Riveting, vivid, fiercely depicted crafted novel of authenticity and power tracing the meteoric rise of George Armstrong Custer from the rank of captain to brigadier general. The utterly engrossing story provides a remarkable inside view of Custer's towering personality as an impulsive and fearless daredevil. The battle scenes are brilliantly written, especially the Boy General leading the First Michigan in one the greatest cavalry charges in military history.

Pierce's historically accurate novel explores the nature of justified defiance. Four different Union cavalry commanders at Gettysburg disobeyed orders, including Custer doing so twice and one officer awarded the Medal of Honor for his justified defiance. The story provides insights into the minds of those disobeying orders and how their decisions contributed to the Union victory over Jeb Stuart's Invincibles on East Cavalry Field.

A remarkable achievement. Like Custer's charging Wolverines, the reader is thrust into the story at a gallop, plunging from page to page. The book recreates a pivotal moment in history with extraordinary authority and insight. *Thundering Courage* is thoroughly compelling — an absolutely gripping read. Truly a great book.

James Stavridis, PhD, Admiral, US Navy (Retired), Supreme Allied Commander at NATO, 2009-2013, Dean, The Fletcher School of Law and Diplomacy (2013-2018)

Until now, generations of Civil War enthusiasts have relied on Bruce Catton, Shelby Foote, and novelists like Michael Shaara and his son Jeff to be our storytellers. And although *The Killer Angels* brought the human emotions of Lee, Longstreet, and Joshua Chamberlain out of the dark, the conflict of East Cavalry Battlefield remained hidden. That pivotal moment that took place three miles east of Gettysburg on the rolling rural fields July 3, 1863, lay yet to be explored.

Enter Terry Pierce. Like a bold cavalry charge, he corrects this oversight with his unique insight, breathing a fresh new voice to those who stood beside cannons and saved the Union flank at Cress Ridge and Rummel Farm. Terry's flair and dedication to detail captures every nuance from Elon Farnsworth's desperado mustache that "looked pasted on," to David Gregg's beaver-tail beard. We feel the pain of General Kilpatrick passing a kidney stone and the tumble of George Custer un-horsed and rescued by Norvell Churchill in the charge at Hunterstown.

With no apologies, General Pleasonton and the cast of supporting characters come to life through Terry's thorough research, capturing nuances of dialogue that's right on, with minute detail, even down to how Custer held his pen. This is the book that has been long awaited to be written.

When I read the last page and closed the book, I knew Terry Pierce had accomplished and written the Last Word on the cavalry action of July 1863 with style, with impeccable research, correctness, and with "Thundering Courage."

Steve Alexander – "Foremost Custer Living Historian"

Thundering Courage is the second book in author Terry C. Pierce's Gettysburg trilogy, building on the story and success of *Without Warning*. From the very first chapter, he takes you on a wild ride, telling the rest of the story of the Battle of Gettysburg and the rapid, unlikely ascension of one of American history's most controversial heroes, Boy General — George Armstrong Custer. While many readers and visitors to Gettysburg's hallowed ground are familiar with the events at Cemetery Hill, Little Roundtop, the peach orchard, the wheat field, and Pickett's Charge, few may know the details of the life-and-death cavalry battles taking place east of the main action or the young cavalry generals who played a pivotal role in securing a Union victory. From its opening pages, Pierce brings to vivid life what it feels like to be in the center of daring cavalry charges again and again. Along the way the reader is introduced to the nascent signs of Custer's greatness and the fatal flaws that would ultimately contribute to his eventual downfall at Little Big Horn. Throughout this exciting and thought-provoking novel, we are introduced to the concept of "justified defiance" and are left to ponder whether it is ever acceptable to disobey an order. It seemed to be for several Union cavalry officers on July 3. I loved *Thundering Courage* — an epic novel grounded in history and the timeless insights of why commanders should be leaders of character.

Steven J. Rauschkolb — Managing Partner, The Crisfield Group,
Board of Directors — Civil War Roundtable Congress

Thundering Courage is truly a masterpiece of storytelling. It is both epic and meticulous in capturing personalities faced with critical decisions and actions while in the chaos of battle. I was totally absorbed by this historically accurate novel. General Meade's controversial promotions of two young Union captains to brigadier generals with their newly formed cavalry brigades, and their coming-of-age command styles, significantly contributed to Meade's victory at Gettysburg. This was so vividly described in *Without Warning: The Saga of Gettysburg, A Reluctant Union Hero, and the Men He Inspired*. I am sure almost everyone is familiar with George Armstrong Custer's inglorious last stand at Little Big Horn, but I, for one, was not familiar with Custer's glorious feats thirteen years before and during the Battle of Gettysburg.

The character-driven story is fast-paced and totally engrossing. The writing is crisp and vivid, and the dialogs convincingly imagined. The battle scenes are graphically written, sometimes shocking, but always gripping. The reader feels as if they are riding with Custer's Wolverines during his daring cavalry charges. The novel is a must-read for understanding the challenges of command and justified defiance. Superb!

Rear Admiral Ronald Christenson USN, retired – former
Commander *USS Theodore Roosevelt* CVN-71

Terry Pierce breathes life into the Union cavalry leaders at Gettysburg. Their character becomes manifest as the reader experiences their behavior with the backdrop of this great battle. *Thundering Courage* details the inner conflict of flawed individuals and is told with clarity and alacrity. I can't recommend this one more highly!

Mike Movius, President
CWRT (Civil War Round Table) Congress

Thundering Courage is a remarkable study in character leadership in the Union Second and Third Cavalry divisions a few weeks before and during the Battle of Gettysburg. From the author of *Without Warning: The Saga of Gettysburg, A Reluctant Union Hero, and the Men He Inspired*, this, Terry Pierce's second novel in his Gettysburg trilogy, is a page-turning story.

Thundering Courage is a groundbreaking feat of historical fiction revealing the heroic role the Union boy cavalry generals and their troopers played in Gettysburg's overlooked cavalry battles. This well-researched novel and powerful narrative reveals the challenges and pitfalls of promoting young cavalry captains to brigadier generals three days before the Battle of Gettysburg.

In this book, Terry Pierce focuses on a youthful George Armstrong Custer and brilliantly captures the whole of Custer's towering personality as he jumps from captain to brigadier general. Upon earning his spurs as a one-star general, Custer believed he was a cavalier of old and dressed outlandishly, imitating Napoleon's cavalry general Prince Joachim Murat's flamboyant dress. Over five days of the battle, Custer challenges fate and leads three remarkable cavalry charges that skyrocket him to national fame. The searing accounts of these cavalry battles were nearly impossible to put down.

Thundering Courage brilliantly reveals the flaws of Custer's passionate yet self-destructive character that will lead to his fate at the Battle of Little Big Horn eleven years later.

In the epic novel *Without Warning*, Colonel George Sharpe, General Meade's intelligence officer, said, "Popularity is overrated. Men want a leader who has strong character. It is character, not charisma, that forges camaraderie and combat effectiveness." When around his men, we witness the full implications of Custer's charm and bravado on the surface and when alone his deep-seated darkness and character flaws underneath. Fortunately, Custer's immediate superior on the East Cavalry Field on July 3, 1863, was a leader of character, Brigadier David Gregg, who directed Custer when and where to attack as if he was moving a key chess piece.

Pierce is a skilled writer, with the rare ability to conduct meticulous research and create a captivating story that shows why military leaders of character possessing the core values of honor, courage (moral and physical), and commitment are so critically important.

This gripping novel is a must-read and should be on the Commandant's Reading List along with *Without Warning*.

General Charles Krulak, USMC, Retired – 31st Commandant of
the Marine Corps

A masterful, detailed, and gripping version of the Union Cavalry's stunning performance and contributions to the Union's Victory at Gettysburg.

Too often, the reader is given the strategic and operational level perspective with notable examples of some of the tactical events sprinkled throughout the story. But in *Thundering Courage*, Dr. Terry Pierce has woven the myriad tactical level events, and the individuals responsible for their execution, into every page of this historical novel... and I couldn't turn the pages fast enough!

Equally mesmerizing was the way Pierce espoused to the reader how all of the units of a well-trained and disciplined ground force (e.g., cavalry, artillery, infantry, intelligence, communications, logistics, etc.) must be synchronized, integrated, and supported to be successful on the battlefield.

But the pièce de résistance in the book is the way Pierce unveils the moral, ethical, and legal dilemmas facing every tactical leader when ordered to execute a task their experience, on-scene knowledge, and instincts know will fail...and worse, might lead to the loss of the overall battle. The most successful leaders learn that the best chance for accomplishing the mission depends on providing good guidance and intent and then training subordinate leaders to develop execution-level details appropriate to the situation and environment they face.

Just as senior civilian and military leaders have used Shakespeare's Henry V in various leadership laboratories, those senior leaders of the future might find, among the dozens of well-documented cases in *Thundering Courage*, perfect examples of how leaders at all levels might better coordinate and synchronize their efforts on the battlefield.

General Gregory (Speedy) Martin, USAF, Retired

Continuing in the tradition of *Without Warning: The Saga of Gettysburg*, Terry Pierce has produced another fine historical novel in *Thundering Courage*. Here he continues the "you are there" style of writing, bringing the reader into a portion of the battle involving George Armstrong Custer and other notables related specifically to the cavalry actions at the Battle of Gettysburg. While we cannot know all the dialog that took place, Pierce comes as close to our imagined dialogue as possible based on meticulous research of the cavalry actions, making for an exciting read. If you enjoy historical novels, especially those written based on solid research, this is the book for you!

Gettysburg Licensed Battlefield Guide Chris Army

A NOVEL

THUNDERING COURAGE:
GEORGE ARMSTRONG CUSTER,
THE UNION CAVALRY BOY GENERALS,
AND JUSTIFIED DEFIANCE AT GETTYSBURG

TERRY C. PIERCE

Heart Ally Books, LLC
Camano Island, Washington

Thundering Courage: George Armstrong Custer, the Union Cavalry Boy Generals, and Justified Defiance at Gettysburg
Copyright ©2023 by Terry C. Pierce
www.TerryCPierce.com
Author website and additional graphic support provided by:
Kim Murray—www.eyegatedesign.com

Cover design: Deranged Doctor Designs
Cover art: *Custer at Hanover* by Dale Gallon - www.gallon.com
Maps created by: Max Shtym

Published by:
Heart Ally Books, LLC - heartallybooks.com
26910 92nd Ave NW C5-406, Stanwood, WA 98292
Published on Camano Island, WA, USA

ISBN-13: (epub) 978-1-63107-052-5
ISBN-13: (paperback) 978-1-63107-053-2
ISBN-13: (hardcover) 978-1-63107-054-9
Library of Congress Cataloging-in-Publication Data

Names: Pierce, Terry C., author.
Title: Thundering courage : George Armstrong Custer, the Union Cavalry boy generals, and justified defiance at Gettysburg / Terry C. Pierce.
Description: Camano Island, Washington : Heart Ally Books, LLC, [2023] |
  Summary: ""Promotions or a coffin!" To George Armstrong Custer, war is the Devil's own fun. And his luck-"Custer Luck"-peaks during the Civil War, keeping him alive against all odds. Yet, for the first two years of the war, Custer luck has not earned him a command-until, three days before a brewing battle at Gettysburg, Captain George Custer is promoted to brigadier general. Possessed with raw courage, rare gallantry, and reckless heroism, Custer becomes the youngest general in the Union army. Hugely spirited, tactically flexible, and fiercely ambitious, Custer, on July 3, 1863, trots in front of the First Michigan cavalry regiment, grips his sheathed saber, and pulls. The blade swishes from its metal scabbard with the sleekness of a swooping hawk. "Come on, You Wolverines!" he yells. And the 23-year-old leads one of the greatest cavalry charges in the annals of warfare. Craving attention, approval, and glory, the boy general with long, flowing, golden locks is an impulsive, fearless daredevil. Commanding the Michigan Cavalry Brigade, Custer is throttled by his vainglorious reporting senior and ridiculed by battle-hardened Wolverines. But the pride that lies in the flesh of all men is thicker in Custer. He loves dancing at the edge of death's doorstep. And he believes that moral courage means leading from the front-but not always following orders. Because he knows that, between orders and duty, blind obedience and justified defiance hang in the balance. Thundering Courage is the riveting story of the Union cavalry's Second and Third Divisions at Gettysburg, boy generals who face crises of justified defiance, and the unsung hero who wisely keeps a human thunderbolt on a tight, short string. Built firmly upon the annals of history, Thundering Courage journeys through the hearts and minds of Union cavalry heroes who face the agony of choosing between blind obedience and justified defiance at the Battle of Gettysburg"-- Provided by publisher.
Identifiers: LCCN 2023028052 (print) | LCCN 2023028053 (ebook) | ISBN 9781631070532 (trade paperback) | ISBN 9781631070549 (hardcover) | ISBN 9781631070525 (epub)
Subjects: LCSH: Custer, George A. (George Armstrong), 1839-1876--Fiction. | United States. Army. Michigan Cavalry Brigade (1862-1865)--Fiction. | Gettysburg, Battle of, Gettysburg, Pa., 1863--Fiction. | United States--History--Civil War, 1861-1865--Cavalry operations--Fiction. | LCGFT: Historical fiction. | Novels.
Classification: LCC PS3616.I35994 T48 2023 (print) | LCC PS3616.I35994 (ebook) | DDC 813/.6--dc23/eng/20230817
LC record available at https://lccn.loc.gov/2023028052
LC ebook record available at https://lccn.loc.gov/2023028053

10 9 8 7 6 5 4 3 2 1

Dedication

For Dick McConn, an Air Force Academy
Distinguished Graduate and a quiet leader of
character who, like victorious Cavalry General
David Gregg at the Battle of Gettysburg, has never
sought fame or glory in doing his duty to his family,
academy, and his nation.
Thank you for your unwavering support
and mentorship.
You are truly one of our nation's great unsung heroes!

Major General George Armstrong Custer

Table of Contents

Thursday, July 2, 1863

Friday, July 3, 1863

Table of Contents

Lt. George A. Custer with dog

List of Illustrations

All photographs in this list are in the public domain unless noted.
The link below each entry will take you to a reliable source.
Maps copyright Terry C. Pierce unless otherwise noted.

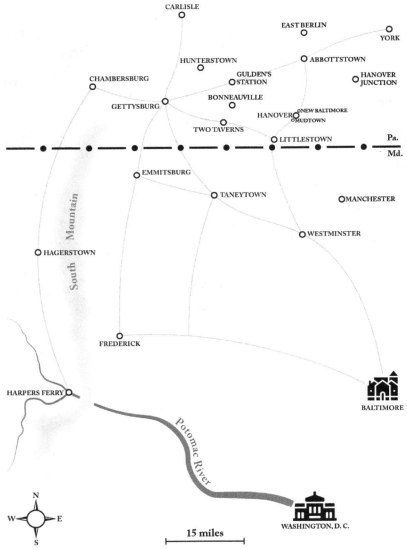

Preface

This story of the Union cavalry at Gettysburg begins two weeks before the battle and ends on July 3, 1863. It is told from the viewpoint of George Armstrong Custer and the other cavalry generals and troopers of the Second and Third Cavalry Divisions of the Army of the Potomac, who fought six engagements in the bloodiest battle of the Civil War.

Most of us have an opinion of Custer's dramatic "Last Stand" at Little Bighorn — good or bad. But when the Civil War ended eleven years earlier, Custer was a national war hero, as mythical in fame as the Greek warrior Achilles of the Trojan War. He had unparalleled success on Civil War battlefields, escaping capture and death several times—something now often called Custer's Luck. Custer and his friends called it Custer luck.[1]

Unlike General George Meade, commander of the Army of the Potomac, who was one of the United States' greatest reluctant heroes of the Gettysburg Campaign, Custer was one of our nation's greatest *willing* heroes at Gettysburg. Custer's rise to becoming the youngest general in the Union army at age twenty-three is quite remarkable. After being court-martialed at West Point, Custer served as a staff officer to several generals for two years and was cited for gallantry for leading cavalry charges at Brandy Station and the Battle of Aldie. When he assumed command of the Michigan Cavalry Brigade, the Wolverines thought he looked like "a circus rider gone mad!" National newspapers hailed him "The Boy General with the Golden Locks." No one took him seriously. On July 3, 1863, the ripsnorter disobeyed orders twice, claiming justified defiance, and defeated Jeb Stuart's larger cavalry force by leading two Napoleonic cavalry charges.

---

1 T.J. Stiles, *Custer's Trials: A Life on the Frontier of a New America*, Vintage Books, New York, 2015, page 180. Also see Endnote 72, page 497. "George Armstrong Custer using the phrase 'Custer luck' in his letter to Libbie Custer February 8, 1869, Folder 7, Box 4, Marguerite Merington Papers, Manuscripts and Archives Division, New York Public Library."

In the context of Custer's actions, other names appear, including the controversial General Judson Kilpatrick, jailed for corruption before Gettysburg; General Elon Farnsworth, who led a suicide cavalry charge; General David Gregg, who was the unsung hero; and Major William Wells and Captain William Miller, Medal of Honor recipients. These troopers' stories provide readers a greater appreciation of the cavalry's contribution to the Union victory.

No facts have been knowingly altered. When possible, key characters' written accounts of their experiences have been paraphrased. As a result, the story is not a work of narrative nonfiction, but a novel of biographical and historical fiction that strives to accurately portray what happened to Custer and the Union cavalry troopers in the Gettysburg Campaign.

Custer was a creature of unlimited ambition, viewing war as the Devil's own fun. He dressed in a flamboyant costume and craved attention and approval. He sparkled with wit, bubbled with enthusiasm, and blinded people with brilliant bursts of charm. The chaos of his inner world was his greatest strength and his greatest weakness. In spite of his reckless, death-defying impulses, which would eventually be his undoing at Little Bighorn and earn him great notoriety as a villain, Custer's bravery during the Battle of Gettysburg skyrocketed him to national fame.

But the seeds of his destruction at Little Bighorn were also on display at Gettysburg. Fortunately, General David Gregg, the unsung cavalry hero of Gettysburg, kept Custer in check, directing the boy general when and where to move like a master chess player, and achieved a great Union victory on East Cavalry Field. Nevertheless, for his heroic style of leadership at the Battle of Gettysburg — his daredevil charges and death-defying quest for glory — and his contributions to the Union victory, our nation owes a great debt to General George Armstrong Custer.

—*Terry C. Pierce*

The Men

These men wore Union blue:

Army Commander
George Gordon Meade, Major General
James Biddle, Major, Aide-de-Camp
Seth Williams, Adjutant General

Artillery Reserve Commander
Henry Hunt, Brigadier General

Intelligence Commander
George Sharpe, Colonel

Cavalry Corps Commander
Alfred Pleasonton, Major General
Lieutenant Colonel Andrew Alexander, Chief of Staff
George Yates, Captain, Aide
James Wade, Captain, Aide
Clifford Thompson, Captain, Aide

First Cavalry Division Commander
John Buford, Brigadier General

Reserve Cavalry Brigade Commander
Wesley Merritt, Brigadier General
Captain Isaac Dunkelberger, Aide

Second Cavalry Division Commander
David Gregg, Brigadier General
Henry Weir, Captain, Adjutant General
Henry Meyer, Captain, Aide-de-Camp
Thomas Jackson (T.J.) Gregg, Lieutenant, Aide

First Cavalry Brigade Commander
John McIntosh, Colonel
Walter Newhall, Captain, Adjutant General, Aide

First New Jersey Regiment Commander
Myron Beaumont, Major
Hugh Janeway, Major
Thomas Cox, Sergeant Major
James Hart, Captain
Francis Brown, Private

Third Pennsylvania Regiment Commander
Edward Jones, Lieutenant Colonel
Dr. Theodore Tate, Assistant Surgeon
William Miller, Captain, Company M, Medal of Honor Recipient
William Brooke-Rawle, First Lieutenant, Company M
Frank Hess, Captain
Charles Treichel, Captain
William Rogers, Captain
Thomas Wier, First Sergeant
John Brandon, First Sergeant
Thomas Gregg, Sergeant
George Heagy, Sergeant
E. G. Eyster, Private

First Maryland Regiment Commander
James Deems, Lieutenant Colonel

Purnell (Maryland) Legion, Company A, Commander
Robert Duvall, Captain

Second Cavalry Brigade Commander
Pennock Huey, Colonel

Third Cavalry Brigade, Commander
J. Irvin Gregg, Colonel

Tenth New York Regiment Commander
Henry Avery, Major
John Kemper, Major, commanding squadron of H and L Troops
Marshall Woodruff, First Lieutenant commanding L Troop
William Peck, Captain, commanding H Troop
Benjamin Lownsbury, Captain, commanding squadron of E and K Troops
Ira Allen, Second Lieutenant
Truman White, Lieutenant
James Matthews, Lieutenant

William Potter, Corporal
Abram Thompson, Corporal
Benjamin Bonnell, Sergeant
David Rines, Sergeant
Edmund Dow, Corporal
William Doan, Bugler

Artillery

First U.S. Horse Artillery, Batteries E and G (Four 12-pounder Napoleons)
Alanson Randol, Captain

Section Battery Commander
James Chester, Lieutenant

Third Pennsylvania Heavy Artillery, Battery H, (Serving as Light Artillery)
William Rank, Captain (One Section: two 3-inch Ordnance Rifles)

Third Cavalry Division Commander
Judson Kilpatrick, Brigadier General
Llewellyn Estes, Captain, Assistant Adjutant General
Eli Holden, First Lieutenant, Aide
Samuel Gillespie, Private, Bugler and Bodyguard from Division Headquarters Guard

First Cavalry Brigade Commander
Elon Farnsworth, Brigadier General
Andrew Cunningham, Captain, Aide-de-Camp
Herman Hamburger, First Lieutenant, Assistant Adjutant General
Charles Bond, Private, Orderly
John Murray, Private, Orderly
Gilbert Buckman, Bugler

Fifth New York Regiment Commander
John Hammond, Major
Amos White, Major, Adjutant
Seldon Wales, Sergeant
Johnnie Catlin, Bugler
Thomas Burke, Private, Troop A, First Medal of Honor awarded in Pennsylvania

James Rickey, Corporal, Troop A
Abram Folger, Private, Troop H

Eighteenth Pennsylvania Regiment Commander
William Brinton, Lieutenant Colonel
William Darlington, Major
Henry Potter, Second Lieutenant, Troop M
William Jones, Lieutenant
William Nott, First Sergeant
Joseph Cooke, Sergeant, Troop A
Henry Lashire, Corporal, Troop A
Isaac Dannenhower, Corporal, Troop M
Frank Street, Corporal, Troop M

First Vermont Regiment Commander
Addison Preston, Lieutenant Colonel
William Wells, Major, Staff Officer, Medal of Honor Recipient
John Bennett, Major
Clarence Gates, Adjutant
Oliver Cushman, Captain, Commander Troop E
Henry Parsons, Captain, Commander Troop L
George Duncan, Sergeant
Stephen Clark, Lieutenant
Willard Farrington, Sergeant, Company L
Henry Pratt, Corporal, Troop H
Samuel Dowling, Sergeant, Troop H
Harry Sheldon, Private, Troop M
George Walker, Corporal

First Vermont Battalion Commanders
First Battalion: *Henry Parsons,* Captain, Companies E, F, I, and L
Second Battalion: *William Wells,* Major, Companies B, C, G, and H
Third Battalion: *John Bennett,* Major, Companies A, D, K, and M

First West Virginia Regiment Commander
Nathaniel Richmond, Colonel

Horse Artillery

Battery E, Fourth U.S. Artillery (Four Ordnance Rifles)
Samuel Elder, Lieutenant

Second Cavalry Brigade Commander

Joseph Copeland, Brigadier General (relieved as Commander June 29, 1863)

George Armstrong Custer, Brigadier General (assumed Command June 29, 1863)

William Colerick, Second Lieutenant, Aide-de-Camp

William Wheeler, First Lieutenant, Aide-de-Camp

Augustus Drew, Captain, Acting Assistant Inspector General

Norvell Churchill, Private, Special Orderly

Peter Boehm, Private, Bugler, Orderly

Joseph Fought, Private, Bugler and Orderly

Johnny Cisco, Boy Groom

William North, First Lieutenant, Quartermaster

First Michigan Regiment Commander

Charles Town, Colonel

Milton Rice, Chief Trumpeter

Dewitt Smith, Sergeant Major

Fifth Michigan Regiment Commander

Russell Alger, Colonel

Noah Ferry, Major, Staff

Luther Trowbridge, Major, Staff

Samuel Harris, First Lieutenant, Troop A

William Dunn, Private, (Major Trowbridge's Orderly)

George Munn, Private, (Major Ferry's Orderly)

Charles Osborne, Sergeant Major

Edwin Bigelow, First Sergeant, Troop B

John Allen, Chief Trumpeter

Lewis Gardner, Private

Sixth Michigan Regiment Commander

George Gray, Colonel

Peter Weber, Acting Major, Staff

Henry Thompson, Captain, Commander Troop A

Stephen Ballard, Second Lieutenant, Troop A

Charles Bolza, Second Lieutenant, Troop B

Edward Craw, First Lieutenant, Troop E

William Keyes, Sergeant, Troop B

James Harvey Kidd, Captain, Commander Troop E

Charles Storrs, Second Lieutenant, Troop G

John Molloy, First Sergeant, Troop G

Thomas Edie, First Sergeant, Troop A

George Patten, First Sergeant, Troop B
Dr. David Spaulding, Assistant Surgeon
Charles Batson, Private, Troop B

Sixth Michigan Squadron Commander Battle of Hanover

Peter Weber, Major, Staff[2]
Daniel Powers, First Lieutenant Company B
Donald Lovell, First Lieutenant Company F

Seventh Michigan Regiment Commander

William Mann, Colonel
Allyne Litchfield, Lieutenant Colonel
James Carpenter, Major, Battalion Commander
George Briggs, Acting Adjutant
James Birney, Lieutenant, Troop C
Heman Moore, Captain, Troop K
George (*Geo) Armstrong,* Captain, Troop D
Edwin Havens, Sergeant, Troop A
Andrew Cline, Sergeant, Troop K
Andrew Buck, Sergeant, Troop F

Artillery

Second United States Artillery, Battery M, Commander

Alexander Pennington, Jr. Captain
John Barlow, Lieutenant
Carle Woodruff, Lieutenant

War Artist

Alfred Waud, Special War Artist for *Harper's Weekly Illustrated Newspaper*

Infantry

Ninth Irish Massachusetts Regiment Commander, Fifth Infantry Corps

Patrick Guiney, Colonel

---

2 Peter Weber was promoted to Major and waiting for the official promotion papers to arrive before sewing on his Major insignia. He was an Acting Major, but the story will call him Major Weber because his superiors and subordinates called him Major Weber.

These men wore Confederate gray:

Cavalry Division Commander
Jeb Stuart, Major General

Cavalry Brigade Commanders
Wade Hampton, Brigadier General
Fitzhugh Lee, Brigadier General
John Chambliss (Lee's brigade), Colonel
Albert Jenkins, Brigadier General

Second North Carolina Cavalry Regiment
William Payne, Lieutenant Colonel

Infantry Commanders

Stonewall Infantry Brigade Commander
James Walker, Brigadier General

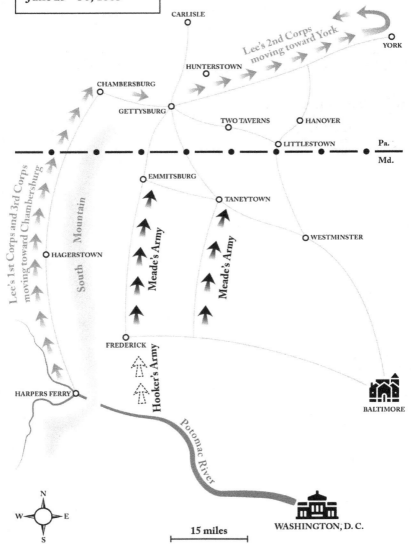

**Roads Leading North
Infantry Marches
June 25 - 30, 1863**

CARLISLE

Lee's 2nd Corps moving toward York

YORK

HUNTERSTOWN

CHAMBERSBURG

GETTYSBURG

TWO TAVERNS

HANOVER

LITTLESTOWN

Pa.

Md.

EMMITSBURG

TANEYTOWN

WESTMINSTER

Lee's 1st Corps and 3rd Corps moving toward Chambersburg

South Mountain

HAGERSTOWN

Meade's Army

Meade's Army

FREDERICK

Hooker's Army

HARPERS FERRY

BALTIMORE

Potomac River

N
W   E
S

15 miles

WASHINGTON, D. C.

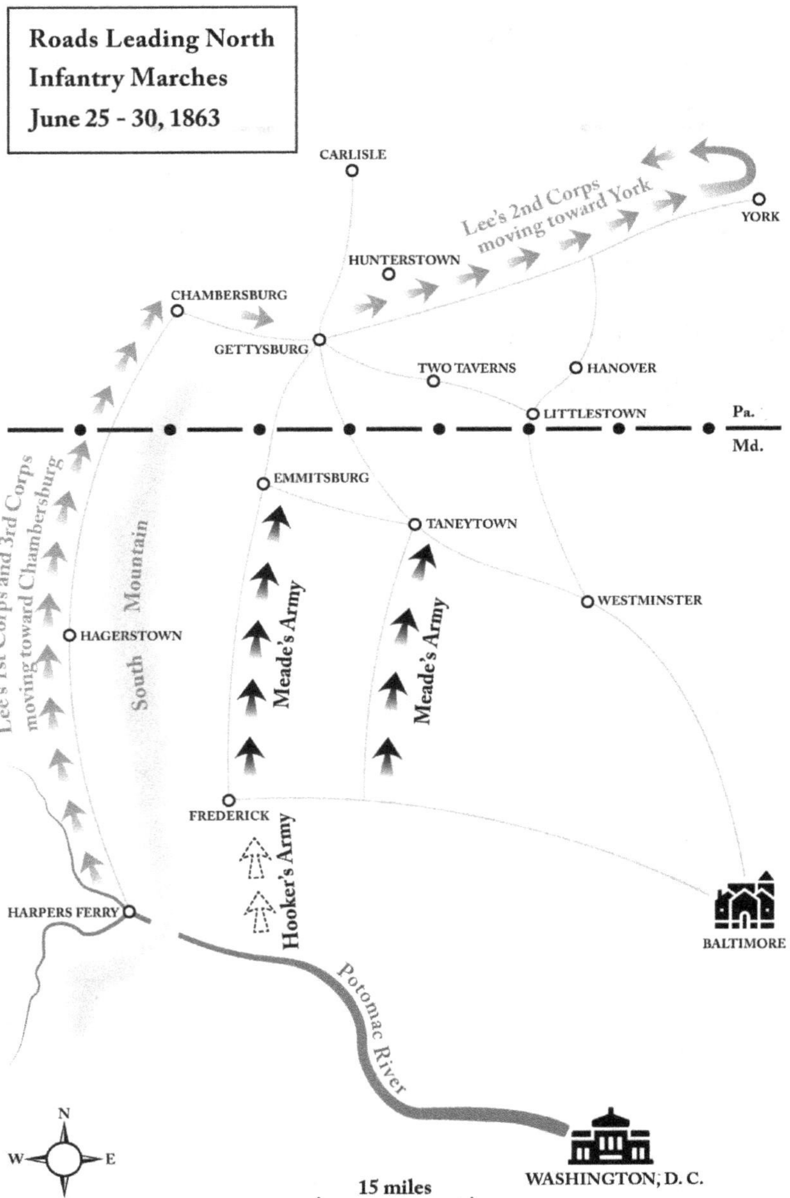

South Mountain

HAGERSTOWN

Meade's Army

Meade's Army

FREDERICK

Hooker's Army

HARPERS FERRY

Potomac River

BALTIMORE

N
W   E
S

15 miles

WASHINGTON, D. C.

xxviii

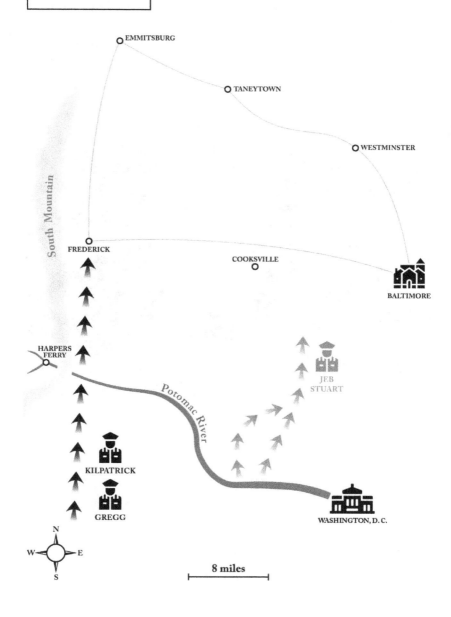

**Cavalry Marches
June 27-28, 1863**

EMMITSBURG

TANEYTOWN

WESTMINSTER

South Mountain

FREDERICK

COOKSVILLE

BALTIMORE

HARPERS
FERRY

Potomac River

JEB
STUART

KILPATRICK

GREGG

WASHINGTON, D. C.

N
W   E
S

8 miles

Custer Charging at the Battle of Aldie by Alfred Waud

1

Custer — Wednesday, June 17, 1863

5:30 p.m. (daylight is waning)
Lieutenant George Armstrong Custer
On a small knoll behind the Snickersville Pike, near the village of
Aldie, Virginia

Lieutenant George Armstrong Custer lowered his wide-brimmed hat against the slanting streaks of sunlight and scanned the landscape, shrouded in a bloody sea of blue dragoons. He shuddered. Hundreds lay unmoving on the ground. Others hobbled and crawled, if they could, back to the Union lines, crying and mewing like bleating lambs. His throat constricted as a little current of heated air dragged a sickly stench of decaying flesh, singeing his nose. *Poor buggers.*

The cracking din of Rebel rifles had dropped to a distant echo, like brittle branches breaking. Where were the rest of the Confederate bastards? Something flickered. He gripped his field glasses and inspected the crest beyond the blue casualties. Along the tree line, drawn sabers started glinting like swarms of flashing fireflies. *Holy hell.* Two long lines of mounted graybacks were reforming and growing. A Rebel saber charge was imminent. His heart leaped as a feverish impulse urged him toward reckless audacity.

He wheeled toward his dithering cavalry commander. General Alfred Pleasonton sat stolid on his mount like a marbled statue, his face cloaked in a dark dread of defeat. A growl gurgled in Custer's throat. *Damn it, General, order a countercharge.* He wiped his sweaty brow. The heat of touched pride was whipsawing him between his duty as Pleasonton's aide-de-camp and his passion for boldness and fame, summoning him to the thin edge of obedience and defiance. He squeezed the saber grip and rattled the sheathed blade as a seething rashness quick-strung

1

his nerves. He didn't give a damn about his mortal soul, but he sorely coveted a chance for immortal glory. What a man did in battle echoed for eternity. *Just unleash your daredevil, General.*

Staccato cracks erupted, and two bullets whined by his head, fluttering his golden locks. He smirked. Didn't the Rebels know he was blessed with an odd vigilance? Custer luck. It saved his ass at West Point, and it would save his ass in this war.

Spiraling smoke puffs blossomed from Confederate sharpshooters popping off shots. The Rebels were still hunkered down behind a stone wall where they had ambushed the charging blue dragoons of the First Massachusetts. A chill slithered through him. The running cavalry battle of charges and countercharges, raging for the past three hours between Jeb Stuart's Invincibles and Alfred Pleasonton's troopers, had shifted in favor of the surging Rebel tide forming on the crest.

Someone shouted, "Here they come!"

Second Virginia Invincibles, sporting plumed hats and brandishing glinting sabers, trotted forward. They threatened to engulf the sea of skedaddling blue dragoons. He bristled, bottling a daredevilish instinct to bolt forward. Gritting his teeth, he stroked the points of his golden mustache. *Gah!* He wanted desperately to charge but had no permission. Charging without permission meant another court-martial. Not charging meant watching helplessly while what remained of the First Massachusetts Regiment was butchered bit by bit.

He bobbed in his saddle like a fishing cork. Uncertainty flowed through him. Perhaps in a few moments he *would* charge, with or without permission. Court-martials be damned.

A banshee scream tore through the air. A brave regimental cavalry commander with the Fourth New York Cavalry pointed his saber toward the Virginians and charged, single-handed.

His dastardly troopers refused to follow.

Devilry. "Yellow-bellied cowards," Custer muttered.

A rattling volley of bullets cracked, and the New York colonel and his horse crashed to the ground in a shower of gravel and dust. The Rebels jeered and waved their battle flags with ruthless insolence at the lily-livered Union regiment. A surly breath burst out from Custer's constricted chest. An enemy bugler trumpeted, and Rebel wolf cries howled, encouraged by the cowardly actions of the Fourth New York. A gray, crested wave spiked with glittering sabers started jogging down the crest.

Disaster loomed, pumping him empty. Enemy cannons thundered, and wispy black tendrils threaded their smoky way toward the Union lines. A sharp twinge of urgency seized him as he mentally raced through his options.

He twisted in his saddle and stared at Pleasonton. The vainglorious cavalry commander was fidgeting, his face blotchy and sweaty. Pleasonton had disobeyed orders. General Hooker, the commander of the Army of the Potomac, had told him to halt five miles east from Aldie. Instead, Pleasonton had pressed ahead. Making matters worse, they had stumbled into a hornet's nest of Rebels at Aldie. If Pleasonton lost this battle, he could be fired for dereliction of duty. A swelling impulse lurched through his mind. *Damn't, Pleasonton. Let me lead the charge.*

With as much restraint as he could muster, he said, "General Pleasonton, we need to countercharge the Rebels, or all will be lost. Do you want me to lead the charge?"

Pleasonton stiffened and barked, "No! You're a staffer. Stay put."

He bit down on his lip, tasting blood. *Son of a bitch.* Didn't Pleasonton see what needed to be done? Only twenty-three, and his leadership and tactical sense were better than his superior's. He gripped the reins and leaned forward in the saddle, struggling to throttle his feverish instincts. Since Pleasonton had ignored orders and created this pending disaster, wasn't he justified in defying Pleasonton and bolting forward, leading a spirited cavalry charge?

Pleasonton gestured for General David Gregg. Custer muffled a grin as the spindle-shanked Gregg trotted up. Nicknamed Old Steady, Gregg sported a bushy beavertail beard and a beat-up service hat. He looked more like Appalachian hill folk than a typical flamboyant cavalry commander. The only cavalry officer dressed more shabbily than Gregg was Custer himself. But Old Steady was a trusted stalwart and gifted cavalry general.

3

"David." Pleasonton pointed. "Countercharge the enemy."

Gregg turned to an aide and shouted, "Order Colonel Calvin Douty's First Maine to charge with Kilpatrick's brigade. Have Colonel Irvin Gregg's Tenth New York, Fourth Pennsylvania, and Sixteenth Pennsylvania form into an extended line and trot behind the First Maine as a ready reserve."

The staffer wheeled and spurred down the hillock. Custer cringed. Kilpatrick had made several attempts to dislodge the Rebels this afternoon and had failed each time. Could the Second Brigade reinforced with Douty's regiment carry the day? Cold creeps welled in the hollow of his bones.

Custer nudged his mount toward Pleasonton. "Beg pardon, sir, I request permission to join General Kilpatrick." He rocked in his saddle, champing at the bit like a high-spirited bronco. *Please Lord, let your dashing thunderbolt turn the tide at Aldie.*

Pleasonton dipped a short nod. "Lieutenant, you have my permission to join the fight with the troopers of the First Maine."

Custer cracked a half-smile under the edge of his blonde mustache. "Promotions or a coffin!" he shouted, then clapped spurs and plunged down the knoll on his skittish black mount, flying with wings ablaze. His skin tingled as a savage craving coursed his veins. God, he loved cavalry charges.

Watching from the knoll, Pleasonton cringed as his young hotspur, sporting long blonde locks girted by a battered straw plantation hat, flew as recklessly as if a bugler had trumpeted attack.

"I see you're unleashing your whippersnapper," Gregg remarked. "But what is that on his head?"

Pleasonton made a gesture of helpless surrender. "Custer claims the regulation cap never stays on his head. Hell, wearing a Confederate hat and those oversized knee boots, he looks more like a Rebel cavalry officer than a Union one. Who knows," he sighed. "Maybe it'll keep him safe." A lone raptor hovered high above Custer with outstretched wings, majestically silent as it floated with the wind. "Perhaps a good omen," he murmured.

"What persuaded you to turn him loose?"

Pleasonton turned to face Gregg. "I was saving Custer from another court-martial. He has been pestering all afternoon to join the fight. I sensed he was going to join the charge whether he had permission or not."

Gregg puffed on his pipe. "Custer has the prey drive of a hunting dog. You just need to point him in the right direction and unleash him."

Pleasonton nodded. "I wish we had more young officers like Custer." He raised his field glasses and watched as Custer tore toward Kilpatrick. Custer was a creature of glory, a reckless, gallant boy, undeterred by fatigue, and unconscious of fear. If anyone could arouse his troopers with sweep and fire, it was this swashbuckling cavalier who loved fighting. "God be with you, George."

Galloping cock-a-hoop over the 400 yards toward the rolling green fields at the bottom of the knoll, Custer pitched forward on his mount, racing past Gregg's three regiments forming up into a long reserve attack line. He hard-gripped the reins and squinted as the breeze buffeted his face. He veered a bit right and aimed for the rear of the First Maine column. Harry's quickstepping hooves slapped against the ground like clapping coconut shells. Custer started humming the Irish air "Garryowen" and shivered with the anticipation of a high-spirited colt as the blue troopers broke into a trot. Finally, he was going to be able to quench his thirst for riding in a glorious cavalry charge. *Thank you, General.*

Twenty yards ahead along the narrow dirt road, hidden Rebel sharpshooters crested a berm and fired a cracking volley into the exposed right flank of the Mainers. Screams erupted and troopers and horses tumbled to the ground. Thick battle smoke spewed like a growing wildfire. He yanked on the reins, veered off the road, and jabbed his spurs into Harry's flanks. "Come on, boy, before they reload!"

He twisted in his saddle and spied Colonel Gregg's reserve regiments erupting into a charge toward the First Maine. *Good.*

In a matter of moments, Gregg's reserves would slam into the Rebels and rescue the First Maine survivors.

He whisked along the column toward Brigadier General Judson Kilpatrick sauntering ahead of the regiment alongside their commander, Colonel Calvin Douty. Custer flitted by the troopers, doffing his Rebel hat and fanning the air. "Three cheers for General Kilpatrick!"

The Mainers responded with great cheer. "Hip hip hurray! Hip hip hurray! Hip hip hurray!"

Custer donned his hat and reined up beside Kilpatrick's sorrel horse, Beppo. He whipped out his long Toledo saber and bobbed it in a dashing cavalier salute, grinning. "General Pleasonton gives his regards and directs you to halt the charging enemy."

Kilpatrick's face flared the same red as Beppo's coat. "Please give my regards to the general and tell him I will carry the day."

Custer mused, a vibrant thrill bubbling inside. "We can both tell him after our glorious charge, when we whip the Rebels."

Kilpatrick glared down his vulture-like nose. "I don't need an escort from the general's staff."

Custer cracked a devilish smile. "General, I'm not here to escort anyone."

Kilpatrick fidgeted like a temperamental mare, his beady little eyes crawling over his overzealous underling. "This is my brigade, *Lieutenant*, and I will lead this damn charge. You're not going to try to steal my thunder like you do everyone else's."

"With all due respect, General, your brigade has been fighting piecemeal for half a day. It's time to end this battle."

"Keep your place, Custer," Kilpatrick snarled, his voice sounding strangled. "You can ride next to Colonel Douty."

Custer nodded and smiled, tight-lipped. *To hell with him.* Cavalry charges were a lure for the bold and a misfortune for the timid. Pleasonton could not afford another botched attack.

Kilpatrick turned and shouted, "Attention for the charge!"

Colonel Douty repeated the order.

"Draw sabers," Kilpatrick bellowed. "Column forward, trot ho!"

Custer reached inside his jacket pocket and gripped the treasured locket. He opened it and stared at Libbie Bacon's ambrotype. His heart pounded against his ribs. *I cherish you, Libbie. I will show Judge Bacon that a poor boy from Ohio[3] deserves your hand.* He placed the locket inside his jacket. He withdrew and raised his burnished saber, clapped spurs, and slewed forward a horse-length behind Beppo. They loped across the rolling field, hundreds of hooves thundering behind. He snarled. Kilpatrick was riding too slow and needed to pick up speed. Anger flamed in his gut as the general's last words swirled in his brain, dismissive and scornful. *Keep your place, Custer.* Kilpatrick's timid charge was doomed to fail again. A bursting impulse beckoned a reckless act. *Justified defiance.*

Custer twisted in his saddle and twirled his saber, shouting, "Come on, boys!"

Old Harry surged forward from a trot to a half-gallop. He sidled up to Kilpatrick.

"Damn you, Custer!" the general snapped.

A flicker of a smile broke across Custer's face as a charming excitement swelled inside him like a magic spell. He pointed his saber forward and buglers brayed, "'Charge!'"

He pitched his mount into a full gallop. His heart roared, pounding in his ears. A cheer burst from behind. His skin tingled, trilling with bliss. Leading a cavalry charge was the most electrifying thrill in the world.

His eyes flicked right, where Kilpatrick and Douty were pulling abreast of Old Harry. A whirl of thrummed energy passed through Custer, like a breeze through tall wheat stalks. Kilpatrick's nostrils were flaring and Douty was howling.

Rebel bugles blasted, voices roared, and red guidons rippled as ribbons of mounted graybacks streamed forward, yelling like demons.

"Gunfire!" Kilpatrick shouted.

---

3 Custer was born and raised in New Rumley, Harrison County, Ohio, with his parents until age ten, when he moved to Monroe, Michigan, to live with his half sister Ann Reed.

Custer pitched forward onto his mount's neck and shot half a horse length beyond Kilpatrick and Douty. The charging Rebels fired a raking volley. Twanging bullets sang overhead, and thumps echoed like sacks of flour hitting the ground. Custer glanced over his right shoulder. Douty screamed, hit twice in the chest, and tumbled dead to the ground next to his slain mount. Beppo had buckled and tumbled down, pinning Kilpatrick underneath.

Custer screamed a blood-lust cry and dug in his spurs, tearing flesh. His mount gobbled up the ground like a bolting mustang as he swept ahead of the trapped Kilpatrick. A wellspring of pulse-pounding exhilaration was gushing inside Custer like a busted steampipe. Nothing could top the thrill of leading a charge like his flamboyant hero General Murat, Napoleon's First Horseman of Europe.

He bounced on his wild ripsnorter, leaping frantically forward at breakneck speed ahead of the blue flying figures. His long blonde curls flapped against his neck, keeping in time with his beating heart. Thundering hooves pounded close behind. He grinned. The lovely old feeling of dancing at the edge of death's doorstep was back. He was the star of the show, racing across an open field for everyone to see.

The charging graybacks were twenty yards ahead. He caught a popping flash out of the corner of his eye, and a bullet whizzed by. He veered slightly, raced for a red battle flag, and swung his saber, cutting the guidon in half. His heart jumped as Harry whinnied and bolted toward a growing gap in the second Rebel line. A Confederate swerved his mount toward his black warhorse and swung his saber like a scythe cutting wheat stalks. Custer ducked and leaned as the blade swooshed over his head. A furious rage pulsed inside. He spun and swung the Toledo, slashing the Rebel's back. Harry thundered on at breakneck speed. Five hundred yards ahead loitered the enemy reserves guarding the Rebel rear.

"Harry, whoa!" he shouted, and pulled hard on the reins, jamming the bit into the back of the mount's mouth. Harry kept up the hell-bent gallop. Twenty yards ahead a Rebel trotted toward him, aiming his revolver. *Crack.* The hot lead whisked by his face. His breath caught and his gut clenched. The grayback yelled and spurred his mount, closing in for the kill.

Custer's ears rang and rang. Hot fury churned inside. *You devil's whore.* He raised his Toledo over his head, flashed it in a circular swing, and sliced the grayback's shoulder. The Confederate screamed and plunged from his mount. Thundering hooves echoed from his left. A Rebel rode up stirrup to stirrup and swung his saber toward his left forearm. Custer wheeled his right-held saber across his chest and parried the blow. Sparks flew. The blade vibrated like a tuning fork, stinging his hand and peppering his arm with needle-like pricks. They raced full speed toward the enemy rear as the Rebel swung again and again at his exposed forearm and, again and again, he parried the blows. *Damn't. Can't return any cuts.*

After his fourth parry, instinct took over and his left hand yanked on the reins, checking Harry. The Rebel shot by. He spurred Harry as the Rebel wheeled about. A jolt surged through him. He twisted and twirled, as graceful as a venomous snake. He swung his saber and cleaved the enemy's skull into a Devil's cloven hoof. Blood sprayed and vaporized, a vanishing mist in the blazing sunlight.

He reined about and halted, his heart thumping in his ears. Harry was snorting and foaming. He patted the mount's neck. "Easy, boy, easy."

My God. He was amidst a gaggle of retreating Rebels jogging by, casting offhand glances in the rustling silence. He peered toward the Union lines. A haunting twang strummed in his mind and a budding dread began to purl. He was a mile away, cut off from the blue troopers. A few Confederates studied him closely but made no attempt to charge. Why? He half chuckled. He was wearing the same Dixieland straw hat as the Confederates, and captured enemy boots. *The graybacks think I'm a Rebel. Custer luck.*

He reined Harry about and started to trot slowly toward the Union lines. One of Jeb Stuart's Invincibles screamed like a crazed cougar and rushed with a raised, glinting saber.

"Damn you, Yankee!" the Rebel shouted.

Custer sucked in a deep breath and held it. He whirled Harry toward the Rebel and parried the blow. Metal clanged against metal. He swung a backhanded arc, catching the Confederate across the face. The Rebel screamed and tumbled off his horse.

A Rebel officer wearing a plumed hat shouted, "Get 'im!"

Custer spurred Old Harry, shot passed the Confederate officer, and dashed toward the Union lines. He hunkered against Harry's neck as they galloped at a dead run. The air cracked and a bullet nickered overhead. His mind snickered. *Missed me. Don't you Rebs know I'm invincible?*

Grinning, he shouted, "Come on, boy, fly!"

His heart raced; wind breathed on his cheeks and whistled in his ears. Two hundred yards from the Union lines he spotted a gray-clad rider wobbling and swaying side to side like a drunk. He drew slightly on the reins and slowed to a canter. The Rebel was gripping his bloody shoulder. Old Harry pulled up, his muscles bunching. It was the trooper Custer had slashed.

"Sir, you're my prisoner. I respectfully request you pass me your saber and revolver."

The Rebel wobbled. "You're the Yankee that clabberclawed my shoulder. You look more like a Confederate than a blue belly." He slowly handed Custer his saber and then his revolver.

Custer said, "Ride next to me. No more harm will come to you."

As they rode toward the Union lines, the prisoner asked, "What is your name, sir?"

"I'm Lieutenant George Armstrong Custer."

"Well, I'll be. I know who you are."

"How's that?"

"I served under your West Point roommate, Captain John "Gimlet" Lee. He told me that at the Battle of Williamsburg he was captured and suffered a badly wounded leg. You cared and fed him for two days and gave him stockings."

Custer grinned. "Yes, that's true."

"Captain Lee told me he was paroled and asked you to be his groomsman. You showed up for the wedding in Union blue

and he wore Confederate gray. You were the talk of Jeb Stuart's cavalry force."

"I was one of General McClellan's staffers, and he gave me permission to attend the wedding. It was a grand old time. I danced nearly the entire night."

They pulled up to the Union lines. A provost guard pointed his pistol at the prisoner. "Get down, Reb!"

Custer leaped to the ground. "Let me help, trooper."

The prisoner moaned as he half slid, and half fell off his mount. Hitting the ground, the Reb swayed. "Thank you for sparing my life, Lieutenant Custer."

Custer smiled. He reached into his jacket pocket and pulled out a *carte de visite* and a pencil. He signed the calling card and handed it to the prisoner. "Please give this signed card to Captain Gimlet Lee when you see him again."

"I will, sir."

Custer nodded, reached into his pants pocket, and gripped a five-dollar bill. "Here, take this. After you visit the surgeon, you can buy a new jacket and shirt, since I shredded the ones you're wearing."

The prisoner's eyes grew wide, and tears streaked down his cheek. "I have no words for your generosity and your compassion, Lieutenant Custer."

Custer reached out and shook the prisoner's hand. "If I'm captured, I hope to be treated as I have done you."

The provost guard stepped forward, pointing his revolver. "He's mine now, Lieutenant." The guard turned to the prisoner and jerked his head toward a field hospital. "Let's go, Reb," he snarled. "I don't got all day."

Safe at the Union defensive lines, still holding the reins while Harry regained his breath, Custer watched closely as the guard led his prisoner away.

"Lieutenant Custer."

He turned to see Alfred Waud reining up, smiling. Custer stood there flabbergasted, while his mind raced and momentarily tied up his tongue. *Waud … Alfred … sketch artist. Famous …*

Oh my God, Harper's Weekly! Custer's heart leaped. Had Waud sketched his cavalry charge?

"My, my, Lieutenant Custer," Waud exclaimed. "Will wonders never cease? That charge was an extraordinary expression of aristocratic glory. Beyond the Devil's handiwork."

Custer grinned, his impetuous pride swelling. Waud's words soared through him like one of his Williamsburg balloon rides over enemy lines. "Did you sketch me?"

"Indeed, my young dragoon." Waud extended the sketch book. "I felt like I was watching Marshal Murat adorned with his three-cornered, white-plumed, ostrich-feathered hat, leading one of his magnificent mounted charges."

Custer gripped the book and stared. There he was, depicted four horse lengths ahead of the thundering pack. Impish glee capered in his chest, vainglorious and divine. "This is a marvelous sketch."

Waud grinned. "I still have some shading. But as Shakespeare said, I'm not going to 'gild the lily.' I've truly captured your moment of glory."

"May I have a copy to send to my dear Libbie?"

"Yes, indeed. Because of you, Lieutenant Custer, this is certainly a great day for the Union cavalry."

Taking his leave of Waud, Custer cocked his hat and rode up the small knoll behind the Snickersville Pike through a breaking silence. Sunlight pierced through overhead branches, casting long, shimmering shadows like dancing giants. The two generals sat silently on their mounts. Pleasonton's face had a steady grin. Gregg puffed on his pipe, his bearded face nodding slightly. Custer's vanity flushed hot on his bubbling cheeks. He summoned all his bursting energy to throttle his overbearing pride. *Remember, Pleasonton is the commanding cavalry general. Must permit the general to start the congratulatory exchanges.* But he had saved the day and, from their expressions, both generals plainly knew it.

He reined up and saluted. Pleasonton waved his hand and started to speak, but Custer blurted rashly, "General Pleasonton,

I led the charge that stemmed the enemy advance, and the Rebels are retreating. Your cavalry corps is victorious."

"George," Pleasanton said, reaching for Custer's hand, "that was one hell of a charge."

Gregg chimed, "Lieutenant Custer, you truly enjoy crashing the gates of hell."

"Thank God for my wide-brimmed straw hat." He winked. "And I was drenched in Dixie Dust. The Rebels thought I was one of them and ignored me. I started for the flank of the enemy line and a Rebel spotted me and charged. I sabered him and put the spurs to Harry, circled the field, and raced back to our lines."

Pleasonton pumped his arm. "George, I'm citing you for valor and I'm sending your name to President Lincoln for a special promotion. I've not witnessed a more gallant man on the field. Whenever there is a daring expedition or hard fighting to be done, you're always among the foremost. Your charge led to the capture of one hundred prisoners and one Rebel flag."

"Thank you, General. I just hope someday I'm able to command a cavalry regiment. That's my dream."

"Be patient, George. Your wish may come sooner than you think."

He stared; frustration echoed in his voice. "Perhaps, General."

Custer saluted and trotted toward the aides' tent. Hooves echoed and at the edge of his vision a lone rider approached, sporting a desperado mustache. Captain Elon Farnsworth, a fellow aide-de-camp to General Pleasonton, reined up. Custer chuckled. Elon's black mustache looked as if it was pasted on.

Farnsworth grinned. "Damn, George. If that don't beat all. That was one hell of a charge. I thought you were a gone goose when you bolted into the Rebel line."

"My Rebel hat and boots and Custer luck saved my britches from being mustered out."

"We were getting ready to divvy up your belongings and draw straws for your prized studhorse, Roanoke."

Custer couldn't resist a tinge of sarcasm. "Knowing your stellar reputation at the University of Michigan, you would have managed to draw the long straw."

"Unlike you, George, I don't charge blindly and I'm not a fiddle-footed gambler. I don't leave matters of great import to chance. Your Iron Gray stallion would have been mine."

He shot Elon a faint half smile. A pause hovered as the heat of wounded vanity painted Custer's cheeks. The spoiled Wolverine collegian was clearly jealous of his glorious exploits and couldn't justify why he stayed out of harm's way, riding Pleasonton's coattails all day. "I don't remember you charging at all today, Elon. Am I mistaken?"

Elon's face reddened. "Pleasonton needed one of his loyal aides to do his duty and stay by his side performing courier duties."

He nodded. No need to keep needling, and his muscles ached. "I'm delighted to hear you're always following orders. Today was a great victory for General Pleasonton."

The deep ruts in Farnsworth's furrowed brow softened. He cracked a half smile. "Again, your crazy charge turned the tide and the Rebels retreated," Farnsworth said. "General Pleasonton sent a courier to General Hooker informing him of a Union victory."

"Thanks, Elon."

"Oh, by the way. Kilpatrick is furious his horse was shot, and you led the charge. When he heard that Alfred Waud sketched you, Kilpatrick went berserk, swearing and stomping about."

"Kilpatrick is a vainglory rogue. I ignored him at West Point and I'm ignoring him now. Good day to you."

He wheeled Harry, giving him his own head. The mount walked toward a big oak where Roanoke was picketed. He glanced at the golden orb slowly descending like the final curtain of a Broadway play. Foreboding fear crept down his throat and gripped his boyish heartstrings. Mercurial urges swirled inside. *Patient. Hmph.* Patience was for losers, not heroes. A dauntless spirit and daredevil exploits were the steppingstones to greatness. Didn't he just show he had a gift for fighting at the Battle of Aldie? Didn't he fight like a medieval knight? Who else in the Union cavalry led troopers like Napoleon's Murat? What more did he have to do to earn a command? His bedeviling critics said he was too young to command a regiment.

He shuddered and dismounted, handing Harry's reins to a groom. Harry's flanks were soapy with sweat. He snuggled his nose near the horse's ear and whispered, "Sorry I rode you so hard, Harry. The groom will take care of you, Old Boy."

The last flash of light from the setting sun shone as he chewed at the inside of his cheek. Without a command, he would never become the First Horseman of the Union army and earn the respect of Libbie's dad, who called him a hellion. *What the damn hell!* His feverish ambitions were being restrained by seniority-based promotions. Young, dashing heroes were not being rewarded with commands. Custer luck could not help him break the iron chains of advancement.

A brittle insecurity filled the pit of his stomach. Would he ever receive a command? *Not likely.*

Brigadier General Elon Farnsworth

2

Farnsworth — Sunday, June 28

11:30 a.m.
Captain Elon Farnsworth
Frederick, Maryland

A bruise-colored cloud scudded across the blue sky, chasing a couple cotton puffs. Farnsworth, his nerves pounding, stood in a patch of oak grass, holding the reins of his mount and General Pleasonton's light-colored charger, Gray Eagle. Beside him, Pleasonton's mounted guidon displayed the corps' cavalry pennant. On his other side, two of Pleasonton's armed orderlies remained mounted. His fingers trembled as he fished out his watch. Half past eleven. For now, he was Pleasonton's aide-de-camp. That could all change in the next few minutes, after Pleasonton's meeting with the army's new commanding general, George Meade.

Why did Meade want to visit with Pleasonton? He cringed. Meade had verbally assumed command at 7:00 this morning. A headquarters courier had visited Pleasonton at 10:00 a.m., requesting his immediate presence at Meade's tent. Was Meade going to fire Pleasonton as cavalry corps commander and replace him with General John Buford, commanding the First Cavalry Division, or General David Gregg, commanding the Second Cavalry Division?

He took another swig of water. Who in the hell was General Meade? What had Meade ever done, except command Fifth Infantry Corps? He shook his head. Hell, Meade looked like one of his dried-up professors at the University of Michigan instead of a flashing Napoleonic army commander.

He rocked back and forth, fidgeting. How would Meade and Pleasonton get along? Meade wore a grizzled beard and a bedraggled uniform and was known as a damned old goggled-eyed snapping turtle. Pleasonton wore a finely trimmed, waxed moustache and was known for his dapper uniform and dandy-like swagger. The two generals couldn't be further apart in taste and temperament. His stomach growled. This meeting couldn't possibly end well. If Meade fired Pleasonton, then he would probably be fired as well. Maybe General David Gregg or General John Buford would let him join their staff after Meade fired Pleasonton.

He stared out across a sea of white tents comprising army headquarters' bivouac. The windless air was thick with humidity and packed with tension. He cringed. God, what a morning. Pleasonton said Meade didn't give a hoot about political connections. He furrowed his brow. How was Uncle John Farnsworth, a former Union cavalry general and now a United States congressman from Illinois, going to help him? Uncle John and President Lincoln and Secretary of War Edwin Stanton were well acquainted and friends. But Meade didn't care who your uncle was and Pleasonton said Meade detested nepotism in the army. Fortune could not smile on this development. *Damn.*

He stiffened slightly, removed a handkerchief, and wiped his wet face. The murderous sun baked his blue jacket and trousers and charred his sweaty skin, chafing against the tightly woven wool. He gripped a canteen hanging from his saddle and took a long swig of warm water. He reached back with his free hand and pulled on his jacket collar. With his other hand, he poured a couple gulps from the canteen on his neck. He shivered as the water cascaded down his back like a sheet of glossy satin.

He glanced at the flaccid flag of the army's commanding general drooping from a pole between two large tents. Terror swirled in his fluttering stomach. A death blow had struck down another general in the morning of his army command. The freshly relieved commanding general, Joe Hooker, and the newly hired commanding general, George Meade, were sequestered in these two tents ten yards apart. A gloomy stillness filled the air as if headquarters camp was draped with an executioner's black hood. No one moved. It felt like he was standing in a petrified forest.

Meade's aide-de-camp, Major James Biddle, was the only officer standing outside Meade's tent. A horde of Hooker's staff officers and aides lingered about their newly dismissed commander's tent like mourners attending the viewing of a recently deceased relative. Inside Fighting Joe's tent, Adjutant General Seth Williams and Hooker were writing the letter to relieve the outgoing commander that both Hooker and Meade would sign before Hooker departed headquarters camp.

What an unbelievable action by Lincoln. He had relieved the army's popular commanding officer a few days before a great battle and replaced him with a dour man who was incapable of arousing anyone's passion by his mere presence. How in the hell could an unpopular commander defeat a popular one like Robert E. Lee? Impossible.

Meade emerged from his tent, followed by Pleasonton. Farnsworth gulped a big breath and held it. They halted under the tent awning and lit cigars. He whooshed the air out of his lungs and his heart thumped. The two generals chatted and smoked, plainly enjoying the moment. Strange. What had happened inside Meade's tent? Pleasonton had said that Meade detested the cavalry corps commanders, calling them pompous aristocrats who failed to coordinate with infantry. Meade also believed the cavalry was ineffective against infantry and artillery and thus of little tactical usefulness.

Pleasonton saluted and strode toward his small cavalcade. Meade lit another cigar and scanned the sea of white tents. Only Major Biddle stood near Meade.

Someone said, "Stand ready, boys, here comes General Pleasonton."

Pleasonton arrived sporting a grin as he mounted his steed. Farnsworth saluted and handed the reins to the general.

Pleasonton said, "I have great news, Elon."

He gulped a breath. "What's the news, sir?"

"I'll tell you as we ride back to the City Hotel." Pleasonton wheeled his horse around and trotted toward the Frederick town square.

Farnsworth swung into his saddle, spurred his mount, and pulled up beside the general.

Pleasonton grinned. "Meade approved my recommendation for you, Captain Merritt, and Captain Custer to be promoted to brigadier generals."[4]

His heart pounded against his ribs. "My God, that's electric news." He flashed a wide grin. "I was worried Meade might relieve you of your command."

Pleasonton shook head. "Just the opposite. Upon my recommendation, Meade has created a Third Cavalry Division. General Kilpatrick will command this new division. Read this."

He reached out and gripped Meade's order. "Brigadier General Farnsworth will command the First Brigade, consisting of the Fifth New York Cavalry Regiment, Eighteenth Pennsylvania Cavalry Regiment, First Vermont Cavalry Regiment, and First West Virginia Cavalry Regiment. Brigadier General Custer will command the Second Brigade, consisting of the First, Fifth, Sixth, and Seventh Michigan Cavalry Regiments." His pulse throbbed in his neck. *My God, I'm a general.*

"Sir, I'm honored to serve as the First Brigade commander." He paused and furrowed his brow. "Will President Lincoln approve our promotions?"

"Yes, he will. Your Uncle, Congressman Farnsworth, has the president's ear and supports your promotion to general. Meade expects the official confirmation by midnight."

He shook his head. What a shocking move by General Meade, promoting three cavalry captains to general. Maybe popularity had little to do with being a great commander.

"General Pleasonton. This promotion is so unexpected and amazing."

---

4 Brigadier General Pleasonton was promoted to major general on June 22, 1863, and was placed in command of the Cavalry Corps by order of General Joseph Hooker. As a staff aide to Major General Pleasonton, Lieutenant Custer was promoted from lieutenant to captain because of Pleasonton's two-star rank.

Pleasonton shot him a devilish smile. "In fact, Elon, General Meade ordered me to pin on your stars by noon. Do you have a one-star general's jacket?"

He chuckled. "No, sir. I was hoping to command a regiment as a colonel. I never expected to be promoted to brigadier."

"I don't want to disobey General Meade's first order to me. So, when we arrive at the City Hotel, let's see if I can scrounge up a general's jacket for you."

12:30 p.m.
Captain Farnsworth
City Hotel, Frederick, Maryland

Farnsworth stood in Pleasonton's hotel room with his hands behind his back. Pleasonton opened a trunk and retrieved a blue jacket with fourteen gold buttons and a star on each shoulder.

"Elon, try this on for size."

"Thank you, sir." Farnsworth reached for the jacket and slipped it on. "It fits fine, General. Thank you."

"It's the least I can do with all the support your uncle gave me when serving as one of my cavalry generals, and the support the congressman is giving to both of our careers."

"I shall wear your jacket with honor, sir."

"It's my lucky jacket. No enemy bullet has ever pierced it. I'm sure it will serve you equally as well."

6:15 p.m. (Sunset 7:44 p.m.)
Farnsworth
Richfield estate

Farnsworth threw his shoulders back and rocked in the saddle, a gleefulness bubbling inside. He was wearing Pleasonton's lucky general's jacket. He pulled in a deep breath, stretching the jacket to its fullest, and slowly let the pride in his mind flow out in a prolonged sigh that came from the very core of his soul. He scrutinized the last blue ribbons of mounted troopers trotting by in Pleasonton's Grand Review of Kilpatrick's newly established Third Cavalry Division. His heart burst with pride as he glanced at the 2,400 First Brigade troopers of his new command. He twisted in his saddle. Near a copse of trees on the bank of the Monocacy River, the First Vermont regimental guidon paused. Farnsworth trotted toward the regiment.

A mounted major approached and saluted. "General Farnsworth. I'm Major William Wells and I'm on the headquarters staff of Lieutenant Colonel Addison Preston, commanding the First Vermont."

Farnsworth returned the salute and smiled. "Major Wells, it's a distinct pleasure to meet you. I was most impressed with the Grand Review and with the First Vermont Regiment."

"Thank you, sir," Wells said. "Congratulations on your promotion to commanding general of First Brigade."

"Thank you, Major."

Wells pointed. "Lieutenant Colonel Preston is visiting with Captain Henry Parsons, commanding Troop L. Captain Parsons commands the First Battalion when we ride into battle. I command the Second Battalion."

Farnsworth nodded as he studied the major. Wells was a distinguished-looking officer with a sharply trimmed black beard, a wide-brimmed hat, sidearm, knee-high boots, and spurs. He looked the ideal mounted knight, rivaling the dashing English cavalier Prince Rupert.

"I'm most honored to meet you, William. I learned about your courageous exploits while serving on General Pleasonton's staff."

"Thank you, General. Would you like me to send a courier to request Colonel Addison's presence?"

"No. I will meet with Colonel Addison tomorrow, after Washington officially approves my promotion." He paused. "Tell me a bit about yourself, William."

"I enlisted as a private at twenty-three in the summer of '61. A few months later, in October, I helped raise Cavalry Company C and was commissioned second lieutenant. A month later I made captain, and in January I was promoted to major. I've been involved in nearly all the engagements of the First Vermont."

"Weren't you captured by Colonel John Mosby and his boys?"

"Yes, sir. I spent seven weeks in Libby Prison and was paroled last month. It's quite a story to tell, maybe on a long ride."

"I look forward to hearing it." Farnsworth smiled. "You and Mosby have something in common. The Gray Ghost was captured last year and imprisoned in the Old Capitol Prison in Washington for ten days before being exchanged."

Wells grinned. "I believe, General, that's all we have in common."

Farnsworth chuckled. "I might have to disagree. You are both quite the horsemen, fighters, and highly respected cavalry commanders. I'm fortunate to have you in First Brigade. And," he added, smiling, "I would choose you over the Gray Ghost any day of the week."

Wells sat up a little straighter. "Thank you, sir."

General Hugh Judson Kilpatrick

3

Kilpatrick — Sunday, June 28

1:00 p.m. (just over five hours earlier)
Brigadier General Judson Kilpatrick
Linganore farm, three and a half miles east of Frederick, Maryland
General David Gregg's headquarters

Cracking rumbles of thunder were closer, and the rushing wind was stiffening. Good. An afternoon downpour would cool down the murderous heat. Kilpatrick dismounted in front of the two-story brick house standing like a chateau overlooking the Monocacy River. He handed the reins to his fire-breathing assistant adjutant general, Captain Llewellyn Estes.

"Llew, this shouldn't take long. General Gregg said he wanted to chat for a few minutes before I meet with General Pleasonton."

Captain Estes nodded and remained mounted.

Kilpatrick stormed up the steps and into the house. His stomach fluttered. This must be good news. He strode into the dining room. Gregg was sitting at a dining table, studying a large map. Gregg's senior aide, Captain Henry Weir, stood with both hands placed on the table, staring down, but glanced up when Kilpatrick entered.

"General Gregg," Weir said, "General Kilpatrick is here."

Kilpatrick straightened his bantam frame and snapped a salute. "General Gregg, I heard you may have some good news."

Gregg glanced up and returned the salute. "Well, Judson, you are quite the rising star. Two weeks ago, Pleasonton recommended you for brigadier general, and Secretary of War Edwin Stanton approved your promotion. This morning you're being promoted to a division cavalry commander."

A prickly jolt cut down Kilpatrick's spine as his wide mouth stretched a Cheshire grin around his perfect teeth. "I heard

President Lincoln fired Fighting Joe Hooker this morning and replaced him with General George Meade. Did Meade promote me?"

"Yes," Gregg said. "General Pleasonton met with General Meade after he verbally relieved Hooker of command at seven this morning. Pleasonton convinced Meade to create a new Third Cavalry Division, and that's the division you will command. Your brigades will come from General Julius Stahel's Independent Cavalry Division."

"This is spanking news, sir! What happened to General Julius Stahel?"

"Since the Battle of Brandy Station, Virginia, on June 9, General Pleasonton has been waging a vigorous campaign to reshape the Cavalry Corps. I've had several discussions with Pleasonton about the reorganization. It is apparent that Pleasonton has deep-seated prejudices about foreign-born officers in senior positions. Major General Julius Stahel is a native of Austria-Hungary and he commands a cavalry division assigned to the Department of Washington. Stahel's command acts independently of the Army of the Potomac and Pleasonton's cavalry. This morning, Meade agreed to Pleasonton's reorganization to have Stahel's independent division transferred to Pleasonton's command."

"So, Meade relieved Stahel of his command?"

"Yes. Stahel's division no longer exists, and his troops now make up Pleasonton's new Third Cavalry Division, which you will command."

"Do you know what brigades I will command?"

"No. But I know that Stahel's three brigades are being re-formed into two large brigades."

Kilpatrick paused and rubbed his chin. Sudden apprehension shredded his swirling delight. "Sir, General Joseph Copeland commands Stahel's old First Brigade—the Fifth, Sixth, and Seventh Michigan Cavalry, and he is senior to me. How can I be his division commander if he outranks me?"

Gregg smiled. "The seniority issue won't be a problem. Upon Pleasonton's request, Meade is also relieving Copeland this morning. Pleasonton wanted Copeland relieved because he didn't know him, and he wanted officers to command now whom he knew. Stahel's two other brigade commanders are also relieved."

Kilpatrick scratched the back of his head. "Do you know who will replace Stahel's three brigade commanders?"

Gregg packed his pipe and lit it. "Captain George Armstrong Custer and Captain Elon Farnsworth are being promoted to brigadier general."

Kilpatrick stared. His throat tightened and his lungs heaved like hounds huffing after rabbits. "My God, is it true?"

"Yes."

"How can Meade promote two junior officers to general?"

"Apparently, when Colonel James Hardie, the army's assistant adjutant general, delivered Lincoln's order for Meade to relieve Hooker, General Halleck, in a separate letter, granted him power to appoint officers to command based upon ability, and not seniority."

"Ability? Farnsworth is not West Point. He is merely a Pleasonton staff protégé, one of the general's chronic coattail-riders. Do you know anything about him?"

"Rumor has it that Elon Farnsworth and General Pleasonton have been currying favor with Elon's uncle, Republican Congressman John Farnsworth, for advancement. And it so happens that President Lincoln and Congressman Farnsworth are close friends."

Fury flamed in his stomach. "So much for ability. Political friendships seem to govern Lincoln's promotions to general. Didn't Lincoln push for that fiendish idiot Dan Sickles, the Democratic Congressman, to be promoted to general and command the Third Infantry Corps?"

"Yep! But that's not the half of it." Gregg smirked. "Sickles killed his wife's lover in cold blood and got off pleading 'temporary insanity.' Lincoln still got him promoted to general."

Kilpatrick shook his head and shuddered. He stared at Gregg and choked out a question.

"Custer, a general? I'm flabbergasted. He graduated *last* at West Point. He is an impulsive daredevil and an incurable romantic who always breaks rules. Hell, West Point court-martialed the hotspur right after his graduation."

"I heard he was arrested for not stopping a cadet fistfight when he was officer of the guard. Apparently, Custer shouted, 'Stand back boys; let's have a fair fight.'" Gregg paused and puffed on his pipe. "Judson, I've heard you were pretty quick with *your* fists at West Point. Your epic forty-minute bout with a cadet twice your size is legendary at the Academy. I don't recall you being court-martialed."

Kilpatrick's face flushed with heat. "The cadet was a damn Southerner, and he was not the only turncoat who hailed from below the Mason-Dixon line that I beat to a pulp. But I wasn't interested in being court-martialed. So, I always fought at an arranged, discreet place."

Gregg puffed on his pipe. "I don't think Custer let the fight last forty minutes. Fortunately, the judge's penalty was a soft slap on the wrist."

Kilpatrick stood straight. Blood pounded in his ears. "I'll tell you one thing, General. If Custer disobeys my orders, he will get more than a slap on the wrist. How he made it through West Point is beyond me."

Gregg smiled, a thin cut erupting through his beard.

Kilpatrick continued, "My concern is that Custer hasn't commanded any unit since graduating from West Point. He has joined in cavalry attacks commanded by others and enjoyed some overrated notoriety. Some of his glory has come at my expense. But this was all done as an aide on several general staffs, including McClellan, Phillip Kearny, and Alfred Pleasonton."

"Did you see the *Harper's Weekly* drawing by Alfred Waud of Custer fearlessly leading *your* First Maine Cavalry at the Battle of Aldie?"

Kilpatrick flared, struggling to collect himself. "Yes, sir. But I'm the one that led the attack until my horse was shot."

Gregg's smile cracked wider, plainly enjoying the moment of throwing Custer's feats in his face.

"Custer is a publicity hound and takes every opportunity to show off when Waud or a reporter is watching."

"That may be true. But after witnessing Custer's daring charge and his slicing through the enemy lines and slaying two Rebels at Aldie, I would take the ripsnorter over any of Stahel's brigade commanders. Custer has a devil-may-care style, but he's a fearless warrior."

Kilpatrick stared. Heat rushed to his face. "With your permission, General, I will take leave and ride to General Pleasonton's headquarters for further orders."

"Thank you, Judson. Permission granted."

He paused. "I enjoyed serving under you, sir." He saluted, stepped outside, and grabbed the reins from Captain Estes.

"How did it go?" Estes asked.

"It's a mixed blessing. I'm Pleasonton's newly formed Third Division commander. It's the smallest of three divisions. I will command two cavalry brigades."

"That's great news, General."

"My two brigade commanders are boys. Twenty-three-year-old Custer and twenty-five-year-old Farnsworth."

"Hell, sir, Custer and Farnsworth are both captains. How is this possible?"

He shook his head. "God knows. But it's the same God that approved my promotion to division commander. So maybe the Almighty knows what he's doing."

Estes muttered, "Maybe I should be talking more with the Creator."

General Wesley Merritt

4

Custer — Sunday, June 28

2:00 p.m.
Captain George Armstrong Custer
The outskirts of Frederick, Maryland

Custer slumped forward in his saddle as he coaxed Roanoke through the dark afternoon downpour pelting the outskirts of Frederick. The former aide-de-camp to "Young Napoleon," General George McClellan, scowled, his pulse rate climbing.

An angry silence descended like a swooping owl. It had been two weeks since he led the victorious cavalry charge at the Battle of Aldie. That victory earned Pleasonton a second star, and the general's new rank required that Custer be promoted to captain. A gust of wind burst against his face; he lowered his chin to his chest and closed his eyes. In that unguarded moment, his mind raced like a jittery squirrel, failing to pull his heart along. His smoldering command hopes were a dying ember.

Roanoke squished and sucked through the sloppy, hoof-deep mud. Custer spurred him, but the steed kept his sluggish stride. Son of a bitch. Like Custer's own creeping cavalry career, Roanoke's feeble progress was mired in muck. Custer's heart hitched, wracking his body with bitterness. Would he ever rise above the rank of a staff captain? Risky boldness and reckless glory were tugging at his fickle heartstrings. Despite his fame for leading daredevil cavalry charges and capturing Rebel flags, he seemingly was doomed to be a staff officer to every cavalry general in the army. He bristled. Would rising to colonel, commanding a regiment, and becoming the *beau sabreur* of the Union cavalry ever come to pass? If it did, his feverish ambition would gallop toward its glorious destiny, a legendary dragoon in his own time. Or was his Custer luck running out, and his stalled career nearing its ultima Thule?

His blinking eyes scanned the distant picket lines. Torrents of stinging rain peppered his face and tattooed his broad-brimmed hat. His muscles blazed as if spit-roasted over a raging fire. He reached back and rubbed his knotted neck, turning toward his bugler and orderly, Joseph Fought. The bugler's mouth erupted into a gaping yawn.

"Joseph, stay sharp," Custer shouted. "No one in this damned army seems to know where Jeb Stuart's Invincibles are. The Rebel cavalrymen are like demonic ghosts and could materialize at any moment in these murky skies."

Fought shouted back over the rain, "My eyes are peeled, Captain Custer."

Custer scowled, his mouth rasping a sigh across his chapped lips. Seven months ago, President Lincoln had fired his boss and mentor, Major General George McClellan, as commander of the Army of the Potomac. Now branded as a "McClellan man," the 23-year-old West Point graduate was once again serving a general as a glorified messenger. The smoldering fire in his chest flared, scorching his throat. Republicans feared the deposed Young Napoleon would be the Democratic nominee for the upcoming presidential election and were hell-bent in killing off Little Mac's friends and aides.

Thunder cracked. Custer frowned and flicked the reins, aiming for the blue videttes hunkered on a low rise. Every hair on his neck stood erect. Many of his West Point schoolmates on both sides were commanding their own regiments and brigades. My God, even the inglorious Hugh Judson Kilpatrick was already a brigadier general and cavalry commander. But not him. His deadheaded career had as much chance of reblooming as a blood-boltered corpse.

He halted his horse at the end of the picket line. Fought pulled up beside him. Two mounted pickets trundled through the mud bath toward them and reined up.

A clean-shaven private said, "Are you two our reliefs? This rain could drown a goose, and we're drenched to the bone. We need a blazing fire to dry out."

A ragged flash flared in the darkish sky, and thunder cracked and hissed overhead.

The other vidette saluted and said, "He's an officer. See the two silver bars on his shoulder strap?"

The private snapped a salute. "Sorry, Captain. It's hard to see much of anything in this bucketing downpour."

Custer saluted. "Stay alert, boys. Fortune favors the bold. The Reb cavalry could be lurking close by." He grinned. "I'm not jesting. Maybe you can nab a few graybacks. In the meantime, I will try to check on your reliefs when I get back to headquarters."

"Thank you, sir."

Custer turned to Fought. "We've checked on the pickets and they need to be relieved as soon as possible before they catch pneumonia."

Custer wheeled Roanoke and started sludging back toward Frederick. He turned toward Fought, riding alongside. "Not a single picket recognized me during our ride along the picket line."

Fought said, "Your yellow locks should have been a dead giveaway."

"It's hard to recognize anybody in this soaker." He wiped the rain dripping from his mustache. "In fact, I'm not sure I could spot the two stars on George Meade's jacket if he trotted up."

"Who is Meade?"

"As of this morning, he's the new commanding officer of the Army of the Potomac."

"Another one? Old Abe sure likes firing generals."

"In Lincoln's reign of terror, the army's leader will most likely get his head lopped off in a matter of months. Meade makes the fourth commander in a year."

"I haven't heard of him. What makes our president think he'll do any better?"

"General Pleasonton told his staff this morning that Meade was the former Fifth Infantry Corps commander."

"What's he like?"

"He's known for his volatile temper, which erupts without notice like a bursting firecracker. Pleasanton said Meade was a straight shooter and will snap your head off if you fail to do your duty. But he's a hell of a lot better than Joe Hooker."

"What are his chances if he fights Lee?"

"Next to zero. Replacing commanders on the eve of a great battle is madness." He paused and grinned. "Honestly, Meade's chances of winning are as great as me being promoted to general in the next couple of hours."

Fought smiled. "Meade's chances are that good?"

"Meade is a McClellan man like me, so he will not last long. Either Lincoln will fire him after the next fight —win or lose — or the Republican congress will demand his resignation."

The rattling downpour started to ebb, and the dark curtain of clouds began to lift. They arrived on the hard-surfaced Frederick and Baltimore Pike Road.

He squinted and spotted Frederick's clustered church spirals. "Joseph, I'm soaked. Let's make a dash back to headquarters."

Custer spurred Roanoke up the Pike. At the edge of town, two bodies dangled from ropes like rag dolls. As he drew near, he spotted signs hanging from their stretched necks. Convicted spies. A stinging, sulphury taste like rotten egg filled his mouth. *No glory in being hung.* He shrugged. The two slithering snakes would hang for a couple of days as warning to other traitors.

He arrived at army headquarters and picked his way through the sea of white, cone-shaped tents until he spotted the dog tent pitched next to one of the twelve-foot-high tepees. He stopped in front of the V-shaped shelter and dismounted. A large white pointer with black eyes and spotted ears lunged from the small tent and loped over the tall grass and licked his knee-high Philadelphia riding boots.

"Hey Rose, how are you doing, girl?"

Custer bent his head and nuzzled Rose's neck.

"Kerchew!"

Custer glanced up. A tattered, hatless boy gripping a brush rushed out of the tent, wiping stringy snot from his nose with his shirt sleeve. Custer frowned at his young groom.

"Johnny, I told you to wear a hat when it's raining."

"It's just drizzling," Johnny blurted.

Fought said, "Your groom is a high-spirited colt, ever chomping at the bit, just like you, Captain."

"I look almost as old as you do, Captain Custer," Johnny sniffed.

"Not quite. I'm twenty-three and you're fourteen. I still have time to make you into a gentleman before this war is over, if you don't die from pneumonia."

"I'm going to go to West Point, like you, Captain Custer. That's where I will learn all that gentleman stuff."

Custer laughed. "I learned all my gentleman stuff at West Point in an off-limits tavern called Benny Havens. If you get an appointment, I will show you where I carved my initials next to the infamous cadet Edgar Allan Poe. A Custer-trained cadet should be well versed in Benny Havens traditions and shenanigans."

Johnny gripped Roanoke's reins and flipped them over the horse's head. "Come on, boy." He led Roanoke toward a large oak. Johnny tied off the reins to a branch and started brushing the stallion's flank. Custer turned and stepped toward the large tepee where Major General Pleasonton's aides were quartered. He threw open the flap and stepped inside. A dense veil of blue-gray cigar smoke waltzed in the air above several aides.

He muttered, "What the hell?"

2:10 p.m.
Custer
Pleasonton's staff officers' tent
The outskirts of Frederick, Maryland

Custer stepped inside the smoky tent. From the back of the tent a haughty voice shouted, "Gentlemen, General Custer has arrived!"

Custer's face flamed. "What the hell! I'm in no mood for any devilry." He was dripping wet, famished, and reeling from fatigue. He removed his hat and slapped it against his thigh, spraying waterdrops.

"General Custer, we are so glad you joined us."

"General Custer, you're in the wrong uniform."

He scowled at each culprit, pressing toward them. Everyone sported giddy grins as if they had pranked some plebes. Again, he muttered, "What the hell?"

Captain George Yates, his friend from Monroe, Michigan, and one of General Pleasonton's aides, stood and saluted. "General Custer, you grace us with your presence."

Molten anger surged upward, searing his throat. He shouted, "Enough of your boyish mockery." He narrowed his eyes, and his nostrils flared like a charging bull. "You may laugh, boys," he stammered. "Laugh as long as you please, but I will be a general yet, for all your chaff. You see if I don't, that's all."

Yates said, "Didn't you blurt out a week ago at Upperville that you intended to be a general someday? Why are you making us wait?"

A burst of high-pitched laugher ripped through the tent, scorching his ears.

Custer clenched his fists and stepped toward Yates, who nearly doubled over with laughter. Yates's eyes flashed and he pointed toward the table as he squealed, "Look on the tabletop."

Custer snapped his head around, spotted a big, fat envelope, and snatched it. *My God ... a War Department envelope.* His eyes riveted on the addressee. To: Brigadier General George A. Custer, U.S. Vols. His heart punched against the back of his throat. "Is this a damn joke?" he shouted.

"No, it's not," Yates said. "General Pleasanton's courier delivered the envelope while you were out gallivanting around in the rain. Did the videttes address you as General Custer?"

"If this is part of your prank, I'm going to thrash you, Yates."

Yates cracked a smile. "You're too damn skinny to kick my ass, boy general."

Custer's fingers trembled as he opened the envelope. His eyes scanned the order. *Oh, my God.* He had been promoted to brevet brigadier general. A prickly chill rattled his spine. He swallowed hard. His mind whirled as tears welled in his eyes. *Don't cry. You deserve this.* He wilted into a chair next to the table. At twenty-three years old, he was the youngest Union general by two years.

"Congratulations, George." Yates slapped his back. "Pleasonton's orderly requested your presence after you read the order."

He nodded. His heart throbbed as mingled wonderment swirled inside. After a moment, he glanced up.

Yates shouted, "Three cheers for General Custer." Several voices shouted huzzahs.

He stood and stared, holding his breath. A waterfall of excitement cascaded down into the bottomless pit of his brittle soul. His mind smiled, even if his face couldn't, just yet. His unexpected promotion from captain to general confirmed his greatness for all to see. The adulation he craved from others was momentarily assuaged.

The staffers shouted, "Speech, speech, speech!"

He clapped on his hat and tilted his head as a curtain raised in front of his feelings. His mind's eye saw him on a Broadway stage, staring at the audience. He raised his arms outward.

"I'm most pleased to be the youngest cavalry general in this great war. The next time you see me I will be in full costume fitting for a flamboyant cavalry general."

They clapped and cheered.

Custer bowed his head. "Thank you, all. I will visit you boys after I pay my respects to General Pleasanton."

He bit his quivering lips as he gazed at Captain Yates. A fierce throbbing pulsed inside; his skin tingled. Custer luck had prevailed. He was finally launching upon his destiny as the Union's greatest horseman. "George, I shall give you my first order as a general. The pickets are soaked and shivering. With the skies clearing, let's have a fresh batch of videttes relieve those troopers early."

"Yes, sir, General Custer."

The boy general paused and smiled.

"I like the ring of General Custer," Yates said.

A thrill shivered through him at the sound of it. "So do I, George. So do I."

2:30 p.m.
Custer
Bivouac tent

Custer surged forward through the dying rain, his boots as light as the paws of an attacking cougar. The heat of pride flushed his face. Custer luck had rekindled glory's flame burning brightly inside. A golden shard of light sliced through the breaking blackness. His breath quickened. He was the youngest general in the Union army. He slipped his hand into his jacket pocket and patted the locket safeguarding his prized ambrotype. What would Libbie's father think of him now?

Ahead, Fought and Johnny were brushing Roanoke's withers with a dandy brush, removing mud and sweat. Roanoke whinnied. "See Johnny, it's just like sweeping a floor," Fought said.

"Joseph," Custer shouted. "Look, Joseph."

Joseph spun around and dropped the dandy brush into Roanoke's grooming bucket. Custer rushed toward him, gripping the letter.

Joseph's eyes widened. "Is it mail call? Do you have one for me?"

Custer skidded to a stop, brandishing the letter like a saber. "I've been made a brigadier."

"The deuce you have," said Fought. He thrust his hand out, and Custer gripped it.

"I had no idea this was going to happen." He grinned. "The new commanding general, George Meade, promoted me today upon General Pleasonton's recommendation."

"Does Meade know you?"

Custer dropped the handshake and wiped his arm across his mouth. "No, I don't think so. But he is rapidly becoming my favorite general after Little Mac. Here, read the telegraph." He handed the order to Fought. The bugler's eyes stared at the order as the corners of his mouth tilted up in a huge grin.

"Let's toast," Fought said. "I have a flask in the tent."

Custer shook his head. "No spirits." He turned toward his groom. "Johnny, grab a water canteen and three tin cups, and we shall toast with water."

Fought gaped and pulled on his ear, plainly shocked by his superior's abstinence.

"Joseph, I shall explain. Two years ago, I swore off drinking during a visit with my sister, Ann, who lives in Monroe. I went out with some local boys one night and became foolishly drunk. Ann was mighty upset, and I swore on God's bones to her I would never drink again. I'm honoring that oath. I don't want liquor to interfere with my revived cavalry career."

Fought nodded.

Johnny passed out the cups and filled them.

Custer raised his cup. "To my swashbuckling dragoons: may they be promoted or die!" They clinked cups like Alexandre Dumas's three musketeers. He gulped a swig, wiped his lips.

"Congratulations, General Custer," Fought said. "I'm proud to serve you." He raised his cup again. "To your *joie de combattre*. I know no one who has a greater love for battle than you."

Custer grinned. "Thank you. I agree."

Johnny piped up. "Can I still be your boy groom, General Custer?"

He frowned. "Johnny, you should say, 'May I still be your boy groom?' The answer is yes. Here's my cup."

Johnny grinned and gripped the cup.

He rubbed the boy's head. "I'll make a gentleman out of you yet."

"Thank you, sir. I'm looking forward to learning the gentlemanly ways of Benny Havens."

Custer turned back to Fought. "I don't have time to get a new uniform." He winked. "I may have a colonel's jacket and a couple of colonel's eagles in my trunk, just in case someone thought I would make a good regiment commander."

"You have a colonel's jacket?" Fought rubbed his head. "The next rank after captain is major and then lieutenant colonel. Were you planning on skipping these ranks?"

"I was politicking pretty hard with the Michigan troopers to sign a petition promoting me to command one of the new Wolverine volunteer regiments. I had a colonel's jacket and couple of eagles just in case I was successful. I wasn't. Now I need a general's jacket and the stars to show my rank."

"Let me see what I can scrounge up. Do you want me to find a Union hat for you?"

"No, I love my Confederate slouch hat." He cracked a devilish grin. "It protects my fair skin from the sun and the Rebels."

Fought grinned and swung aboard his mount. "I will see what I can find in Frederick."

"Johnny, keep a good eye on Rose. I've been summoned to pay my respects to General Pleasonton."

Johnny shouted, "Will do, General Custer!"

3:00 p.m.
Custer
General Pleasonton's headquarters, City Hotel
Frederick, Maryland

Custer reeled with breathless exuberance, trotting down West Patrick Street. What an epic achievement! His feverish ambitions had been exceeded beyond his wildest dreams. He was the youngest general in the Union army.

"General Custer! Congratulations."

Warmth flooded his face. General Pleasonton was leaning over the second-floor balcony railing of the four-story City Hotel, grinning and waving.

Custer snapped a smart salute, tethered Roanoke to a rail, and sprung into the lobby of the white-bricked hotel. He bounded up the stairs and skittered down a hallway. His heart hitched like a jerked rope. He halted before a sentry standing outside Pleasonton's room.

The sentry saluted, saying, "General Pleasonton is expecting you, sir," then knocked on the door and opened it.

He stepped inside. Pleasonton rushed through the balcony door and gripped Custer's hand with both of his. "Congratulations, George! I'm most proud of you."

"Thank you, sir." Custer stood with his legs apart and his hands clasped behind his back. His stomach was a spinning whirligig. Pleasonton ambled over to a writing table sitting next to a brick fireplace and put on his reading glasses. He was short and slight of build, and his trimmed, waxed mustache flowed into his ducktail beard.

Pleasonton pointed to a fruit bowl. "George, would you like to eat?"

"No thank you, sir. I'm well."

The general picked up a piece of paper. "I met with General Meade this morning after he assumed command from Hooker. Meade asked me to recommend which cavalry officers should be promoted to brigadier general. He wanted aggressive leaders who would take the fight to the enemy, because he is ordering the cavalry tomorrow to search for the Rebel army. I recommended you, Captain Elon Farnsworth, and Captain Wesley Merritt."

"I'm honored you would recommend me, sir, and that General Meade approved your decision." Custer paused and swallowed. His face tightened, and his insides started rattling like an earth tremor. "But are you sure the president will appoint me? I'm young, I hold a low rank, and, being a McClellan man, I don't have a single friend at Court."

"General Meade told me that the president will approve your promotion."

Custer's lungs froze as he struggled to breathe. Fire from his heart flared to his face, searing his cheeks. Amazing. Beyond belief. After a few erratic heartbeats, he grinned and shook his head.

Pleasonton reached into the bowl and picked up an apple slice. "I've relieved Brigadier Copeland of command of the Michigan Cavalry Brigade." He bit the slice. "I don't know about his leadership abilities, and I want only subordinates on whom I can rely. I do know about your fighting abilities, George."

"I love fighting, sir."

"I know you do. Your performance two weeks ago at Aldie with the First Maine Cavalry was spectacular. When surrounded by Rebels you somehow cut your way out. That's why we need you, George. A general who will take the fight to the enemy and not only survive, but win."

"Aldie was a close shave, as they say."

Pleasonton grinned. "George, I'm sure you will face numerous more close shaves, and I expect you to survive them. Would you care to assume command of the Second Brigade?"

"Absolutely, sir." If electrical charges could escape his body, he would have been a lightning bolt.

"Good. The Michigan Brigade consists of the First, Fifth, Sixth, and Seventh Cavalry Regiments."

Custer grinned. "All Michigan boys."

"The brigade's full strength is 4,800. But it's only mustering about half the number of sabers due to casualties it has suffered in previous campaigns." Pleasonton drew a breath and beamed. "The Fifth and Sixth Cavalry Regiments are armed with the new seven-shot Spencer repeating rifles. In a minute's time they can get off a dozen .52-caliber rounds. Those two regiments will hit hard with rifles such as those."

"What about artillery support?"

"Your brigade is supported by the three-inch rifled guns of Battery M, Second U.S. Artillery. This is a regular U.S. Army battery and it's fought in over twenty engagements and every major battle, from the Battle of First Bull Run to the recent fight at Brandy Station."

"Isn't it commanded by Alexander Pennington?"

"Yes. Weren't you and Pennington at West Point together?"

"Pennington was two years my senior at the Military Academy. What's his current rank?"

"Pennington is still a Brevet Captain."

Custer paused. "That's hard to believe. Pennington is an excellent officer."

"I agree. Pennington will be promoted soon, with Brigadier General Henry Hunt now commanding the artillery arm of the army. Pennington's regulars are tenacious fighters and perhaps the best unit at throwing shot and shell accurately.

"Meade also promoted Kilpatrick today to command the Third Cavalry Division. Kilpatrick's division will consist of two brigades—yours, and Farnsworth's First Brigade. So, I'm assigning you to take command of Second Cavalry Brigade, in Kilpatrick's Third Cavalry Division."

"Yes, sir." He bristled as he bit on his lip. His West Point schoolmate was a frothy braggart with the raging fury of a fighting cock. During impetuous Kilpatrick-led cavalry fracases, his commanders seemed to drop like scythed cornstalks. But the fiery Irishman always emerged unscathed. Kilpatrick was a glory hunter and had no qualms about riding over the graves of his men to fame.

"When do I assume command?" His voice tautened, breaking the momentarily muffled silence.

"As soon as your promotion is confirmed by General Halleck. General Meade said that he believed the confirmation telegraph will arrive by midnight." Pleasonton reached into the bowl and picked out a couple of olives and popped them into his mouth.

Custer let out a muted sigh. "Good." Surging excitement flooded his face. His mind swirled, trying to fathom his meteoric rise to general. *Unbelievable. Just unbelievable.* General Meade didn't know him but risked his career promoting him from captain to general, based upon Pleasonton's recommendation. *What type of leader does this?* He made a promise then and there to himself. *As God as my witness, I will prove Meade and Pleasonton did right by promoting me.*

"I'm riding out to the Richfield estate. That's General Stahel's former headquarters, and that's where two of your four regiments are bivouacking, along with Pennington's Battery M. I'm going to spend the evening there. Now that you're a general, you're welcome to spend the night in this room here."

"That's most generous of you."

"In fact, why don't you ride with me to the Richfield estate, and you will be able to get a glimpse of the First Michigan and Seventh Michigan Regiments and say hello to your old friend Captain Pennington. I plan on holding a Grand Review of the new Third Cavalry Division at five o'clock on the Richfield farm fields. You're welcome to observe."

"I would be honored to accompany you, sir."

Custer trotted next to Pleasonton down a road cutting through a green meadow covered with waving stalks of corn. He felt like crowing. *God, what a glorious moment.*

Pleasonton pointed. "There's the Richfield manor."

Ahead was a white, two-story mansion sitting on a plateau. The estate was a vast tract of land easily accommodating the three thousand horsemen from Farnsworth's new cavalry brigade and half of Custer's new cavalry brigade. Captain James Wade, Pleasonton's acting aide-de-camp, approached.

Wade reined up. "General Pleasonton, your headquarters are ready."

Pleasonton nodded. "Very well."

Custer's mouth curled into a devilish smile. "General, with your permission I would like to visit Captain Alexander Pennington while you're settling in at your new headquarters."

"Permission granted. When you are done visiting, I would like for you to call on me at the manor."

"Yes, sir."

Wade pointed. "General Custer, Pennington's battery is in that copse of trees next to the Monocacy River."

Custer cantered toward the trees shading Pennington's Battery M, spotting six three-inch rifled cannons and caissons along the way. Spindle-shanked Pennington glanced up and waved as Custer trotted up. Custer's six-foot tall West Point friend had a chiseled face and piercing, light-blue eyes. His flat, circular-top kepi cap with a leather visor was cocked slightly to the right and forward, the front panel decorated with the number 2 sewn atop two gold-crossed cannons. He wore a Van Dyke beard with lengthy stubble reaching up to the bottom of his ears.

Pennington waved. "Fanny, it's great to see you again," he said, using Custer's nickname from West Point. He cracked a sly grin. "Are you mossing around the Michigan cavalry boys trying to petition them again to be their regimental commander?"

Custer swelled with pride as he dismounted. Pennington and his fellow West Point upperclassmen had given him the pet name Fanny for his long, golden locks. He reached out and shook Pennington's hand. "Alexander, I have some stunning news. General Meade just promoted me to brigadier general and General Pleasonton gave me command of the Michigan Brigade."

Pennington raised an open right hand toward Custer. "Fanny, please keep your voice down. My boys might think you are serious. I don't want them calling you a foolhardy jokester behind your back."

Custer winked. "I'm not joking."

"Come on, Fanny. The first requirement for being a general is that you can grow a beard."

"I have a mustache and locks of golden hair."

"Hell, Fanny, most of the officers in my battery and the Michigan Cavalry Regiment sport a full face of whiskers, and I'm not sure you can. With that baby face of yours, you still appear to be a fumbling, beardless cadet two years my junior at West Point."

Custer frowned. "Growing a beard doesn't make one a leader of men. Napoleon's greatest cavalry commander was Marshal Joachim Murat, and he didn't wear a beard."

"Well, Shakespeare said that 'He that hath a beard is more than a youth, and he that hath not beard is less than a man.'"

"I don't recall studying any battles at West Point that Shakespeare fought. But I did study Murat's beardless cavalry victories at Jena and Austerlitz."

"Fanny," Pennington gasped. "You're not fooling, are you? You're being honest."

"Yes, Alexander. General Meade is expecting President Lincoln to confirm my promotion by midnight."

Pennington gawked like a gaping fish. A silence erupted as the cannoneer stared, his mind apparently struggling. Plainly flabbergasted, he shook his head and held out his hand. "Congratulations, George. You have my total support."

"Thank you."

Pennington chuckled. "What an ironic twist. The screw-up 'goat' graduating last in his class at West Point is now a brigadier."

Custer grinned. "What about those two 'goats,' Pickett and Heth, now Confederate division commanders? I just think we goats had more fun than you and the other cadets."

"You may be right. I know one thing. Except for cadet Edgar Allan Poe, you goats hold the cadet record for stealing off the West Point grounds and scurrying a mile south to Benny Havens."

"I loved that little tavern just as much as Poe. I agree with Edgar when he called Benny 'the sole congenial soul in the entire Godforsaken place.'" He cracked a smile. "The forbidden locality of Benny Havens possessed stronger attractions for me than the study and demonstrations of a problem in Euclid."

"I still remember the illegal graduation party you and a few other delinquents hosted at Benny Havens for Stephen Ramseur, Wesley Merritt, and me."

"God, what a drunken night!" Custer grinned. "I call sneaking out of the academy that night justified defiance."

Pennington laughed. "Oh, is that what you call it?"

"You know, I'm lucky to be alive. I almost broke my neck darting down those mountain goat steps in the cliffside."

"Didn't Jefferson Davis almost break his neck on those same steps when he was a cadet?"

"Yes, but that was thirty years ago."

Pennington said, "Didn't you tell me once that Jefferson Davis signed your appointment to West Point when he was Secretary of War?"

"Yes, he did. Maybe Jeff Davis was hoping I would fight for the South."

Pennington grinned. "After several mugs of flip rum that night, I remember us singing 'In the army there's sobriety, promotions very slow. So, we'll sing our reminiscences of Benny

Havens, oh!'" Pennington slapped him on the back. "But your news, George, of bolting from staff captain to brigadier general in one leap, means we will have to add another verse to Benny Havens, oh!"

First Lieutenant Carle Woodruff rode up and saluted. "Captain Pennington, Battery M is ready for your inspection prior to General Pleasonton's Grand Review."

"Thank you, Carle. I'll be right along after finishing with Brigadier General Custer."

Woodruff cracked a suspicious smile and held it. After a momentary pause, the lieutenant departed, shaking his head, plainly not convinced of Custer's new rank.

"I think Lieutenant Woodruff believes you were pranking him," Custer said.

Pennington paused and pursed his lips. "I would recommend you not visit the senior officers of the First and Seventh Regiments this evening until your confirmation comes through. This will give me time to let them know you will be arriving tomorrow morning as their new commander."

"That makes sense. I'm not expecting a warm reception. But I'm looking forward to turning this brigade into the Flying Devils of Michigan."

"Are there any other changes I should know about?"

"Yes. General Stahl is relieved of his command. General Kilpatrick is going to assume command of the newly formed Third Division, consisting of the First Brigade commanded by Elon Farnsworth, whom Meade also promoted today to general, and the Second Brigade, commanded by me. Meade also promoted Captain Wesley Merritt to brigadier general, and Wesley is going to command the Reserve Brigade in General Buford's First Division."

Pennington shook his head. "My God, Meade promoted three cavalry captains to general today. This is the most unbelievable jump in rank that I've ever heard of. Meade is really risking his reputation to promote three young captains."

"I'm not going to let Meade down. But I'm a little concerned about Kilpatrick commanding our division. He was a class ahead of me at West Point and a class behind you. He sure enjoyed running it on me my plebe year. He could be a heartless fiend. What are your thoughts about him?"

"I have the same concerns as you do, Fanny. Kilpatrick was a feisty little man and when insulted erupted like a volcano with his fists. I just remember Kilpatrick was the leader of the Abolitionists at West Point. All the cadets south of the Mason-Dixon line hated him. He was spring-loaded to fight any Southerner."

"One of his big faults is that he exaggerates his accomplishments on the battlefield." Custer scowled.

Pennington's brow furled. "His biggest weakness is that he acts blindly and violently when faced with a tight situation. It seems he resorts back to his cadet days of just fist-fighting until his opponent gives up." Pennington snickered. "Didn't Kilpatrick spend three months in Old Capitol Prison, charged with conduct unbecoming an officer?"

"Yes. Six months ago, he was finally released after being arrested for several illicit misdeeds."

Pennington's eyes narrowed. "Illicit misdeeds?"

"I've heard a couple stories. One is that he took a twenty-dollar gold bribe from an army sutler."

"Why?"

"Kilpatrick used his influence to get the man a contract to sell one hundred horses to Kilpatrick's regiment."

"My God!"

"Another story is that he was convicted of rounding up horses on Virginia plantations along the Potomac River. Then he gave them to sutlers, who acted as Kilpatrick's agents in selling them to the army."

Pennington shook his head. "Why would he do that?"

Custer took a deep breath. "You know Kilpatrick, he loves staying in fancy hotels that cost a lot of money."

"I haven't had much of a chance to observe him in a fight," Pennington said. "I just read about his exploits in the newspapers. The newspapers claimed he was a hero for gallantly leading a charge at the Battle of Big Bethel, and for being the first Union officer wounded in the war."

"That story is hogwash." Custer's face flamed. "A Rebel gunner shot a gust of grapeshot toward Kilpatrick's group and one of the pellets scratched his rump. How could Kilpatrick be nicked in the arse while supposedly facing the enemy and leading a charge?"

Pennington chuckled. "Maybe Kilpatrick knows how to lead with his back toward the enemy." The half-amused look slid away and he narrowed his eyes. "Do the soldiers respect him?"

"Despite his feisty nature, he is not a leader I want to follow into battle. In a fight he becomes highly excitable and nervous, acting on impulse and making rash decisions. Besides his arrogance and thirst for glory, I'm concerned he has no loyalty for his troopers."

Pennington glowered.

Custer scowled. "His men call him Kill-Cavalry. He loves slipping behind enemy lines and conducting raids. Then he makes ridiculous claims about his success and feeds these stories to the nearest war correspondent he can find. But he has no shame ordering his men to certain death."

Pennington's face turned bright red as he cursed a flagrant oath. "What a vainglory bastard."

Custer cocked his head at the echo of trotting hooves, and a colonel and guidon carrying the Seventh Cavalry Pennant approached.

Pennington pointed. "That's Colonel William Mann, commander of the Seventh Cavalry Regiment."

"Then you have work to do. I'm going to take my leave, Alexander. I will see you early tomorrow morning."

Pennington smiled and saluted. "Congratulations again, General Custer."

"Thank you, Alexander." He returned the salute. "I know I can depend on you when the shells and shot start flying. Hopefully, I will see you early tomorrow morning, wearing my stars." He mounted Roanoke and trotted toward the Richfield estate.

His mind bounced in step with Roanoke's clapping hooves as he rode toward the Richfield manor. A big battle was brewing, and he had little time to whip the Wolverines into Flying Devils. He had a previous experience whipping the First New Jersey Infantry Brigade into shape as a staff officer under the tutorship of the Human Thunderbolt, Fighting Phil Kearny. The One-Armed Demon of Battle had his arm blown off during the Mexican War and had served as military attaché with the French army in Italy and Algeria, twice winning the Légion d'honneur. From Kearny he had learned the value of brutal discipline in forging hard-as-nails troopers.

He arrived at the Richfield estate and found Pleasonton standing next to a large window.

Pleasonton glanced up. "George, when I learn of your promotion confirmation, I will send a courier to the City Hotel."

"Yes, sir." A torrent of uncertainty swirled inside. What if the president turned down the promotions? Lincoln despised McClellan boys.

"General Meade is in a foul mood, learning that General Hooker didn't have a plan for pursuing and engaging Lee's army. Meade is a planner. He said he would develop a plan and have it delivered to his corps commanders by midnight. He plans to start marching the army early tomorrow morning."

"Does Meade have a feel for what the enemy is doing?"

Pleasonton shook his head. "No. Intelligence on Confederate movements is poor. Meade doesn't know where the Confederate's three infantry corps are. He believes one of Lee's infantry corps is marching toward York and the other two are west of South Mountain. But Meade received reports that Jeb Stuart's cavalry is operating near Washington, D.C."

"That doesn't make sense. Since the cavalry screens infantry movements, does Meade believe Lee's army is east of Frederick and threatening the capital?"

"Meade doesn't know because he has received conflicting intelligence reports that are more like rumors than precise information. He doesn't know why Lee's cavalry is operating east of us. But he said that Lee would never let Jeb Stuart gallivant about on his own. Lee is a master planner, and Meade believes Lee is using Stuart's cavalry to set up a trap."

"I hope Meade doesn't lollygag about like Hooker. The new commanding general should march the army rapidly northward to fight Lee."

Pleasonton nodded. "Despite being filled with uncertainty, Meade is leaning toward extending the army's front twenty or so miles to the northeast like a fan."

Custer pulled on a golden lock. "Why doesn't Meade march the army directly north? That way he might catch one of Lee's corps operating independently and destroy it before Lee can mass his three corps?"

"Good idea. I suggested this plan. But General Halleck ordered Meade to cover Baltimore and Washington at all times. By marching straight north, Meade would risk Lee scooting around our eastern flank, threatening Baltimore."

"If that's the case, and Jeb Stuart is operating east of us and potentially screening the movements of Rebel infantry, why not march the army forward on a sharp northeast vector?"

"The problem is if Lee's two out of three infantry corps are operating west of South Mountain, Meade would risk uncovering Lee's western flank, allowing him to simply swing around us and gain a clear shot at the capital."

"Damn. General Halleck's orders to cover Baltimore and Washington at all times has severely restricted Meade's freedom to maneuver as he sees fit."

"Meade is not pleased with Halleck's order." Pleasanton paused and wiped his face. "To screen the army's fan-like movements to the northeast tomorrow, I proposed, and Meade agreed, that General Buford's First Cavalry Division would screen to the north and northwest. General Kilpatrick's Third Cavalry Division would screen to the northeast. General Gregg's Second

Cavalry Division would screen to the east, searching for Jeb Stuart's cavalry."

A jolting adrenaline rush tingled Custer's skin. Maybe Kilpatrick's division would run into Stuart's cavalry. What an opportunity for a Napoleonic cavalry battle.

"I'm ordering Kilpatrick's Third Division to march to Littlestown tomorrow. The Fifth and Sixth Michigan Regiments are operating today near Gettysburg. I've ordered those two regiments to ride to Littlestown. When they arrive, you will assume command of them."

"Yes, sir."

Custer paused, shifting his feet. "With your permission, sir, I would care to defer the Grand Review at five o'clock. I want to be confirmed by Washington as a general before meeting my brigade."

Pleasonton paused and scratched his chin. "I concur. The purpose of the Grand Review is so I can get a feel for the condition of Stahel's former cavalry division."

"Thank you, General." He saluted and was stepping toward the door when Pleasonton stopped him. "General Custer."

He stopped and turned.

"You're going to need a new uniform, with a pair of stars and a brigadier insignia."

"Yes, sir." He cracked a grin. "I'm working on that."

"You need to select a staff."

"Yes, sir." Custer saluted, whirled, and swept outside toward Roanoke. Impish glee fluttered in his stomach, as if he had swallowed swirling snowflakes. Soon he would be a general commanding a brigade. Custer luck.

5:10 p.m.
Custer
Custer's tent, near Frederick, Maryland

Custer paced outside his tent.

Private Peter Boehm strode up and saluted. "Reporting as ordered, sir."

Custer returned the salute. "Private Boehm, General Meade just promoted me to brigadier general. I would like for you to be my bugler and orderly."

Boehm grinned, showing his large, beaver-like teeth. "I'm honored to be on your personal staff, sir."

"Good. Are you familiar with the Irish drinking song "Garryowen"?

"I've played it a few times."

"Well, practice up, because that's the song that reminds me of a roaring and trampling cavalry charge." He paused and grinned. "Be prepared to blow your trumpet loudly, because I'm going to lead many cavalry charges, just like my boyhood hero, Captain Charles O'Malley, the Irish Dragoon."

"Will do, General."

"Private Fought will also be on my personal staff. Johnny Cisco, who reminds me of a loyal stray dog, will stay as my groom and help care for the headquarters' horses."

Boehm nodded.

"As I'm no longer a staff officer messing at General Pleasonton's table, I shall need a cook. Can you cook?"

"No, sir."

"When I visit with General Kilpatrick I will ask if I can borrow one of his mess cooks until we can secure one."

5:30 p.m.
Custer
Near Custer's tent

Custer leaned under a large oak, standing like a lone sentry on a grassy mound. Roanoke, untethered, grazed beneath the tree's canopy. The bright sun jostled with Frederick's church spirals as it dipped toward the South Mountain range. He wiped his brow with a handkerchief and tilted the brim of his felt slouch hat toward his eyes. Under his breath he hummed the Irish jig "Garryowen." He murmured, "Our hearts so stout have got us fame. For soon 'tis known from whence we came. Where'er we go they fear the name, of Garryowen in glory." A trooper trotted toward him.

The officer halted and saluted. "General Custer, I am Second Lieutenant William Colerick. General Pleasonton directed Colonel Charles Town to appoint an aide-de-camp from the First Michigan to your staff. Colonel Town selected me, sir."

Custer smiled. "Please dismount, William." Colerick was nearly as tall as he was and had grey eyes, a mustache, and a long goatee. "Why did Colonel Town select you?"

"General Pleasonton told Colonel Town that he was to select a former enlisted trooper who had performed well and had been promoted to an officer. I joined the First Michigan as a First Sergeant, Company L." Colerick paused and lowered his gaze. After a long moment, his darting eyes glanced up and his face twitched.

Custer studied the second lieutenant, who was fidgeting like a condemned prisoner standing before a firing squad. The weighted pause was unnatural. Something was amiss. "Well, spit it out."

Colerick's breath hitched. He said with a throaty rattle, "General Pleasonton also said he wanted your first aide-de-camp to be a few years older than you, sir."

Custer stared like a stalking cougar. A muffled silence. His jaw tightened as he curbed the searing rage rising in his throat. Pleasonton must be wary of the rugged Wolverines' jolting retort of a boyish greenhorn assuming command. Many of the older First Michigan troopers had sons who looked about his own age. Having an older fighter like Colerick on his staff made sense. It was a good move by Pleasonton.

"How old are you, William?"

"I just turned thirty-six this month, sir."

"I'm twenty-three. We're going to get along fine. I'm delighted to have a ripsnorter like you on my personal staff. Where are you from?"

"Almont, Michigan."

"A mere ninety miles north of my hometown, Monroe. Let's ride to the City Hotel, where I will set up my temporary headquarters."

Colerick beamed, plainly relieved with the unexpected stay of a verbal lashing. Warmth settled Custer's mind. Colerick's talents were fighting, and that was why Colonel Town selected him to be his aide-de-camp.

5:45 p.m.
Custer
Riding toward Frederick

Custer headed toward Frederick with Colerick riding alongside. Custer grimaced, his ragged breath lurching from a dark, empty core of insecurity. The pure excitement flooding his body for the past few hours had ebbed. He was not a full-fledged brevet general until President Lincoln approved Meade's promotion recommendation. Pleasonton seemed assured the promotion would be approved before midnight. But self-doubt squeezed like a tight fist around his hope. How could a staff captain make a sudden leap to general?

He glanced at the sinking sun and shook his head. No news. The witching hour was nearing. His lungs burned like hell's everlasting fires. He was a character in a Greek tragedy, fated to fail, not because of disaster, but of his youth.

He turned to Colerick. "William, I can't make any plans, or staff decisions, until Lincoln has approved my promotion."

"Are you worried about the promotion being approved?" asked Colerick.

"I have a case of the nerves. Given my age and low rank, and the fact that I don't have a single friend at Lincoln's court, I'm not sure of my chances. It might not happen. Maybe in another year or so. But not now."

"Colonel Town told me that General Pleasonton was sure it would be approved. General Meade supports your promotion."

"I almost wish Pleasonton had not informed me of his decision to recommend me for general until the promotion had been approved." He stiffened. "I'm hopeful because I have a gift for fighting. I honestly believe I will be a great general someday, perhaps the greatest cavalry general of the war. But being a McClellan man and hated by Republicans, I'm not feeling like a high-spirited colt, relying on the magic of Custer luck to carry the day."

"I have a strong feeling sir, that your confirmation will arrive soon."

He drew a deep breath and scanned the horizon, his gaze resting on the clustered church spires of Frederick. "We shall see."

9:30 p.m.
Brigadier General George Armstrong Custer
City Hotel, Frederick, Maryland

Custer paced in his hotel room, chewing on a dry toothbrush. At a knock on the door, he jerked, his breath catching as if he had plunged into icy water. He placed the toothbrush on the vanity. "Come in."

The door flew open and Colerick stood on the threshold, gripping an envelope and sporting a large grin.

"General Custer. I have grand news! General Pleasonton's orderly just delivered this telegram from General Halleck in Washington. It's dated 9:00 p.m. Your promotion to brigadier general was approved by President Lincoln. Congratulations, sir."

"Is it true?" His pulse purred in his ear. He gripped the telegram and read. "Oh, my God. President Lincoln approved my promotion." He looked up at Colerick, stunned. "I'm the youngest general in the Union army." Goosebumps erupted across his suddenly chilled skin.

He laid the telegram on the vanity and reread it. A brilliant burst of light flashed in his mind like an exploding shell. His compulsive craving for rank and command had been quenched. He glanced into the vanity mirror and smiled. When the curtain rose for the next major battle, he would be standing center stage in his new costume, as the lead actor in his own Broadway play, featuring flying dragoons and sparkling saber duels.

"William," he said, basking in the glow of his newly acquired authority, "we will depart tomorrow at four-thirty in the morning and ride to the Richfield estate. Ensure that Orderly Joseph Fought, Bugler Peter Boehm, and my groom, Johnny Cisco, are ready to ride." He pointed. "Have Fought load my trunk into my supply wagon at four in the morning."

Colerick nodded. "The Wolverines are in for a big surprise tomorrow."

He smiled. "Bigger than you expect. What fun and excitement! It will be a grand show."

11:00 p.m.
Custer
His room at the City Hotel

Custer bent over, rummaging through his trunk. He set aside several letters wrapped in yarn. Next to his sister's package was a hatbox, and nestled in the hatbox was a small black box. It was a gift from Libbie, but he would not open it. *Not yet. Not until I have proven myself worthy of you.* He kissed Libbie's precious gift, and the memory of her tender beauty permeated the room, nearly lifting him off the floor. "Libbie," he muttered softly, "this evening I believe, more than ever, in destiny. And after I lead my Wolverines to glorious victory," he drew a long breath and let it out, "you will be mine." He placed the small black box back into the hatbox.

He gripped a package and unwrapped it. A huge smile took over his countenance. He gently lifted his tiny military suit of velvet out of the package and laid it on the bed. A breathless rapping like a Northern Flicker hammered outside his closed wooden door.

"General Custer. It's Private Fought."

He glanced up. "Enter." The door swung open and Fought came in carrying a bundle and a small box. "How was the hunting expedition? It looks as if you bagged something."

"I went through every place in Frederick where they might keep old uniforms," Fought said. "I found scraps for uniform furnishings. But I didn't find a general's jacket."

Custer frowned. "The stars are the most important. Did you find any?"

"I did, finally. I stumbled into a small store owned by an old Jewish sutler. He had a box of old uniforms and some stars. I bought two big stars."

"Grand!" Warmth ran through him with the speed of rushing rapids. "Let me see them."

Fought handed him the large silver cloth stars. He held them up to the flickering candlelight.

"They're magnificent. They remind me of the Star of Bethlehem perched on top of a Christmas tree."

"I thought you would like them." Fought rubbed his chin, plainly feeling nervous. "I'm sorry I didn't find a jacket for you."

Custer smiled and pointed. "Look what I found."

Fought stepped toward the bed and picked up a child's velvet military coat. He chortled. "General, I don't understand. This is a child's jacket."

"It's the military suit my sister Ann made for me during my hobbledehoy days. She mailed it to me along with a few other surprises in the trunk. My father, Emanuel Custer, was a farmer from Ohio, but he attended the military drill meetings in our town. I wore my military jacket with its big buttons. I had a small wooden rifle and wooden sword and could execute all the commands in the manual of arms."

"General, this is a fine officer's jacket, but don't you think it's a bit too small?"

He chuckled. "Maybe my Custer luck can make my old jacket work?"

Fought shook his head. "Hang the luck!"

"You must have a little faith in my magic. President Lincoln does." He reached into the trunk and retrieved a dark blue shirt with a broad falling collar. "I bartered for this navy shirt from a sailor serving on a Union gunboat on the James River." He laid the shirt on the bed and placed a star on each collar.

Fought said, "You want the stars sewn on the sailor's shirt?"

He nodded. "Yes, on the wide collars."

"For a short second I thought you wanted me to sew them on your boy's military jacket. But shouldn't the stars go on your general's jacket?"

"Yes, they should. But since I lack a general's jacket, I want the stars sewn on the collars of the blue shirt. Can you find needle and thread?"

"Let me scratch around and see what I can find. I will be right back."

After several moments, Fought knocked and reentered Custer's room. "Look what I found." He was holding up a needle and thread.

Custer said, "That's great. Where did you find a needle and thread at this hour?"

"I have my own magical ways."

He hooted a devilish laugh. "This clearly is a fairy-tale night."

"The hotel owner's wife had a stash of needles and thread. She was most helpful. She even volunteered to sew on the stars, but I said I would do it."

Fought grabbed Custer's blue sailor shirt, threaded the needle, and started sewing on the two stars. When he was finished, he handed the shirt to Custer.

Custer removed his captain's blouse, donned the sailor shirt, and stared at the stars in the vanity mirror for several moments. A prickly jolt cut down his spine. "What do you think? Are the stars big enough?"

"You look like a full-fledged brigadier general, minus the jacket."

"The youngest brigadier general in the army. Meet me in the hotel lobby at four a.m." He winked. "That should give me enough time to produce some sort of uniform. Then we will ride to the Richfield manor to take command of the Wolverines."

"Yes, sir." Fought smiled. "If you're able to transform that boy's garment into a man's general's jacket, I'm going to have to report you to General Pleasonton for practicing black magic."

"Custer luck *is* black magic."

Fought smiled and departed.

His fingers trembled as he reached into his trunk and pulled out a wrapped bundle. He read the note penned on the bundle. "Open when you make Colonel, but not before." Had Ann made him a colonel's jacket? Since he had vaulted over the rank of colonel to general, Ann would understand if he opened the surprise. He unwrapped the package and stared at its contents. A colonel's jacket resembling his boyhood military jacket. Ann had also made him velveteen black trousers adorned with a yellow strip on the outside of each pant leg. Quill feathers seemed to tickle him from within. "Thank you, sister Ann," he murmured.

He slipped the black colonel's jacket over the blue sailor shirt. He stared into the vanity mirror and grinned. He turned sideways. The jacket fit perfectly. Now he would be ready at sunrise to take command.

He reached into the trunk and retrieved a rare tinted postal card of Francois Gerard's portrait of his cavalry hero, Joachim Murat. He leaned the likeness against the vanity mirror and stared at Napoleon's greatest cavalry general. Murat was a prancing peacock, distinguished by his gold-embroidered velvet costume and his black velvet cap adorned with high ostrich-feather plumes.

"Now, Murat is how a cavalry commander should look."

He flicked the star-studded collar on the outside of the black velvet jacket. He reached into the trunk and retrieved a large red scarf and tied it around his neck. "The red scarf is my feathered plume." Murat would be proud of his costume.

He stood and stared into the vanity mirror. A yellow flame flickered from a candle sitting on a dresser. He smiled. Yes, indeed. Custer luck once again had prevailed today, and his deadheaded career had rebloomed.

He reached for pen and paper. *Must write to Ann and thank her.* Before he started scribbling, he stared out the window into the soft darkness, spotting a church steeple. He took a deep breath and held it for a moment before exhaling slowly. "Thank you, dear sister," he whispered.

President Lincoln's approval had jolted him with the staggering force of an earthquake. He still couldn't believe it. Today, he had made history by becoming the youngest "Big Boot" in the Union army. Tomorrow, his surprise would expand, hitting the Wolverines and the world with an enormous aftershock. A new prancing peacock was prepared to remake history by surpassing the glorious feats and outlandish appearance of the greatest cavalry general since Napoleon's General Joachim Murat.

This dauntless spirit was General George Armstrong Custer.

HARPER'S WEEKLY.

A JOURNAL OF CIVILIZATION

Vol. VIII.—No. 377.] NEW YORK, SATURDAY, MARCH 19, 1864. [PRICE TEN CENTS.

Wood engraving of Brigadier-General George A. Custer

⌘ 5 ⌘

Custer — Monday, June 29

4:00 a.m. (Sunrise 4:46 a.m.)
Custer
City Hotel, Frederick, Maryland

Custer's flushed cheeks tingled, and his boot spurs jingled as he paced the hardwood floor. He chewed on the salted bristles of his cow-bone toothbrush. He was corralled in his hotel room, champing at the bit like a high-spirited colt. He checked his watch: 4:00 a.m. Sunrise was in almost an hour. Why had time slowed? He had been bedecked in his uniform for over an hour. He shook his head, cursing the endless waiting. It was as if his mind had jumped into a sluggish brook.

He glanced at the glowing candles illuminating the vanity mirror. He gulped a big breath and held it. The flickering flames danced like the footlight wicks lighting a theater stage. His skin prickled like thrummed fiddle strings. God knew how much he loved Broadway plays and the hypnotic theater lights, and how audiences clapped and admired a great performance. He exhaled, a long, sighing wind. His heart danced. He had the greatest regard for lead actors and famous cavalry generals, such as Napoleon's Murat. The similarities were remarkable. Both performed in costume and played to large crowds and became national heroes. Like a fairy tale coming true, he was the new star actor in this arresting drama of Civil War, and his stage was the battlefield.

He paused his pacing and glanced out the window into the pitchy blackness. His lips started moving soundlessly, rehearsing his opening lines to his brigade. It was as if he were onstage, waiting for the curtain of darkness to rise and reveal the breaking dawn of his glorious performance as a cavalry general. After a few silent beats, he stepped in front of the vanity mirror, puffed out his chest, admired his costume. He smiled and retied the devilish red scarf around his neck. He had conquered his greatest fear. No longer was he an ordinary staff officer whose heroic feats enabled others to achieve glory. He was now a general, and glory was his for the taking.

A knock on the door. "General Custer, it's Private Fought."

He stuck his toothbrush into his hat and sprang toward the door and opened it. "Come in, Joseph."

Fought stepped into the room. "I came to pick up your trunk."

He skittered in front of the vanity candles and paused. "Well, what do you think of my general's uniform?"

Fought's eyes bulged, and his mouth gaped. "How did you make the bantam velvet jacket grow?"

"Custer magic."

"Remarkable. My God, you do practice black magic. The bright stars I sewed on look huge on your collar, like two full moons."

He glanced into the mirror and smiled. "I think I've surpassed the costume of Napoleon's greatest cavalry general, the beardless Marshal Murat. This uniform is splendid." Custer chuckled. "I don't want General Meade or the enemy to mistake the Army of the Potomac's youngest star general for someone else."

Fought cracked a grin. "You wanted me to help create a flamboyant outfit. I think I accomplished my task, sir."

Another knock at the door. "General Custer, it's Lieutenant Colerick."

"Please enter, William," Custer said.

Colerick opened the door, saluted, and stepped into the flickering room. "General Custer, I came to see if Private Fought had retrieved your trunk?"

"I'm here, Lieutenant Colerick." Fought picked up the trunk and carried it out of the room.

"Good." Colerick turned and stared at Custer. "General. Is that your uniform?"

Custer grinned. "One must dress appropriately for cavalry charges in this *glorious war!*"

Colerick frowned. "With respect sir, I've never seen such a garish general's uniform."

His heart quaked. "Yes, I was hoping not only to resemble Murat, but to exceed his colorful outfits. But my uniform is more than a getup. It's the romantic style of a heroic dragoon leading a handsome charge."

Colerick smiled tightly and shook his head. "There's no doubt you will be conspicuous on the battlefield with that gawdy getup."

"Perfect. I want my men and the enemy to know where I am on the field of battle."

A knock. Fought opened the door. "Lieutenant Colerick, General Custer's trunk is loaded in the wagon. Also, General Farnsworth is mounted outside the hotel, and said he is waiting for General Custer."

"Thank you, Private Fought. We will be right down." Colerick turned. "General Custer, are you ready to meet the Michigan Brigade?"

The boy general's heart punched against his ribs. "Let's go, William, and make glorious history!"

4:30 a.m.
General Elon Farnsworth
Outside City Hotel

Farnsworth's nerves fluttered. His first full day as a brigadier general. In the eastern sky an orange awakening edged above the horizon into the ebbing darkness. Young Johnny stood beside him, holding the reins of Custer's horse. The hotel's main door swung open and a hatless figure with long, bouncing locks whirled outside, gripping his hat. He smiled. Custer romped toward him like a boy racing out to play, pulled up, and lurched onto Roanoke's saddle.

"Can you believe it, Elon?" Custer exclaimed. "Washington approved our promotions from captain to general."

"George, I'm amazed," Farnsworth replied with a wry smile. His mind raced as silence shuffled in. *My God, what a garish costume.* He throttled the laughter that was about to burst.

Custer looked like a foolish medieval jester. After a few heartbeats, he said, with the most sincerity he could muster, "General Kilpatrick's courier requested our presence at the Richfield estate at sunrise to assume command of our brigades."

Custer flashed a smile. "I'm ready." He placed his soft Confederate hat on his curly blond hair that nearly touched his shoulders. He had cut down the black cover's crown and widened the brim, turning it down rakishly on one side. "Well, what do you think, Elon?"

Farnsworth stared as dawn's breaking rays tunneled toward Custer, illuminating his uniform like theater limelight. "Sheer madness," he muttered.

Custer's bedizened black velveteen jacket was adorned with five gold loops covering each sleeve nearly to his shoulder. Underneath the jacket, he wore a dark blue sailor shirt with a large silver star sewn on each corner of the large collar, worn over the lapel of the jacket. Around his neck he wore a large red scarf tied like a sailor's neckerchief. His velveteen trousers had a bright gold strip down both pants legs, which were thrust into his knee-high riding boots adorned with glimmering, gilted spurs.

Farnsworth snickered and shook his head. "George, you look like a crazy circus rider."

Custer grinned. "I was emulating Murat, or the dashing cavalier look ... like Prince Rupert of the Rhine and his Roundheads."

"George, the Cavaliers were fighting the Roundheads. But you definitely will cause heads to turn—Cavalier or Roundhead."

"So do you, Elon," Custer laughed, then stared. "Where did you get that tattered brigadier jacket? It is too small for you."

"General Pleasonton loaned me one of his old jackets. I hadn't time to secure a brigadier uniform with proper insignia, like you, George." Farnsworth chuckled. "Do you not love the tailored fit?"

"You're nearly a foot taller than Pleasonton. Now who's the circus clown?"

Farnsworth smiled. "Let's go."

4:40 a.m. (Sunrise 4:46 a.m.)
Custer
Riding from Frederick to the Richfield estate

A streak of lighting flashed in the dawn sky, announcing daybreak and the curtain rising on the youngest general in the Union army. Custer smiled. He was the lead actor, stepping onto the nation's stage. Less than an hour ago, he was as cool as the proverbial cucumber, rehearsing his opening lines. Now his breathing sped, and his stomach buzzed like bees swarming over newfound honey. *God, what a glorious moment.* He trotted northward, chased by Rose, bounding at a spirited gait. Farnsworth rode alongside. Custer shivered with excitement. *Unbelievable.* His craving for command was granted. He was now the lead actor of a two-thousand-man troop of actors—a brigade! The national attention he deserved would follow. His heart pounded like a runaway horse. *What a great day!*

"It appears your new staff is following us," Farnsworth said.

Custer twisted sideways. "Yep, it's my supporting cast. It's Lieutenant Colerick, my two buglers, Private Fought and Private Peter Boelm, and young Johnny, my groom."

"Damn, George. You were really prepared for this moment. Somehow you had the makings of an outlandish general's uniform ready and your personal staff hanging around like a bunch of ladies-in-waiting."

Custer grinned. "It took a while last evening for Private Fought to find the right-sized stars and sew them on. I wanted to be in full costume this morning when the curtain rises and I take command of the Michigan Brigade. I also wanted my personal staff ready to play their parts as supporting actors."

Custer studied Farnsworth. The 25-year-old, tall, dark-complexioned young general sported a thick gunfighter's mustache. Although Elon had attended the University of Michigan, they would have made great classmates together at West Point. Custer suppressed a grin. He had graduated the "goat" at West Point and Elon had been expelled his junior year, when a fellow Wolverine died during a notorious drinking party. Well, he himself had been court-martialed at graduation for not stopping a fight between two cadets.

Yes, Elon and he would have had fun finding mischief together at the military academy.

"George, were you not schoolmates with General Kilpatrick at West Point?" Farnsworth asked. "Can you tell me a little of what to expect from our new commander?"

"Yes, Kilpatrick was a year ahead of me, but my class graduated a year early, a month after his class graduated."

Custer pursed his lips, stopping his tongue mid-lick. A sudden silence confronted his racing mind. A strained silence, like watching a condemned spy dangling at the end of a rope. *Careful. Kilpatrick is your senior.* He nudged his horse ahead of Farnsworth's mount and they crossed, single file, over a small rock bridge spanning a bubbling brook. Hooves on the cobblestones clopped in the air. He followed the pony trail easterly and squinted into dawn's breaking light streaking across wide, grassy fields. Beyond the stretched fields, thickly sprinkled groves swelled against the yellow light.

A voice whispered in his head. *Without bias, how would you describe Kilpatrick?* His mind traveled back to West Point. Kilpatrick's favorite pastime was vicious hazing. Judson loved "running it" on new plebes in the most brutal way. Fright gripped his insides as he recalled that unforgettable late summer night his plebe year. Kilpatrick burst into his room like a wet banty rooster, screaming and shouting. Judson braced him to attention, bared his fangs, and then showered his face with hissing spit like a king cobra. His eyes burned as Judson refused to let him wipe his face. Kilpatrick shouted over and over, "I love your shock of golden curls, Fanny! Did you ever get your tail wet, Fanny?"

The next evening, before the ritualistic hazing started, he stood in front of a mirror, eyeing the tears flowing down his cheeks, and sheared off his golden fleece. He had not known that a baldie was not a regulation haircut; they forced him to wear a wig for several weeks. His stomach lurched. *Damn Kilpatrick and his cronies.*

Farnsworth bounced in his saddle. A dark cloud sailed in front of the swelling sun, shadowing Farnsworth's face.

"I was not a great fan of Kilpatrick my plebe year, but I was not a fan of any of the plutes."

Farnsworth snapped his head around, plainly confused. "Plutes?"

He smiled. "A plute is an upperclassman."

A flashing movement up the road. A jackrabbit halted, standing on its back legs. Rose burst by in full sprint, yelping. The jackrabbit bounded into the grassy field, with Rose giving chase. "Damn't, Rose," he shouted, "come here, girl!"

Rose ignored his call and raced into the field. Johnny galloped past in chase. "I'll get her, General Custer. I'll get her."

Farnsworth chuckled. "George, does Rose's impulsiveness and refusal to obey orders remind you of anyone?"

He grinned. "I can't think of anyone."

"Anything else I should know about Kilpatrick?" Farnsworth asked.

"He loved to fight at the academy, especially with Southern cadets. Judson is hot-tempered and makes rash decisions under pressure. He doesn't think things through."

"I agree. We both observed him at the Battle of Aldie. Kilpatrick is prone to launching uncoordinated and unsupported cavalry assaults."

Custer nodded. "My main complaint is that he does not lead from the front."

Farnsworth furrowed his brow and shook his head, plainly disgusted. "What did the Southern cadets think of Kilpatrick?"

"Hated him. Behind his back they accused him of being a lying, barbaric worm."

Farnsworth shook his head as if in disbelief.

After a moment, Custer said, "Elon, please take this to heart. Kilpatrick will bully you if you disagree with a bad decision. Defend yourself. Once Kilpatrick learned I would speak up for myself at the academy, he left me alone and picked on others."

Farnsworth nodded thoughtfully. "George, thank you for sharing your experiences with Kilpatrick. Since my expulsion from the University of Michigan, I've tried hard to follow all the rules, and that means I will follow Kilpatrick's orders." He smiled. "I don't anticipate any problems with Kilpatrick. I can handle him and his orders."

Bright sunlight lit the road again. Custer glanced skyward; the black cloud blocking the sun had passed.

"Again, George, thank you for your thoughts on Kilpatrick." Elon smiled as the shadow faded from his face. "I have a thought for you, but more positive. Captain James Kidd is serving in the Sixth Michigan Cavalry. We attended the University of Michigan together. He is a good man. You can depend on him."

"Thank you, Elon. I will introduce myself to Captain Kidd when I get a chance." He grinned. "Then I'll get the ins and outs on you."

Farnsworth chuckled. "Good luck. I pay Kidd lots of money to say nice things about me."

"Good. Then the new intelligence should take only a few seconds."

6

Kilpatrick — Monday, June 29

4:46 a.m. (Sunrise)
Kilpatrick
The great room of the Richfield estate

Kilpatrick strutted like a banty rooster along the length of the great room lit by flickering candles. His small, crafty hands fidgeted as his whirling pride churned. A newly promoted divisional cavalry commander, he was equal in status to the hard-nosed General John Buford, commanding the First Cavalry Division, and the reserved General David Gregg, in charge of the Second Cavalry Division. General Pleasonton had given him the opportunity to go after Jeb Stuart's Invincibles, operating somewhere to the east. He licked his lips, tasting the notoriety that would soon be his. Those cadets at West Point who doubted his future would soon be envious of the newspapers' celebration of his victories. With luck, he could capture the public's imagination and surpass Buford as the best cavalry general in the army.

An orderly entered the great room. "General Kilpatrick. General Custer and General Farnsworth have arrived, sir."

"Good. Send them in." He stepped to the head of the long table and bent down to study the map. For a couple heartbeats, silence hovered like a warm blanket. The kind of silence he wished would linger a bit longer. The door crashed open and a gentle whoosh of air feathered his face, as spurs jingled and boot heels clicked crossing the parquet flooring. The candles on the table flickered. He grimaced and glanced up, eyeing the impulsive Custer storming up like a cocky boy claiming his prize. Farnsworth was trailing behind. Dread dripped down his throat. Custer was always crashing through doors and making pompous entrances. Why West Point didn't expel him was a great mystery.

That was a mistake. He will never amount to anything. Now I have him. For Christ's sake, would the rash hotspur follow his orders? Did Custer follow anyone's orders? That was a question for the ages.

Custer snapped to attention and shouted, "General Kilpatrick, General Farnsworth and General Custer reporting as ordered, sir!"

Groaning inwardly, he glanced at the two young generals standing erect and holding their salutes. The first strings of sunlight angled through the paned French windows, radiating about them.

He returned their salutes. "Congratulations, Elon, and George, on your new commands." Kilpatrick froze. He studied Custer for a few moments. "George, your uniform is a mingled wonderment."

Custer smiled. "It's something I prepared on the spur of the moment. I didn't have time to be creative."

He shook his head. "At the academy I could smell you coming a mile away, with your cinnamon-perfumed hair. We always joked that you took your French classes too seriously. But now, I can *see* you coming a mile away with that crazy outfit."

Custer grinned. "I've heard that a lot of those fancy Southern cavalry boys also like to perfume their hair, and I didn't want you mistaking me for them. I wanted to give you another way to watch my glorious exploits."

Kilpatrick stared. *Damn this vainglory imp. I should have weeded him out of the academy.* "Well, at least I won't have a hard time spotting you on the battlefield." He turned to Farnsworth. "Elon, why in the hell are you wearing that tight jacket? It's two sizes too small. You look like an overstuffed straw man. Do you think dressing as a scarecrow will ward off rebels?"

"The jacket is a temporary loan from General Pleasonton," Farnsworth said, "until I have time to be properly fitted for a jacket."

"For a minute I thought Cinnamon might have given you the jacket and was pulling one of his puckish pranks on you. George was famous for those at West Point."

Farnsworth turned to Custer. "*Cinnamon?*"

Custer said, "That's the moniker General Kilpatrick and the other upperclassmen gave me for oiling my golden locks in cinnamon."

Farnsworth grinned. "Cinnamon, I should have been one of your classmates at West Point. Sounds like it was a happy-go-lucky place."

"You would have fit right in, wearing a jacket like that," Kilpatrick said. "You and George would have been best friends, competing for the most demerits." He suppressed a grin. "Now, down to business. General Meade ordered General Pleasonton to protect the army's front and flanks as it marches north to find Lee's army. Meade emphasized that the cavalry provides him reliable intelligence of the presence of the enemy, his forces, and his movements."

Kilpatrick paused as Custer and Farnsworth nodded their heads.

"Pleasonton has ordered Buford's First Cavalry Division north toward Gettysburg. Buford's task is to locate General Longstreet and General Hill, rumored to be west of Gettysburg along the Chambersburg Pike, which cuts through South Mountain. Gregg's division will cover the southeast and is tasked with locating Jeb Stuart's cavalry, possibly somewhere between Washington and Baltimore. My Third Division will cover the middle, directly east and northeast of Frederick. My task is to move toward York, where portions of General Ewell's corps are rumored to be. Any questions?"

Custer said, "Does Meade know if Longstreet and Hill's corps are marching through the South Mountain passes toward Gettysburg?"

"Meade's intelligence officer, Colonel George Sharpe, believes both Longstreet and Hill are still west of the mountain. It's Meade's hope that the Third Cavalry Division can find Ewell's corps before they reach York and Harrisburg."

Farnsworth asked, "Is Stuart screening Ewell's infantry as it marches toward the Susquehanna River?"

"Sharpe doesn't think so. He said Stuart's cavalry is operating independently from Lee's infantry."

Custer shook his head. "That's strange. One of the roles of cavalry is to screen the infantry. Lee is up to something. At Chancellorsville, Lee divided his force in two, against a much larger Union army, and won. It appears he has divided his force again, with Lee and Hill operating west of the mountain, and Ewell and Stuart maneuvering on the east side of the divide. What devious plan is Stuart executing for Lee?"

Kilpatrick grinned. "I don't know what surprises Lee and Stuart have up their sleeve, but I have a surprise for *them*. Third Cavalry Division is going to rush toward York like a wicked storm. When we find Ewell's infantry, we are going to slice them up like sausage."

The generals nodded.

Kilpatrick's pulse quickened. "Here are my orders. Elon, your brigade and Elder's battery will depart Richfield estate by eight o'clock this morning. You will travel northeast, by way of Woodsborough, Bruceville, and Taneytown, to Littletown, Pennsylvania. George, your brigade and Pennington's battery will depart after Elon's brigade and travel northward by Utica, Creagerstown, and Graceham to Emmitsburg. From Emmitsburg you will move east toward Littlestown. When the Fifth and Sixth Michigan Regiments arrive at Littlestown you will assume command of them."

He turned to Farnsworth. "Since your brigade is at full strength for today's march, the logistics train of Third Division will follow your brigade and will encamp near General Pleasonton's cavalry headquarters near Middleburg." He paused and drew a breath. "I want you to detach a squad of forty troopers that will trail one mile behind your brigade. They will act as the rearguard and protect the division train. Tell them to keep a sharp lookout for the enemy in the area."

"I will give the rearguard assignment to Lieutenant Colonel William Brinton, commanding the Eighteenth Pennsylvania," said Farnsworth.

"Good." He glanced up at Custer. "George, the First and Seventh Michigan Regiments are here at Richfield estate." He pointed at the map. "Your Fifth and Sixth Michigan Regiments are departing Gettysburg today and traveling south, down the Emmitsburg Road. Pleasonton has sent them orders to turn left at Emmitsburg and scout southeast toward the Westminster area. They are to arrive at Littlestown by the morning of June thirtieth. On that morning, my entire Third Division will be together."

"Do my Fifth and Sixth Regiments know that Stuart may be in the area they are supposed to scout?" Custer asked.

"Yes. Pleasonton is sending a courier to them this morning. Besides providing the two Michigan regiments the latest intelligence on Stuart's possible whereabouts, the courier is also delivering an order from headquarters, relieving General Joseph Copeland as commander of the Michigan Brigade."

Custer's mouth expanded into a devilish smile. "Who will be the acting commander of the two regiments as they march toward Littlestown?"

"Colonel Russell Alger, commanding the Fifth Michigan, will act as the officer in charge. Any other questions?"

Custer and Farnsworth shook their heads.

"Very well," said Kilpatrick. "George, I want you to be headed north toward Emmitsburg by eleven o'clock this morning. I want Third Cavalry Division to put a real twist on Ewell's boys. Now go over and assume command of your brigades."

Both generals saluted and departed.

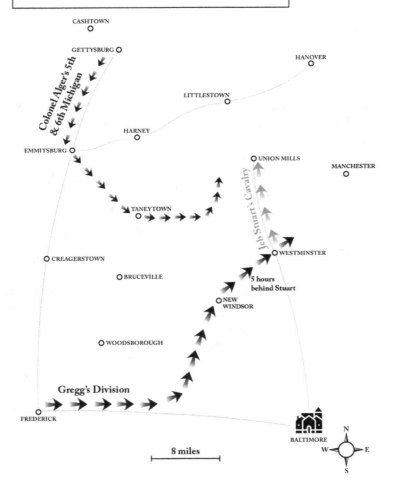

Searching for Stuart

Colonel Alger's 5th & 6th Michigan Cavalry March
Gregg's 2nd Cavalry Division March
June 29, 1863

CASHTOWN

GETTYSBURG

HANOVER

Colonel Alger's 5th
& 6th Michigan

LITTLESTOWN

HARNEY

EMMITSBURG

UNION MILLS

MANCHESTER

Jeb Stuart's Cavalry

TANEYTOWN

CREAGERSTOWN

WESTMINSTER

BRUCEVILLE

5 hours
behind Stuart

NEW
WINDSOR

WOODSBOROUGH

Gregg's Division

FREDERICK

BALTIMORE

8 miles

N
W   E
S

7

Custer — Monday, June 29

Custer's body radiated with growing warmth as he and Roanoke trotted eastward from the Richfield estate. The night's dark curtain had risen, and the glowing sunrise glared into his eyes, spotlighting his ride across the world's stage, debuting his performance as the Union's youngest general. He had changed his bars for stars and was eager to start realizing his dream of becoming an epic hero and legend in his own time. He reached up, adjusted the scarlet cravat around his neck, and smiled. Colerick, Farnsworth, and Kilpatrick had laughed at his costume and his red scarf. But they'd see. After his brilliant first cavalry charge, his scarlet neckerchief would become the Wolverines' emblem of courage, as were the black hats of the Union's famous Iron Brigade.

Racing alongside Roanoke was Rose. He twisted in his saddle and spotted his two buglers, Privates Fought and Boelm, riding behind him, followed by Johnny. He was riding to take command of the Michigan Cavalry Brigade. He started humming "Garryowen." His skin prickled with excitement as the radiant dawn glinted off the Monocacy River one hundred yards ahead.

The fickle muse of irony was on full display today. A month earlier, he had begged Michigan's Governor Blair to be made colonel of the Fifth Michigan Cavalry regiment. Then he had visited the Fifth Michigan and asked their officers to sign a petition to the Governor to appoint him as their colonel. Lieutenant Colonel Alger from the Sixth Michigan cavalry was the heir apparent to take command of the Fifth—and his competition. He tried to outmaneuver him, but Alger learned of his politicking and nearly spit in his face, saying he was too young. Some officers of the Fifth signed the petition, but most of the officers of the Fifth rejected Custer as being an outsider and a regular officer who graduated from West Point as a citizen of his native Ohio. They wanted a homegrown commander. And they said Custer was just a boy. Governor Blair promoted Alger to colonel and appointed him commander of the Fifth.

His dog raced ahead and he whistled. "Rose, get back here."

Rose halted and sat down on her haunches, wagging her tail.

They trotted up to her. "Good girl. Now follow behind with Johnny."

He turned his head and trotted toward the bivouac of the First Michigan and Seventh Michigan Regiments. He glowered, his cheeks growing hotter. His challenge was earning the respect of his Wolverines instantly, a nearly impossible task. Colonel Alger was a threat. Alger's men were loyal, and Alger disdained him. The 27-year-old lawyer was a rags-to-riches success. His impoverished parents died when he was twelve, and he helped raise his brother and sister. Later he became a Republican and a lumber baron, before the war. Although not from West Point, Alger was a fearless leader and fighter who had earned the respect of his troopers.

Alger was a problem, for he was the man Custer had been trying to be a few months ago—a fearless colonel and regimental commander—and Alger still saw him as a young boy, trying to be something he was not: a commander of men. But now he was the man he was supposed to be. A general commanding a brigade—including Alger's Fifth Regiment.

He cracked a devilish grin; the new general had a surprise for Alger and all the doubting Thomases in the Michigan Brigade. His former boss, Brigadier Philip Kearny, the "Dashing Dragoon," had taught him well. Fighting Phil's father was a founder of the New York Stock Exchange, leaving him millions. But Kearny preferred fighting, once saying, "I love war. It brings me an indescribable pleasure, like that of having a woman." Kearny often quoted Napoleon, saying, "To him the smell of gunpowder and the whine of bullets were as perfume and music." General Winfield Hancock said that soldiers would follow Kearny to the very gates of hell.

Custer shook his head. West Point had taught him how to play soldier. Kearny had taught him how to kill like one. Under Kearny's watchful eye, he learned to hold a tight rein on the men of Kearny's New Jersey Infantry Brigade. Kearney had encouraged him to lead with *physical torture* to ensure the soldiers were hard as nails. Kearny often said, "Drill them until they fail, and if need be, shoot a few to make them love discipline." He didn't shoot anyone, but he did whip Kearny's brigade into a killing force.

Now he was riding to take command of the First and Seventh Michigan, as well as Pennington's elite U.S. Artillery Battery M, consisting of four three-inch rifled guns. When he met the Fifth and Sixth Michigan on June 30 in Littlestown, he would take command of them as well.

Every hair on his head stood erect beneath his soft hat he'd found on the battlefield. He tilted the wide-brimmed hat into a rakish angle, shivering. He and Napoleon's dashing Murat both believed in glorious destiny. Murat would be proud.

He studied Colerick, riding his charger alongside like a knight in full chain mail. William looked like his favorite childhood hero, Charles O'Malley, the Irish Dragoon in the novel by Charles Lever. Warmth blanketed his heart. Colerick sat tall in his saddle and, like O'Malley, was rangy, handsome, had well-set eyes, a strong chin, and bore evidence that no great urging was necessary for him to fight and kill. His face had cocksure immunity against death by sword, shrapnel, or bullet. Just the type of fearless dragoon you would want riding next to you in battle. He was struck by a premonition: Colerick was going to be a loyal and faithful aide.

"William," he said, "what do you think the Wolverines' reaction will be this morning when I take command?"

Colerick turned and stared. "Truthfully, General, it's going to be tough. You're dressed like a prancing peacock, and you look like you haven't reached your sixteenth birthday."

An answer charred his tongue. "Every lead actor has their special costume. This is mine. General Kearny taught me something. He once told me an old tale: A newly crowned king met with his minister. 'Minister, I want to be the hero, and you the bad villain.' The minister agreed. After six months of being the hero, the king told the minister that he couldn't accomplish anything. It seemed everyone took advantage of him. So, he wanted to change roles. He would be the villain, and the minister the hero. Two months later, the people revolted under the king's harsh regime, cut off his head, and made the minister the king."

"I understand," Colerick said.

Rose raced past them with Johnny on his mount in hot pursuit. Twenty yards ahead, Rose stopped, and Johnny reined up and dismounted. The groom rushed over and collared the dog. He attached a long leather leash to the collar and remounted.

Custer turned to Colerick and pointed. He shouted sharply, "What's the moral of the story, Second Lieutenant Colerick?"

Colerick glared with a flushed face, plainly confused as he rubbed his brow.

Custer pulled out his long sword and thrust it toward Colerick's neck. "What's the damned answer, Colerick? You have three seconds, or I will run you through."

Colerick gaped, plainly shocked. After a couple heartbeats, he erupted into laughter. "I get your point, pun intended."

Custer grinned.

Colerick said, "When a new leader assumes command, it's wiser to be hard at first, then loosen up, but going the other way is foolish and disastrous. The troopers would think they are

80

being betrayed just as I felt a moment ago after being scolded for no apparent reason."

"Precisely."

5:41 a.m.
Captain Alexander Pennington
Michigan Brigade headquarters
Copse of trees next to Monocacy River, Richfield estate

Pennington stood next to 23-year-old Colonel William Mann, commander of the Seventh Michigan. Sitting on a stool next to Mann was Colonel Charles Town, the 36-year-old commander of the First Michigan. Pennington turned around. The brigade's field officers stood perhaps twenty yards behind, in clumps. Some smoked pipes, some were chatting. They all appeared relaxed, enjoying the quiet morning.

Standing behind Pennington and the two regimental commanders were their staff officers and company commanders. Town reached inside his jacket and removed a white handkerchief. He lurched forward as if he had been shot in the gut. He coughed several sharp times, splattering blood on the handkerchief. He wiped his mouth. "*Damn.*"

Pennington said, "Charles, did the surgeons give you anything for your consumption?"

"No, there is nothing they can do. I eat as much as I can, but I continue to lose weight."

"General Custer should be arriving soon. Are you going to be okay?"

"Yeah, just give me a moment."

Pennington spotted a rider approaching. The rider had golden locks bouncing on his shoulders and was being followed by a small cavalcade. "William, Charles—here comes General Custer."

Town started to stand on his wobbling legs and faltered. Mann grabbed the collar of Town's jacket and pulled him up. Custer arrived and dismounted.

Pennington shouted, "Form companies!"

Custer stood at parade rest, his legs straight and heels in line. His arms were behind his back, fully extended, his fingers straight and joined, pointing toward the ground, palms facing outward. His head was immobile and up, and his eyes stared straight. That was one thing he had learned to do correctly at West Point.

The officers rolled their eyes and wore wolfish grins as they moseyed into ranks with the clumsy gait of condemned prisoners climbing the gallows. The cavalrymen griped as they formed up behind their officers in their troops.

A chorus of low mumblings split the early morning air.

"Who is this kid?"

"General *Custerd*."

"His shoulder-length hair curls just like a girl."

"It's our new general, boys. The baby brigadier."

"General?—Oh, sugar."

"A madcap harlequin."

Custer stood, frozen as a marble statue. Hot blood surged, flooding his face like a dam about to burst. Rose bounded forward toward the men, launching a loud volley of barks like a sheepdog prancing around. Johnny pulled on the long leash. "Come here, girl!"

Panic ripped through Custer like a barb. He felt like a hapless plebe with a bad case of stage fright. *They don't respect or trust you. Some of these men are old enough to be your father, and most of the troopers can grow beards. Don't. Show. Fear.* He snapped to attention. This was going to be a challenge.

Custer bellowed, "Ah-Ten-Shun."

The cavalcade slowly stood erect at attention, standing in two ranks.

"Hand salute," Pennington shouted. The colonels and lieutenant colonels gave sloppy salutes.

Custer snapped a sharp return salute.

Someone in the back row muttered, "Where did they find this West Point popinjay?"

"Pretty dandy with girl's hair," said another.

His temper flared. *This pretty dandy is going to be a hell-driver martinet and your worst nightmare.*

Custer shouted, "Eyes right. Dress, right dress."

The brigade formed around the soldier on the far right. Every man raised an arm parallel to the ground, touching the shoulder of the man next to him. Then they all locked their heads toward the man on their right.

"Ready front!"

Every man snapped their head forward, some rapidly, some slothfully. He emitted a low, guttural growl. *This disrespectfulness is going to end.*

"Gentlemen. I am Brigadier General George Armstrong Custer. General Pleasonton has ordered me to assume command of the Michigan Cavalry Brigade. After an inspection of each squadron, I will lead the Michigan Brigade north to Emmitsburg, whence we will ride to Hanover, Pennsylvania, where we will bivouac. The Fifth and Sixth Michigan Regiments are on detached duty, scouting from Gettysburg to Emmitsburg today. When they reach Emmitsburg they will ride southwest toward Westminster and then join the brigade tomorrow morning."

Custer paused and surveyed the brigade from left to right, glaring into each man's eyes. When he finished, he glared at Colonel Town and Colonel Mann, standing in front of their regiments. "I want to make something clear. I expect every man to do his duty courageously. When we go into battle, I expect us to win, because winning means victory. We do not leave our wounded on the field. And after we win, we will bury our dead."

He paused and took a step forward. "This is what you can expect from me. I love fighting and will lead all charges. I will always dress thus, so you may see me during a fight.

"Now here is my promise to you. Come hell or high water, the Rebels will come to fear the Michigan Cavalry Brigade more than any other fighting force." He paused, glaring. "One day the men of the Michigan Brigade will be heralded as unequaled in every trait essential to soldiers. You will be known as the *Flying Devils.*"

Moans and guffaws erupted from the ranks.

"Now mount up and prepare for inspection."

The officers broke ranks and hustled back to their companies, shouting orders. Almost in unison, one thousand men mounted up and formed into their companies. Custer vaulted into his saddle, slipped on a pair of clean white gloves, and started the inspection with Colonel Town's battle-hardened First Cavalry Regiment, proudly displaying their bullet-gashed guidons. He paused before each trooper, stared the man in the eyes, and asked their names and where they were from. He glanced at their uniforms and their mounts and ended by finding some nitpicking discrepancy. He spared none from his brutal eye. Finishing the inspection, he signaled for the two regimental commanders.

Colonel Town and Colonel Mann rode up and halted. He glared at them, holding his gaze for several seconds. Using a sharp tone that could cut a diamond, he said, "Regimental discipline is lax, and that's something I will not tolerate. I expect you to be martinets and lick 'em into shape immediately. If you don't, I will fire you and find someone who can whip them into a disciplined fighting unit. Do you understand me?"

They both stared, their faces bright red.

"You are dismissed."

They wheeled and trotted back to their regiments, shaking their heads.

11:00 a.m.
Custer
Richfield estate

Custer chuckled, agreeing with a Shakespearean thought. "O for a horse with wings!" Now riding that kind of mythical horse would make him an instant epic hero.

Private Boehm pulled up, gripping his bugle.

Custer turned. "Colonel Town, lead out with your regiment. Colonel Mann, you will follow in trail. By column of fours, at the gallop!"

Both colonels saluted and trotted back to their regiments.

He shouted, "Bugler, sound 'Boots and Saddles'! We're moving out."

Boehm snapped the bugle to his lips and pierced the air with the familiar pitch of alternating notes. A beehive of activity erupted as troopers mounted their horses, and sabers and canteens clinked.

Colerick rode up. "General Custer, your personal staff is ready to move out."

"Good. Keep an eye on Johnny today. I plan on riding at best speed throughout the day and night without a horse faltering."

"Will do, sir." Colerick reined his mount around and trotted back to the brigade staff.

Custer trotted to the head of the brigade as it formed into columns of four.

Colonel Town shouted, "First and Seventh Regiments are formed up, General Custer."

Custer shrilled, "Column forward, trot!" He waved his arm forward. "March."

He clapped his gilded spurs to Roanoke's flanks and sprang forward. The dull, slipshod sound of thousands of hooves echoed in the muggy midday air. He stared ahead. The sun cast a hazy glow of rippling waves off the road. He glanced over his shoulder at the blue ribbon of troopers snaking forward like a sidewinder scooting slowly across hot sand. He floated in his saddle as if on a winged horse. A bolt of energy spiked through him. His skin tingled and his heart fluttered. He glanced skyward and whispered a prayer. "Thank you for allowing me to command my own brigade and giving me the chance to become the greatest cavalry general of the war."

1:45 p.m.
General Joseph Copeland
Road from Gettysburg, Pennsylvania, to Emmitsburg, Maryland

A two-day-old knot loosened inside General Copeland's gut as he led half of his brigade from Gettysburg. Although the townspeople had reported Confederates roaming the Gettysburg streets a few days earlier, his two regiments had not spotted any graybacks. Gettysburg was the center hub of ten roads feeding in from all angles of a compass rose. He had expected at any moment Jeb Stuart's cavalry to come flying down one of those roads.

He glanced behind; the Sixth Cavalry was first in line, followed by the Fifth. He nodded and stroked his long lumberjack's beard. He glanced over at the popular and brave Captain James Harvey Kidd, Commander of Company E, Sixth Cavalry Regiment. The boyish-faced Kidd was a University of Michigan graduate, sitting tall in the saddle. He stood five and a half feet tall, like most cavalrymen, weighing about 140 pounds.

"James," Copeland said, "riding into Gettysburg yesterday was so festive. All the townsfolk were out, in their best Sunday attire, welcoming the blue troopers."

"I don't think I will ever forget the sound of the church bells ringing and the masses of beaming faces lining the streets," Kidd said.

"I felt like we were marching in a victory parade up the Capital's Pennsylvania Avenue."

Kidd patted his stomach. "I liked the ladies spoiling our boys with bread covered with apple butter. I had three slices."

"The bread was delicious." Copeland grinned. "Didn't you receive a flower wreath?"

Kidd shook his head. "I guess only generals are privy to flowers."

"We also get them at funerals," Copeland replied wryly.

Kidd pointed. "Look, sir. A courier!"

"I see him. Let's pull off to the side of the road."

The courier halted and saluted. "General Copeland, I have an order for you from General Meade's headquarters." The courier reached into the leather satchel on his hip and handed the order to Copeland.

Copeland opened the envelope and read it. "This must be a mistake." His heart tumbled and his lungs seized. "I'm being relieved of command immediately by Brevet Brigadier General George Custer. My God, when did Custer jump from being a captain to a general?"

"General Meade promoted Custer to brigadier yesterday, sir," said the courier.

"Damned Meade doesn't have authority to promote Custer to a general! This is illegal!"

"It's a legal order. President Lincoln gave General Meade authority to promote men regardless of seniority. General Copeland, you are no longer in command of the Michigan Brigade. You are to appoint Colonel Russell A. Alger, commander of the Fifth Michigan, to assume temporary command until this unit meets up with General Custer. You are to ride ahead and report to General Pleasonton in Frederick, who will give you further orders. I will escort you, sir."

Copeland's heart roared, pounding in his ears. He would protest, and in writing. *Damn you, Pleasonton, you unscrupulous little dandy.*

2:00 p.m.
First Lieutenant Samuel Harris
In the rear of Fifth Michigan Cavalry
Traveling toward Emmitsburg from Gettysburg

Harris bounced on his brown Kentucky Saddler, Billy, plodding along a good distance behind his regiment. He squinted, peering through the dirt road's swirling dust, spotting the last troopers of his regiment nearly a hundred yards ahead. He reached up with his gloved hand and adjusted the chevron flap of the blue neckerchief wrapped around his mouth. He grimaced. He was no more than a hapless dolt, relieved of his duties and told to stay out of the way.

What a strange situation. He had been accused unfairly of letting a farmer pass his picket post. But he had received no order during the relieving of the picket post that said he could not let anyone pass. Colonel Gray said he was not to blame, but that he would let the new commander of his regiment, Colonel Alger, handle the inquiry. So here he was, riding behind his regiment, deprived of his command, yet not under arrest, and no charges preferred against him. His instincts told him to remain silent until he could address his situation to the new regimental commander. He expected to get this chance soon, as rumors of a big battle were brewing.

He smiled and wiped his brow. The warm glow of blackberry wine still shined inside him like the sweetness of the sun. Riding at the back of his regiment had its benefits. As the Wolverines departed Gettysburg and rode down toward Emmitsburg this morning, a lady stood in her front yard and waved her handkerchief. As the last rider of the column, he paused and asked her for a drink of water. She motioned for him to follow her, and he did. She said her name was Mrs. Codori. They sat at the kitchen table, and she produced two generous tumblers of potent wine. He managed to finish most of one, before gliding out to Billy and catching up with his regiment.

He squinted and spotted Carrick's Knob ahead, the summit overlooking Emmitsburg. At its base was St. Mary's College. Maybe he would meet some girls like those in Gettysburg. No such luck. His regiment had turned left onto the Taneytown Road, and he pulled on the reins and followed them. Thundering hooves echoed from behind. His stomach recoiled.

A sharp voice shouted, "Stand clear!"

"Oh, my God," Harris muttered. "What a sight!"

A circus-dressed boy covered in black whipped the reins as he blasted by like a cannon shot. His long, golden curls hanging under his big hat whipped in the breeze like an ensign flying from a fast-moving warship. Close behind was his cavalcade: a second lieutenant, escort buglers, a tattered waif, a white dog.

The lead rider held up his left hand and skidded to a stop. Harris turned his horse and halted. He shook his head. *Unbelievable.* The lead rider was the same boy who a month ago asked the officers of the Fifth Michigan Regiment to sign a petition to the governor to have him appointed colonel and command the Wolverine regiment. *My God, the lead rider was George Armstrong Custer.*

"Where is the Michigan Brigade?" Custer yelled.

Harris's mouth dropped open. Custer was wearing big white stars on his wide blue collars. How could that be? Custer was a captain. Now he was a brigadier? Harris pointed down the

Taneytown Road. "There, down there a considerable way." He pointed.

"Is it the Fifth and Sixth Michigan?"

"Yes."

Custer tipped his hat with his right index finger and cracked a smile. "Are you bringing up the rearguard of the Wolverines?"

"I am, General."

"Well, I'm the new commanding officer of the Wolverines. I look forward to leading you into battle."

Custer turned in his saddle and spurred his horse northeast up the Harney Road. His four other escorts raced after him.

Harris removed his hat and scratched his head. He spotted the lead elements of the First and Seventh Michigan Regiments, two hundred yards behind Custer. "My God, what a crazy war. We now have circus performers leading our brigade."

4:00 p.m.
Custer
Six miles from Harney, Maryland

The muffled echo of leather saddles squealing and bridle chains jingling filled the air as Custer swung in the leather, trotting eastward on the Harney Road. The searing sun baked the road, and dust mushroomed around scuffing hooves and clung in the air. He breathed the heavy air, dripping with humidity. A feverish smile creased his lips. For all the demerits, puckish pranks, and madcap shenanigans at West Point, including his proud achievements of graduating last in his class of 34 and being recognized as the class daredevil, he discovered he loved being a cavalry officer.

He shook his head, thanking Custer luck for this moment. After graduation he was denied accompanying his classmates to Washington because he was court-martialed for insisting on a fair fight between two cadets. He pleaded guilty and miraculously received a reprimand for conduct unbecoming an officer and a gentleman. Traveling to war alone from West Point, he assumed command of Company G of the Second Cavalry assigned to McDowell's army.

His heart lightened in the warmth of the memory of his first battle at Bull Run. He had heard artillery shells fired many times at West Point, but never fired at him. Above the roar of thousands of crackling rifles and thundering cannons, the serpentine hissing of a Rebel cannon shot passed overhead, crashing near his cavalrymen.

A few moments later he had spotted several thousand butternut troops pouring from the woods. The enemy formed into a line and surged forward, screaming a strange yell like hundreds of screeching cougars. The Union flank crumbled, and the blue soldiers panicked, skedaddling to the rear, clogging the bridge crossing Cub Run stream.

He'd clapped spurs to Old Wellington, leading his troopers over the smoky field to cover the retreat. He screamed at the skedaddling poltroons to "stand and fight." The wild-eyed cowards cursed him and continued sprinting toward the bridge. He clenched his jaw, enraged by their cowardice. A swarm of blue soldiers halted in front of the suspension clogged with overturned carriages. *Damn civilian spectators.* There was no other crossing available. Suddenly, three enemy shells plunged and ripped up the macadamized causeway leading to the bridge. The screaming mass of retreating soldiers froze like spectators watching a spy dangling from a hangman's tree.

He spurred his mount, galloped to the smoke-laden span, and leaped off his horse. A smashed buggy and a capsized ambulance were blocking the bridge. He flung forward, gripped the wooden wheel of the ambulance, and dragged it aside. A high-pitched shriek like a screeching hawk plunged toward him. Every muscle contracted and he knelt on a knee, covering his head. The shell burst twenty yards away, showering him with dirt and rocks. His ears deadened and the blast pulsed his chest. The taste of blood filled his mouth. The battle's din was momentarily muffled into a silent roar. He stood, gulped a breath, and gripped the buggy, dragging it aside. He ordered his company to fan out on either side of the road. The Company G line sprayed the charging Rebels with a sheet of lead. A cheer erupted and the blue-clad soldiers scampered across the Cub Run.

After the last soldier reached the far bank of Cub Run, he had ordered his troopers to cross. Standing alone, he fired his pistol at the charging Confederates. He flinched as gunfire crackled and bullets whizzed by his cheeks. Once his troopers were safely across, he'd wheeled Old Wellington and dashed across the span.

With glorious pride, he was last to leave the field and was cited for bravery for personally leading the rear-guard action.

6:00 p.m.
Custer
Outside Harney, Maryland
Eight miles southwest of Littlestown, Pennsylvania

Custer raised his hand and shouted, "Column!" He glanced over his shoulder as the column gathered their horses, preparing for the next command.

"Halt!" he shouted and turned to Colerick. "William, tell the regimental commanders that we will rest here at Harney for thirty minutes before moving again."

He dismounted and gave the reins to Johnny. "Give Roanoke a good brushing after you feed and water him."

He turned and stepped, stiff-legged, toward Battery M. Pennington was leaning against an artillery and chatting with some officers. "Alexander."

Pennington glanced and saluted. Custer returned the salute. "Let's take a stroll." Custer and Pennington stepped several yards out into a field. "Alexander, how did the men react to my talk and inspection this morning?"

"Well." Pennington stared. "Do you want the truth?"

"Yes, I do."

"They thought you were cold and distant. You were accused of 'West Point conceit.' You were called an 'affected dandy' with 'girl's hair.' A lot of these men are seasoned veterans, especially the men in the First. They didn't take kindly to your approach."

"Good. I'm young, just as Napoleon was when he first took command. Napoleon treated his colonels coldly at first because he didn't want them clapping him on the back and giving him advice. I don't want my colonels slapping me on the back and offering advice, either. I was promoted to general because I rarely follow anyone's guidance. That's why I conducted a harsh inspection this morning."

"Oh," Pennington said. "One of the University of Michigan boys said you looked 'showy, akin to Murat' in your fantastic garb."

Custer chuckled. "Now, you have given me a good evening. I was hoping someone thought I resembled my flamboyant hero Murat."

"George." Pennington paused for a moment. "I'm going to be blunt with you. All this spick-and-span inspection stuff and your flamboyant dress doesn't mean dad-sizzle if you don't lead these men well in battle. That's the proof in the pudding. Can you lead these men in battle to victories?"

Custer smiled. "The Michigan Cavalry Brigade will soon learn that I love leading a mounted charge. It's one of the most majestic sights of war. I can't wait to lead my Wolverines."

8

Farnsworth — Monday, June 29

12:30 p.m. (Five-and-one-half hours earlier)
Farnsworth
Halting at Taneytown

Farnsworth trotted around a bend in the murderous noon heat. He pulled out a handkerchief and wiped his wet brow. His butt ached. His First Cavalry Brigade had been marching since eight a.m. He turned to Private Charles Bond, his personal orderly and trusted trooper from his old Troop K of the Eighth Illinois, riding a horse length behind. Bond caught his eyes and cracked a smile. He nodded and glanced beyond Bond. A wave of warmth coursed through his veins. He was leading two thousand troopers stretching for nearly two miles. Spirits were high and no one had faltered. Damn, he was proud of his troopers.

He turned to Captain Andrew Cunningham, his aide-de-camp, riding alongside.

"Andrew, I want to feed and rest the horses when we arrive at Taneytown."

Cunningham nodded. "General, how long do you plan to stay?"

"About three-quarters of an hour."

His orderly, Private John Murray, reined up and saluted. "General Farnsworth, the village of Taneytown is a quarter of a mile ahead. The townspeople heard you were coming, and they've prepared refreshments for the troopers."

"Good. Any reports of Rebel cavalry?"

"No one has sighted the enemy near Taneytown. The rumors are that Jeb Stuart's cavalry may be riding toward Westminster, Maryland."

"Stuart's cavalry is heading toward Westminster?" His pulse rate climbed. He twisted in his saddle. "Andrew, Westminster is seventeen miles southeast of Taneytown. If Stuart's cavalry is moving northwest today, they could be approaching Taneytown now. If the Rebel cavalry is moving northward up the Baltimore Pike, they could be near Union Mills and approaching Littlestown."

"Do you want to post extra patrols?" Cunningham asked.

"Yes. Have a patrol ride southeast for five miles toward Westminster and another patrol ride five miles ahead toward Littlestown."

Cunningham saluted and departed.

Farnsworth gestured to Private Charles Bond.

Bond rode up alongside. "Yes, sir."

He pointed. "Charles, there is Taneytown. The troopers are going to enjoy refreshments the kind folks of Taneytown are providing."

"I hope there's apple pie waiting for us."

Farnsworth nodded. "Before I head into the village, let's check on the division's supply trains." He reined around and trotted back down the road toward the column's rear guard.

A short while later, they passed by the last troopers of the column, heading toward Taneytown. He lowered his hat and squinted down the road. A cloud was whipping up like a dust devil about 1500 yards down the road. He pointed. "Look, Charles. That must be Lieutenant Henry Potter's rear-guard squad of forty troopers from Companies L and M of the Eighteenth Pennsylvania."

"If that's Lieutenant Potter's squad, then the supply trains he is protecting must be safe," Bond said.

Farnsworth nodded. "I agree."

He spurred his mount and rode toward the dust cloud. One hundred yards away, an officer, yellow scarf covering his mouth, and an aide emerged from the devil duster. *Must be Potter.*

Lieutenant Potter reined up and tugged down his sweat-soaked scarf. Farnsworth chuckled. Potter's grimy face looked as if he were a theatrical mime.

"General Farnsworth. I'm Lieutenant Henry Potter."

"Good afternoon, Henry. I wanted to ride back and meet you and see how you're doing."

Potter paused, removed a white handkerchief from his blue coat, wiped his gritty face.

Farnsworth let the silence ride a moment as he studied the boyish 22-year-old lieutenant. He curbed a smile. Potter was sprouting a five-day, dark-stubble mustache, the whiskers barely poking out of the skin. He looked even younger than Custer, who, at twenty-three, was growing an impressive mustache.

"No major problems so far," Potter said. "We've been trailing about a mile behind your brigade. There's been no sign of Rebel cavalrymen."

"Any problems with cavalry stragglers?"

"No."

"Good. The brigade is going to depart Taneytown around 1:15 p.m. When you arrive at Taneytown, rest and depart by 1:45 p.m. That should give you enough time to water the horses and for the troopers to enjoy snacks from the townspeople."

"Yes, sir. Do you expect the rear column to run into any enemy cavalry?"

He shook his head. "No. We're heading northeast, trying to catch one of General Ewell's infantry divisions dillydallying as they march toward York. The Rebel cavalry is supposedly operating well east of us. That's where General Gregg's Second Division is patrolling. Gregg's boys are rabid coonhounds and will flush out any Rebel cavalry well away from us."

"That's good. Our Pennsylvania regiment has had only a few small scrapes since we formed up last fall."

"I still want you to keep a sharp lookout for Rebels. They probably have scouting parties that may slip through Gregg's troopers."

Farnsworth and Bond turned and trotted back toward Taneytown.

"Do you think Potter's boys will run into any Rebels?" Bond said.

Farnsworth shook his head. "No, they have an easy detail. I just wanted to check on Potter and introduce myself."

7:30 p.m.
Farnsworth
A quarter mile from Littlestown

Farnsworth gripped his field glasses. The outline of steeples and buildings splintered against fading sunlight. He yawned and turned to Bond and pointed. "Look, Charles. I see Littlestown. We're in Pennsylvania."

A huge, booming cheer erupted like a roaring freight train. He twisted in his saddle, smiled, and turned back around. "The Pennsylvania boys are whooping it up. We're riding on the free soil of the Keystone State."

"Why do they call Pennsylvania the keystone state?" Bond asked.

"In the newly formed Union, Pennsylvania was like a keystone, because it was centrally located among the thirteen original states and played a key role in holding them together."

"Are you saying that if we lose this upcoming battle in Pennsylvania the war is lost?"

Farnsworth paused and nodded. "It would be a grave defeat. Losing a battle in Pennsylvania would be like removing the Republic's keystone. I fear if that happened the Union would collapse forever into a divided North and South."

7:44 p.m. (Sunset)
Farnsworth
Approaching Littlestown town square

Farnsworth rode onto King Street leading to the town square. Ahead, Lieutenant Eli Holden, from General Kilpatrick's staff, and a private approached.

"Good evening, General Farnsworth," Holden greeted him. "General Kilpatrick established his headquarters at the Barker House this evening, and he has reserved a room for you. I will escort you, sir."

"Thank you, Eli. Did General Kilpatrick designate where he wanted my brigade to bivouac?"

"Yes, he wanted your brigade east of the town, next to Piney Creek, where you can water your mounts." Holden pointed. "Bugler Samuel Gillespie will show you the site."

Farnsworth turned to Private Bond. "Charles, inform the regimental commanders that Bugler Gillespie will lead them from here. I will meet you later at the Barker House."

Holden said, "It's on the northwest corner of the town square."

Bond nodded, reined his mount around and departed. Farnsworth turned toward Holden. "Let's go, Eli."

As they rode up King Street a cheer erupted, echoing off buildings, booming as loud as a packed audience in Manhattan's Park Theater. Farnsworth felt an encouraging gleefulness bubbling up inside. Children stood on a hotel balcony waving handkerchiefs and Union flags. Men and women stood on the streets belting out the "Battle Cry of Freedom."

"Yes, we'll rally around the flag, boys,
We'll rally once again,
Shouting the Battle Cry of Freedom."

"Eli," he said, "this is a much different reception than we've been accustomed to by the inhabitants of Virginia."

"When Kilpatrick arrived ahead of you, I thought they were going to crown him king."

Farnsworth smiled, tight-lipped. Kilpatrick would have enjoyed that but preferred to be crowned an emperor, like Napoleon. Both men were the same height and they believed that king was not ambitious enough.

7:55 p.m.
Farnsworth
Barker House, Littlestown

Farnsworth dismounted in front of the two-story, red-brick Barker House and stretched his aching legs. He handed the reins to a private acting as a groom, climbed the steps of the white-columned porch, knocked, and entered the house. A lovely gray-haired woman wearing a large apron and a sweet smile greeted him.

"I'm Mrs. Barker," she said. "Welcome. I have hot brewed coffee or cold milk to go with hot muffins and honey."

"Thank you."

She pointed. "General Kilpatrick is in the dining room with some of his staff. I will bring your milk and muffins to you in there. When you have finished speaking with General Kilpatrick, I will show you to your room upstairs." She paused as a tear dripped down her cheek. "I'm so incredibly grateful you're here, General Farnsworth. I feel safe now."

He smiled; a satisfying warmth wrapped itself around him.

"Please follow me. General Kilpatrick is this way."

He followed her as she stepped into the dining hall. General Kilpatrick was bent over a large table, studying a map. He halted and saluted. "Good evening, General Kilpatrick."

Kilpatrick glanced up, returned the salute, and grinned. "Great to see you, Elon. How was the march?"

"The brigade did well. They are settling in near Piney Creek for the night. Any intelligence reports from the scouting parties?"

Kilpatrick shook his head. "No one seems to know where Stuart is after the clash in Westminster."

"What clash?"

"When I arrived in Littlestown, I was given a telegram from Pleasanton. The vanguard of Stuart's cavalry arrived in Westminster at 4:00 p. m. The First Delaware Cavalry regiment defending the town drew sabers and charged. Stuart's larger force drove the Delaware cavalry from Westminster and then the Rebels cut the telegraph wires."

"Do you believe Stuart is still in Westminster?"

"I'm not sure. But if Jeb is, he won't stay there long with Gregg's cavalry division searching for him."

"What's your plan?"

"I'm going to let Gregg chase Stuart and I plan to race toward York and tangle with Rebel infantry supposedly loitering up there. I'm itching for a fight."

Mrs. Barker strode into the room and set the refreshments on the table. Farnsworth's nose tingled as wafts of warm muffins filled the air. He licked his withered lips, thirst throbbing in his parched throat. He gripped the glass of creamy milk and gulped it down like a waterfall.

He turned to Kilpatrick. "What time do you want my brigade to depart tomorrow?"

"Sunrise. When Custer's two regiments arrive around midnight, I'm going to have them ride through town and bivouac near the Alloway Creek. Since he will be north of you, he will start moving toward Hanover an hour before sunrise."

He nodded. "Do you still want the supply trains to follow a mile behind my brigade?"

"Yes. How did Lieutenant Potter's rear guard perform?"

"Despite being a bunch of greenhorns with little fighting experience, Potter's squadron did well."

"That's the best place for these inexperienced Pennsylvania troopers on this march, because it's the safest." Kilpatrick paused and grinned. "My guess is that they will be mighty lucky if they spot a mounted grayback scurrying around the trains, and if they do, it will be a mourning dove flying about searching for cracked corn."

He smiled. *So Kilpatrick does have a sense of humor.*

"Good work today, Elon. Get some rest and let's hope we can surprise Rebels tomorrow. I don't want Buford or Gregg doing all the fighting and getting all the glory. I need to make a name for this Third Division, and you only do that by fighting and winning."

Farnsworth beamed. "I have a feeling if we find Rebel infantry tomorrow, we will get a good twist on them. Good night, sir."

He departed. Kilpatrick was going to be mighty disappointed tomorrow about gaining glory because it was going to be a boring marching day. He paused and yawned. *Can't wait to get a couple hours of Ole Shut-eye.*

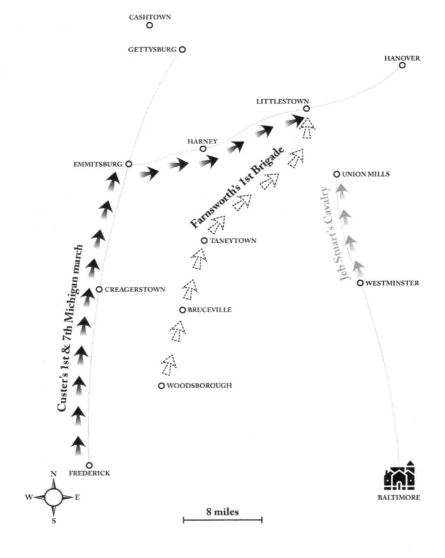

Custer's 1st & 7th Michigan Cavalry March
Farnsworth's 1st Brigade Cavalry March
June 29, 1863

CASHTOWN

GETTYSBURG

HANOVER

LITTLESTOWN

HARNEY

EMMITSBURG

Farnsworth's 1st Brigade

UNION MILLS

Jeb Stuart's Cavalry

TANEYTOWN

Custer's 1st & 7th Michigan march

CREAGERSTOWN

WESTMINSTER

BRUCEVILLE

WOODSBOROUGH

FREDERICK

N
W   E
S

8 miles

BALTIMORE

100

9

Custer — Monday, June 29

11:45 p.m.
Custer and his First and Seventh Michigan Regiments
A quarter mile from Littlestown, Pennsylvania

The nearly full moon hung overhead in a graphite sky. Custer and aide-de-camp Lieutenant William Colerick rode alongside each other at the head of the First and Seventh Michigan Regiments and Pennington's artillery battery. Crickets chirped alongside the muddy road, seemingly in time with the thousands of hooves plodding through oozing muck.

Custer grimaced and stood in his stirrups, stretching his chafed thighs and his saddle-sore fanny. His Wolverines had been riding nearly twelve hours. He leaned forward and patted Roanoke's drooping neck, whispering, "We're almost there, boy."

He glanced over his shoulder. His hungry and weary Wolverines were hunched over and clung to their mounts as if stranded on sagging dogwood branches. He smirked. So, the crack Wolverines were human after all. Before departing Frederick that morning, his bearded and rugged troopers had looked at him with scorn and shock, whispering, "The *beardless* boy general." When he pressed them to ride faster and ignored pleas for rest, they had muttered "iron-arse" and "hell-driven." They were going to be in for a big surprise when they learned he was a predatory beast who loved war. He craved the reckless risk and sheer excitement of leading cavalry charges. No one in blue excelled more than he did in unleashing the sheer shock power of a mounted saber strike. No one.

Colerick pointed. "Look, General. The church steeples of Littlestown. Also, there's a picket line ahead."

"Good. I see the spires." Warmth flooded him. They looked like the spires of St. Paul's Chapel, Grace Church, and Trinity

Church along Broadway. His mind drifted. God, he loved Broadway plays.

"When we arrive, I will pay a call on General Kilpatrick. I want a report on the Fifth and Sixth Regiments, and when we can expect them to join the brigade. Also, I want to learn if any of Kilpatrick's scouts have located Stuart's cavalry."

Colerick said, "I believe that's General Kilpatrick's aide-de-camp, Lieutenant Eli Holden, trotting from the picket line."

Custer nodded and suppressed a grin. He reached up and stroked the large stars sewn on his shirt collars. A booming chorus of "Garryowen" swept through his heart. He shuddered. His fear of remaining an inglorious supporting actor, performing in the cloaked shadows of center stage, was gone. Fame's spotlight would soon shine on the youngest general in the Union army. Come hell or high water, the Michigan Brigade was his instrument for glory.

Holden approached. *What an unbelievable moment.* A puppy-like eagerness bubbled up in him. His mind pictured the brave and brash Murat leading a cavalry charge. Like him, Murat surely craved the heart-pounding, nerve-wrenching thrill of being a harum-scarum daredevil. Nothing matched the intoxicating jolt of shouting *Charge!* and racing ahead of saber-twirling dragoons.

He closed his eyes for a moment. Who would have believed that four days ago he was a captain aide-de-camp and now he was the youngest general in the Union army, leading his cavalry brigade? Who would have believed he would be given a chance to exceed Murat's glory? Custer luck had not forsaken him.

Colerick spoke up. "Getting out of Old Virginia is like getting out of a graveyard and into paradise."

"I'm sure the citizens of Pennsylvania will treat us better than those south of the Potomac." Custer's stomach growled. Excitement or hunger? Maybe both. His breath quickened and a chill surged through him as if he had plunged into a tumbling, icy creek.

Holden halted and saluted. "Good evening, General Custer. General Kilpatrick is anxiously awaiting you. Did you run into any Rebel cavalry?"

"No signs of Rebel cavalry." His face flared hot. "But I expected to find my Fifth and Sixth Michigan Cavalry Regiments waiting for me at Emmitsburg. Instead, I found Lieutenant Samuel Harris from the Fifth Michigan at Emmitsburg. I learned from him that the two regiments had passed through Emmitsburg and were scouting to the southeast. Have they arrived at Littlestown?"

"Not yet. An hour ago, a Sixth Cavalry courier reported to General Kilpatrick that your two regiments would arrive at Littlestown tomorrow about six a.m."

He shook his head. Confronting Colonel Alger would have to wait. At least Alger was aware that he had taken command. "I would like to speak with General Kilpatrick."

"Yes, sir. He is waiting for you at the Barker House. He also has reserved a room for you. I will escort you."

"Did General Farnsworth's brigade arrive?"

"Yes, he arrived around ten p.m. to a grand reception by the Littlestown folks. It was like an early Fourth of July celebration. The townsfolk waited around until about eleven thirty p.m. for your brigade to arrive and then they retired. The streets are quiet now."

Damnation. Farnsworth beat him to Littlestown. A hushed anguish swerved through his nerves. Even though First Brigade had a couple hours' head start, he had pushed his half-sized brigade like a cruel martinet, shouting and cussing, but he still lost the race. He breathed deeply and collected his bruised pride. *That's not going to happen again.*

"Where is General Farnsworth's brigade bivouacked?"

"Southeast of the town, near Piney Creek."

"Did General Kilpatrick say where he wanted my brigade to camp?"

"Yes. He wants you to place your brigade northwest of Littlestown, near the Alloway Creek." Holden twisted in his saddle and pointed. "General Kilpatrick's bodyguard and bugler, Private Samuel Gillespie, will escort your troopers to the Alloway Creek."

He nodded. *Good.* His brigade would be closer to Hanover than Farnsworth's. He turned to Colerick. "William, lead the brigade to the creek."

"Do you want the brigade to dismount when you visit General Kilpatrick?"

"Yes. They can have victuals and rest for a bit, and water the horses in the creek. Hanover is only six miles up the road. I will request permission from General Kilpatrick to depart Littlestown tomorrow morning at five o'clock. If we press, our troopers can arrive first at Hanover, and we can rest them and the horses."

Colerick turned to Bugler Gillespie. "Lead the way, Private. The brigade will follow you."

Holden said, "Please follow me, General Custer, and I will escort you to General Kilpatrick's headquarters."

"Let's go." He spurred Roanoke and trotted next to Holden. Blood pounded in his ears. Farnsworth had beaten him to Littlestown and half of his brigade was roaming around without orders from him in territory lurking with Stuart's cavalry division. Damned Kilpatrick should have ordered the Fifth and Sixth Michigan Regiments to wait for him at Emmitsburg. Hot-headed Kilpatrick was horrible at connecting all the big-picture dots.

11:58 p.m.
Custer
Kilpatrick's headquarters, Barker House, Littlestown, Pennsylvania

Custer and Holden dismounted in Littlestown square and strode toward Kilpatrick's armed guards in front of the Barker House, the town's first-class hostelry. A sergeant saluted. "General Kilpatrick is expecting you, sir."

Custer returned the salute. "Thank you, Sergeant."

He stepped inside the Barker House, its inside lit by several glowing lanterns. A middle-aged woman wearing an apron skittered toward him. "Good evening, General Custer. I am Rose Barker, the owner's wife. I have been waiting for you. General Kilpatrick is in his room."

"I will fetch the general," Holden said.

"General Custer, please sit at the dining room table," Mrs. Barker said, pointing the way. "I made some venison stew, my specialty. Would you care for some and something to drink?

"Yes, and some hot coffee."

He stepped to the dining room table and plumped down in a French Renaissance chair. He chuckled and wondered if Murat had sat in one of these chairs when he was campaigning.

Heavy boots clomped against the wooden floor. He glanced up as Kilpatrick lumbered into the dining room, gripping his lower back. Kilpatrick winced in the flickering lantern light. Custer stood and saluted.

"I'm glad you finally made it, Cinnamon." Kilpatrick paused and sneered, wiping his sweaty face on his jacket sleeve. Dripping sarcasm, he said, "Even though Farnsworth had the more direct route to Littlestown, I thought for sure you would beat him here."

An icy silence swelled in the room even as a blazing hearth fire flared within him. "General Kilpatrick, my First and Seventh Regiments and Pennington's Battery M have arrived in Littlestown. They are proceeding to their bivouac at Alloway Creek."

Kilpatrick nodded. He shuddered, gripped the chair arms, and swiveled softly downward like a floating feather. "Please sit." He tumbled into the cushions.

"Are you alright, General?"

"I'll be fine if I rest for a while. My kidneys flamed up during the long ride. I haven't been able to pass water in twelve hours."

Custer grimaced. Until this moment, he had been unaware that Kilpatrick had a kidney ailment. He absorbed the information, letting a moment pass. "Will Elon be joining us?"

"No. He rode over to his brigade's bivouac. But he has a room here at the Barker House. You also have a room."

"Thank you, sir."

Mrs. Barker scampered over and placed hot coffee and a bowl of steaming stew on the table. "Here you go, General Custer. I just made the coffee. I put a bay leaf in your stew to tone down its gaminess." She stepped back and paused.

He whiffed the stew and his stomach growled. He glanced up at Kilpatrick.

Kilpatrick smiled. "Cinnamon, please."

He gripped the large soup spoon and scooped up a heaping portion. The venison melted in his mouth, and his body warmed as if Rose Barker had draped him in a quilt. "Mrs. Barker, this stew is heartwarming. Thank you."

"Thank you, General Custer," Rose replied. "I used my own recipe." She glanced at Kilpatrick. "I told this story to General Kilpatrick. Three days ago, on June 27, a band of Rebel soldiers led by General John Gordon stopped at the Barker House. They requested a meal. I refused to provide them service and left the house."

Kilpatrick said, "Rose's husband, Mr. Barker, heard that Early's infantry division was on its way to York."

Custer wiped his mouth with a cloth napkin. "My guess, Judson, is that Stuart is probably heading to York."

"Well, at least we know where some of the enemy is."

"How far is York from here?"

"Northeast about twenty-eight miles."

Holden entered the dining room. "General Kilpatrick, Captain George Yates, from General Pleasonton's staff, is here with orders."

Yates walked toward Kilpatrick, saluted, and handed him a sealed order. Kilpatrick remained sitting. He opened and read the order before glancing up. "General Custer, General Pleasonton has ordered Third Cavalry Division to march tomorrow to Hanover and Abbottstown. My division is to provide a screen for General Henry Slocum's Twelfth Infantry Corps, which is marching to Littlestown tomorrow. If no rebels are found in Hanover and Abbottstown, I am to head northeast toward York and fix Ewell's corps and track them. General Meade believes Ewell's corps may have turned and is no longer threatening Harrisburg. But he wants to make sure." He turned to Captain Yates. "Where does Meade believe Ewell's corps is headed?"

"Either Carlisle or Gettysburg."

Kilpatrick turned back to Custer. "I want to catch Ewell before Buford gets all the glory for finding him in Carlisle or Gettysburg."

Custer shot out of his chair and grinned. With heart pounding, he said, "My brigade is bivouacked the furthest away, north of Littlestown. When may I depart for Hanover?"

Kilpatrick cringed and stood, grabbing his lower back. A long moment stretched longer while he squinted, plainly in severe pain. "George, I want you to move out from Littlestown before first light." He paused, gulped a breath, and bent over and pointed at the map on the table.

Custer studied Kilpatrick's stony face.

Kilpatrick took a deep breath. "When you reach Hanover, you can let your boys rest there for a bit. Then proceed north through Pigeon Hills gap and head for Abbottstown. It's about six miles north of Hanover. I will ride ahead of Farnsworth's column. I plan on meeting up with you around Abbottstown and then we shall head northeast toward York, hopefully catching Ewell by surprise."

"What about Stuart?"

"Pleasonton believes that Jeb's boys are southeast of us, and Gregg's division is supposed to find him."

"Do you have any news on the whereabouts of my Fifth and Sixth Michigan?"

"Yes, they are south of here and should arrive in Littlestown before six a.m. I expect they will catch up with your brigade in late afternoon after you've passed through the Pigeon Hill range three miles north of Hanover on your way to Abbottstown."

Kilpatrick pointed to the map. "Pigeon Hills is a ridge range that towers above Hanover. You can cross through Pigeon Hills through this gap."

He nodded. "I'm looking forward to having the Fifth and Sixth joining the brigade. Having those two regiments with their Spencer rifles is critical if I get into a scrap. They could turn the tide in a fierce fight." Kilpatrick writhed and rubbed his back.

"With your permission, General, I'm going to check on my brigade and the picket line before turning in. See you near Abbottstown."

Kilpatrick nodded. "Permission granted."

Custer saluted and turned toward Rose. "Thank you for your hospitality, Mrs. Barker, and for the information about Gordon. That's useful." Custer bowed his head and rushed outside. Joseph Fought was holding Roanoke's reins.

Custer dashed toward his orderly. "Joseph. I'm going to sleep a few hours here at the Barker House. But first, let's ride over to the Alloway Creek and see how my Wolverines are doing."

10

Sixth Michigan — Tuesday, June 30

4:45 a.m. (Sunrise 4:49 a.m.)
Captain James Kidd
Sixth Michigan Cavalry Regiment
One mile from Littlestown, Pennsylvania

Captain James Kidd, commanding company E, squeezed his eyes shut, promising his mind he would only nod off for a minute or so. His mount stumbled and he snapped awake as light rain beaded a silvery sheen on his jacket, like morning dew. How long had he dozed off? He yawned. Twenty yards ahead, he peered at Colonel George Gray commanding the Sixth. The Irish-born attorney was thirty-nine years old and sported a carefully groomed beard. He swallowed. A martinet, Gray was swift to plant a spurred boot on the backs of officers wearing shabby uniforms. Kidd's back throbbed, remembering a swift kick from him. He respected Gray's toughness. The colonel was fond of alcohol, however. Maybe too fond, as he sometimes suddenly plunged into erratic behavior.

Kidd glanced sideways at his friend Acting Major Peter Weber riding alongside, a regimental staff officer. Web was dirty, bedraggled, unshaven, just as he was. Maybe Gray would spare them a boot kick after riding all day and night from Gettysburg. Maybe.

A gentle swoosh of air feathered his face, and his neck tensed. He whirled his head and spotted a large owl racing noiselessly downward with its forked talons outstretched. The kill was quick, and the night predator soared upward.

"Did you see that?" Web said.

"Yes. It glided right over my head, and I froze."

Web chuckled. "I spotted you yawning so I asked the owl to spook you. I didn't want you falling asleep and tumbling to the ground."

Kidd shook his head and yawned. "You might have to call the owl back for another pass. My body is dead tired."

"So is mine. This twenty-four-hour ride from Gettysburg has been brutal. Over thirty miles to Emmitsburg, then scouting south of Taneytown, and then riding up to Littlestown..." He shook his head.

"Well, at least the roads are passable, despite the heavy rains the past couple of days."

"At least for us," said Web. "It's going to seem like a gateway to hell if you're one of the troopers and beasts bringing up Kilpatrick's division rear guard and trailing in the path of thousands of hooves and artillery wheels churning the road into sticky mud."

Kidd pointed. "Look. A church steeple, a real tall one. We're almost to Littlestown."

"Good," Web said. "The boys and their horses need a rest after this all-night march."

Something like relief dared to stir in Kidd's gut. "I'm anxious to arrive in Littlestown. Dozens of troopers are struggling along on foot with their saddles slung over their shoulders. Their weary horses gave out a few miles back."

5:15 a.m.
Captain James Kidd
Sixth Michigan Cavalry Regiment
Christ Church
Littlestown, Pennsylvania

Kidd pulled up at Littletown's Christ Church. Farnsworth's brigade was breaking camp and trotting north. Where was Custer's Second Brigade?

Web rode up. "Kilpatrick's courier delivered orders that Colonel Gray's Sixth Michigan is to remain in Littlestown. We are to scout the area and guard the rear of Farnsworth's brigade as it marches north toward Hanover. A squad of ten troopers from Company E of the Sixth is to scout east of Littlestown."

"What about company B?"

Web pointed. "I'm sending a squad of ten men from Company B to the northeast to scout. After an hour, we are to send squads to replace the scouting parties so they and their mounts can get some rest and food."

"What about the Fifth Michigan?"

"Colonel Alger's regiment has been ordered to ride south toward Westminster and scout for rebel cavalry."

"Poor bastards," Kidd said. "They're going to be saddle-sore for days."

"I'm worried about our mounts and the fraying and tattering of horseflesh." Web paused and glanced backwards. "I must compliment you, James. Colonel Alger told me you had the best-looking lot of horses in the regiment, and I agree with him."

Kidd smiled. "Thanks. I can only merit such a compliment by compelling the men to take care of their mounts. I am becoming more and more a believer in the strictest form of discipline. The men won't *do* it if left to themselves."

"After we complete our scouting task, the regiment will ride toward Hanover. We may run into a squad of troopers from Brinton's Eighteenth Pennsylvania. They are the rear guard of Farnsworth's brigade and escorting the division's logistics train. The leader of the rear squad is Lieutenant Henry Potter."

Kidd nodded. "When are we going to meet up with our brigade?"

"Probably late this afternoon. Custer and the First and Seventh, and Pennington's Battery M, are the vanguard of Kilpatrick's cavalry division and have ridden forward to Hanover. I'm guessing we will meet them after we've passed through Hanover, probably near Abbottstown."

Elizabeth "Libbie" Bacon

11

Custer — Tuesday, June 30

5:20 a.m.
Custer
A quarter mile from Hanover, Pennsylvania

Custer's brain was racing like a diving raptor. His Wolverines were leading Kilpatrick's division, and he was fervently hoping they would be the first to encounter the enemy. A ghostlike figure galloped down the Hanover Road toward the column. His aide-de-camp First Lieutenant William Wheeler reined up and pointed. "General Custer, do you see that tall cupola with a dome roof?"

He adjusted his binoculars and spotted the protruding upside-down cup in the first flush of hushed gray light. "Yes, I see the bell tower."

"That's the German Reformed Church. It's in the middle of the town on Abbottstown Street near Hanover Square. The local townspeople must have heard that we were coming, because when we rode past the Central Hotel, several were standing out front, including the hotel's proprietor, Thomas McCausland."

Custer smiled. "Are they a friendly gaggle?"

"Yes, sir. They were breaking out Union flags and hanging them on the hotel and buildings."

"Good." Custer turned to Lieutenant Colerick. "William, I want to rest the men and horses a bit when we arrive in Hanover."

"Yes, sir. We were lucky that the six miles from Littlestown to Hanover was relatively flat terrain with a few rolling hills, and no steep grades."

"Agreed. But I'm a bit worried for the horses after we depart Hanover and ride toward Abbottstown. That's hill country and we have to cross through the narrow gap of the Pigeon Hills range."

Colerick nodded. "There's a lot of mounts with sore backs. Do the regimental commanders have permission to unsaddle the horses and care for the animals' backs?"

"Yes. I want to depart for Abbottstown by eight a.m."

Colerick saluted, turned, and rode back down the column.

6:30 a.m.
Custer
Central Hotel, Hanover, Pennsylvania

Custer trotted up the Littlestown Road, turned onto Hanover Square, and reined up in front of the three-story red-brick-and-mortar Central Hotel. It was adorned with white window frames and shutters. The blushing red sun lit up the Union flags draped from the windows. His heart leaped. Townsfolk lined the street, cheering and waving. The spirited welcome was inspiring. Two white-haired men approached, flashing huge grins.

"General Custer, welcome to the friendly town of Hanover. I'm Thomas McCausland, and this is my hotel. This is Reverend W.K. Zieber, pastor of Emmanuel Reformed Church. Your scouts told us you would be arriving."

"Good morning, Reverend Zieber, Mr. McCausland. My brigade is the vanguard of General Kilpatrick's cavalry division. Following an hour behind me is General Farnsworth's brigade. So be on the lookout for a hungry lot of Yankees soon."

"How long will your troopers be in Hanover?"

"Not long. Little over an hour. We need to rest and water our horses."

"I told the townspeople that you would be arriving," Reverend Zieber said, "and they are preparing food and drinks for you and your troopers."

Custer's skin tingled. The corners of his mouth curled upward into a huge smile. "That's most kind of you, Reverend Zieber. It's great to be back on the free soil of Pennsylvania, with the Stars and Stripes to cheer us on."

He reined Roanoke around, trotted up Abbottstown Street, and halted at the Hanover Branch Railroad tracks.

"I'm glad the Wolverines are getting the same treatment that General Farnsworth's troopers received when they arrived before us in Littlestown," Lieutenant Colerick remarked.

Custer nodded and gritted his teeth, his cheeks flushing. He should have pushed his brigade harder to Littlestown. Farnsworth arrived first and stole the Wolverines' thunder of a hero's welcome and refreshments. His brigade had trotted into a ghost town. Never again would he be beat out. By Farnsworth or anyone else. Never.

He glanced at Colerick.

"Murat became Napoleon's most dashing dragoon by being first in everything. First to execute an order. First to arrive at a destination. First to lead a charge. That's me. There is no glory in being second in anything. I've played a supporting role for the first two years of this war. I'm now in command, and this brigade is a deadly thunderbolt that will always strike first." He pointed at Colerick. "That's the last time I'm second to anyone." An uncontrollable urge burst into his throat. "To glory...or death!"

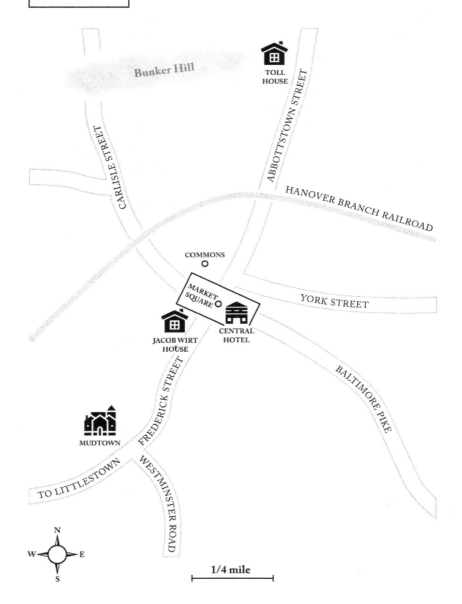

Hanover
June 30, 1863

Bunker Hill

TOLL
HOUSE

ABBOTTSTOWN STREET

CARLISLE STREET

HANOVER BRANCH RAILROAD

COMMONS

MARKET
SQUARE

YORK STREET

JACOB WIRT
HOUSE

CENTRAL
HOTEL

FREDERICK STREET

BALTIMORE PIKE

MUDTOWN

TO LITTLESTOWN

WESTMINSTER ROAD

N
W — E
S

1/4 mile

12

Farnsworth — Tuesday, June 30

6:30 a.m.
Farnsworth
Barker House
Littlestown, Pennsylvania

Farnsworth exited the Barker House. The sharp echo of hooves approached.

"General Farnsworth. Lieutenant Henry Potter of Company M of the Eighteenth Pennsylvania reporting as ordered, sir."

"Lieutenant Potter, good work during yesterday's march. Once again, I am assigning you rear guard. When the brigade pulls out in a few minutes, I want you and forty men from Companies L and M to act as a rear guard for the marching column. Follow a mile behind the column."

"Are we expecting any enemy this morning?" asked Potter.

"No." Farnsworth shook his head. "It's going to be a quiet morning, just like yesterday."

"Good."

"The only activity you might encounter is Custer's Fifth and Sixth Michigan overtaking you before we reach Hanover. They arrived just south of Littlestown a bit after sunrise and are going to linger for a while, scouting the area south of here and screening some of General Slocum's Twelve Corps infantry marching northward toward Littlestown. When Slocum's infantry arrives near Littlestown, Custer's Fifth and Sixth will ride toward Hanover."

"Where are Custer's other two regiments and artillery?"

"They departed for Hanover a couple of hours ago. Custer was anxious to push forward to Abbottstown, thus his brigade got an early start."

Potter saluted. "Yes, sir. I will use the same forty troopers from yesterday and will trail the column a mile behind." He wheeled his horse and trotted back toward the end of the brigade column, shaking his head.

Farnsworth turned to Bugler Gilbert Buckman, whose face was rosy red from yesterday's torrid sun. "Let's saddle up the brigade."

Buckman snapped the bugle to his lips. The brassy notes of "Boots and Saddles" echoed over Littlestown. Several regimental buglers joined in, shrilling the call to mount up.

Farnsworth twisted in his saddle and gazed down the column as troopers threw saddles over the backs of horses and braced their knees against their flanks to cinch them up. Nearly in unison the brigade jumped into their saddles to the creaking of stirrup leathers and the rattle of sabers.

"We're marching forward and moving ahead," he shouted. He stopped and drew a breath. "At the walk...march!"

Buckman trumpeted a piercing "Forward Walk" order, the shrill notes echoing throughout Littlestown, accompanied by a chorus of trilling bugles. Farnsworth's horse lurched forward toward Hanover. The general turned to his bugler. "I'm guessing the citizens of Hanover will be excited to see the Yankee troopers this morning. Maybe we will get a chance to rest the brigade."

"A couple hours of rest sounds heavenly." Buckman paused. "Maybe the patriotic citizens of Pennsylvania will provide hospitalities. My throat is still choking from yesterday and eating all that dust from the road."

"Maybe you're right about receiving some refreshments as we did in Littlestown. We should arrive in Hanover around eight a.m."

13

Kilpatrick — Tuesday, June 30

Kilpatrick and his advance guard trolled ahead of Farnsworth's brigade. A dull ache radiated from his lower back. Damned kidneys still smarted from yesterday's ride. A knot tightened inside. A great deal rode on his division finding Rebel infantry near York and cutting their rear guard to pieces. He licked his lips, tasting fame. He spotted a young boy dressed in overalls, sitting on a wooden fence, watching the approaching troopers.

Kilpatrick pulled off the road and reined up in front of the boy. "Good morning, son. What's your name?"

"George Spangler. Are you a Union cavalry officer?"

"Yes I am, George." He flashed a grin. "How did you guess?"

"You are wearing a blue uniform and you're wearing lots of stars and you're riding at the head of the column. If I was a cavalry officer, I would be riding in front of everyone like you are."

He grinned again. "George, would you like to accompany us into Hanover?"

"I would rather remain on the fence," the boy said.

"Why is that?"

"I want to see all the soldiers pass by, and I might miss them if I go into town."

"George, all the troopers are going to pass through the town so you can watch them from there. How about it? You can ride with me."

George paused a moment. He scratched his head as if he was pondering the offer. He said, "Okay, let's go. I don't want to miss any of the cavalry soldiers."

"Good. Hop up." Kilpatrick reached down with his right arm and grabbed the back of the boy's overall straps and pulled. The boy lurched upwards and landed behind him. Kilpatrick peeked over his shoulder. "Are you ready?"

"Yes, let's ride!"

Kilpatrick pulled back onto the road and rode at a trot. After covering a couple hundred yards, Kilpatrick cocked his head. "Do you know where Mr. Jacob Wirt lives?"

"I sure do. Why do you want to visit with Mr. Wirt?"

"I heard he has some maps of the area."

"I will point out his house when we arrive in town."

8:20 a.m.
Kilpatrick
Jacob Wirt's home on Frederick Street, just off Hanover Square
Hanover, Pennsylvania

A swelling savor, sweet as sin, beckoned to his senses. A flood of civilians holding baskets of food and drinks. *Whew!* What a lovely sight.

George pointed. "That's the Wirt house."

"Good." Kilpatrick pulled up to the two-story white brick house. "George, you jump down first."

George jumped down and Kilpatrick dismounted.

"Thank you, George, for riding into town with us. You can see all the troopers from here as they pass through the town."

"You're welcome." George stuck out his hand. "What is your name?"

"I'm General Hugh Judson Kilpatrick, and I'm the commander of this cavalry division."

"Well, good luck fighting the Rebs, General."

"I've been fighting those southern traitors since my cadet days at West Point, and I never lose to those cowards."

Kilpatrick tied his horse up to a large tree in the front yard. He trundled up the five steps to the front porch and knocked on the door. He quaked and grabbed his lower back. He dry-heaved as a sharp stabbing like a glass shard sliced through his kidneys. He wiped his mouth with the crook of his right arm.

A boy who looked about thirteen answered the door.

"I'm General Kilpatrick. I'm looking for Jacob Wirt. Is that your father?"

"Yes, Jacob Wirt is my pa. I'm Calvin Wirt. But he's not home. He is the president of the Hanover bank and he and my ma have taken the bank's holdings to a safe place because the Rebel cavalry is rumored to be in the area."

"I heard your father had a map of York County. May I come in?"

"Sure. Follow me."

Kilpatrick followed Calvin into the front parlor. The boy stopped and pointed to a large map on the wall.

"This is an excellent map," Kilpatrick said.

Calvin reached up, unhooked the map from the wall, and laid it on the dining room table.

"May I have my headquarters staff join us in the dining room so we can study the map with you?"

"Sure. Also, General Kilpatrick, you can take the map with you when you depart. I'm sure my father won't mind."

He smiled. "Thank you, son."

8:25 a.m.
Farnsworth
Jacob Wirt's home, Hanover, Pennsylvania

"General." A young lady skittered down Abbottstown street carrying a picnic basket.

Farnsworth halted and smiled a lopsided grin.

"General, I made something for you. We are so grateful your troopers have arrived in Hanover." She reached into her basket and handed him a slice of warm bread spread with apple jam.

"Thank you so much." He nodded as the bread melted in his mouth. "This is delicious. How did you know I was a general?"

She laughed. "Early this morning a very funny-dressed boy general with golden locks leading several hundred troopers arrived. I gave him a piece of bread. He said the bread was wonderful and to watch out for his friend who was also a general that wore a black gunfighter mustache."

He cracked a grin. "So, you met the infamous General George Custer."

"Yes, I did, and he was very dashing and happy-go-lucky."

He cracked a grin. "General Custer is very beguiling around attractive young ladies. You have a good day, Miss. Thank you for the bread."

Moments later he stepped into the Wirt front parlor. A slight breeze through an open window swirled the bitter-pungent cigar smoke lingering above a table. Kilpatrick's voice cut through the fog. "General Farnsworth, please join us."

He squinted his eyes, sliced through the haze, and saluted. "General Kilpatrick, my brigade is arriving."

"Good." Kilpatrick gestured to the young boy beside him. "This is Calvin Wirt. He lives here."

"Good morning, Calvin." Farnsworth reached across the table to shake the boy's hand.

"Calvin has been kind enough to offer us the use of his father's map." Kilpatrick pointed. "Look here."

Kilpatrick's right index finger moved north along the Abbottstown Road, stopping on the Pigeon Hill range.

"Here is the gap in the Pigeon Hill ridge," Kilpatrick said. "Calvin, tell us about this area."

Calvin complied. "The Pigeon Hills start about three miles north of Hanover. They are a range of rolling big bumps and rising steep slopes. The ridgeline is about three hundred feet higher than Hanover. The narrow gap cutting through the range rises and falls like waves from 20 feet to 80 feet above Hanover."

Kilpatrick nodded his head and smiled at the boy. "Thank you, Calvin. That's good information."

"You seem to know the area quite well, Calvin," Farnsworth said.

Calvin grinned. "There's a great swimming and fishing hole up there that my buddies and me go on Saturdays. We even built a secret hut there."

Farnsworth chuckled. "Maybe after the war you can show me."

Calvin sprang up like a young buck and said eagerly, "I can take you there now, General."

"Not today. Hopefully soon, Calvin. I do love fishing."

Kilpatrick turned to Farnsworth. "It's going to take longer than usual to ride through here as we approach Abbottstown. Custer departed Hanover before first light, and I told him to take his time traveling through this Pigeon Hill area. I want the horses as fresh as possible when we depart Abbottstown for York."

Farnsworth dipped a quick nod. "What time are you departing Hanover this morning?"

Kilpatrick reached into his blue jacket and pulled out his watch. "I'm going to depart at nine o'clock. I'll ride ahead of your brigade and close with Custer's brigade. I don't want Custer to get too far forward of me and get into mischief before I arrive and I have to pull his chestnuts out of the fire."

"The Fifth New York Regiment arrived a few minutes ago and are occupying Hanover Square and Abbottstown Street. I'm going to give them a chance to rest a bit. Some of the troopers are in bad shape. Allowing the patriotic citizens to feed the New Yorkers will do them good."

"Agreed. I want my division as fresh as possible if we are lucky enough to run into Confederates today."

"The Eighteenth Pennsylvania are bringing up the rear, and when they arrive in Hanover, I'm also going to give them a chance to rest before departing for the Pigeon Hill gap and Abbottstown," Farnsworth continued.

"That is well," Kilpatrick said. "I will be out in a bit. But first, I want to ask Calvin about the country roads, streams, and nearby towns."

Farnsworth turned to Calvin. "Thank you for the detailed information." Calvin beamed. "By the way, what kind of fish are you catching up in the Pigeon Hills?"

"Striped Chars and Artic Graylings."

He grinned. "Don't forget you promised to take me fishing someday." He turned to Kilpatrick. "My brigade will be ready to ride at nine a.m., General."

Hanover Union Rear Guard Collides with Confederate Lead Elements

June 30, 1863

10:00 a.m.

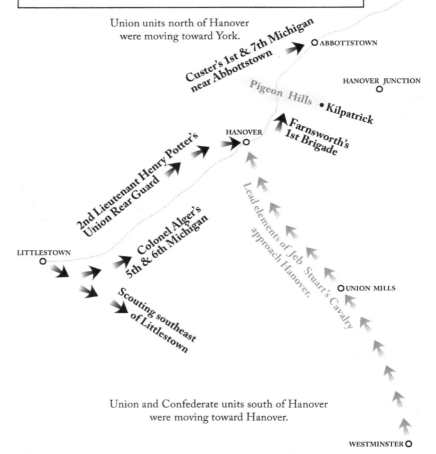

YORK

Union units north of Hanover
were moving toward York.

Custer's 1st & 7th Michigan
near Abbottstown

O ABBOTTSTOWN

HANOVER JUNCTION

Pigeon Hills • Kilpatrick

HANOVER

Farnsworth's
1st Brigade

2nd Lieutenant Henry Potter's
Union Rear Guard

Colonel Alger's
5th & 6th Michigan

LITTLESTOWN

Scouting southeast
of Littlestown

Lead elements of Jeb Stuart's Cavalry
approach Hanover.

O UNION MILLS

Union and Confederate units south of Hanover
were moving toward Hanover.

WESTMINSTER O

Pigeon Hills — a prominent elevation located just north of Hanover
All of Hanover was visible
in the valley below Pigeon Hills.

N
W — E
S

2.5 miles

14

Eighteenth Pennsylvania — Tuesday, June 30

10:00 a.m.
Lieutenant Henry Potter
Approaching Mudtown, Pennsylvania
One-half mile south of Hanover, near intersection of Westminster and Hanover-Littlestown Roads

Plum Creek babbled underneath a bridge twenty yards ahead. Potter raised his hand and halted his forty troopers from the Eighteenth Pennsylvania Cavalry. He twisted in his saddle as First Sergeant William Nott, a horse length behind, pulled up. "First Sergeant, let's dismount here and water the horses."

Sergeant Nott turned and rode back along the fifty-yard column. Potter dismounted and led his horse into the stream. The water burbled around the horse's hooves. A horse neighed close behind him; he turned and spied Lieutenant William Jones coaxing his horse toward the stream.

"How in the hell," Jones grumbled, "did we pull this rearguard duty two days in a row, while the rest of the Eighteenth is relaxing in Hanover?"

"My guess is that Lieutenant Colonel Brinton believes we have the best-looking horses to show off to the residents of Mudtown."

"Yeah, ten families, total, and probably no handsome women."

Potter grinned. "All the handsome young women are in Hanover, socializing with the rest of the Eighteenth."

"If that's the case, let's trade in our horses for some ugly mares, so we don't get this rearguard duty again."

Behind them, a trooper shouted, "Lieutenant Potter, a man with a gun is yelling and running toward us."

Potter turned. An old farmer trundled toward him, wielding a flintlock musket. Whatever the old codger's complaint, he didn't have time for it. He steeled himself for whatever trouble was lumbering toward him.

"The Rebs have taken my horses and cows!" the farmer yelled.

Jones cracked a smile. "Watch out, Henry. Davy Crockett is as mad as a wet hornet."

The farmer halted in front of Potter, gasping for breath. "Are you in charge here, sonny?"

"Yes," Potter said.

"The Rebs just emptied out my barn of most of my livestock."

"Show me."

Potter mounted his horse and followed the farmer, who scuttled across the field, swearing devilish oaths. He reined up and dismounted, following the farmer toward a red barn with gables. He gripped his pistol, stepped through the barn doors, and halted. His shoulder muscles tightened as he gazed through the dim light at the hayloft. Nothing. He quickly scanned the stalls.

"See, sonny! All the stalls are empty."

Sure enough. A clean sweep. "Who took the livestock?"

"Follow me!" The farmer dashed out of the barn and pointed. A small gaggle of troops in the distance were riding away with an old-fashioned Conestoga wagon. "That's the sons of bitches. That's them, sonny!"

Potter gripped his binoculars. "Those troops have blue coats."

"I'm telling you, they're Rebs. I know a damned Reb when I see one. Just like I knew what a Redcoat was in 1812."

Fury flared in his gut. "I will get your stock back." He mounted his horse and galloped toward the stream. He spied Sergeant Nott, sitting on his horse halfway between the barn and stream, gripping a pistol. He pulled up.

Nott holstered his pistol. "I followed you, Lieutenant Potter, because I wasn't sure if that old griper might shoot you."

"The old coot's blood is up, but his barn is empty. Have a couple of troopers ride over and investigate that wagon and those boys escorting it."

"I'll send Corporals Frank Street and Isaac Dannenhower." Nott trotted toward the creek.

Potter put the field glasses to his eyes, scanning the entire area. He shook his head. All he saw were blue-uniformed troopers. Was the old farmer imagining Rebels?

Lieutenant Jones rode up. "What's happening?"

"I'm not sure. The troops escorting the wagon are wearing blue coats. But the old farmer swears they're Rebs."

Potter stared at the two corporals trotting across the field. Street and Dannenhower paused thirty yards from the wagon.

"Why did they stop and now they are turning back?" The old farmer squawked. "Are they afraid of those Yellowbelly Graybacks?"

A cold misgiving slid down his throat. "William, something is not right. Let's go." He spurred his mount and galloped toward the creek. He reined up and shouted, "Everyone. Let's mount up."

The column formed up in twos. The two corporals and Sergeant Nott pulled up and saluted.

Corporal Street said, "Lieutenant Potter. We checked them out from a safe distance. We believe they are from Captain Freeland's Company E. They were one of the flanking patrols detached from Littlestown and riding on a small road to the left of Hanover Road."

Fragments of uncertainty coursed through his mind. He drew a deep breath and forced it out.

"I will speak with Captain Freeland when we arrive in Hanover." He turned to Nott. "Let's move out, Sergeant."

"Forward, march," Nott bellowed.

Potter spurred his mount and turned to Lieutenant Jones. "William, something is not right. I've been watching Freeman's boys riding parallel to us this morning. Captain Freeland's scouting squadron had a dozen troopers. Do they look like they have a dozen troopers?"

Jones gripped his binoculars and scanned for a couple moments as his breathing grew heavier. "Damn, Henry. My guess is that their numbers are double that or more."

"I would swear their guidon is red."

"You're right. It's very red. Something is rotten in the state of Denmark."

"Let's stay alert," Potter said. "I know how that Shakespeare play ends."

"Look, Henry, about seven or eight rods over there." Jones pointed. "The road that gaggle is on merges with ours."

A bloodcurdling yell like the screams of several cougars erupted from the thick trees. His eyes flicked toward the chilling cries. Sixty gray-clad troopers burst forth like a pack of wolves and blocked the road. His breast locked up as an icy chill swept through his body.

"Christ almighty!" Jones shouted.

A Confederate officer wearing a large, soft, black-plumed hat galloped towards them with his pistol pointed just over their heads. He pulled hard on the horse's reins and halted about forty yards away. His gray gelding stood champing at the bit with his nostrils flared.

The Rebel officer shouted, "Don't shoot! You must surrender. We've just captured some of y'all, and their wagon, and they did not shoot."

A jolt surged through Potter as Sergeant Nott pulled up even with him. He bent his head slightly and whispered. "They must have captured Freeman and his boys."

Nott nodded. "Yep. Old Davy Crockett was right. Rebels stole his livestock."

"Tell the boys we are going to ride slowly forward and, on my signal, shoot and ride like hell to Hanover."

"Will do, sir." Nott said. The sergeant eased back toward the column.

A muffled interlude like silent lightning reigned for a few electrified moments—an interlude that every man present knew would end in a few thumping heartbeats. And that ending would be either peaceful or deadly.

"Ride toward us and drop your weapons, and we won't shoot," the Confederate officer admonished.

Potter's jaw stiffened; sweat poured off his brow. Nott eased back up next to him.

Nott said, "Everyone is ready, sir."

He nodded and started to ride forward in a four-beat walk. He glanced over his shoulder and spotted his troopers forming a V-shape behind him. He snapped his head forward and locked his eyes onto the enemy officer. He said, "Sergeant, let's keep the pace as if we are going to comply with the Rebel's surrender order."

"Will do, sir," Nott said.

The V-shape closed to twenty yards of the Rebel officer. He lightly spurred his mount and the V-shape picked up speed. The Rebel's face turned ashen, and his eyes swept from side to side like a swinging pendulum.

Ten yards away, Potter gripped his pistol and ripped it out of its holster. "Charge!"

He spurred his horse and leaned to the right. His jaw muscles flinched as a bullet zipped past his ear. He aimed his pistol and pulled the trigger. *Crack.* The Rebel officer grunted, lurched forward, and tumbled off his mount.

Sergeant Nott shouted, "Fly like the devil, boys!"

Potter gulped rapid breaths and narrowed his eyes as he raced toward the enemy horsemen. He aimed his pistol and fired. A Rebel dragoon threw up his arms and slumped forward on his mount. A fissure erupted through the enemy gaggle like a light shaft through a storm cloud. His heart leaping, Potter plunged his galloping mount into the gap. *Holy hell.* It felt like he was riding the whitewaters of a narrow gorge and the rocky walls were lined with Rebels.

"We're right behind you, Lieutenant," Nott shouted. "Ride like you're chasing the Devil himself!"

Revolvers cracked and gunfire roared from the charging V, scattering the enemy as they galloped through the Rebel gauntlet. Screams and shouting and cursing and horses neighing rent the air.

Potter cleared the gap and spurred his horse into a breakneck gallop. They raced up the Hanover-Littlestown Road to the clattering thunder of Union horse hooves.

He swiveled 'round and bellowed, "Come on, boys. Just a half mile to go!"

Hot sweat sprayed off his brow like a leaky pump, scalding his eyes. He squinted and wiped his brow as he rounded a bend. His heart hammered to the beat of galloping hooves. When Hanover's church spires came into view, a torrent of relief swept through him.

One hundred yards ahead, at the southwestern edge of town, was the rear of his regiment, dismounted, rifles ready along Frederick Street. Twenty yards away, a stone-and-wood fence lined both sides of the road. At the beginning of the fence a blue-clad sergeant popped up behind it, pointing a carbine, nearly stopping his breathing.

The sergeant shouted, "Keeping riding! We've set up an ambuscade behind the fences."

"Thank you," he gasped. "The Rebels are right behind us."

As he neared the Eighteenth Pennsylvania's defensive line along Frederick Street, he slowed down and twisted in his saddle. His wide-eyed troopers raced past him, with some crashing through Kilpatrick's division wagons and ambulances.

The teamsters shouted, "Slow down, you're going to kill somebody!"

Potter spotted the enemy cavalry galloping around the bend and firing their pistols as they approached the fences. A Union officer stood and shouted, "Now!"

The Pennsylvanians hidden behind the two road fences rose and fired a thunderous volley. Shrieks split the air as several Rebels tumbled to the ground. The shocked Confederates skidded to a halt, turned, and skedaddled back around the bend, as if chased by Death's own scythe.

After his last trooper cleared the defensive line, he followed. Screaming teamsters started driving the supply wagons and ambulances toward the center of Hanover Square.

He halted, reined his mount around, only to witness a large gaggle of Rebels reforming.

He turned to Sergeant Nott. "My God, the Rebels are preparing to charge through the town."

A booming voice shouted, "Lieutenant Potter, what the hell is going on?"

Potter turned around. It was Major William Darlington of the Eighteenth Pennsylvania. He saluted. "Sir, we were ambushed by Rebel cavalry about a mile south of Hanover."

"In what strength is the enemy?"

"A hell of a lot." Potter wiped his face. "I believe a detachment of fifty or sixty enemy troopers attacked my rear guard. But an entire enemy regiment is now attacking up the Hanover-Littlestown Road."

"I will stay here and take command of the rear guard," said Darlington. "Have someone ride into Hanover Square where the rest of Eighteenth Pennsylvania are enjoying refreshments along with Fifth New York. Inform Major John Hammond, commander of the Fifth New York Cavalry, of the enemy attacking, and tell him we need reinforcements. Now!"

Potter turned to Lieutenant Jones. "William, follow Major Darlington's orders and inform Major Hammond of the situation."

Jones saluted and spurred away.

He glanced back down the road, eyeing the charging Rebels. He had blind faith in the surprise power of a sudden cavalry charge.

He turned to Major Darlington. "Sir, I'm going to lead a countercharge with my rear-guard detachment. I believe I have the strength to rout their frontline."

"Very well," Darlington said, "I will stay here and take command of the New York reinforcements when they arrive."

10:30 a.m.
Potter
Littlestown Road, Outskirts of Hanover

Potter turned back around and shouted, "Rear guard, right-about. Face the enemy!"

"A column of twos!" Sergeant Nott barked out.

Potter glanced at the rear guard forming up quickly. "Sergeant, it looks like some of the New York troops are joining our Eighteenth Pennsylvania boys. My guess is that we have about a hundred troopers for a countercharge."

"That's good," Nott said. "I think we're tangling with the vanguard of a large cavalry force."

"Perhaps. Let us find out." He turned and thundered, "Charge!"

He pitched his mount forward as hundreds of hooves pounded behind him. He rounded the bend. He scanned the Rebels loitering beyond the range of the dismounted Pennsylvanians firing behind the fences.

"I think the Rebs are getting ready to charge again," Nott shouted.

Potter galloped toward enemy troopers and fired at the enemy guidon that held the staff of the treacherous red flag. A Confederate officer pulled up, whirled his saber, reined his horse about, and skedaddled back down the road. His detachment turned and followed him, galloping down the Hanover-Littlestown Road and then veering left down the Westminster Road.

"We have them on the run!" Nott shouted.

Potter turned down Westminster Road. He drew his saber and waved it above his head. Pounding hooves like a cattle stampede echoed behind. Beyond the enemy detachment displaying the one red battle flag, he spotted four more red battle flags sailing toward him like a flotilla of ships. He cringed. The Rebels drew sabers, screamed a bloodcurdling yell, and plunged into a mounted charge. A chilling terror galloped down his spine. He leveled his saber and spurred his mount.

The two forces crashed like runaway trains. Men and horses tumbled and collapsed in withering heaps. The Pennsylvanian vanguard sliced through the enemy in a wild, boiling mass. Sabers clashed against one another. Shrieks and groans filled the air. Sergeant Nott raced past, stabbing and hacking like a berserker. He lost his hat, and his long hair flew in the wind.

Potter's heartbeat sped with a fighting spirit. His eyes darted as he searched for the next target. A bullet whizzed by his face, sounding like a hornet. He ducked. His lips trembled and his throat tightened as cold fear racked his body. *That was close.*

A Southern voice shouted, "Retreat, fall back!"

The Rebels broke and scattered, and the bloody melee fractured into pockets of saber fighting and clanging metal. Potter halted and twisted in his saddle. His skin prickled with pride. His troopers had fought gloriously, never losing their rank, and closing gaps as casualties occurred.

Thunder rolled overhead. He glanced up and spotted slender tendrils streaking through the sky. *Oh, my God.*

The Rebels were shelling the town.

Nott pointed and screamed, "Lieutenant, a Rebel unit is going to hit our left flank. We must pull back."

He turned, spotting the vanguard of gray troopers racing toward his column's flank. Yards behind them a red battle flag flapped, marking the edge of the rushing Rebel storm.

He turned. "Retreat back to the town! Retreat!"

"Every man for himself and the Devil take the hindmost!" Nott bellowed.

Potter spurred up Westminster Road and aimed for the belled cupola of the German Reformed Church, a mile away. Several shells swooped overhead, striking like lightning bolts. The ground rumbled and fissured as hell's flames and brimstone burst forth. Pennsylvanian troopers galloped past him like bounding rabbits. A plunging shot stopped, shrieking as if suspended in air. His heart clutched. *Oh, my God, it's coming for me.* The missile swooped, hitting with a thunderous crash and flashing fire.

His horse bucked and shot him upward. His heart floated into his throat during his fall. He crashed and tumbled off the road, landing against a rail fence. Confederate horsemen charged past him, screeching the rebel yell and firing their pistols. *Don't move. Play dead,* his mind screamed. He held his breath and squeezed his eyes shut. The rattling storm raced ahead. His heart thumped against his rib cage. Within moments, the clattering hooves faded like a passing train.

A distant voice sounding like Sergeant Nott grew louder. "Lieutenant Potter! Are you wounded?"

He opened his eyes and stared at Nott kneeling beside him. He hesitated as his mind searched for pain. He rubbed his bruised shoulder. That was it. "I fell on my shoulder. No blood."

"Get up, sir. We have to run. The Rebels will be riding back."

Potter stood and glanced up and down the road. No enemy horsemen.

"Follow me," Nott said. "Run for the tree line." Nott gripped his revolver, jumped the fence, and started sprinting.

He leaped over the fence and sprinted after Nott. Reaching the trees, they halted. He glanced toward the town's church steeples. "Sergeant, we can run north along the tree line until we reach Hanover Square."

"Let's go, Lieutenant."

He started bounding through the trees like a spooked deer. Nott was running with him. He lengthened his stride. *Must reach Hanover Square before the enemy overruns it.*

10:30 a.m.
Major John Hammond, Fifth New York
Hanover Square

His New York Regiment was drawn up in a column of fours in Hanover Square surrounded by young ladies distributing pies and cakes. He spotted his 14-year-old bugler, Johnnie Catlin, chatting with a pretty girl his age. She was holding a pie and held it out to Johnnie.

Hammond turned to his adjutant, Major Amos White, sitting on his horse beside him. "Our visit has turned into an early Fourth of July feast."

White smiled. "Yes, and I think your young bugler might have found his first sweetheart."

The sharp report of artillery thundered from the hills south of town. The shell streaked across the southern sky, pitching down near the Winebrenner Tannery on the Hanover-Littlestown Road.

Hammond turned to his adjutant.

"Have you seen any artillery?" asked Hammond.

White shook his head. "No. Lieutenant Elder's artillery battery supporting Farnsworth's brigade departed Hanover about twenty minutes ago. Captain Pennington's artillery battery supporting Custer's brigade departed Hanover over a couple hours ago."

Hammond rubbed his chin. "How strange. Maybe the citizens are firing a salute in our honor."

White grinned. "Or maybe in honor of Johnnie and his young lass."

A second report ripped through the air like shrieking wind. The shell burst south of the town square with a blinding white flash, and scorching metal shards whizzed into the ground like pelting rain. Young ladies hosting the troopers screamed and raced pell-mell toward the town's buildings.

"People don't fire exploding shells for a salute," said White. "That's enemy artillery."

"Damn. Let's go."

Hammond trotted toward the town square, worming his way through the screaming crowd. He arrived in front of the Central Hotel. "Citizens," he announced, loudly enough to be heard above the clamor, "please go to your homes and into your cellars. In a few moments there will be fighting in your streets."

A solid shot shell plunged down as a hailstone of iron, throwing up a cloud of dirt and dust as it screeched up the street.

Hammond yelled, "Men, take cover! That's Rebel artillery!"

The New Yorkers glanced into the sky, where two black tendrils looking like long, slithering snakes streaked overhead. They started riding through Hanover Square up Abbottstown Road.

Hammond's eyes strained as a Union officer rushed toward him, waving his hands. Lieutenant Jones halted, gasping for breath.

"Major, the enemy is attacking our rear guard south of town along Littlestown Road. They are routing the Pennsylvanians, who are skedaddling both north and south on the Hanover-Littlestown Road."

A rumbling stampede echoed throughout the town square. Teamsters driving ambulances and logistic wagons thundered up the street, their long whips snapping above the horse teams.

"Oh, my God," Hammond muttered, every muscle contracting. "This is a major attack, at least a brigade." Hammond ducked as a rattling storm of bullets whizzed through the air. "Gather up your Pennsylvania boys and join my New York Regiment and we'll make a stand here. Farnsworth will send reinforcements and join us soon."

10:30 a.m.
Kilpatrick
Beyond Pigeon Hills
North of Hanover near the York Pike

Kilpatrick rubbed his throbbing lower back. It felt like he had been mule-kicked. He dismounted on a grassy knoll dotted with large shade trees, north of Pigeon Hills. The scorching sun charred his neck and back, but his flaming skin paled next to his fiery kidneys bleeding jets of hot lava. He mopped the sweat from his huge, stringy sideburns. His staff had congregated underneath the raked shadows of a giant eastern hemlock. Grimacing, he squinted southward at Farnsworth's endless blue ribbon of troopers meandering toward the Pigeon Hills gap like a chattering mountain creek. *Damn kidneys.*

Hooves thundered and a rattling horse snorted behind him. Captain Llewellyn G. Estes approached; his horse was sputtering froth. Kilpatrick flashed a smile. If only his cavalry division had more fire-eating officers like Estes. The 20-year-old was cut from the Kilpatrick mold, a fearless fighting cock sporting a dapper, drooping, black mustache. Estes pulled hard on the reins and the horse slid to a stop, rearing up on his hind legs as his front hooves lashed out.

"General Kilpatrick, Custer's brigade is arriving in Abbottstown, about two miles up the road. General Custer sends his respects and is waiting in Abbottstown as you directed, before proceeding to York."

"Good. I'm delighted Custer is obeying orders. Let's rest the headquarters' staff a few minutes here before riding to meet Custer's brigade and leading them to York."

A dull, booming clap rumbled overhead. Kilpatrick peered at the sky over Hanover. "Llew, was that thunder?"

Llewellyn gazed southward. "I'm not sure. The sky is clear. Where are the thunderheads?"

Kilpatrick reached into his jacket and pulled out his pocket watch: 10:30 a.m. He glanced through his binoculars at the blue troopers moving northward from Hanover on the Abbottstown Road.

"It looks as if the head of Farnsworth's brigade is a few miles north of Hanover, passing through the village of New Baltimore. I'm guessing the rear of the brigade is still in the northern part of Hanover."

"The Eighteenth Pennsylvania, the rear guard, are probably still there," Llewellyn replied.

A second clap of thunder boomed overhead. Kilpatrick fidgeted. Then a mighty din rocked the sky.

"That's artillery." Kilpatrick vaulted onto his horse. Fangs of fire scorched his insides. "Damned Rebels! They must have at least a brigade, supported by a battery, shelling Farnsworth's rear detachment."

"Stuart's boys?"

"Must be." He motioned for Lieutenant Eli Holden. "This is our chance to give him a licking. Stuart doesn't know he is facing a whole cavalry division."

His aide rode up. "Eli, ride north to Abbottstown and tell General Custer that the Rebels are shelling Hanover. I'm riding back to Hanover with my staff. Tell Custer to countermarch his brigade to Hanover at his best speed."

Lieutenant Holden saluted and spurred his horse northward to Abbottstown.

Kilpatrick turned to Llewellyn. "I'm racing ahead to Hanover. Private Samuel Gillespie will ride with me. You lead the rest of my headquarters staff to Hanover. I will meet you there."

Kilpatrick turned to his bugler, mounted on his horse ten yards away. "Private, let's ride like hell to Hanover!"

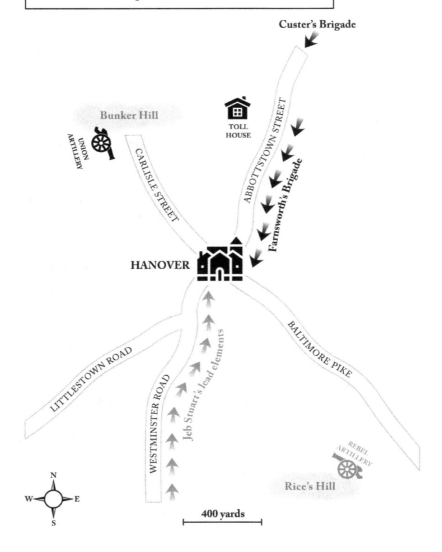

Battle of Hanover
Farnsworth's Brigade Fights Jeb Stuart's Division
June 30, 1863
10:30 a.m. - 12:00 p.m.

Custer's Brigade

Bunker Hill

UNION ARTILLERY

TOLL HOUSE

ABBOTTSTOWN STREET

CARLISLE STREET

Farnsworth's Brigade

HANOVER

LITTLESTOWN ROAD

WESTMINSTER ROAD

Jeb Stuart's lead elements

BALTIMORE PIKE

REBEL ARTILLERY

Rice's Hill

N
W—E
S

400 yards

15

Farnsworth — Tuesday, June 30

10:30 a.m.
Farnsworth
Hamlet of New Baltimore
One mile north of Hanover

Farnsworth's muscles stirred, riding at the head of his brigade at a swinging trot. Hundreds of saber scabbards rattled against his brigade's troopers' pant legs. He took a deep breath. A quietness hung in the thick air, smelling like fresh-mown grass.

He turned to his aide-de-camp Captain Andrew Cunningham. "General Kilpatrick said he is not expecting us to run into Rebels today."

"That's good. Maybe we can give the regiments in the rear guard time to enjoy Hanover's hospitality."

"They deserve a respite, even if it's only for an hour."

From the town, rifles and pistols popped and crackled.

Farnsworth's brow furrowed. "Do you think the townspeople are celebrating?"

"It could be those Eighteenth Pennsylvania boys, happy to be back in their home state."

A volley of rifles cracked like a whip.

"That sounds more like a severe affair," Cunningham said.

"I agree." A thundering boom echoed over the brigade. What was that sound? He glanced into the bright sky and saw no storm clouds. A second sharp report thundered over Hanover.

Farnsworth shuddered. "That's more than a severe affair. That's enemy artillery. There must be at least an enemy brigade attacking our rear guard."

"Do you want me to send a courier to General Kilpatrick?"

"No. He will hear the artillery and come racing back. Let's countermarch and push forward as rapidly as possible. I will lead the advance." Farnsworth reined his mount around and faced the column. Cunningham and Bugler Gilbert Buckman turned and rode alongside.

"Forward by fours at a gallop!" Farnsworth yelled. He spurred his horse toward the middle of the approaching column. The blue troopers cleaved left and right off the road like an ax splitting wood.

Cunningham shouted, "Follow General Farnsworth!"

Farnsworth twisted in his saddle. The blue columns were turning around and moving their mounts toward Hanover. His heart thumped in time with the beating of horses' hooves. He suppressed a grin. *Hang on, Eighteenth Pennsylvania. We're going to surprise these Rebels with a full brigade.*

10:35 a.m.
Major John Hammond
Hanover Square

Hammond felt the sharp breath of a flight of enemy shells approaching and instinctively glanced up. They flew leisurely upward in a rainbow arc. Hitting their peak, they bent downward and accelerated in a thickening scream, striking with a violent flash of yellow light, clawing the ground with murderous shards of steel. *Damn.* The Rebels were softening up the Union defenses and preparing to charge. He stood in the middle of Hanover Square and cast his gaze toward Frederick Street, wiping his face in the sweltering late-morning heat. An attack plan quickly cobbled itself together in his mind.

"Sergeant Selden Wales." He pointed south toward Frederick Street. "The Rebels will be coming up that road. I want half the regiment to dismount and form a battle line. Prepare to fire carbines."

"Yes, Major!" said the Sergeant. Wales dismounted and dashed down Hanover Square, gripping his horse's reins and shouting orders.

A shell shrieked through the sky. Hammond glanced up and spotted a black tendril as the shell swooped down, hissing like a large bull snake. A few gawking citizens stood frozen, staring into the sky. He hollered, "Take cover! Run into your cellars! The fight is on!"

The shell burst with a thunderous crack just north of Hanover Square on the Abbottstown Road, lightning radiating from a puffy white cloud. Hot iron hailed like a screeching wind, and an ear-piercing shard sliced past his ear. A prolonged hiss heralded the approach of another shell. Then the hissing seemed to stop. The shell hung suspended momentarily like a distant star. *My God, this shell is close.* The missile hit twenty yards away with a blinding fury, tearing and plowing the ground. *The enemy is shelling the townspeople. Sons of bitches. This isn't civilized warfare.*

Hammond turned to his bugler, Johnnie Catlin, holding a pie. "Stay mounted behind this barricade. The enemy is going to burst into Hanover Square."

He started to turn his horse, then looked back over his shoulder at Johnnie. "And save that pie. I'm going to want some later."

"Yes sir, Major."

"See, look!" Hammond pointed. A swelling gray wave rumbled toward Hammond's dismounted troopers, thrashing retreating enclaves of blue Eighteenth Pennsylvania troopers.

Hammond shouted, "New Yorkers! Hold your fire! Hold your fire until they are four rods away!"

Confederate horses pounded a thundering din as the enemy stormed up Frederick Street, brandishing sabers and screeching howls.

"FIRE!" Hammond screamed.

Two hundred carbines from dismounted New York troopers unleashed a jarring sheet of yellow fire, and screams echoed. A sulphury arch of smoke stretched across the street. The first enemy wave crashed and broke, whirling away in every direction like ocean spray.

Hammond turned to his bugler. "Johnnie, 'Charge!' You stay here!"

Johnnie put his bugle to his lips and blasted out "Charge."

Hammond spurred his black charger and leaped over the battle line, firing his pistol with his left hand and slashing his sword with his right. Private Thomas Burke of Company A spurred his horse past Hammond and slashed a Rebel across the face. Two hundred dismounted New Yorkers rushed forward, screaming like howling wolves. The enemy splintered, spilling into alleys, backyards, and side streets.

Hammond pointed. "Chase those Rebels out of town!"

Dismounted New Yorkers sprinted after the enemy. Within minutes, several small-scale battles broke out. Fierce saber fights erupted in pockets around Hanover Square. Carbine fire deepened and rolled. Hammond spotted a dismounted Rebel officer with a plumed hat firing his pistol into the backs of blue troopers rushing into the melee. Rage surged over him. Hammond spurred his horse. The Rebel turned his head, his eyes wide and plainly filled with fright. Hammond yelled and slashed his sword downward across the enemy's throat. The Rebel screamed and fell to the ground, bright blood spurting from his sliced carotid.

Volleys blazed and leaped, pounding the air like a rampaging storm surge. He reined his mount around. The violent melee had turned into a hand-to-hand slashing and knifing, like the vicious New York City gang riot between the Dead Rabbits and the Bowery Boys.

Hammond's New York staff officer Major Amos White shouted and pointed. "Major Hammond, look!"

Hammond twisted in his saddle and searched toward the rear of the New Yorkers.

White shouted, "The Rebels are using the alleys to flank us!"

Hammond stiffened as he gazed at a horde of enemy troopers bursting forth from the Frederick Street alleys, chasing fleeing Pennsylvania troopers. Thunderous booms erupted skyward, thumping his face with their pulsing beats. Enemy artillery shells started raining a hundred yards in front of his regiment. A torrent of fright swept through him.

"Amos, we are in a pickle. The Rebs keep pouring troops on us."

"Major! Major!" White pointed again.

Hammond twisted in his saddle and glared at an old man with long white hair and beard.

"Major, over there is an ideal place for your regiment. It's called the Commons." The old man pointed westerly toward a vacant field near the railroad depot.

Hammond scanned the open field, then turned to the old man and tipped his hat. "Thank you, sir."

He rode several yards back to Johnnie, still cradling a pie. "Johnnie, blow 'Retreat' and follow me."

Johnnie stood and trilled "Retreat." Hammond rode toward the vacant lot, waving his sword, and looked behind him. *Good.* The New Yorkers were following him. He pulled up. His breath caught in his throat.

"Major White!" he shouted. "Order the men to line up in a line of battle and draw sabers."

White rode toward the arriving troopers and pointed. The dragoons started lining up.

Hammond turned and shot a glance at his bugler. *My God.* Johnnie's face was smeared with blue pie. "Johnnie did you try to swallow the blueberry pie whole?"

Johnnie wiped his shirt sleeve across his mouth. "Yes."

Hammond smiled and nodded. "Let's charge."

Johnnie took a deep breath and lifted his bugle to his purple lips. He blew so hard his cheeks puffed out. A metallic shriek pierced the air.

Hammond raised his sword. "*Charge!*"

The New Yorkers spurred their horses and thundered forward through the streets toward the enemy line of battle. Hammond scanned the streets as bullets flew thick, like swarming locusts. Women stood in the doors of their houses, waving white handkerchiefs and cheering. *My God, these are brave women.*

Sergeant Selden Wales screamed and plunged ahead of his company as if madness took him. The enemy fired a roaring volley. Bullets streaked by and thudded into his troopers. Wales screamed and clutched his jacket, plunging from his horse. *Damn!*

Hammond pulled up next to Major White, hunched forward on his skittish mount. White's face was as pale as a ghost. "Amos, are you wounded?"

"I have been shot in the leg just above my ankle and my boot is filling with blood. I felt a crack, so I think surely the bone is broken."

"Amos, turn around and get medical treatment."

"I will. Just as soon as the enemy starts fleeing."

Hammond spurred ahead, slashing and firing. Searing rage spilling into his veins, he howled as he chased the Rebels a mile down the Hanover-Littlestown Road. Beyond the fleeing Confederates, he spotted a large Rebel reserve force drawn up in the road, sporting three red flags flaunting half the stars of Old Glory. A long, cracking volley of murderous bullets whizzed by from the enemy line, raking the air, eliciting screams from his regiment, and emptying several saddles. He held up his sword and halted. The rattling storm threatened to reap his regiment from their steeds like a scythe cutting wheat.

He turned to Johnnie. "Blow 'Retreat.'"

The blue-faced bugler shrilled out "Retreat." Hammond rode back toward Frederick Street. The street was littered with bodies and dead and dying horses. Women were rushing out of buildings and tending to the wounded.

10:49 a.m.
Farnsworth
One-half mile north of Hanover

Farnsworth's heart pounded in his ears as he galloped down Abbottstown Street. Half a mile ahead, rifle and pistol volleys echoed over the town square. On a hill south of town he spotted yellow flashes of Rebel artillery thundering. Booming shells arched high in the sky and screamed downward, raining death on his troopers and trapped townspeople.

"General Farnsworth."

He turned to Lieutenant Colonel Addison Preston, commanding officer of the First Vermont.

"That's the Toll House on the right, about twenty rods ahead," Preston said. The Toll House marked the northern edge of Hanover.

"I see it." Farnsworth shuddered, his pulse climbing. How would Preston and the First Vermont respond to the upcoming battle? The regiment had been through a bevy of colonels, and now a lieutenant colonel was leading them. Maybe Preston was the right man. The lieutenant colonel, with his chiseled face and handlebar mustache, was popular with his troopers. Colonel or lieutenant colonel, he would soon find out if Preston could lead the Vermonters in battle.

He reined up at the Toll House, gripped the binoculars hanging around his neck, and peered through them at the fighting in Hanover Square and on Littlestown Road.

"General, look." Preston pointed. "An enemy column flying a red battle flag is approaching the New Yorkers." He turned and pointed again. "Over there in that field west of town are some blue troopers forming up."

Farnsworth scanned the area. "Lieutenant Colonel Preston, send a Vermont battalion to support the Fifth New York and countercharge that enemy column."

"Yes, sir," Preston said.

Preston turned in his saddle and waved. "Major John Bennett."

Farnsworth squinted. The 27-year-old officer approached. Bennett was a brawny brute with a full black beard covering his angular face. He had heard Bennett was a fierce fighter and respected by his troopers. Bennett saluted Farnsworth and Preston.

Preston pointed and said, "Major Bennett, I want your Third Battalion to form up in the Commons Field and support the New Yorkers in a countercharge."

"Yes, sir," Bennett said. "We will push the Rebels out of town." He saluted and departed.

Farnsworth pointed toward Bunker Hill, a sloping rise beginning at the Toll House and running west for eight hundred yards. "Addison, I'm going to place Lieutenant Samuel Elder's battery on that hill. I want you to send two companies to protect

Elder's artillery battery and act as the brigade's reserve in case the Rebels break through."

"Yes, sir." Preston turned to his adjutant, Clarence Gates. "Clarence, order Captain Parsons's First Battalion to protect Elder's artillery battery that will unlimber on Bunker Hill."

"Addison," Farnsworth said, "let's ride to the Commons just north of the town square."

He spurred his mount toward the fighting blossoming in Hanover Square. He gritted his teeth and suppressed the butterflies fluttering in his gut. His first battle as a brigade commander. *Must prove to Pleasonton that he made the right choice recommending me for general.* He and Preston reined up in the Commons. Waiting for him were the First West Virginia, commanded by Colonel Nathaniel Richmond, the Fifth New York, commanded by Major John Hammond, and the Eighteenth Pennsylvania, commanded by Lieutenant Colonel William Brinton.

His heart quickened. "Major Hammond, please give us the latest intelligence on the fighting."

"Second Lieutenant Potter and forty troopers from Eighteenth Pennsylvania were a mile behind the rest of the regiment, pulling rear guard duty. They were about a half mile from Hanover when they were attacked and shelled. Potter and his men raced into Hanover, where the Fifth New Yorkers were enjoying refreshments from the citizens. The enemy raced into the town square, chasing Potter's troopers. The New Yorkers regrouped and did a countercharge, supported by the Pennsylvanians. We pushed the enemy down the Hanover-Littlestown Road until we met a large enemy reserve. Outnumbered, we retreated back into town."

"Let's form up for another countercharge," Farnsworth proposed. "The Rebels are going to be surprised when they are facing a brigade."

The four regimental commanders nodded.

Farnsworth continued. "I want the West Virginians to attack through town and then split off southeast toward Baltimore Street. The Vermont Third Battalion commanded by Major Bennett will form up in the Commons open field on our right, and attack through town and support the New Yorkers and Pennsylvanians fighting along Frederick Street. I want to push the enemy through Frederick Street south onto Hanover-Littlestown Road as far as we can go. I will lead Major Hammond's remaining New Yorkers in the cavalry charge. Let's form up."

The regimental commanders departed to their ordered areas and wheeled into line. Farnsworth glanced left, then right. *Good.* "Draw...sa*bers!*"

A chorus of rattling steel filled the air. He glanced toward Bugler Buckman. "Let's go."

Buckman trumpeted the air with a high-pitched "Charge."

Farnsworth raised his saber. "*Charge!*"

Hundreds of horses surged forward, thundering abreast of Farnsworth. The blue boys waved their sabers and screamed. A thrill quaked through his body. The aftershock felt like sparks igniting across his skin. He was leading his first cavalry charge as a brigade commander, at lightning speed.

The stunned enemy turned and raced out of Hanover. Farnsworth reached the center of town. He spotted Second Lieutenant Potter and several disorganized companies of the Eighteenth Pennsylvania. "Lieutenant Potter," he yelled, "form the Pennsylvanians in a line of battle."

Potter shouted back. "Yes, General."

Farnsworth waved his sword high. "Line up, men. Line up."

The Pennsylvanians formed up. Farnsworth rode in front of them. "Don't shoot until you see the color of their Rebel eyes."

The troopers cheered.

"Let's support your fellow New Yorkers," Farnsworth yelled. He turned toward Bugler Buckman. "'Charge'!"

For the second time in six minutes, Buckman blew "Charge."

Farnsworth pointed his sword and surged forward. Ahead, he spotted the red battle colors of a Rebel regimental flag floating. Two Fifth New Yorkers galloped past him. The troopers raced ahead about one hundred yards when Hammond pulled up.

Farnsworth reined up. "Who are those troopers?

Hammond grabbed his binoculars. "The one in the lead is Corporal James Rickey. The one behind him is Private Thomas Burke."

Farnsworth's eyes widened and his jaw dropped. *What rare courage.* Suddenly, Corporal Rickey flew from his horse. Both tumbled to the ground. Rickey stood up, but his horse did not. Burke raced past Rickey, firing his carbine and darting toward the Rebel flag. Burke pounced on the six Confederates protecting their treasonous flag. He disarmed several enemy troopers of their rifles, swords, and pistols, grabbed the enemy flag, and turned and marched his mounted prisoners back to Hanover.

"My God, John." Farnsworth marveled. "I think Private Burke is rushing his captured Rebels and their flag back to your lines. I want you to write him up for a Medal of Honor. That's the most courageous act I have ever seen."

"Yes, General."

"I'm riding over to Frederick Street to see how the Vermonters are doing."

11:10 a.m.
Farnsworth
Retreating back into Hanover

A shiver sliced through Farnsworth. When would the rest of his brigade arrive, and Custer's brigade? He turned to Captain Cunningham and Bugler Buckman. "Follow me."

A line of dismounted Vermonters at the intersection of Westminster and Hanover-Littlestown roads were pouring lead into a line of dismounted enemy. Smoke filled the air like low clouds. His chest tightened. Major John Bennett yelled and bolted forward, leading over a hundred horsemen. At a full gallop, they leaped over a line of 90 dismounted Vermonters. Bennett fired his pistol and started slashing Rebels. His troopers joined the melee. The Rebels broke and fled down Littlestown Road.

"Let's follow them," Farnsworth shouted. He spurred his steed and raced toward Bennett and his troopers. The hills south of town seemed to grow in height. Farnsworth climbed the first hill and halted on its summit, next to Bennett.

Farnsworth wiped his brow. "What is happening?"

"The hills south of town are masking enemy movements," Bennett said. "We can't move forward unless we have a plan."

Farnsworth frowned. He hated halting the attack with such strong momentum, but he had little choice. Continuing the countercharge risked being overpowered by larger numbers of enemy troops hiding in the hills.

"I agree," Farnsworth said. "We are not in position to continue the attack."

"When will Custer's brigade arrive?" Bennett asked.

"Not for another hour or so. I have no idea when Custer's two other regiments will be arriving from Littlestown. If we are fighting Stuart's boys, they have three brigades south of town to our one brigade in town."

Bennett said, "I think this fight is a draw for now. I recommend we pull back into town."

"I agree. Let's pull the Vermont and New York boys back into town and regroup."

Union Cavalry Leaders & Raiders: Averill, Kilpatrick, Kautz, Gregg,
Sheridan, Custer, Streight, Grierson, Wilson,
Stoneman, Merritt, and Torbert

150

16

Kilpatrick — Tuesday, June 30

Kilpatrick yanked hard on the reins. His Confederate States of America–branded horse slid on all fours on the grassy ridgeline. The horse gasped and snorted, a frothy wheezing. Kilpatrick snapped his riding whip across the animal's neck.

"Damn you traitorous horse. Just get me to Hanover before you die."

He grabbed his binoculars and scanned the Abbottstown road, jammed with an endless blue column of troopers and caissons snaking their way toward Pigeon Hills. He snarled. *Can't bust my way down the road.*

Hoofbeats clapped from behind, and he twisted in his saddle. Gillespie pulled up, his face red and dripping wet.

"General…sir." A beat passed as Gillespie struggled to catch his breath. "You're going to kill your horse riding it at breakneck speed."

"It's a branded Confederate animal. It needs to die, just like every one of those traitorous West Pointers who ride them."

Gillespie shook his head.

"The road is jammed up. We're going to ride through the fields on the west side. Let's go."

Kilpatrick whipped and spurred his horse. The horse bolted down the ridge and sprinted toward the road. Kilpatrick aimed for a small gap between two marching companies. He snickered.

151

This should be amusing. A glaring young officer held up his right hand and yelled, "Halt!"

The column started bunching up like an accordion.

Kilpatrick shot three yards in front of the officer's horse. "Thank you, boys."

Someone shouted, "My God, that's General Kilpatrick, our divisional commander!"

Kilpatrick grinned, dashed into saddle-high wheat, and raced south toward Hanover. Whipping and spurring the mount, he shouted, "Come on, you traitorous horse, don't die until we reach Hanover." He bounced up and slammed down into the saddle. His kidneys flamed as if scorched by a cherry-red branding iron.

11:00 a.m.
Kilpatrick
Arriving at Hanover Square just as Farnsworth's charge repulsed the enemy

Kilpatrick whipped his mount as he galloped into Hanover Square and down Frederick Street. He pulled up in front of the Vermont line of battle guarding the southern approach to Hanover and turned to Gillespie. "Pass me my flag."

Kilpatrick stood up in his stirrups and waved his divisional flag. "Men of Vermont, you don't know me; I don't know you. Today we make an acquaintance on the battlefield. I know I shall like you; I think you shall like me."

The Vermonters raised their carbines and cheered. A shiver speared down his back. *I love commanding a cavalry division.*

He trotted back through Hanover Square and reined up in front of the Central Hotel. Scores of dead and dying troopers and horses lay along the dusty streets. He dismounted and gave his mount's reins to Gillespie. The Confederate horse gasped and swaggered before crumbling forward on its knees. Blood-laced foam spurted from the animal's mouth, and it collapsed, dead.

Kilpatrick snickered and scooted into the hotel. *If only it were that easy to kill all the Rebel traitors.*

11:15 a.m.
Kilpatrick
Top of the Central Hotel, Hanover

Kilpatrick burst into the Central Hotel and bolted up the stairs. He paused on the fourth-story rafter attic and gasped, bending over and grabbing his lower back. A silent scream sliced through his brain. *Damned kidneys.* He stood and spotted a wooden ladder leading to the roof. He clambered up the ladder and stepped onto the roof. He braced himself against a wide brick chimney extending six feet above the roof's peak. In one frantic heartbeat, his eyes skated over the town square and down Frederick Street. The stairs groaned below, and he spied General Pleasonton's chief of staff, Lieutenant Colonel Andrew Alexander, leaping onto the roof, followed by Captain Estes and bugler Private Gillespie.

"There was one hell of a fight here," Kilpatrick said.

Gillespie pointed. "My God, look at all the dead horses and blue and butternut coats sprawled along the streets and on the sidewalks."

"It's hard to tell the Yankees from the Rebels with all the blood and dust covering them," Alexander said.

Kilpatrick scanned the Hanover-Littlestown and Westminster Roads. An eerie silence shrouded the streets and roads, a deafening stillness like an empty cathedral. "It appears there is a lull in the fighting and the town is under Union control." He scanned south of the town; 1,500 yards away, silent enemy artillery batteries ringed the crest of Rice's Hill.

"Are we fighting Stuart's boys?" Estes asked.

"Yes, and my guess is they are Jeb's Invincibles," Kilpatrick said.

"Do you think it's Jeb's entire cavalry division south of us?" Alexander asked.

"I'm not sure. But we are probably facing at least two Rebel cavalry brigades." Kilpatrick pointed south. "Look there on Rice's Hill. That's where the Rebel batteries fired the opening shots. As long as the enemy is occupying those hills, they are a threat to our boys defending Hanover."

Estes pointed north. "General, here comes Lieutenant Elder's battery down Abbottstown road."

Kilpatrick turned. A swirling dust cloud chased Elder's artillery batteries down the road. He pointed. "Llew, that's Bunker Hill. Tell General Farnsworth that as soon as Lieutenant Elder's battery arrives, I want them there. Tell him to start firing at the enemy artillery battery on Rice's Hill."

"Yes, sir." Estes swooped down the ladder.

Kilpatrick gazed up Abbottstown road. Smoldering anger ignited in his belly, leaping up his throat like flickering flames. "Where in the hell is Custer? And his two regiments and Captain Pennington's artillery? I expected the brash daredevil to be here by now." He sighed. Perhaps the happy-go-lucky prankster was not cut out for brigade command.

"General Custer's First and Seventh Regiments should arrive around noon today, and Pennington's battery should be right on their tails," Alexander said.

"When they arrive, have Pennington's battery limber up next to Elder's battery, just west of Carlisle Road. For now, order the New York and Vermont troopers to help barricade the streets. I expect we will be hearing from the Rebels again."

17

Farnsworth — Tuesday, June 30

11:35 a.m.
Farnsworth
Hanover Square

Farnsworth rubbed his chin as he rode along the defensive line. The dismounted men stood ready behind the barricades, gripping their carbines. Twenty yards behind the barricade, every fourth trooper held the reins of the horses of his dismounted comrades.

A whistling enemy shell sailed overhead, exploding north of the town. As if in reply, another hissing shell sailed over them, heading south. He shot a glance toward Rice's Hill. The shell burst near the Rebel battery.

Farnsworth turned to Adjutant Herman Hamburger and Captain Andrew Cunningham. "That's Elder's battery."

Two more ear-piercing projectiles shrieked overhead, crashing like metal hailstones south of town. The fiery jaws of the Rebel cannons thundered in reply.

"Andrew," Farnsworth said, "order Lieutenant Colonel Preston and the First Vermont to replace the Fifth New York. Hammond's troopers have been carrying the brunt of the fight."

Cunningham saluted and departed.

"Herman, order Major Hammond and his Fifth New Yorkers to pull out of town and ride up and support Elder's battery when the First Vermonters relieve them."

11:45 a.m.
Major Hammond
Hanover Square

Hammond's horse whinnied and pitched its head amid the rattling roar of rifles mingled with the booming thunder of artillery.

He pursed his lips as the serpentine line of his eight depleted companies mounted their horses. The troopers gripped the reins hard-handed and cursed the Rebs for killing and wounding several New Yorkers and shelling innocent townsfolk. Beyond his companies, he spotted Captain Estes galloping toward him. Estes pulled up and saluted.

"Major Hammond, General Kilpatrick orders you to flank the enemy's position and capture the enemy battery on Rice's Hill."

"I've just been ordered by General Farnsworth to move from the town to Elder's position on Bunker Hill when the First Vermont relieves us. My regiment has suffered several casualties. We've been fighting for nearly an hour and our ammunition is low."

Estes sneered. "General Kilpatrick's orders override General Farnsworth's orders. I will inform General Farnsworth of the commanding general's orders."

Hammond glared. A sharp twinge of realization stabbed at him. *Kilpatrick doesn't know what the hell is going on.* He shook his head. "I understand. I will execute General Kilpatrick's orders." He saluted and spurred his horse.

11:52 a.m.
Farnsworth
Frederick Street, Hanover

Farnsworth fished out his watch. Nearly noon. He pulled on the reins, halting on Frederick Street, and turned to First Lieutenant Hamburger. "Herman, did you order Major Hammond to ride up to Bunker Hill?"

"Yes, his regiment is mounting up."

Captain Estes rode up. "General Farnsworth. General Kilpatrick sends his respects and wishes to inform you that he has set up his headquarters at the Central Hotel."

"Thank you for the news, Captain Estes. Has the general orders for my brigade?"

"Yes, he has ordered the New Yorkers to conduct a flanking attack on the Rebel artillery battery. I have delivered that order to Major Hammond."

Farnsworth seethed. "I just ordered Major Hammond to pull out and ride up to Bunker Hill."

"General Kilpatrick has ordered the First Vermont to ride up the hill to protect Elder's battery."

Farnsworth's face tightened and, somewhere inside him, something scoured his gut. "I'm the brigade commander. Why isn't General Kilpatrick issuing his orders through me?"

"General Kilpatrick didn't know where you were. He felt it imperative that Elder's batteries be protected, and the First Vermonters arrived after the Fifth New York, so that's why he ordered the Vermonters to Bunker Hill."

"Damn it, Major. That's why we have a chain of command. I expect the commanding general to use it. Those New Yorkers have carried the fight from the very start. Their companies are depleted, and they need to regroup. Most of the Vermonters are fresh and are the right unit to execute the flanking attack."

"I'll pass on your concerns."

His face heated. "As soon as I observe the New Yorkers execute the flanking attack I will ride to the Central Hotel."

"Very well." Estes saluted and departed.

Farnsworth muttered, "You're a damn fool, Kill-Cavalry!" He spurred his horse toward Major Hammond's Fifth New Yorkers.

12:05 p.m.
Custer
Arriving at the Hanover Toll House

Custer flew past the Toll House on Abbottstown Street with Lieutenant Colerick riding alongside. The spirited din from the Union and Rebel artillery cracked and thundered like a volcano. The metallic storm was nearby. Custer grinned. A tingling thrill surged through him like an arching spark. His muscles pulsed, craving bloodlust moments like this. Dash, surprise, and swiftness had vaulted him from captain to general, and he would use these fighter's qualities today against Stuart's boys.

He shouted over the din. "I hope Farnsworth left some fighting for the Michigan Wolverines!"

Colerick yelled back. "This sounds like a serious fight, General!"

Lieutenant Eli Holden galloped up and halted. "General Custer, General Kilpatrick sends his regards. He requests you deploy your regiments northeast of town between York and Abbottstown Streets. He also requests that Captain Pennington's battery unlimber behind the First and Seventh Michigan."

"Very well," Custer said.

"General Kilpatrick has set his headquarters in the Central Hotel. He recommends you set up your headquarters at Jacob Wirt's house on Frederick Street. After you've set up your headquarters, General Kilpatrick requests the honor of your presence."

"Thank you, Lieutenant Holden. Please give my respects to the commanding general and tell him I will pay him a visit soon."

Holden saluted and galloped back toward town.

Custer glanced up Abbottstown Road, his hunger for greatness pulsing inside. Colonel Mann, leading the seven hundred sabers of the Seventh Michigan, rode up and saluted.

Custer pointed and said, "Colonel Mann, deploy your regiment east of Abbottstown Street and north of York Street. Dismount four companies and form up two squadrons to act as advance skirmishers. The rest of the regiment will remain ready to attack. The First Michigan and Pennington's battery will deploy and dismount and unlimber behind your regiment."

"Yes, sir."

Custer turned to Lieutenant William Wheeler. "Inform the First Michigan and Pennington's battery of my orders. I'm riding ahead to set up headquarters at the Jacob Wirt house and then I'm visiting with General Kilpatrick."

"Yes, sir," William said.

Custer turned to Lieutenant Colerick. "Let's ride into Hanover."

Pulse thumping, Custer spurred Roanoke into a gallop. The hunger for greatness ached inside as if he had been starving for days.

12:15 p.m.
Custer
Jacob Wirt's house

Custer's heartbeat pounded in his ears as he galloped into the yard of Jacob Wirt's two-story colonial brick house. He dismounted and tied his horse to a stout maple tree. "William, please tell Johnny to take care of Roanoke when he arrives. My iron thoroughbred has been ridden hard today."

"General Custer?"

Custer turned. An elderly man stood on the porch, resembling Moses with his glowing white hair and beard.

"I am Jacob Wirt. General Kilpatrick's courier came by about an hour ago. He requested the use of my house for you as your headquarters. I said of course. Welcome."

"Thank you for your generosity, Mr. Wirt. How did you know I was General Custer?"

Wirt cracked a big smile. "When you rode through Hanover early this morning, some of the townsfolks caught a glimpse of you. They said you were a Viking of old, with a great mass of blond curling hair under your hat, and wearing a bright red necktie."

Custer smiled. "I wear the necktie to alert the Rebs of my presence." He winked. "Like Napoleon's Dandy King Murat, the flamboyant necktie also enhances beauty and nobleness on the field of battle."

Wirt chuckled. "You did impress quite a few young women who I'm sure would like to make your acquaintance someday."

Custer shuddered with pride. "As the Union's youngest bachelor general, I would be honored to have tea with the young ladies after I become the nation's hero."

"Please come in. I have a small map of the town and surrounding area that might be useful."

Breathing fire, Farnsworth stormed into the great hall of the Central Hotel and glared at Kilpatrick. Kilpatrick glanced up from the large map lying on a large table.

"Welcome, Elon. Great job on deploying your brigade and thwarting the enemy attack this morning."

Farnsworth scowled. "I would like to speak in private with you, General Kilpatrick."

A puzzled look crossed Kilpatrick's face. He narrowed his eyes. "Yes, by all means." He glanced at his staff. "Gentlemen, please give me and General Farnsworth a moment."

The staff stepped out of the great hall. "Well, Elon. What's on your mind?"

Farnsworth swallowed hard. "I'm formally protesting you violating the chain of command." His face grew hotter. "You circumvented me in giving orders directly to the Fifth New York and First Vermont."

Kilpatrick cracked a ghost of a smile. "I know we've only worked together for two days. But this is my cavalry division, and I can give orders to anyone I want. Do you understand me?"

Farnsworth stepped closer, standing tall, towering over the five-foot-five-inch Kilpatrick. "These are my troops. I'm their commanding officer. I demand that you give your orders to me to execute, and that you not circumvent me."

Kilpatrick grunted and clenched his fists until his quivering knuckles turned white. He lunged forward, shoved his chest out, stopping inches away. His red face contorted, his eyebrows knitted together, his eyes protruded, and his nostrils flared like a fanged pit viper.

"Do you have anything else to say?" Kilpatrick hissed, spraying spit.

Farnsworth clasped his hands behind his back and glared down at the small, sneering firebrand. Locked in a vicious staring contest, the two combatants were as confined by silence as much as by proximity, and the first to blink would lose. He had to make Kilpatrick understand.

Farnsworth broke the stillness with a snort. "The Fifth New Yorkers have carried the brunt of the fight since it started. Major Hammond led the first countercharge into the enemy. Then his New Yorkers fought in the second countercharge that I led. Hammond's companies are depleted. That's why I ordered them to Bunker Hill to rest and regroup. Except for two First Vermont companies, Lieutenant Preston's troopers are rested and eager to conduct the flanking attack."

"You don't have the big picture." Kilpatrick thumped his finger into his chest. "Elder's battery was unprotected. Pennington's battery hasn't arrived yet. The Vermont boys were closest to Elder's battery."

Farnsworth gritted his teeth. He had made his point, and to continue would breed worse evils than necessary now. The enemy was the Rebels, not Kilpatrick. He took a deep breath and held it. He would discuss this event with General Pleasonton at the first opportunity. But someone had to back down. He blinked and took a step back. "If you give direct orders and circumvent me you must take responsibility."

"I take responsibility for everything that happens in this division." Kilpatrick cracked a tight-lipped smile and unclenched his fist. "Now, tell me the details of your actions this morning."

12:28 p.m.
Custer
Central Hotel

Custer strode into the great hall, his spurs clicking against the oak floor. He halted in front of General Kilpatrick and saluted. "General, I've established my headquarters at Jacob Wirt's house. First and Seventh Michigan have deployed as you ordered. Pennington's battery has arrived and is unlimbering for action behind the First and Seventh."

"That's good, George. Do you have new intelligence on the Fifth and Sixth Michigan?"

Custer shook his head. "No. I haven't heard from them. But I expect they should arrive in Hanover midafternoon."

"That's a concern," said Kilpatrick. "I'm not sure of the enemy's strength. Have we been fighting two or three brigades?"

"My guess is that we've run into Stuart's three brigades," said Farnsworth.

"Damn!" Kilpatrick shook his head. "Here is the broader situation." He pointed to the map table. "Meade is moving his army headquarters to Taneytown this afternoon. That's fifteen miles southwest of Hanover, and Littlestown is halfway between. It's critical the Hanover-Littlestown Road remain open, because that's our line of communication to army headquarters and General Pleasonton."

Custer said, "The good news is that the Fifth and Sixth Michigan will be traveling up the Littlestown Road to join us in Hanover."

"True. But I'm troubled with the Rebel brigade posing a threat from the high ground southwest of Hanover along the Littlestown Road."

"George," Farnsworth cautioned, "My brigade was able to push the enemy down the Hanover-Littlestown Road. But once we hit the hills we had to stop. Those hills are like a floating castle in the sky, occupied by the enemy."

"That's risky," said Custer. "The Fifth and Sixth must somehow navigate safely past the enemy brigade and artillery batteries when they arrive. If they don't, they will be cut off from the rest of the division."

Kilpatrick picked up a piece of paper lying on the map table. "Here is a dispatch we intercepted that says Fitz Lee's brigade is approaching from the southwest." He gave the dispatch to Farnsworth and turned to Custer.

"George, I feel fairly good that we have the southeast portion of Hanover secured. But I'm concerned about the southwest portion. I want you to shift Pennington's battery to Bunker Hill and place it west of Carlisle Road next to Elder's battery that is east of Carlisle Road."

Custer nodded. "What about the First and Seventh? Do you want them to deploy with Pennington's battery to provide protection?"

"Yes," Kilpatrick said. "Bunker Hill is much more than a grand artillery platform. The hill is like the Rebel's Rice's Hill and can also serve as a reserve staging area. Reserves can rush into town to support other Union troopers, or rush to counter a Rebel flanking attack."

Custer bobbed his head. "General Kilpatrick, if you would excuse me momentarily, permit me to relay your orders to my staff."

Kilpatrick nodded.

Custer stepped out of the great hall and gestured for Lieutenant Colerick. He relayed Kilpatrick's orders for the First and Seventh and Pennington's battery and stepped back into the great hall after Colerick departed. He glanced at a tall Union private holding his pistol on an unarmed Confederate lieutenant colonel. The Rebel officer was stained brown from head to toe, including his face, hair, gray uniform, and white gloves.

Kilpatrick pointed and chuckled. "Look, George, at who Private Abram Folger captured. May I introduce you to Lieutenant Colonel William Payne from the Second North Carolina Cavalry."

Custer smiled. "Greetings, Lieutenant Colonel Payne. What's that nasty whiskey-colored liquid you're drenched in?"

"General, sir. It's the brown dye liquid of the tannery vat that I was obliged to take refuge in when Private Folger discovered me." Payne grinned, his white teeth contrasting with his caramel-dyed face. "If I may say so, that's quite the uniform, General Custer."

"I made it myself," Custer said. "What's the story of you soaking in a tanning vat?"

Kilpatrick interrupted. "Private Folger, why don't you give us your side of the story first."

Folger obliged. "Well, Generals, the Fifth New York was being attacked by these here Rebels." He pointed toward Payne. "I was knocked from my horse. When I got up, this here

Confederate officer captured me. As I was being marched back toward the Rebels' lines, I escaped down an alley, where I found a carbine. I picked it up and moved back to the street. I spotted the Rebel officer who had captured me, and I shot his horse. He tumbled to the ground, got up, and ran into the tannery, where I found him hiding in a vat."

"Okay Private. Thank you. You're dismissed."

The private saluted and departed.

"What's your side of the story, Lieutenant Colonel Payne?" Kilpatrick said.

"One part of the private's story is true," Payne replied. "He did find me sitting in a barrel of brown dye. I was looking down at my side and trying to stop the bleeding from a saber cut when I heard someone above say, 'You're my prisoner.'"

"What's the rest of the story?"

"My regiment pushed you Yankees into Hanover Square," Payne said. "Then the bluecoats counterattacked and regained control there. As my regiment was pushed back down Frederick Street, the fighting turned into a tangled melee. Suddenly my horse collapsed and tumbled dead, headlong under me. I jumped to my feet and was knocked down again by a Yankee horse. I crawled out, hoping that a Rebel countercharge would recover me."

Kilpatrick said, "How large is the enemy force we are fighting?"

Payne said, "You are fighting General Jeb Stuart's entire cavalry corps numbering twelve thousand troopers."[5]

Custer's mouth slackened and an icy shiver shot down his spine. *My God, Kilpatrick's division numbers less than four thousand and is short the Fifth and Sixth Michigan.*

Kilpatrick's eyes started blinking rapidly. "Are you sure? Twelve thousand?"

Payne said, "Yes." His face remained fixed like a stone.

A sharp blast from several cannons rocked the Central Hotel.

---

5 Eric Wittenberg & J. David Petruzzi, *Plenty of Blame to Go Around*, Savas Beatie, New York, 104. Payne lied. Stuart's force was not 12,000 troopers but was nearly 7,000. Payne's ruse worked, however. Kilpatrick believed Payne and his decisions the rest of the day were tempered with a good deal of caution.

Custer said, "Those cannons must be from both Elder's and Pennington's batteries." He glanced out a panoramic window. Rebel cannons from Rice's Hill blasted and shell tendrils whistled overhead toward Bunker Hill. The dueling cannonade erupted into a hideous storm, shaking the windows.

Kilpatrick said, "Lieutenant Colonel Payne. Thank you for your cooperation. My staff will escort you to receive medical treatment for your wound."

Payne bowed, executing a sweeping hat salute with perfect grace and respect. "I shall take my leave, gentlemen." He turned his head slightly, winked at Custer, and departed under an escort.

Custer's mind stirred with anticipation. Adrenaline pumped through his veins. *Glory awaits me today.*

Lt. Robert Clarke, Capt. John C. Tidball, Lt. William N. Dennison,
and Capt. Alexander C.M. Pennington
August 1862

18

Sixth Michigan — Tuesday, June 30

12:29 p.m.
Captain James Kidd
Sixth Michigan departs Littlestown

Captain James Harvey Kidd stood outside the Barker House in Littlestown square, grooming his horse. The mare whinnied as he flicked a curry brush through her flank, whisking out dirt. "That feels good, doesn't it?" The horse turned her head and nickered. "Yes, I know you like this."

A door banged open and Major Peter Weber bolted out of the Barker House.

"James," Web said, grinning. "Colonel Day wants to saddle up the regiment at one p.m. and start riding toward Hanover. He said a courier from General Slocum's Twelve Corps reported the lead elements of his infantry division are about an hour's march away."

"That's great news." Kidd smiled and checked his watch. "You have about half an hour to groom Dolly."

"That's good. Dolly has been begging for a grooming, haven't you girl?" Web stepped toward his horse, tethered with a long rope to a tree.

"Web, I'm anxious to rejoin the brigade and to meet our new commander, George Armstrong Custer. Meade has sure made a lot of drastic changes to the Union cavalry since we rode through Gettysburg two days ago."

Web reached under his charger and unhooked the strap. "The old goggled-eyed snapping turtle sure didn't waste any time replacing a bunch of old men with young bucks." He reached up with both hands, gripped the pommel, pulled the rawhide-covered McClellan saddle off the horse, and laid it on the ground near the horse's head.

Kidd said, "I heard Kilpatrick is twenty-seven, Farnsworth is twenty-five, and Custer is twenty-three."

Web snickered. He reached into his saddle bag, pulled out a body brush, and started combing the horse's coat. "Apparently, if I was just a year older, General Meade might have placed me in command of the Michigan Brigade instead of Custer."

"You look like you are seventeen instead of twenty-two," Kidd said. "But you do have the right military air about you. The only problem is that army commanders don't usually promote former librarians to be generals."

Web laughed. "They should, because being a librarian means I am exceptionally well-read. I'm not sure all those West Point officers like Kilpatrick and Custer can say that."

"But they can march." Kidd paused and drew a breath. "My classics professor at the University of Michigan's favorite epic was Homer's *Iliad*, and his favorite character was Achilles."

"My favorite character in the Trojan War is Hector," Weber said. "He always rides at the front and throws his heart into his troops."

Kidd smiled. "Achilles finds Hector loitering behind his charging troops and slays him."

"Yes, but it's a heroic death."

Web grinned. "If Kilpatrick read the classics, he didn't learn anything. Custer, however, might have paid closer attention to them, because from what I've heard, the boy general envisions himself Achilles."

"Achilles was the world's most famous warrior when he died."

"Maybe that's what Custer hopes to do. Die as our nation's most famous warrior."

"What about Farnsworth?" Web said. "Weren't you two college classmates?"

"Elon attended the University of Michigan with me." Kidd frowned. "He didn't graduate, however. During our third year Farnsworth and a bunch of his buddies got silly drunk, and one student died from intoxication. They expelled Farnsworth and some others for that."

"What about Custer? What do you know about him?" Web said.

"Custer and Kilpatrick graduated in the same year from West Point. But Kilpatrick was a year ahead of Custer. That's all I know."

"Well," Kidd said, "we will find out soon enough about those two West Pointers when we arrive in Hanover."

Shouting split the air. Kidd glanced up. A middle-aged man was hurtling toward them. The man stopped and put his hands on his knees, panting.

"What's wrong?" Kidd said.

"A large Rebel cavalry force is about five miles out, riding hard toward Hanover."

Kidd shuddered. Colonel George Gray lumbered out of the Barker House and stood next to Kidd and Web. "What the hell is going on?" Gray shouted. His cheeks glowed rosy.

Kidd whiffed whiskey. His nose scrunched. The Irishman was too fond of alcohol. "This man reported a large Rebel force marching toward Hanover."

Gray shouted, "Damn jackanapes." He waved his arm. "'Boots and Saddles.' We're moving out now!"

The regimental bugler blared. The troopers rushed to their horses. Web raced to finish saddling up Dolly. Kidd placed a folded six-layer indigo-blue blanket on his own horse's back. Using both hands, he smoothed it out, with the fold facing the animal's head. He jerked up the saddle and hoisted it into place over the blanket, reached underneath the horse and cinched the strap tight. He strapped on his two-inch-wide black leather belt and clasped it in place with a rectangular brass belt plate embossed with an eagle and wreath. He hooked his cavalry saber to the left side of the belt. His .44-caliber Colt revolver was cradled butt-first in a black leather holster that rested on his right hip. He slung a broad black leather belt over his left shoulder and suspended his Spencer repeating rifle from a snap swivel hook attached to the leather belt.

Web shouted, "Let's go, James."

Kidd sprang into the saddle and swung into line. The bugler blasted "Forward March" and he kicked his heels into the horse's flanks, urging him forward. Something flashed on the column's flank. He turned his head. *Unbelievable*. Several citizens were running alongside the regiment, carrying muskets and shotguns, trying to keep pace with the cavalry. He smiled. These loyal Pennsylvanians were eager to scrap with the enemy.

1:15 p.m.
Colonel Gray
Approaching Hanover

The Sixth Michigan flowed northward like a blue stream snaking through a narrow gulch. Colonel Gray rode at the front of the column of fours. The knot in his stomach tightened. He needed a drink. He cursed.

He should have never ordered Company A to scout in the direction of Union Mills and Westminster. He should have left that mission up to Colonel Alger and the Fifth Michigan, who were scouting southwest and east of Littlestown. He chaffed. Without Company A, he had only 550 troopers riding toward Hanover.

He turned to Major Weber riding next to him. "Peter, I'm not sure about this enemy force reported near Hanover. Do you think they're Stuart's boys?"

"They could be, Colonel."

"If so, this means that a Rebel force of undetermined size is between us and Kilpatrick's division."

Gray and Weber crested a rise and slowed their mounts to a walk. Gray glanced to the northeast, toward an open field with clumps of trees lining the meadow.

Weber said, "The map we examined in Littlestown labeled this Hanover area as Mount Pleasant. On the summit of this rising mound is the Samuel Schwartz farm."

Gray glared. "I think you're right, because dead ahead on that broad hill is the Schwartz schoolhouse."

"This means we are about two miles from Hanover," Weber said.

Gray's eyes flicked to several dismounted gray-clad skirmishers scurrying toward the Sixth Michigan. His heart pounded in his ears. He pointed. "Peter, look: skirmishers."

"I count about thirty or so, dismounted enemy."

"Agreed." Gray turned to his bugler. "'Charge'!"

The metallic notes of "Charge" pierced the air. Gray spurred his horse with his saber raised. The enemy glanced up, turned, and started sprinting up Mount Pleasant Hill. After galloping 150 yards, Gray reined up. Down the eastern edge of the hill, he spotted a brigade of Rebel cavalry loitering. His heart lurched. Behind the brigade were hundreds of wagons.

"Peter, we must have stumbled into the enemy's rear."

Several enemy cannons sitting 500 yards away on a hill fired. Gray stared at the yellow flames and black smoke spewing from them. Shells shrieked long and sharp and erupted 50 yards in front of the Sixth Michigan column.

Gray yelled. "Bugler, sound retreat!"

The bugler trumpeted. Gray reined to his left and galloped back toward the Hanover-Littlestown Road. Out the corner of his eye a blurring regiment wheeled around behind him. Good, the enemy artillery was doing little damage.

Weber shouted, "My God, Colonel! Look behind us to our right and rear. There must be at least one thousand Rebels charging us!"

His jaw tensed. "We're outnumbered and they are surrounding us. We are in danger of being encircled. Peter, take companies B and F, and fight a holding action while I lead the rest of the regiment into Hanover."

1:30 p.m.
Major Peter Weber
One mile south of Hanover

Weber's stomach plunged and his throat constricted. A bitterness swirled in his mouth. Gray had ordered him to sacrifice two companies to save the regiment. He rode up to First Lieutenant Daniel Powers of Company B and Lieutenant Don Lovell, commanding Company F.

"Don, Daniel, Colonel Gray ordered me to take command of a squadron, consisting of Companies B and F. This squadron will act as rear guard and cover the regiment's escape to Hanover."

A bullet flitted past, and Weber flinched. His heart rate quickened.

He glanced southward toward the Schwartz schoolhouse. "Let's deploy the two companies in the patches of woods on either side of the road. Daniel, you take the left side, and Don, you take the right."

"Shall we remain mounted?" asked Lovell.

He gulped. "Several of the men have Spencer rifles, which is a huge advantage.[6] Troopers with Spencer rifles dismount. It's too hard to shoot them accurately on horseback. The men with Burnside rifles should remain mounted and use their carbines, Colt revolvers, and sabers."

"What's the plan if the enemy encircles us?" Powers asked.

"If we get cut off and can't reach Hanover we will hide in the woods and make our way back after dark."

Both officers saluted, rode back to their companies, and started deploying their troopers.

A bugler trumpeted "Gallop." Weber twisted in his saddle. Dust swirled up as several hundred Wolverines galloped northward. Fear gripped him like a fist and squeezed. James Kidd was his closest friend. Would he ever see—

A howling shriek disrupted his thought. Down a narrow lane he spotted a Rebel flag and enemy cavalry racing in a fury toward his line. Without warning, a host of stubby twenty-two-inch-barreled Spencer rifles cracked, raking the charging enemy with a murderous yellow volley. Screams erupted as several Rebels plunged to the ground. Before the enemy survivors fired, the Spencer rifles unleashed a second rattling storm of sheltered volleys. Ghost-gray smoke twirled in the tense space between the opposing forces.

The Rebel cavalry charge halted like a storm surge hitting a massive breakwater. Weber yelled to his bugler, "'Charge'!"

He spurred his steed and burst from the tree line. Pounding hooves thundered from behind as the mounted cavalry squadron roared from the trees. The blue dragoons smashed into the enemy and slashed the Rebels with their sabers, shooting the graybacks with their revolvers. The Confederates yelled and skedaddled. Weber pulled hard on the reins and held up his gloved hand.

---

6 Some of Weber's squadron of 120 troopers had Burnside carbines and others had Spencer rifles. See Mark S. Stowe, *Company B, 6th Michigan Cavalry*, CreateSpace, North Charleston, South Carolina, 2012, page 33. "Those men with Spencer rifles found it too hard to shoot accurately while on horseback."

He turned to his bugler and yelled, "'Retreat'!"

The squadron hurled back to the trees and reformed their line. Weber's eyes burned from the sweat dripping from his brow, and he wiped his sleeve across his face. He opened his eyes and glared at the enemy, now charging for a second attack. The Spencer rifles cracked and unleashed another murderous volley of hot lead.

Again, he yelled, "Charge!"

He spurred his horse and led the second charge from the woods, galloping hooves pounding behind. A dismounted Rebel aimed his pistol and fired. Weber flinched as a bullet grazed his neck. He raised his saber. The Rebel gasped and stared, wide-eyed. Weber grunted and slashed downward. The Rebel shrieked as the blade sliced into his fleshy neck. Blood squirted out of the jagged wound. The grayback crumbled to the ground. The wound was mortal.

Weber glanced up. Lieutenant Powers blazed by on his charger. Weber spotted three or four enemy tracking Powers with their rifles. He shouted, "Daniel, look out!"

1:45 p.m.
Lieutenant Daniel Powers
Near Schwartz schoolhouse, one mile south of Hanover

Powers pulled on the reins and veered left, glancing back at Weber. A branch cracked and seared the side of his face like a branding iron. He flew back in his saddle and his hat flew off. A volley of pistols cracked, and the bullets zipped past him. *Am I hit?* A second pistol volley rattled. A metallic thud struck his scabbard. His thigh throbbed as if a mallet had belted his leg. He reeled and peeked down. Hot blood spurted, drenching his left boot. *Who was hit?* A bullet wound should hurt more. He reached down on his charger's left flank and flicked a gaze at his glove. *Christ Almighty.* His glove was covered in the horse's blood. *Damn.*

He steadied his breathing and spotted seven Wolverines surrounding four Rebels, including a hefty Confederate lieutenant. A Union private shouted, "Let's shoot this bastard!" The

Wolverines aimed their pistols and cocked them, several clicking sounds renting the air.

Powers shouted, "No!" He spurred his mount and charged the private. He swung his saber, knocking the pistol to the ground. He halted and turned back. "We don't shoot prisoners!"

He turned to the Rebel officer. "Surrender your weapons!"

The prisoner handed him his pistol and saber. "Thank you, I owe you my life."

Powers nodded.

Weber shouted from behind. "Here they come again!"

Thundering hooves rumbled like the guttural roar of an approaching avalanche. He stiffened, aimed at the lead Rebel of the charging cavalcade, fired his pistol. *Missed. Damn!* "Retreat and reform!"

Powers turned and galloped for the woods. He glanced over his shoulder; Company B was staying with him. Good. He reached the tree line and waved his saber. "Fall in. Fall in."

He sheathed his saber and gripped his pistol. He reached into the cartridge box attached to his waist belt, scooped up several rounds, and reloaded.

"We're being flanked!" It was Sergeant William Keyes.

"Sergeant, ride up the road a ways and get out of range! I'm going to ride forward and try to figure their plans."

"Be careful, Lieutenant," Keyes said. "You're riding back into a hornet's nest."

Powers trotted forward, hatless. He rounded two large trees and rode into a tall wheat field. Thirty yards into high stalks of wheat he stopped and scanned the area. Dismounted Rebel skirmishers jumped up and fired. His horse whickered a sharp cry and stumbled. Powers hit the ground and tumbled. He pushed himself up to one knee, gasping in half breaths. He shot a glance toward the thumping boots. A tide of graycoats rushed forward. He stood and threw his pistol like a whirling rock. Four Rebel skirmishers raced up and surrounded him.

"Where did you toss that pistol, Yankee boy?"

Powers pointed to his left. "I threw it that way."

"You're a damn little cuss," a Rebel corporal said. "I seen you throw it to your right."

"No, I threw my pistol that way," Powers said. He pointed to his left.

"You're a liar and I'm going to shoot your ass." The Rebel raised his pistol and cocked it.

His heart raced and his throat shut.

"Hold," shouted a hefty Rebel lieutenant on horseback.

Powers locked eyes with the officer. "You're the same officer I captured earlier."

The Rebel officer tipped his hat. "Yes, and one good deed deserves another." He turned to the Rebel skirmishers. "Treat this officer with respect."

2:15 p.m.
Colonel Russell Alger
Fifth Michigan commanding officer
One-and-one-half miles from Hanover

Dust steamed up around the column of nearly five hundred troopers of the Fifth Michigan, trotting northward. Colonel Russell Alger, riding at the head, turned to Sergeant Major Charles Osborne, riding alongside.

"Mudtown should be a mile or so ahead," said Alger. "The hamlet is about half a mile from Hanover."

"We've made good time in an hour," said Osborne.

Rattling, popping noises echoed overhead. "Was that gunfire?"

"I believe so, Colonel."

Alger trotted around a bend, his eyes riveted on a horde of Union dragoons galloping toward the Fifth Michigan.

"Rebels are chasing those Wolverines," Osborne shouted.

"Rebs!" yelled the Union troopers as they raced toward Alger.

"'Charge!'" Alger shouted to Bugler John Allen.

Allen shrilled a piercing "Charge."

Alger unsheathed his saber and spurred his mount down the middle of the road toward the riptide of Sixth Michigan troopers racing toward him. The retreating blue troopers split apart and pulled to both sides of the road like waves around a ship's bow as the Fifth Michigan sailed through them.

Alger shouted, "Sergeant Major Osborne! Order Companies A and F to dismount into the fields on either side of the road and advance!"

"Yes, sir!" The sergeant pulled out of the racing column.

Alger aimed for the lead enemy cavalryman fifty yards ahead, who had halted and turned his mount. The Rebel was shouting and waving his saber, trying to halt the Confederate charge. The enemy vanguard started bunching up as the rear Rebel cavalryman momentum crowded the front soldiers into a motionless mass.

Alger half smiled. *You're no longer chasing outnumbered skedaddlers.* Thirty yards away, he aimed and fired his Colt. A Rebel shrieked. Hitting the Confederates was like shooting blindfolded spies. *Don't aim, just fire.* His skin prickled. Twenty or so blue cavalrymen pulled even with him, brandishing their swords. They pounced on the Rebels at full force like a pack of rabid wolves, snarling as they pressed the attack. A devilish fury of flames erupted inside as his saber slashed and sliced like a rotating whirlwind. Shreds of flesh and clothing flew into the air, raining down on gray-clad bodies bathed in blood. Groans and cries filled the air.

The enemy vanguard melted away. Alger reined up. He needed to grasp the fight. Were they winning? A thundering river of blue cavalrymen swept by him and washed over the second and third ranks of enemy with the force of a breached dam. The surviving Rebels broke and raced for the thick trees.

Alger rode to a mound. He scanned the terrain. South of Hanover, a curtain of hills dominated the entrance to the town like freestanding watchtowers. *Need to control those hills if the regiment is to reach Hanover.* Alger spurred his horse toward the main body of Wolverines. He rode up to Sergeant Major Osborne.

"Sergeant Major." Alger pointed. "Dismount the regiment. We are going to attack eastward toward those hills."

Within minutes, three out of four Wolverines had dismounted and handed their reins to the fourth trooper, who remained mounted. The dismounted troopers readied their Spencer rifles. Alger snickered. The Rebels were in for a shock. The Fifth and Sixth Michigan Cavalry were the only troopers in the whole Army of the Potomac to carry these devastating new weapons. The Wolverines advanced eastward on foot with fangs bared. Alger gently heeled his mount and eyed the assault with binoculars. Abruptly, the Wolverines halted, aimed, and fired, volley after volley cracking the air like a thunderstorm. Brilliant bolts of yellow lightning slashed from the Spencers and streaked across the hills. The Rebels shrieked; several fell dead to the ground. The survivors turned and retreated.

Alger turned to his bugler. "'Mount up.'"

Bugler Allen blared piercing notes. The Wolverines turned, sprinted back, mounted their horses. Alger gritted his teeth and galloped up the Hanover-Littlestown Road, his eyes focused on Hanover's German Reformed Church steeple.

3:00 p.m.
Major Peter Weber
The woods near Schwartz schoolhouse

Weber gazed through the patches of trees. The Fifth Michigan were throwing a cloud of dust as they galloped up the Littlestown Road toward Hanover. Five hundred yards behind the last Wolverine, the lead elements of Rebel vanguard raced after the bluecoats.

Weber turned to Sergeant William Keyes. "Sergeant, we are cut off from Hanover. Rally the men and tell them we are going to stay hidden here. Then after dark, we are going to ride North in a roundabout way to Hanover."

"Yes, sir." Keyes stretched out a hand. "Major, you did one hell of a job today."

Weber smiled, gripped the sergeant's hand, and shook it. "The boys fought well today. There were a few times when I didn't think any of us were going to make it. I think the Rebels captured Lieutenant Powers. That's a huge loss."

"Despite our losses, you did a masterful job, Major. We held off the Rebels, outnumbered five to one. Most important, the squadron allowed Colonel Day and the rest of Sixth Michigan to ride to Hanover."

"Well, I hope they made it to Hanover. We shall find out after we depart this evening and make our way to join up with the regiment."

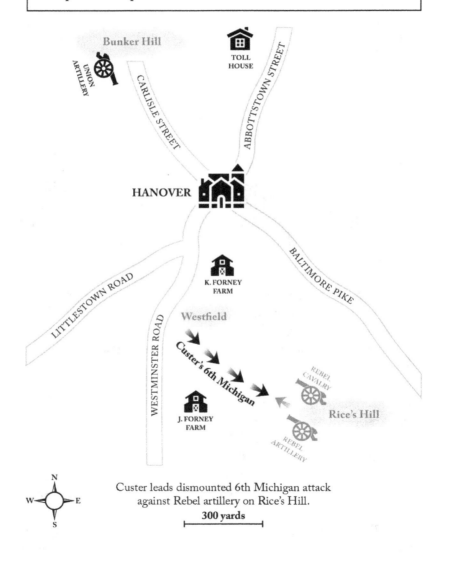

Battle of Hanover

Custer Leads 6th Michigan Attack on Confederate-held Rice's Hill

June 30, 1863

3:50 p.m. - 6:00 p.m.

Bunker Hill

UNION ARTILLERY

TOLL HOUSE

CARLISLE STREET

ABBOTTSTOWN STREET

HANOVER

BALTIMORE PIKE

LITTLESTOWN ROAD

WESTMINSTER ROAD

K. FORNEY FARM

Westfield

Custer's 6th Michigan

J. FORNEY FARM

REBEL CAVALRY

REBEL ARTILLERY

Rice's Hill

N
W — E
S

Custer leads dismounted 6th Michigan attack
against Rebel artillery on Rice's Hill.

300 yards

⤕⤕ 19 ⤔⤔

Custer — Tuesday, June 30

C uster lightly touched his spurs against Roanoke's flanks and dashed north on Abbottstown Street. Union batteries boomed atop Bunker Hill. The Toll House loomed ahead. He swiveled and glanced at Lieutenant Colerick, galloping alongside.

"William," he shouted, "when we pass the Toll House we will turn left and ride up Bunker Hill."

Custer glanced left up Bunker Hill. A feathery cloud of white battery smoke engulfed the summit. He rode another hundred yards, turned, and trotted up the backside of the hill, Colerick close behind him. Elder's batteries, protected by the First Vermont, blasted flames from their iron jaws. He crossed Carlisle Street and rode up to the First Michigan, protecting Pennington's batteries. Colonel Charles Town rode up and saluted.

"Good afternoon, General," Town said.

Custer returned the salute. "What's the situation?"

"Pennington's batteries have been firing since we arrived. Neither the First Michigan or Seventh Michigan have engaged any enemy cavalry."

Custer grinned devilishly. "That's about to change."

Colonel Mann rode up and saluted. "The Seventh Michigan is deployed and protecting the western flank of the division." He pointed south. "I've deployed a squadron of two companies down near the Gettysburg railroad in case the Rebels try to skirt our flank."

"Good."

179

Town said, "I'll tell you, General. I've been mighty impressed with Pennington's artillery boys. They are a well-oiled machine, and they are as accurate as hell. They have developed a miraculous science in the way they throw shot and shell. I swear they can knock the beak off a hungry vulture perched five hundred yards away."

Captain Pennington rode up and saluted. "General Custer, Battery M is having good execution in firing at that enemy counterbattery."

"Good job, Alexander. How is your ammunition?"

"We're fine. We've shot about two hundred rounds. We have one thousand rounds in reserve."

Custer beamed. "Gentlemen. As soon as the Fifth and Sixth Regiments arrive, I'm going to propose to General Kilpatrick that we maneuver as close as we can to the enemy battery on Rice's Hill and remove it."

He turned to Pennington. "Alexander, when we get close to Rice's Hill, I would appreciate if you would not fire any short shorts. I still remember you and Kilpatrick thumping my ass during my plebe year at West Point."

Pennington grinned. "I don't remember it that way," he said with a sarcastic laugh. "My classmates were trying to thump Kilpatrick when he was making a run on you and your fellow plebes. We would have spared you a thumping if you and Kilpatrick hadn't seemed like such tight first cousins."

Custer smiled and winked. "Oh, that's right. I forgot Kilpatrick and I were best friends at the academy. Okay, gentlemen, keep up the good work."

3:20 p.m.
Custer
Lofty Steeple of St. Matthew Lutheran Church

Custer raced up the winding steeple staircase of St. Matthew Lutheran Church. He stepped onto the landing and next to Kilpatrick, who was gripping his binoculars and surveying the hills south of Hanover.

Kilpatrick glanced up. "George, I've been impressed with Pennington's battery. Those boys can lob shells like nobody else."

"I agree, General." Custer gazed toward Bunker Hill. In the open ground west of St. Matthew Lutheran Church, the Sixth Michigan were arriving. Behind them, riding in a column, approached the Fifth Michigan. His skin prickled with pride. The Michigan Wolverine brigade had reunited.

"General Kilpatrick, look." Custer pointed and grinned widely. "The Fifth and Sixth Regiments are arriving. My entire brigade is in Hanover."

"Finally. My entire division is here on the battlefield."

Custer gripped his binoculars and scanned south. "That Rebel artillery battery on Rice's Hill appears to be unsupported. With your permission I will lead the Sixth Michigan against the enemy battery. The Fifth Michigan will follow behind and act as a reserve."

Kilpatrick smiled. "That's a good plan, Cinnamon. That Rebel battery is protecting enemy skirmishers near the Hanover-Littlestown Road. The enemy skirmishers are acting as a covering force. I need that road free from the enemy, so the division has an open line of communication with General Meade's headquarters in Taneytown."

Custer's chest swelled and his heart pounded. A cavalry charge was imminent.

Kilpatrick continued, "I want the Sixth Michigan to dismount and form a single battle line west of town." Kilpatrick pointed. "Deploy skirmishers and advance through the Forney farm field."

Custer gazed beyond Kilpatrick's pointing finger and nodded. "I see the farm." He grinned. "That should give the Rebs a bit of a shock." Custer saluted and departed.

He mounted Roanoke and galloped to meet an officer coming toward him, with a bugler carrying the Sixth Michigan Regimental flag. The officer pulled up and saluted. "General Custer, I'm Colonel Gray, commanding the Sixth Michigan Cavalry Regiment."

"My pleasure to meet you, and I'm delighted you arrived," Custer replied and returned the salute. "We don't have time to chat. I want your regiment to conduct a dismounted attack against that enemy battery on Rice's Hill that's been giving us fits all day. The Fifth Michigan will act as a reserve. I will lead the attack."

3:50 p.m.
Captain James Kidd
Sixth Michigan
Crossing the Littlestown branch of the Hanover and Gettysburg Railroad

Kidd gripped his Spencer rifle and stepped in line with the dismounted troopers over the railroad tracks. Rice's Hill loomed in the sky about a mile east. The monstrous mound was about a quarter-mile long. White smoke billowing up from the enemy batteries curled up and danced on top of the hill.

Kidd halted and held up his hand. "Pass down the line. On your hands and knees. Crawl forward."

Company E fell forward and started snaking its way through brushwood and blackberry vines toward the Forney farm. After a distance, Kidd halted and lifted his head above the brambles. The Forney house was five hundred yards ahead. Beyond the house was a vast, golden wheat field. It flowed eastward up to a low, steep ridge running parallel to the Hanover-Littlestown Road. Forney's ridge was three hundred yards away from Rice's Hill.

4:20 p.m.
Captain James Kidd
Entering the Forney wheat field

The Sixth Michigan crawled to the edge of the waist-high wheat field. Kidd stood up and shouted, "Company E, stand and crouch as we step forward to Forney's ridge."

He gripped his Spencer rifle as the line squat-walked into the wheat field. His thighs flamed with every step. His lungs burned with every breath.

"Keep even, Wolverines. Keep even," someone shouted behind Kidd. The voice was clear, calm, and confident.

Kidd glanced backwards. Whose voice was that? His eyes riveted upon a man a few feet away, sitting tall on his charger. He chuckled. A staff officer dressed like a circus performer was giving the orders. He must be conveying commands of his chief. Kidd turned his head and strode toward Rice's Hill.

"Wolverines, keep the line straight." The officer rode his mount ahead of the line, his saber drawn. "You're looking good, men."

Kidd shook his head. This young, boyish-looking officer must be in command of the line. He stared. Was this officer wearing a red scarf trying to copy Henry of Navarre, who wore a white plume so his men would know where he was in the thickets of the fight?

Kidd shouted, "Sharpen up the line. We're drifting." He glanced left and right. The assault line was nearly a quarter-mile long. He snickered. This boy officer was as showy as Napoleon's Murat.

Lieutenant Colerick rode past Kidd. "William, who is that officer?" Kidd asked him.

"That's Brigadier George Armstrong Custer, our new brigade commander."

"Are you a member of his staff?"

"Yes, General Custer chose me to be his aide-de-camp."

"Goodness, congratulations."

Colerick rode forward next to Custer. Kidd chuckled and stared through his field glasses. Custer looked as if he were 18 years old. Tall, lithe, active, muscular, straight as an Indian, and as quick in his movements. He was clad in a suit of black velvet, elaborately trimmed with gold lace, and a necktie of brilliant crimson was tied in a graceful knot at the throat, the lower ends falling carelessly in front. A soft, blank hat with a wide brim, adorned with a gilt cord, and a rosette encircling a gold star, worn turned down on one side, gave him a rakish air.

Kidd chuckled along with the war gods, eyeing the foppish costume. *Well, well. I hadn't realized that West Point offered acting classes.* Intended or not, he had to admit that the shavetail boy general was as magnetic as any good actor. The Mad Cavalier showed no fear. Kidd shook his head. *Prancing peacock. One minute he's petitioning to command Fifth Michigan, and the next he's a brigadier general.* He forced his attention back to the assault line, his head still shaking slightly in disdain, and continued creeping slowly through the wheat field toward the enemy.

It's only a matter of time before the prancing peacock has his fine feathers plucked.

4:45 p.m.
Custer
East of the Forney farm

Custer's ears pulsed as earsplitting thunder cracked from the Rebel cannons on Rice's Hill. Roanoke nickered, and he patted the warhorse on the neck. "You're doing great, boy. Those shells are not meant for you." He trotted ahead of the line of Wolverines through the wheat field, toward the enemy skirmish lines. He twisted in his saddle. The Sixth Michigan was spreading out with several yards between each dismounted trooper. The Wolverine line was three-fourths of a mile long, moving like a slow, crawling wave. He pulled on the reins and paused on the western side of the crest line, scanning Forney Ridge. No enemy. Good. The ridge masked the movement of the regiment.

"William, let's stay here out of view of the enemy until our line is in position behind the crest."

Colerick turned and rode back to the advancing line. Custer dismounted and gave his horse's reins to Bugler Joseph Fought. He crawled up Forney's Crest and peeked down the other side. Three hundred yards ahead was Rice's Hill. A devilish tremor rippled under his skin. Mounted enemy skirmishers were loitering at the bottom of the hill. *Excellent.* The Rebels didn't know the Wolverines were advancing. Excitement rushed through him, strong and fast. *In a moment, they're going to be in for a shock, tasting hot lead from Spencer rifles.*

He crawled back down the ridge and stepped into the saddle. He grinned at Colerick. "It's time to show the enemy what the youngest general in the Union army is capable of."

Custer glanced up and down the Wolverine line resting just beneath the ridge. What a sight. He climbed the crest and pointed his saber. "Fire!"

The concealed Wolverines scurried up and knelt on the crest. Hundreds of rifles blazed and cracked, raking the enemy troopers. Several Rebel skirmishers screamed and crashed to the ground. The uninjured Confederates eyed the ridgeline, plainly in shock. The Spencer rifles fired again and again. The popping din sounded like a hailstorm pelting stained-glass windows.

Custer studied the summit of Rice's Hill. The enemy batteries stopped firing. Rebel artillerymen were fleeing their batteries. His heartbeat sped up. *We got them on the run.*

"General," said Colerick. "The enemy skirmishers are racing back up Rice's Hill.

"Let's chase them." Custer turned to his bugler. "'Charge.'"

Custer raised his saber and spurred Roanoke. A chorus of hoots and yells assaulted his ears. Out of the corner of his eye he caught the yellow flashes along the long line of Wolverines rushing forward, firing. He raced ahead, firing his pistol. A thrilling rush like a high cliff dive pulsed through his body. The furious blue wave was a powerful pulse of energy bursting up the base of the hill.

A den of screeching graybacks erupted. He glanced up the hill. The mountainous rumbling intensified as an avalanche of enemy cavalrymen crested from the summit, sliding down in a great, howling gray sheet, enveloping him like a shroud of murderous fury. *My God, the Rebel force is the size of a brigade.*

He shouted, "Let's pull back to the ridge and regroup. Bugler, sound 'Retreat.'"

He turned and raced back to the ridge. "We will regroup here!" he bellowed, pointing his saber along the ridgeline. The Wolverines sprinted back to the ridge and hopped over. They knelt, reloaded their rifles, and aimed.

Custer yelled, "Wait. Wait!"

The last Wolverine leaped over the ridge. The charging Rebels were fifty yards away. "Fire!" he shouted.

Rattling fire raked the enemy line.

The vanguard of the enemy countercharge melted away like a spring snow before a merciless sun.

The Rebel batteries on Rice's Hill thundered and enemy shells started raining down one hundred yards behind the ridge. *Well, apparently the fleeing Rebel artillerymen have returned to their cannons.*

Off to his left a cracking boom splintered the air. He glanced toward Bunker Hill. A shell hissed toward Rice's Hill, paused, hung suspended for a moment, and vanished in smoke and fire near the Rebel cannons. Pennington and Elder's batteries. In an instant, a blinding fury of bursting shells hissed and growled, crashing on top of Rice's Hill.

Great streams of lead poured into the enemy horsemen from the Wolverines' rifles. Over Forney Ridge, occupied by half of Custer's brigade, stretched a sulphury arch of smoke. Rebels littered the field. Custer peered through the smoke and a rush of pride flushed his cheeks. The enemy were pulling back to the base of Rice's Hill. Glory erupted in his brain like a sprouting geyser. He took a deep breath and held it. His sweaty hands tingled as calm flooded his mind. He was the Union's dashing dragoon, and he was preparing to lead a charge.

He turned to Colerick. "The enemy can't take this ridge. The Spencer rifles have too much firepower. I'm considering attacking again."

Colerick shook his head. "General, attacking Rice's Hill again—and the enemy batteries—with one regiment is not wise. The Rebel artillery sitting atop that mound have been reinforced with perhaps two brigades. Ordering an attack would have the same butcherous result as General Burnside's foolish Fredericksburg attack against the fortified ridge of Marye's Heights."

Custer glared at Colerick. A chill flowed through his veins, cooling the rage ignited by his aide-de-camp's words. If his entire brigade were on the field, he would attack. *Damn. What a missed opportunity for a glorious charge.*

He gulped a breath. "Perhaps you're right, William."

"How long do you plan on holding the ridge?"

"Until dark. That will prevent the enemy from using Littlestown Road. If Stuart wants to continue north, he will have to move east around Hanover, then toward York. He won't be able to use the Carlisle Road."

7:30 p.m. (Sunset 7:44 p.m.)
Custer
Near Rice's Hill

Custer pinched his lips. His brain felt like it was tied in knots. *Damn, I could have taken Rice's Hill if all four regiments had been deployed for an attack.* He shook his head. The reddish orb was a sliver above the horizon. *Sunset in the next few minutes.*

"William, let's pull back to the ridge." He drew in a frustrated breath, wishing he could have taken Rice's Hill. "We've achieved our tactical goal of opening up the Hanover-Littlestown Road. I'm not certain of the enemy numbers on Rice's Hill."

Colerick said, "My guess is that a few thousand Rebel cavalry are up there."

"Bugler Fought," Custer yelled, "'Retreat!'" Bitter bile erupted up his throat. God, he hated retreating.

He reined about and started riding toward the Forney farm. He turned to Colerick. "William, we're going to ride back to the field near the railroad and reform."

"Yes, sir!"

"I'm proud of the Wolverines," Custer said. "They never faltered once today."

"They fought well, General."

"Damn Kilpatrick for sending the Fifth and Sixth Regiments on a goose chase this morning. If I would have had my entire brigade, I could have taken Rice's Hill."

Norvell Churchill's Sword and Grave Marker

20

Kilpatrick — Tuesday, June 30

The scrape of boots and spurs rolled into the hotel room. Kilpatrick grimaced and glanced up as Custer and Farnsworth strode toward him, smiling. He smirked. There was a vanity, a kind of overbearing assurance in the way Custer entered the room. You could almost hear drums beating ruffles and the bugles blowing flourishes. He started to stand, but the muscles in his lower back strained as if attached to a torture device. *Damn kidneys throb like hell.* He slouched back down into the chair at the head of the small dining room table.

"Gentlemen, please take a seat." He poured a glass of bourbon. "Would you like a drink?"

Custer shook his head. "No, I will have a glass of water." Custer reached for the water pitcher and poured. "I'm as thirsty as hell."

"Well, George," Kilpatrick said, "I'm surprised. At West Point I could always count on you having a shot of America's native spirit with me."

"That's true. But after we graduated from the academy, I promised my sister I would abstain from spirits."

Kilpatrick sneered. "What about you, Elon? I know you were a hell-raiser in college."

"I'm going to have water. I'm drained," Farnsworth replied.

Custer poured Elon a glass of water.

Kilpatrick shook his head. Maybe the Jim Beam would douse his flaming kidneys. He tipped the glass and gulped half of his bourbon. The Kentucky spirit slipped across his tongue, tingling

189

the back of his mouth as the fiery warmth sank down his throat. His eyes watered.

"Both your brigades fought well today in our first fight. Elon, you responded well, darting back to Hanover and organizing a successful counterattack. George, you also did a fine job, scurrying to Hanover and conducting the attack against Rice's Hill."

"Major Hammond performed superbly today," Farnsworth said. "The Fifth New York saved our bacon."

Custer added, "Colonel Gray's Sixth Michigan ran into a Rebel hornet's nest about a mile from Hanover. He was nearly surrounded. He ordered Major Peter Weber to command a squadron from B and F Companies and fight a holding action while Gray raced to Hanover with the remaining Sixth Regiment."

"What's the status of Weber and his men?"

"I am uncertain. My guess is that they hid in the woods near the schoolhouse and will make their way back after dark."

"Keep me informed when they return." Kilpatrick paused and took another swig of bourbon. "An army headquarters courier today said that both Meade and Pleasonton are anxious to hear how the Spencer rifles performed in battle for the first time. The Michigan Cavalry Brigade is the first and only unit to be issued the Spencer rifles thus far."

"Nearly all of the Fifth Michigan, well over four hundred troopers, and two companies of the Sixth Michigan, over ninety men, had Spencers today," Custer said. "The Wolverines firing the seven-shot Spencer rifle were getting off fourteen rounds a minute. A much larger Rebel force, by my guess brigade-size, counterattacked down from Rice's Hill. We retreated behind the Forney Ridge and delivered a continuous sheet of lead for twenty minutes that halted the Rebels."

"Did Weber's squadron have the Spencer rifles in the holding action?"

Custer grinned, jubilance bubbling inside. "Yes, and that's why his one hundred twenty men were able to hold off the enemy while Gray's regiment made it back to Hanover."

"Well, gentlemen, let us toast. We achieved a great victory today. The first victory for the new army commander, General Meade." Kilpatrick held out his bourbon glass and clinked it with Custer and Farnsworth's water glasses. "Bottoms up!"

"A great victory?" Farnsworth asked.

Kilpatrick poured another glass of Jim Beam and took another swig. His face grew hot.

"Yes, a glorious victory, Elon," Kilpatrick said. "I sent a dispatch to General Pleasonton, who is at General Meade's army headquarters in Taneytown. I said that after a fight of about two hours, in which the whole command at different times was engaged, I made a vigorous attack upon their center, forced them back upon the road to Littlestown, and finally succeeded in breaking their center."

Farnsworth and Custer nodded, tightlipped.

"My loss is trifling," Kilpatrick said. "We shall bivouac tonight at Hanover. We have plenty of forage and the men are in good spirits, and I don't fear Stuart's whole cavalry."

"I'm not sure we broke Stuart's line," said Farnsworth. "For several moments, the issue hung in the balance."

Kilpatrick slapped the table. "That's hogwash. We crushed Stuart today. It was a stunning victory, led by me. One I imagine will be reported in all the national newspapers. It was also General Meade's first victory over Lee's army. But you may be right that the battle hung in the balance until I arrived at Hanover. Once I assumed command of all action, I knew I would hand old Jeb his ass."

Custer shook his head. "We were lucky today. We should have discovered Stuart's division at Union Mills. They were only twelve miles from army headquarters at Taneytown. Stuart caught us with our pants down."

"That's crap, George." Rage flamed its way down his gullet and lodged near his kidneys. "Gregg's Second Cavalry Division had the responsibility for scouting the Union Mills and Manchester area for the enemy cavalry."

He stared at Custer. "Gregg let us down. I will tell that to General Pleasonton when I see him."

"General Kilpatrick." Farnsworth paused and rubbed his chin. "What are your plans about pursuing Stuart?"

"I've ordered Captain Estes from my staff to form a detail of one hundred troopers to trail Stuart. I always prefer to be the aggressor. But after we interrogated Lieutenant Colonel Payne this afternoon and learned Stuart's forces number 12,000 mounted troopers, we must be cautious. My division numbers 4,000 men."

Custer interrupted. "After fighting the enemy forces on Rice's Hill, I think Stuart's division is just slightly larger than yours, General Kilpatrick, numbering about 7,000."

"No, I disagree." He slapped his open hand against the table, rattling the glasses. "My instincts tell me Payne was telling the truth. It's at least 12,000."

Custer scowled, plainly disagreeing.

Kilpatrick's face flared, and his lower back throbbed. "I didn't graduate last in our West Point class, George. I know what the hell I'm talking about. Late this afternoon my staff had the opportunity to gather intelligence from our scouts and the local citizens. I believe the bulk of the Army of Northern Virginia is in the vicinity of East Berlin. That's about ten miles north of here."

"What?" Farnsworth said. "Lee's army of nearly 90,000 infantry is ten miles north of us and we are permitting his cavalry division of 12,000 to join him unmolested?"

Custer added his support like a jackal joining the kill. "We should at least harass Stuart's cavalry as it moves north and try to recapture or destroy his slow-moving train. I don't need to remind you that those are captured Union trains, sir. These trains could replenish Lee's army with food and ammunition."

Kilpatrick shook his head. "I sent a courier to General Pleasonton, asking for cavalry reinforcements and to inform General Meade of the whereabouts of Lee's army at East Berlin and that Jeb's cavalry is moving to join him. I'm not trading our glorious ass-whipping of Stuart's cavalry today for an inglorious ass-whipping by Lee's entire army. That's George Meade's job."

Farnsworth shook his head. "Stuart does not have a direct way to East Berlin because you have denied him the use of

Pigeon Hills pass. You have General Geary's infantry division from Slocum's Twelfth Infantry corps sitting six miles south of there in Littlestown. Merritt's cavalry division is operating below Littlestown, and they can rush up and support you."

Kilpatrick fidgeted and shook his head. He stood, scowling. He reached back with hands and grabbed the lower part of his ribcage on both sides of his backbone. Nausea filled his throat. He grabbed and held the table and took deep breaths. He needed more bourbon.

"That's all, gentlemen," he growled. "My kidneys took a terrible pounding on that harrowing ride from Pigeon Hills to Hanover."

Custer stepped outside the Central Hotel and paused, bristling. Nothing had changed. Kilpatrick was a flaming idiot. Bootsteps echoed off the floorboards. Farnsworth strode outside the hotel, scowling, his face beet-red.

Custer said, "I would like to invite you over to my headquarters at the Wirt residence. I'm first going to meet with my four regimental commanders and Captain Pennington. But I would like to chat with you about today's events afterwards."

Farnsworth nodded. "I also need to meet with my regimental commanders. I will join you after."

Russell Alexander Alger
1899

21

Custer — Tuesday, June 30

8:30 p.m.
Custer
Wirt house

Custer's body vibrated with excitement. For the first time since assuming command of the Michigan Brigade, he was meeting with all four of his regimental commanders. He sprang into the Wirt house parlor room. The regimental commanders, sitting at the table, stood and saluted. Custer returned the salute.

"Good evening, gentlemen. Please sit." He glanced at Colonel Russell Alger, commander of the Fifth Michigan. Alger stared back with narrow eyes and a furrowed brow. He was perturbed that a boy general was commanding the brigade instead of him, and he made no attempt to hide his anger.

Colonel Gray spoke up. "Before we start, General Custer, I would like to say a few words, with your permission."

Custer nodded.

"I want to compliment you, General, on the way you rode forward and the led the charge against Rice's Hill. Several of the Sixth Wolverines were a bit surprised with your flashy attire when you appeared on the battlefield. But after sunset, when we fell back to Hanover, every man I spoke to said how proud of you they were, and how you lead from the front."

Except for Colonel Alger, they all—the other three colonels and Captain Pennington—nodded their heads in approval. Custer glared at Colonel Alger, as still as a fresh corpse.

"I'm proud to be commanding the Michigan Wolverines," Custer said. "All four regiments performed superbly today." He pointed to his red scarf. "I'm wearing this so you will always be able to spy me on the battlefield."

He paused, letting the swirling excitement inside well up. God, he wished his dear Libbie Bacon's father could see him addressing his four Michigan colonels. His cravings for approval had been allayed, except for the disgruntled Alger. He would deal with Alger in a moment.

"One final comment: I will lead every charge. I will never ask you to charge while I remain behind and observe."

He paused, letting the silence grow. After several heartbeats he said, "Colonel Gray. Please let me know when Major Weber and his squadron return to Hanover."

"Yes, sir."

"Get some rest. I expect that we will be riding again about noon or so tomorrow. Great work today, gentlemen. I'm most proud to be your commander. You're dismissed."

All four regimental commanders were walking out of the room, and Custer said, "Colonel Alger, just a moment."

Alger turned and stopped. Custer tightened his lips and braced for an argument.

"Colonel Alger, I understand you may be perturbed that General Pleasonton chose me to command this brigade. That's understandable. You probably felt it was your brigade to command."

Alger nodded.

"You're the best regimental commander of this brigade. I not only respect you, but I need you to be your best in the upcoming battle, as we are facing Lee's army."

He bit his tongue as a sucking vacuum descended, clenching his throat. He let the silence last ridiculously long; if looks could kill, he would have been mincemeat by now. This was a moment of reckoning for Alger, and Custer hoped the colonel realized that the shadow that ran from one of the general's cheekbones to the other was a darkening, imminent thundercloud. He broke the silence just before the cloudburst.

"I would hate to lose you as a regimental commander because of your pride or some other nonsense. Understand?"

Alger glared, his fists tight.

Custer stared back. Too bad he didn't have more time to work things out with Alger. But this was going to get solved, one way or another, in the next few moments.

Alger lowered his eyes, saluted, and held it. "You have my total support, General Custer. I, too, was impressed with you leading the Sixth Michigan this afternoon, and so were my Fifth Michigan Wolverines as we observed from the road."

Custer's eyebrows shot up, his mind shimmering. He had won. He smiled and returned the salute. Warmth flowed through his veins. He held out his hand. Alger gripped it and shook.

"Get back to your regiment, Russell. I'm looking forward to working with you."

Alger saluted, turned, and stepped out of the house.

9:00 p.m.
Custer
Wirt house

Custer slid into the dining room chair. The aroma from the bowl of steaming stew wafted through the evening air. His stomach growled. When was the last time he had eaten? He shook his head. Five this morning. He gulped down a spoonful of stew. Pitter-pattering feet flitted into the dining room. He raised his eyes and peered at Mrs. Wirt grinning ear to ear, carrying a bowl of biscuits.

"These are hot out of the oven, General."

"Mrs. Wirt, you're a godsend. My staff and I are lucky to have you."

"Slow down, General. You're wolfing down that stew. I made plenty for you and your boys." She plopped the biscuits down beside his bowl. "Look what else I have for you." She held out a jar of strawberry jam.

"What a treat. Thank you. Did Johnny eat yet?"

"He hasn't stopped eating since the stew finished cooking. He is learning bad habits from you because he wolfs his food down, too."

Custer smiled. "He needs to learn to eat fast so when he's at West Point he won't starve his plebe year."

Bugler Fought stepped into the room. "Sir, General Farnsworth is here."

"Please show him in."

"I will bring out a bowl of stew for the general," Mrs. Wirt said, and pattered out of the dining room.

Custer gestured. Farnsworth yawned, lumbered into the dining room, and sat down.

Elon wiped his brow. "Our two brigades did a pretty good job fighting Stuart's boys today. I must confess, George. It was nip and tuck for a while this morning. A lot closer than Kilpatrick said it was."

Mrs. Wirt placed a bowl of stew in front of Farnsworth, who ate voraciously. "This is good," he said around mouthfuls, looking up at her. "Thank you."

Custer spread butter and jam on a biscuit. "This is the first lighthearted moment all day, Elon."

"It is, and I don't want to interrupt the pleasantries, but I want to discuss Kilpatrick's behavior. There was an incident that occurred today before you arrived."

Custer glanced up and narrowed his eyes. "Go ahead."

Farnsworth's face flushed crimson. "I ordered the First Vermont, who had just arrived, to replace the Fifth New York, which had been fighting since the opening shots. Major Hammond's ranks were depleted. Kilpatrick's fire-eating aide-de-camp, Captain Estes, located me in the town square and told me the commanding general had ordered the First Vermont to protect Elder's batteries on Bunker Hill. The Fifth New York was to form up east of town and conduct a flanking attack."

Custer nodded.

"I protested the order but carried it out. It angered me that Kilpatrick violated the chain of command. It also angered me that Estes wears Kilpatrick's stars and enjoys being a little Napoleon as much as Kilpatrick does. Estes delivered the order with a visible sneer."

Custer stared at Farnsworth, who was plainly tired and angry.

Farnsworth continued, "When I confronted Kilpatrick about him countermanding my orders, he flew into a rage, and for a moment I thought he wanted fisticuffs. The meeting ended with Kilpatrick saying he could give any damn order he wanted at any time, and he was the chain of command."

Elon paused, gulped a breath, and speared Custer with a stormy gaze without blinking. He was plainly angry, and an ominous silence erupted.

Custer shifted in his chair; his breath quickened. Farnsworth was finally experiencing the sneering and vainglorious Kilpatrick he had warned him about the morning they took command. For the good of his brigade, Elon had to learn to stand up to Kill-Cavalry or the results could be disastrous.

Farnsworth leaned toward him over the bowl of stew. "I'm reporting Kilpatrick's egregious conduct to General Pleasonton. But in the meantime, I wanted to know your thoughts about him, since you two knew each other at West Point."

Custer ran his hand through his hair and blew out a thoughtful sigh.

"I know that Kilpatrick can be one hell of a damned fool. But the chain of command was iron law at West Point. So, there is no excuse for him violating it and threatening not to follow it."

"Then I don't understand why my conversation with him became a matter of honor? I wasn't sure he was going to let the incident pass without challenging me to a fistfight or a pistol duel."

"At West Point, Kilpatrick was constantly attempting to advance himself by his fists and bluster. Being small and cocky, he saw himself as a vicious banty rooster. He would fight anyone at the drop of a hat, no matter how big they were. During our plebe year, the upperclassmen, including Pennington, who's commanding Battery M, enjoyed taunting him. I once witnessed Kilpatrick fighting a cadet twice his size, for forty minutes."

Farnsworth nodded.

"Things really got tawdry at the academy in 1858. That's the year after the Supreme Court denied Negroes the right to become citizens in the Dred Scott decision. Kilpatrick went absolutely beside himself. He led the antislavery group at West Point and started stalking and fighting Southern cadets."

199

"Did you get along with Kilpatrick?"

"Sure, I tried to get along with all my schoolmates, Northern and Southern. What bothered me most about Kilpatrick was his cruel treatment of horses and the Southern cadets. It didn't bother him a bit about running a horse until it dropped dead or beating a Southern cadet senseless. I heard Kilpatrick killed a horse today by riding it too hard."

"Yes, that's true." Farnsworth took another bite of stew. "My men have started using Kilpatrick's nickname, Kill-Cavalry, for ordering the reckless charge at Second Bull Run. His troopers were slaughtered while he watched."

"That's why I believe in leading men into battle," Custer said. "I don't send them unless I'm in front."

Farnsworth nodded. "I believe that, too. Leaders lead from the front. Here's my question." He leaned one arm on the table and looked Custer straight in the eye. "Is Kilpatrick a moral man?"

Custer paused, letting his mind race. "I was aware at the academy that Judson enjoyed frequent visits with ladies of the evening, and I've heard that he continued to see them after he was married."

"So, he is an immoral officer?"

"Yes, he is immoral, and he is dishonest. He spent three weeks in the Washington, D.C. jail in 1862 for a graft scheme. He sold confiscated Confederate horses to the Union army for personal gain."

"I'm not pointing a finger," Farnsworth said. "While on a drunken spree at the University of Michigan, one of my classmates died because I was irresponsible."

"That sounds more like college boy antics that went too far. But from what I know, you are morally sound."

Farnsworth looked down at his stew. "I'm trying. That's why I tried to restore my honor by tackling the Far Western Frontier and becoming civilian forager for the U.S. Army in the 1858 Mormon War."

"Aren't we all trying to be morally sound, except perhaps Kilpatrick?"

"Since college, I've tried to be a rule follower, including honoring and obeying the chain of command." Farnsworth paused and scratched his chin. "How do we obey an immoral officer who issues immoral orders?" Farnsworth asked.

"I'm not sure I can answer that question," Custer swayed backward and stroked his blond mustache. "Here is what I believe. We are morally required to disobey an immoral order."

Farnsworth stared.

"Elon, it's important to stand up for yourself and your brigade. If Kilpatrick tries to goad you into doing something that you believe will needlessly kill your men, then you have a moral obligation to disobey the order. Your job is not to sacrifice your brigade like Kilpatrick's horse this afternoon. Please remember this. With one exception, I don't recall Kilpatrick leading a cavalry charge. But he sure likes to order one, and then take all the glory."

"My goal is to follow the rules since I've broken some big ones."

"You have to know when to break the rules. Five days after graduating from West Point, I was waiting orders to join my classmates and report to the adjutant general of the army in Washington, D.C. I was the officer of the day when a plebe reported to my tent and said that three upperclassmen were taunting him. Suddenly one of the upperclassmen punched the cadet. I didn't think that was fair. I told everyone to stand back and let's have a fair fight. I was arrested and court-martialed for not stopping the fight. I was found guilty of neglect of duty but received no punishment and received orders to join my classmates."

"Why didn't you follow the rules?"

"Fairness and sensibility sometimes supersede rules. You must know when to break them. I have no regret for letting the two cadets have a fair fight."

Farnsworth nodded and stood. "Thank you for the supper, George." He pushed his chair back, scraping the wooden legs on the floor.

Custer jumped up. "You're welcome. Mrs. Wirt is a grand cook. One more thing, Elon. You must resist being cowed by Kilpatrick's bullying. He loves verbal duels and can easily wound your honor. Don't let chivalry trump morality."

22

Weber — Tuesday, June 30

9:10 p.m.
Acting Major Peter Weber
Hanover Commons

Hanover stood undaunted against the fading twilight. A sudden lightness struck Weber's mind. He flicked the reins and skirted along the western side of the Hanover Branch Railroad tracks, aiming for Bunker Hill, looming five hundred yards northward from the railroad tracks.

"Halt!" Two vedettes holding carbines appeared.

His gut seized. "Don't shoot. It's Major Weber from the Sixth Michigan."

The mounted sentries trotted forward. A sergeant said, "Good evening, Major. Colonel Gray is eagerly awaiting your arrival. Please follow me."

They trotted along the railroad tracks and halted in a large open field. The sergeant pointed. "This is the Commons, and the Sixth Michigan is bivouacked here."

"Thank you, Sergeant." He trotted toward the rows of white tents.

"Web!"

He turned and spotted Captain James Kidd waving. His heart lurched and he broke into a huge grin, doffed his hat, and waved.

"I'm back!" He dismounted.

Kidd sprung forward and clutched him in a bear hug. "Web! We thought you and your detachment had vanished for good."

Weber grinned. "It was a hellish hailstorm until darkness, when we hightailed it back like scurrying swamp rats."

Kidd slapped him on the back. "Colonel Gray is worried about you. Follow me."

Weber followed Kidd toward a tent flying the Sixth Regimental flag. Colonel Gray glanced up and grinned.

"Web, it's great to see you. Follow me. General Custer has been needling me every twenty minutes about the condition of the detachment. You can tell him firsthand what happened."

Weber and Kidd trailed Colonel Gray into the Wirt house. Custer was writing at a dining room table and chewing on a toothbrush. They walked up and saluted. Weber stared, muffling a laugh. Custer's velvet-and-gold garb and gaudy red tie was absurdly farcical.

Custer glanced up, removed the toothbrush, and returned the salutes.

"General Custer," Colonel Gray began, "this is Major Weber who led the rear guard detachment that enabled my regiment to arrive safely this afternoon."

Custer erupted from his chair, creating a fluttering current of air. "Major Weber, it's my distinct pleasure to meet you. I congratulate you on the fine job of holding the Rebels in check for the Sixth Regiment's main column to break away and reach Hanover." He pulled on his blond mustache. "Major Weber. Why are you still wearing captain's bars?"

"General, I'm waiting for my official promotion papers to replace Major Elijah Waters."

"Well, as far as I'm concerned you are *Major* Weber."

Weber gulped and shifted his boots a foot apart, moved his hands behind his back and interlaced his thumbs. He took a deep breath and held it, hoping to hide his amazement. Custer stood nearly six feet tall, lithe and muscular like a big cat. His golden locks fell to his shoulders and his upper lip was garnished with a blonde mustache. The boy general's complexion was as fair as a schoolgirl's, his blueish eyes fiery, and his voice spirited, possessing a dauntless tone.

Custer grinned. "Now, please give me the details of your rear guard fight."

Weber let out a slow breath. Despite the fantastic costume and Custer's meteoric rise in rank, there was something magical about the boy general. A warmth tingled inside. Weber liked him immediately. "General, my detachment of B and F companies consisted of six officers, including myself, and one hundred twenty-five troopers," Weber replied. "I ordered the detachment to dismount and form up into a line of battle on the eastern side of the Hanover-Littlestown Road. Twenty-five troopers served as horse-holders. They removed all the horses to the west side of the road and sheltered in a grove of trees."

"So you had an effective fighting force of about one hundred dismounted troopers?"

"Yes, General. That's right."

"Was your detachment armed with the Spencers?"

"Yes, some of the troopers had Spencers. The Sixth Regimental companies that all have the Spencer rifles are A, D, E, and H. The rest of the six companies in the regiment, including my detachment of B and F, have mainly the single-shot breech-loading Burnside carbine and Colt army revolvers. But yes, some of the men in my squadron had Spencers."

Custer turned to Gray. "Colonel Gray, does the Fifth Regiment have a mix of Spencer and Burnside rifles?"

"No. Colonel Alger's Fifth Regiment is completely armed with the Spencer rifle."

Custer nodded. "Continue, Major Weber."

"I deployed the troopers in a short skirmish line facing southeast toward the Rebels. We stopped three mounted cavalry charges with minimal losses. Being outnumbered, the Spencer rifle proved to be a Godsend. A second Rebel force circled behind us and blocked our retreat route to Hanover. I ordered my detachment to ride into the trees on the west side of Littlestown Road. We waited until dark and then rode north to Hanover."

Custer said, "Major Weber, your bravery in facing this extreme danger showed your high sense of honor and duty. Your daring and dashing conduct is exemplary, and it's what I expect from all my officers."

"Thank you, General."

"That's all, gentlemen. You're dismissed."

The officers departed. Custer smiled. Weber was a good officer, reminding Custer of himself. He could depend on Weber in a tight situation. He was sure they would face one in the next few days. Or at least he hoped so.

23

Custer — Wednesday, July 1

Custer stood fidgeting in the Central Hotel dining room, staring out a window, feeling rage clutching at his throat. Kilpatrick's dawdling was strangling his killer instincts. Didn't he realize there was an opportunity to ambush Stuart's rear guard, lumbering along with several hundred captured wagons? *God almighty.* He felt like a caged cougar with bared fangs, eyeing its prey slipping away. Boot spurs clinked and Farnsworth strode into the room.

He waved a hand. "I'm over here, Elon."

Farnsworth yawned. "Good morning, George. Is General Kilpatrick going to join us?"

He shook his head. "I sure as hell hope so. Stuart's boys departed Hanover last night at 10:00 p.m., and here we are nine hours later, still waiting for orders."

First Lieutenant Eli Holden stepped into the room. "Gentlemen. General Kilpatrick will be down shortly. He had a pretty restless night."

Custer stared. His gut coiled tightly, like a threatened rattlesnake. Grunting and thumping echoed beyond the room. *What the hell?* Judson Kilpatrick rounded the corner, bent over and clutching his lower back, creeping toward them like a dark mist sliding across the floor.

Kilpatrick mumbled, "Please sit down, gentlemen." The general gripped the back of a chair, winced, and slumped down. His stony face was pale and gaunt, like a ghoul.

"General," Custer asked, "are you suffering from a wound?"

"It's my kidneys. They hurt like hell after galloping back from Pigeon Hills to Hanover."

Holden stepped into the room, carrying a pillow. "Here you go, General."

Kilpatrick twitched. Plainly in pain, he placed the pillow behind him and leaned back. "Thank you, Eli. I had a restless night, not getting much sleep."

Custer smirked. *Neither did Jeb's troopers, riding all night to escape our clutches.*

"Do you need anything else, sir?" Holden inquired.

"Yes. I'm not going to be able to mount a horse today. Find an ambulance for me to ride in when we depart Hanover."

"Yes, sir." Holden departed.

Kilpatrick winced as he twisted in the chair. "George and Elon. I want to congratulate you both on your brigades' performances yesterday. Elon, you reacted quickly to the Rebels' attack on the division's rear guard, and you thrust the enemy out of Hanover. George, your attack on the Rebels' left prevented the Confederates from cutting off my line of communication to Littlestown and army headquarters and forced Stuart to flee during the night." Kilpatrick moaned and adjusted the pillow. "This was my first great victory as Third Cavalry Division Commander."

Custer fumed, fighting to control his daredevil impulses. The opportunity to put a twist on Stuart's cavalry was fading like a slackening rain. "General, with your permission, I would like my brigade to depart immediately and start pursuing Stuart." He thrust forward in his chair. "We have a chance to crush the Rebel cavalry."

Kilpatrick stared. "No. I sent a hundred-man detachment commanded by Lieutenant Colonel Andrew Alexander along with Captain Estes to reestablish contact with the Rebel cavalry. Once they do, Alexander is to follow them and see where they go."

Custer bristled. "General, Jeb's troopers departed Hanover last night at ten o'clock. They have a big head start on us. We're going to need at least a brigade to tangle with the Rebel rear guard. Alexander's detachment is too small, and the Rebels will swat them away like a mosquito."

Kilpatrick's brow furrowed. "Damn it, Custer. The Confederate officer we took prisoner yesterday told us that Jeb's force is twelve thousand strong. That's three times larger than my division. I reported to Meade's headquarters last night that Lee's headquarters is in East Berlin. Lee's entire army is about twelve miles north of us. That's Meade's job to fight Lee's infantry, not mine."

"General, did your scouts spot this large Rebel force?"

Kilpatrick shook his head. "No. My intelligence is based upon reliable and patriotic Pennsylvania citizens spotting the enemy moving through the area."

Custer's stomach reeled as if snake venom were dripping down his gullet. "Sir, as you know, General Meade said yesterday that the most important duty of his cavalry was to gather accurate information on the enemy's movements. If you believe Lee's infantry corps are near us, we need our troopers to locate their exact positions."

Kilpatrick held up his hand. He turned to Holden. "Eli, I need another pillow." He turned back to Custer. "Go ahead, General Custer."

A lump clogged his throat. He swallowed around it. "You tasked Lieutenant Colonel Alexander only with trailing Jeb's cavalry. If I move my brigade now, I can send out several patrols to locate both the Rebel infantry and cavalry, and my brigade is big enough to sting the Rebels like a wasp and make them do something they didn't plan."

Kilpatrick flinched, closed his eyes, and waved his hand. "That's enough, George." He shifted back in his seat, took several shallow breaths, and opened his eyes. "I'm content to move cautiously forward and follow the Rebel cavalry." Kilpatrick turned to Farnsworth. "Elon, your brigade will depart first today. George, your brigade will follow Elon's."

Custer's chest locked up. "General Kilpatrick, my brigade is already two miles north of Elon's. I should go first."

Kilpatrick shook his head. "No. I don't want my division spread out all over Pennsylvania. Your brigade will follow Elon's." He twisted in his chair, plainly in pain. "Elon, I want your brigade to depart Hanover by eight a.m. You're both dismissed."

Custer stood and vaulted out of the room. His mind screamed as if it had crashed through a thorny thicket and frayed his thoughts. He had never known Kilpatrick to skirt a fight. The general was letting the Rebels bat him around like a frail shuttlecock.

10:00 a.m.
Custer
Custer's brigade marching to East Berlin via Abbottstown

A suffocating mugginess crouched in the still air. In the distance, heat waves fluttered along the road, shimmering like puddles. His mind was hissing like a short artillery fuse; any second it would ignite the rage roiling in his bones. *Damn Kilpatrick. Throttling the division's movement northward so he could mope along, riding in a wagon like a shunned skunk. Instead of lollygagging northward as though we're on a Sunday stroll, my brigade should be rushing forward like a surging torrent and swamping Stuart's rear guard. But no, Kilpatrick is worried about bragging rights—too cowardly to unleash the emerging beau sabreur of the Union army and too proud to risk being outshined again.*

He scowled and glanced at Colonel Mann, trotting next to him at the head of the Seventh Michigan Regiment anchoring the rear of his brigade. Thunder erupted like a distant drumroll. He glanced toward the west. The sky was filled with cotton balls, slowly sailing on streamlets of wind. No swirling storm clouds.

"Colonel Mann. What do you make of the thundering? Is it artillery?"

"I believe it is, sir." He pointed. "Gettysburg is about nine miles west of us. My guess is that a fight has erupted there."

Custer's animal instincts pulsed. Maybe a fight was brewing. "I agree. I'm going to ride back and talk with General Kilpatrick. We're moving too slowly."

He spurred Roanoke and rode to the end of his brigade. He reined up behind a large Moses ambulance wagon, lumbering along and flying the Third Division Cavalry flag. He smirked. Kilpatrick was curled in a curious pose on a bed of seat cushions, as if stretching his lower back.

"General Kilpatrick. I believe the distant thundering we're hearing is artillery from Gettysburg. Isn't Buford's First Cavalry Division occupying Gettysburg?"

Kilpatrick contorted and tilted his head upwards. "Yes."

"Sir, if Buford has run into Confederates, they have to be Lee's infantry, because Stuart is north of us."

Kilpatrick grunted and sat up. "What's your point?"

"My guess is that Lee's main army is west of us, near Gettysburg, and not north of us. Stuart and his wagons are north of us and are perfect pickings. If we race ahead, we can attack Jeb before his force turns west and links up with Lee's infantry."

Kilpatrick's face turned beet red. "You are wrong, General Custer. Lee's headquarters is north of us, near East Berlin, and that is where his main army is. I am content to trail Stuart's cavalry and then determine what Lee's plans are. Now fall back in with your brigade. You are dismissed, sir."

A silent scream wracked his brain. Anguish and rage surged through his veins. Saluting, he trotted back toward the head of his brigade. He turned to Colerick. "Kilpatrick is making a terrible blunder by not vigorously pursuing the Rebel cavalry."

"I agree. We had Stuart on the ropes, and we are letting him escape."

"I thought I could appeal to Kilpatrick's reckless nature and convince him to dart forward." Custer's voice hardened. "Kilpatrick hasn't changed since West Point. He is a frothy braggart without brains."

4:00 p.m.
Custer
Riding toward East Berlin

Rage rattled around in Custer's lurching stomach, searching for a way to escape. God, Kilpatrick was a flaming idiot. Normally, the fiery Irishman would have unleashed his division, looking for another fight. But not today. Custer pulled in a hard breath, his rib cage rising and falling as Roanoke trotted. Echoing behind him was a chorus of clacking carbines and clattering sabers harmonizing with clopping hooves.

Colerick and a private pulled up stirrup to stirrup. Colerick grinned. "General Custer. You said you wanted another orderly on your staff. Colonel Town has nominated Private Norvell Churchill from Troop L, First Michigan."

Custer studied Churchill. The chiseled, clean-shaven face featured a faint mustache. The lanky, wiry private rode erect, like a Roman Centurion. Although he appeared to be about five feet seven inches tall, and no more than 130 pounds, there was something powerful about him. Swift and stealthy, like a prowling jaguar.

"Private Churchill," Custer said, "do you have any experience serving as an orderly?"

"Yes I do, General. I served as an orderly for General Nathaniel Banks. Then I was assigned as escort orderly to Major General Mansfield at the Battle of Antietam."

"Were you with General Mansfield when he was wounded?"

"Yes, I was."

"Tell me what happened."

"General Mansfield rode ahead of his men through heavy fire, trying to keep them from firing on what he believed were Union troops. They were wearing gray coats and I galloped after him, calling for him to turn back. General Mansfield turned and said, 'Yes, you're right.' At that moment his horse was shot, and the General tumbled to the ground under his horse. I raced up and pulled him from the horse. Another soldier and I carried the general back to our lines. A Rebel bullet had pierced his lung. The general died the next day."

Custer nodded. "Well, it sounds like you have the dash to serve as my orderly. I just hope you're not bad luck and I end up like General Mansfield."

Churchill smiled. "Well, if you do, General Custer, I promise I will pull you back to our lines so you can die among friends."

He laughed. "How old are you, Norvell?"

"I turned 23 a few days ago."

"Good. That means I'm six months older than you."

Churchill rubbed his left eye.

"Is your eye giving you problems?"

"It's been bothering me a bit since Antietam. I came down with typhoid after the battle."

"Were you treated at a hospital?"

"No, I just gutted out the fever. I feel fine now except my eye gives me problems from time to time."

Custer nodded. "Welcome aboard as my orderly."

"Thank you, sir. I won't let you down." Churchill grinned. "As long as you don't fall on my left side."

Custer chuckled. "I will make sure I'm always riding on your right side."

10:00 p.m.
Custer
Bivouac between East Berlin and Abbottstown

Custer sat on a stump, petting Rose and chewing on his toothbrush. Hundreds of flickering campfires dotted the rolling farmlands, like geyser pits jetting reddish-orange lava. Heat licked his face and his throat tightened as he swallowed down surging bile. Damn Kilpatrick had let Stuart's cavalry slip away uncontested after Hanover. Was it fear or incompetence that made Kilpatrick incapable of seizing the initiative and taking decisive action? A vein in his forehead throbbed. Whatever it was, Kilpatrick's shameful blundering was despicable.

Clapping hooves approached; Farnsworth reined up and dismounted. He handed his mount's reins to Johnny and ambled toward Custer.

"Good evening, George," Farnsworth said.

"Elon, how was your day?" Custer grinned. "Did you find any Rebels?"

Farnsworth shook his head. "No. My West Virginia Regiment entered East Berlin and found no evidence of Rebel troopers. The citizens of East Berlin said that General Early's infantry division had passed through yesterday and were headed west toward Gettysburg."

"When I heard the artillery firing near Gettysburg late this morning, I tried to convince Kilpatrick to sprint forward and find Stuart's boys." Bitterness was unmistakable in Custer's voice. "But Kilpatrick was content to ride in the back of the ambulance and write his report on his great victory at Hanover."

"We moved like slugs today," Farnsworth lamented. "I swear infantry troops marched faster than we did."

Custer studied Farnsworth as the campfire flickered on his shadowy face. He let the silence ride a moment as his shoulder muscles tightened and a chill slid down his back. It was plain from Farnsworth's tone that he was losing confidence in Kilpatrick, who believed in little but himself.

He drew a deep breath and sighed. "My scouts found no trace of Stuart's boys. I think Stuart moved on a northeasterly track today instead of riding straight north like we are doing."

"I ordered Major Hammond and his entire New York Regiment, along with one two-gun section of Lieutenant Elder's battery, to ride northeast toward York in hopes of finding Stuart's boys," Farnsworth said. "Hammond's courier arrived a few minutes ago and said they didn't find any Rebels and they were returning."

"That's no surprise."

Farnsworth glowered. "Kilpatrick missed a great opportunity to pursue Stuart. Instead, he was content to let Stuart escape, insisting to Pleasonton and Meade that he had located Lee's army. That's pure claptrap."

"I agree."

"As the booming guns proved today, Lee and Meade's armies were tangling near Gettysburg." Farnsworth shrugged. "I'm beginning to wonder if Kilpatrick is a bad general whose troopers will meet a bad end?"

Custer shook his head. "I'm not going to let Kilpatrick destroy my Michigan Brigade." He suppressed a grin. "I hope the artillery thundering we heard near Gettysburg is more than a

one-day skirmish. I don't want Buford's cavalry boys to have all the fun."

Farnsworth smiled. "I hope Kilpatrick is more on his game tomorrow. Hopefully July 2nd will be more eventful than today."

"If it's up to me, I'm sure it will be. No more lollygagging."

Colerick strode up, escorting Captain George Yates. Yates grinned and saluted.

Custer stood and slapped Yates on the back. "What is General Pleasonton's aide doing galivanting around at this time of night?"

"General Custer and General Farnsworth. General Pleasonton sends his respects and wanted me to provide you a report of today's battle in Gettysburg. I've just briefed General Kilpatrick."

Custer's heart pounded. "How did Buford do against the Rebels? I heard the artillery guns thundering today from Gettysburg."

"Buford's cavalry division performed well. On June 30, Buford was patrolling around Gettysburg. Town citizens informed Buford that a Rebel column was northwest of the town along the Chambersburg Pike. Buford sent a scouting party west along the Pike and they encountered some Rebel infantry. No shots were fired, but Buford knew he had probably located the vanguard of Lee's army. Buford bivouacked west of town that evening and flung vedettes in a semicircle around Gettysburg."

"Did Buford deploy pickets west of Gettysburg along the Chambersburg Road?"

"Yes," Yates replied. "At first light the next morning, Buford's pickets spotted Confederate infantry marching down the Chambersburg Road toward Gettysburg, and shots were exchanged. By midmorning an all-out firefight had erupted. Buford was heavily outnumbered and fought a skillful delaying action waiting for General Reynolds's First Infantry Corps to arrive. Buford's troopers' quicker-loading carbines outgunned the Rebel muzzle-loading rifles. Buford's goal was to prevent the Confederates from occupying the Cemetery Hill and Culp's Hill just east of Gettysburg."

"When did General Reynolds arrive at Gettysburg?" Farnsworth asked.

"Reynolds's First Corps arrived midmorning and relieved Buford's troopers." Yates paused, his lower lip quivering, then drew a sharp breath. "Sadly, General Reynolds was killed by a sharpshooter shortly after deploying his corps."

"My God, Reynolds is dead?" Custer's mouth gaped. "Reynolds was Commandant of Cadets at West Point and was my cavalry instructor." He shook his head in sorrow and disbelief. "He was beloved by all the cadets. This is a great loss."

"After Reynolds's death, General Howard's Eleventh Corp arrived, and Howard took command of First and Eleventh Corps."

Custer shook his head. "I hope to hell Howard did better than the Battle of Chancellorsville, where his corps was nearly decimated by Stonewall Jackson's evening attack."

Yates nodded. "General Meade had the same concerns as you, General Custer, and he ordered General Hancock to Gettysburg to take command of all troops there. Hancock arrived in early evening, rallied the retreating Union troops, and held on to Cemetery and Culp's Hills."

"What's Meade's plan for tomorrow?" Farnsworth said.

"When I departed Taneytown, Meade was preparing to ride to Gettysburg. He had ordered all seven infantry corps to Gettysburg."

"Was Jeb Stuart's cavalry at Gettysburg?" asked Custer.

"No."

"Damn," Custer shouted. "Kilpatrick was wrong. Most of Lee's army *was* west of Gettysburg. If Kilpatrick would have unleashed my brigade this morning, I could have perhaps recaptured several of the Union logistics wagons Stuart had confiscated."

Farnworth shook his head. "Kilpatrick missed a great opportunity to find and fix Jeb's cavalry and perhaps even prevent him from reuniting with Lee at Gettysburg."

A soaring thrill rippled across Custer's skin. "I just feel it my bones, Elon. Tomorrow, I'm going to lead my first cavalry charge as a commander of the Wolverines. I just know it."

General David Gregg

24

Gregg — Wednesday, July 1

12:00 p.m. (Ten hours earlier)
Brigadier General David Gregg
Four miles from Hanover Junction
Hanover Junction is ten miles Northeast from Hanover

Brigadier General David Gregg pressed the canteen's spout against his cracked lips and took a small swig, swirling the tepid water against his parched throat before gulping. He swiped his tongue across his salty lips, craving the taste of melting ice. The noon air was hot and heavy. The rhythmic clop of iron horseshoes hitting the dirt road and the clattering of steel scabbards hanging from saddle rings echoed behind him. He glanced over his shoulder. The miles of motley blue columns were shrouded in white dust.

He glanced sideways, letting the silence ride a moment, staring at Lieutenant Thomas Jackson Gregg. His 20-year-old brother had joined his staff prior to the Chancellorsville campaign. Thomas wobbled in his saddle, his eyes closed.

"T.J.! Wake up!" he shouted. "You're going to fall off your horse."

T.J. frowned and opened his eyes halfway. "I'm awake."

"Drink up."

T.J. gripped his canteen and swigged a gulp.

"Stay awake. We're almost there." T.J. nodded.

Gregg lowered his hat's brim, shading his eyes from the fiery sunlight. He muttered an oath. It was as if hell's fires blazed, braising his troopers in the Devil's cauldron. Four miles until Hanover Junction. Hopefully, his boys could rest there for a while.

He shot a glance at Major Henry Avery riding on the other side of him. The 27-year-old officer commanded the Tenth New

219

York Cavalry, riding as the vanguard of four thousand troopers of Second Division. Avery was part of Colonel Irvin Gregg's brigade, which was followed by Colonel John McIntosh and Colonel Pennock Huey's two brigades. He suppressed a grin. Avery looked like a villainous saloon gambler with his drooping black pencil mustache.

Gregg said, "I appreciate you leading the division in singing 'John Brown' when we crossed into Pennsylvania this morning. I even sang a couple verses."

Avery grinned. "You called that singing? You're a much better general than a vocalist."

"You have to admit, the spontaneous outburst of loyal voices was quite a moment."

"When we reach Hanover Junction, I'm hoping we can bivouac there," Avery replied.

Gregg wiped his brow. "I agree. The troopers and horses need a prolonged rest." Both men and animals were reaching a breaking point. The horses' ribs protruded like a sickly coyote's. Being in the saddle twenty out of twenty-four hours since crossing the Potomac at Edward's Ferry three days ago had been brutal.

"I'm worried we are losing too many horses." Avery twisted in his saddle and pointed toward the rear of the column. "They are dropping by the score."

"How many of your New Yorkers have lost their horses from exhaustion and are at the rear of the division carrying their saddles and bridles?"

"Thirteen troopers have joined the dreaded dismounted *Company Q* and are trudging along in hopes of finding new horses along the way or at Hanover Junction. *Company Q* has grown to fifty troopers from the division's three brigades who are slogging it on foot."

Gregg wrestled with the worry that was worming its way through him. "The troopers are exhausted. They keep pinching themselves so they don't fall asleep and fall and break their necks."

Avery nodded, tight-lipped.

Gregg pulled on his monstrous black beard. On instinct, he stood in his saddle, trying to relieve the throbbing in his legs.

"Look, General." Avery pointed. "Thick columns of black smoke."

"I see it. My guess is that Jeb Stuart's boys beat us to Hanover Junction." Gregg gestured. His 19-year-old aide-de-camp, Captain Henry C. Meyer, rode up. "Henry, ride forward with ten troopers from the headquarters security guard. Take T.J. with you so he stays awake. Don't mix it up with the enemy. I just want to know what the Rebs are up to."

Meyer saluted. "Come on, T.J." They spurred their mounts and galloped toward the billowing smoke.

Gregg smiled. His clean-shaven aide looked like a 15-year-old schoolboy and almost as young as the daredevil Custer. But he was a fearless officer like Custer, and he wouldn't trade him for any troopers in the division.

1:45 p.m.
General David Gregg
One-quarter mile from Hanover Junction

Thundering hooves approached and Gregg peered through the dust whirl toward a galloping rider. Meyer reined up.

"The Rebels tore up the railroad tracks and the railroad ties are burning fiercely. They also cut the telegraph wires. Our security detail captured a couple of Stuart's rear guard lurking around the depot. The prisoners claim Stuart is heading for York."

Gregg grimaced.

Meyer continued. "General, do you see the two jutting buildings at Hanover Junction?"

"Yes."

"As I recall from a previous visit to Hanover Junction, the two-story brick building with the pointed roof is the Hanover Junction Hotel. The two-story building across the tracks with the flat roof is the Hanover Junction Railroad Station."

"I'm surprised the Rebels didn't torch the buildings."

2:00 p.m.
General David Gregg
Hanover Junction, ten miles Northeast of Hanover

Gregg rested in the dining room of the Hanover Junction hotel, gulping down his second glass of water. He passed the water pitcher to Colonel John McIntosh, commanding the First Brigade. Colonel Pennock Huey, commanding the Second Brigade, was across the table, and next to him was Gregg's cousin Colonel Irvin Gregg, commanding the Third Brigade.

"Gentlemen, I've sent out details to scour the roads north and northeast of Hanover Junction to see if they can spot Stuart's boys." He fished for his watch. Four hours or so until sunset. "Let's bivouac here for the evening."

"That's a great idea," McIntosh said. "Company Q's dismounted troopers are hoping to buy or acquire new horses."

Gregg turned a smile on the 34-year-old colonel sporting a full, V-shaped beard. Although not a West Point graduate, McIntosh had received a regular commission as a lieutenant in the Second U.S. Cavalry. He was one of the best brigade commanders in the Army of the Potomac. He was a born fighter, a strict disciplinarian, and a dashing leader. Despite his tough exterior, he was a polished gentleman. Most important, Gregg could count on McIntosh to identify and exploit enemy weaknesses.

Colonel Irvin Gregg said, "Do you have orders for tomorrow?"

Gregg turned to Irvin. "Not yet."

Colonel Pennock Huey's aide burst into the room and gestured. Huey turned to General Gregg. "With your permission, General, I will be right back."

Gregg nodded.

Irvin reached for the water pitcher and poured another glass. David studied the profile of his older first cousin. They looked somewhat alike, except Irvin's bushy beard was not as long. They were both tall, but Irvin was a bit taller. His troopers called him Long John. Irvin was not a professional soldier, but he could fight, and he was a natural leader of men. He had volunteered to fight in the Mexican War and was quickly promoted to an officer.

After the war he had returned to running his Pennsylvanian iron foundry.

When the Civil War broke out, both cousins had joined the newly formed Sixth U.S. Cavalry. Irvin received a captain's commission. He was steadfast, and during battle his movements were as precise and timely as a Swiss watch.

McIntosh rubbed his lower back. "I'm damn sore from all this riding the past few days. Maybe I should have joined the infantry." He chuckled. "General. How in the hell did you end up in cavalry?"

Gregg turned to McIntosh. "After graduating from West Point in the class of 1855, I opted for a lieutenancy in the dragoons. I loved riding horses." He grinned. "But I had weak wrists and did not excel at wielding a saber." He glanced upward. His mind whispered a thank-you. "But somehow I was blessed and allowed to become a dragoon."

"Were you in the First or the Second Dragoons?" asked McIntosh.

"I started out in the First Dragoons, but five months later I transferred to the Second Dragoons." He paused and stared at Irvin Gregg and John McIntosh. "I will tell you something. In 1857 I was a green lieutenant, and I led a troop from Fort Tejon, located near Los Angeles, to Fort Vancouver, along the Columbia River in the Washington Territory. We then traveled up the Snake and Spokane Rivers and tangled with the Palouse, Spokane, and Coeur d'Alene Indians."

Irvin cracked a hard grin, splitting his black beard. "I'm delighted you didn't get scalped as you romped around the Pacific Northwest."

A laugh burst from Gregg's throat. "Me, too. That excursion from Los Angeles to Fort Vancouver, and then out to Snake River, doesn't compare to the marching we've done the past four days."

He stood and stepped over to the window. Dark smoke billowed. The Rebels would be in for quite a surprise when General Herman Haupt, the Superintendent of U.S. Railroads, arrived. He was an engineering magician whose sorcery could repair the railroad in less than a day. Meade would need this railroad to resupply his army if he defeated Lee.

Colonel Irvin Gregg peered at the clock on the wall. A few minutes past two. He shot a glance at his 30-year-old cousin. David was spare and tall. A humble and gentle man, David exemplified the highest ideals of West Point. The general was a bold and dashing leader who skillfully applied the principles of war. What he admired most about David was his impeccable character. He cared about his troops, and they cared about him.

Irvin suppressed a grin. David was also a skilled and intimidating chess player, brilliant at moves and predicting opponents' plays. His favorite opening move was the Queen's Gambit, in which he sacrificed a wing pawn for better control of the center of the board.

David stepped back over to the table and plopped down. "Let's wait until Pennock gets back and then I will provide orders for tonight's bivouac defenses." He reached into his pocket and retrieved three cigars. "We deserve these after our recent hard marches."

Irvin lit his cigar. He smiled and asked, "Do you think *my* favorite first cousin, Pennsylvania Governor Andrew Curtin, is going to pay us a visit while we're romping around his state?"

David grinned. "I thought I was your favorite first cousin."

"You are until Governor Andrew shows up. He treats me better than you do and lets me win at chess."

"That's why you're still a colonel and I'm a general. I don't let anyone beat me when it comes to strategy and chess."

2:07 p.m.
General David Gregg
Hanover Junction

David spotted Huey stepping back into the dining room. A dust-covered lieutenant was behind him.

"General Gregg," Huey said, "I discovered General Pleasonton's courier outside asking for you."

David stared at the lieutenant. "Do you have orders from General Pleasonton?"

The lieutenant said, "Your division is to proceed south through Manchester toward Baltimore."

Gregg stiffened. What had changed? "I don't understand. My cavalry division was in Manchester early this morning, headed for Hanover Junction."

"A general engagement is being fought at Gettysburg today. General Meade is still in Taneytown with General Pleasonton."

"Why doesn't Meade travel to Gettysburg?"

"General Buford's First Division fought the Confederate infantry this morning as they were advancing toward Gettysburg from the west along the Chambersburg Road. About ten this morning General Reynolds's First Corps arrived at Gettysburg, followed by General Howard's Eleventh."

"We have only two infantry corps and Buford's cavalry division at Gettysburg?"

"Yes!"

"Is Lee's entire army at Gettysburg?"

"I am not sure. But Meade believes he is tangling with a large force."

"What is General Meade's plan?"

"Meade's first choice is to execute his Pipe Creek Line defense. That would entail the forces at Gettysburg falling back to the Pipe Creek Line, about four miles south of Taneytown. That's why he has not ordered his other five infantry corps to Gettysburg."

"What is the Pipe Creek Line?"

"It's a high ridge beyond Pipe Creek running west to east from Middleburg to Manchester. Meade's chief engineer,

225

General Warren, said the Pipe Creek Line was as strong as thick castle walls."

"It seems like my cavalry division would be more useful if it traveled to Gettysburg, where there is a fight, and where it could provide screening for the infantry corps."

"General Halleck ordered Meade to maintain a force between the enemy and Baltimore and Washington, D.C. If the enemy breaks through at Gettysburg, they will have a clear shot at Baltimore, traveling down the Baltimore Pike. That's why General Meade is ordering you to Manchester."

Gregg stifled a welling rage. A forever moment ticked by as his mind churned. *Too bad the Rebels cut the telegraph wires.*

"Very well." Gregg turned to Irvin Gregg, John McIntosh, and Pennock Huey. "Gentlemen, let's saddle up. Pennock, your brigade is the vanguard, marching south, followed by Irvin's brigade and then John's."

Gregg turned to Captain Henry C. Meyer. "Henry, have the bugler sound 'Boots and Saddles.'"

2:30 p.m.
General David Gregg
One-quarter mile south from Hanover Junction

Hundreds of clattering hooves followed him as Gregg led his division, heading for Manchester. The blistering heat and mugginess were like riding through a steam bath. The throb in his head sharpened. *We were just in Manchester. The fight is at Gettysburg, and now we're riding away like yellow-bellied skedaddlers.*

Captain Meyer shouted, "General, a courier is approaching."

A dust-caked lieutenant pulled up. Both the officer and the horse were sweating and panting.

"General Gregg." The lieutenant paused and wiped his face. "General Pleasonton orders you to turn around and ride as rapidly as possible to York."

"What?" His pulse rate climbed.

"General Pleasonton believes a portion of Stuart's cavalry may be operating near York."

"I just received orders fifteen minutes ago from General Pleasonton's messenger, ordering my division south to Manchester."

"Those orders are superseded by your orders to march to York. General Kilpatrick's division fought Stuart's cavalry yesterday at Hanover. Kilpatrick reported that the Rebel cavalry numbers twelve thousand. Kilpatrick is pursuing Stuart but is heavily outnumbered. Your cavalry division is needed to even things up."

Gregg glared. His brain shrilled a hellish oath that could melt a mountain. "Very well, Lieutenant. Do you have any recent information on the fight at Gettysburg?"

"I'm not sure how Buford's cavalry division and First and Eleventh Infantry Corps are faring, sir."

2:45 p.m.
General David Gregg
One-quarter mile south from Hanover Junction
Heading north to Hanover Junction and York

Gregg scowled, his shoulders tightened. He stood up in his stirrups and turned to Captain Meyers. "Henry, I'm not sure General Meade and General Pleasonton know what the hell they're doing, except having us march up and down the same road."

"It appears Meade is determined to execute his Pipe Creek Plan and not fight at Gettysburg. Are you familiar with Gettysburg?"

Gregg nodded. "As a boy growing up in Bellefonte, I visited Gettysburg a couple times with my folks. I remember some large hills just southeast of town. If Reynolds and Howard are occupying those heights, then they should be able to put up a good fight until other forces come up."

"General, I see another courier approaching."

Gregg scowled. "Another damn order?"

The captain reined up, panting hard. "General Gregg, I have orders for you."

His throat tightened, bottling the bubbling rage. "This is the third order I've received from General Pleasonton in the last forty-five minutes!"

The captain said, "You are ordered to dispatch a brigade to Westminster, Maryland, to protect the rear of the army and the logistics trains assembled there."

Gregg gritted his teeth. What foul demons were torturing him? "I don't understand. My division was in Westminster on the twenty-ninth. There was an adequate force protecting the supply depot."

"General Reynolds, commanding First Corps, has been killed." The captain's breast rose and fell with a rapid gasp. "General Meade fears the enemy may break through the Union army's scattered defenses near Gettysburg and threaten Westminster."

"My God...John Reynolds is dead?" Gregg bit his lip as a chill crackled his bones. "What is Meade's plan?"

"When I departed headquarters, General Meade was discussing ordering General Hancock to Gettysburg to determine if the ground was suitable. If so, Meade was going to order the whole army up. If not, he was going to pull back to the Pipe Creek Line."

Gregg snapped, "Do you have any *other* orders?"

"Yes, sir," said the captain. "The balance of your cavalry division is to move with all possible speed in the direction of Gettysburg, about twenty-five miles away, where Meade may concentrate the army."

Gregg's stomach twisted into a knot. How could his exhausted troopers survive an all-night 25-mile march? He glowered in the unnatural silence that dropped like a death shroud. He had wasted most of the morning riding up and back on the same stretch of road, wearing out his men and their horses. His jaw tightened. *This better be the last order I receive today, and if it isn't, I'm disobeying it.* "Very well."

The captain continued, "One more thing. General Pleasonton wants you to report to army headquarters when you arrive near Gettysburg. General Pleasonton believes General Meade will ride forward soon to Gettysburg."

Gregg bristled as he stroked his beard. "Understood."

The courier saluted and departed.

Gregg turned to Captain Meyers. "What a perplexing situation. Do I expect a fourth order in the next few minutes?"

"Which of the three recent orders are you going to follow?"

He stroked his soaked beard. Uncertainty plagued his mind. He drew a deep breath. "The last one. Since Colonel Huey's is the last brigade in the column, I will have him turn around and ride south to Westminster. I will lead Colonel Gregg and Colonel McIntosh's brigades to Hanover Junction and then we will turn toward Hanover."

Gregg turned and rode down the road toward Huey's brigade. He peered at Colonel Huey at the front of his brigade and pulled up.

"Pennock, I just received my third order from General Pleasonton in the last forty-five minutes. You will turn around and march your brigade back to Westminster, along with the six 3-inch rifled guns of Lieutenant William Fuller's Company C, Third U.S. Artillery."

Huey's mouth flared like a cottonmouth. "My God, General, you're depleting your division of 1,400 men, along with an artillery battery, and the damn fight is at Gettysburg. Does General Pleasonton know what the hell is going on? We were in Westminster yesterday."

Gregg stared. "Understood. It's an important task, Pennock. If the enemy breaks through at Gettysburg they will rush toward Westminster, and then the national capital."

Huey skewered him with a grisly glare. "Yes, sir. Understood." Huey saluted.

General Gregg turned and rode up the column, whose depleted numbers were now 2,600. He forced an outward calm that belied the roiling anger inside. He stopped and explained the new orders to Colonel McIntosh and then to Colonel Gregg. He arrived at the front of the column and pulled up next to Meyer.

"Henry, this is going to be a tough march. We will have to use all our wits to protect the men and animals as much as possible."

Meyer shot him a tormented gaze. "I pity those Company Q troopers. They found no mounts to ride to Gettysburg."

Portrait shows from left: Wesley Merritt, David McMurtrie Gregg, General
Sheridan, Henry Eugene Davies, James Harrison Wilson, Alfred Torbert.
Photographed between 1861 and 1865

25

Gregg — Thursday, July 2

Gregg's weary mind begged for sleep. He yawned as Captain Henry Meyer reined up. "General Gregg, Hanover is just ahead. The town is a sleepy hollow. Jacob Wirt is a resident and noticed our advance scouts lingering about in the town square. I spoke with Wirt. He said General Custer used his house as his headquarters during the Battle of Hanover two days ago. He is waiting to speak with you."

Gregg's eyes closed and his eardrums stretched as another unexpected yawn erupted. He exhaled the air slowly and wiped his watery eyes. "Good."

"Wirt said his wife boiled coffee for you."

"Sounds delicious. I wish she could fill several barrels of coffee for the troopers. Lead the way, Henry."

Gregg locked his eyes on Henry's horse and trotted a horse-length away in the inky darkness. He followed Henry into Hanover's public square. The reek of rotting meat wafted through the morning air. Queasiness wormed in his bowels like a slithering snake. Dead horses lay in the streets. The streets were barricaded with boxes, ladders, hay bales, wagons, and old carriages. *There was one hell of a battle here.*

He pulled up to a two-story house and tied his horse to a large tree in the front yard. His butt muscles twinged like torn ankle ligaments. He trundled up to the front door and knocked. A white-haired man with flinty blue eyes opened the door.

231

The man turned and shouted, "General Gregg is here." A woman stepped outside, carrying a cup of coffee.

Gregg smiled. "Thank you." He reached for the hot brew and took several sips.

"I'm Mrs. Wirt. Please have your staff dismount. I have coffee for them, and I've sliced some bread, meat, and cheese."

"Thank you so much, Mrs. Wirt. Your generosity is most appreciated." He turned to Meyer. "Henry, have the headquarters staff dismount. I want to be marching toward Gettysburg by three a.m."

Gregg turned back to the elderly owner of the house. "Mr. Wirt, which roads are the most direct route to Gettysburg?"

Wirt pointed. "That way, General. Take the Littlestown Road for about seven miles. When you arrive at Littlestown, turn and go north for eleven miles on the Baltimore Pike. Thank God for you and your men."

Gregg tipped his hat and took a sip of coffee. The hot brew jolted his brain.

3:05 a.m.
Captain Henry Meyer
Hanover

Meyer was dreaming of standing barefoot on the shore of a cold mountain lake, holding his fishing pole. "Henry! Henry! Wake up." Fingers dug deep into his shoulder and shook.

"Henry, it's me, Henry Weir. We've moved out. General Gregg asked where you were. I came back looking for you."

Meyer opened his eyes and glanced, blurry-eyed, at Captain Henry Weir, adjutant general to General Gregg.

"Get up. General Gregg departed a few minutes ago. Let's go!" Weir said.

Meyer struggled to sweep the grogginess from his brain. He glanced at his right hand gripping the reins of his horse. He sat up and looked around at the fish stall he had been sleeping in. That explained the fish in his dream.

Weir plugged his nose. "How did you end up in this fish stall? You stink!"

"I'm not sure. I must have dozed off." He whiffed a foul odor; the biting air stung his eyes. He snapped awake. His stomach lurched.

"Let's go," Weir said.

Meyer mounted his horse. "I will follow you, Henry."

3:14 a.m.
General David Gregg
Two miles outside of Hanover on the Littlestown Road

Gregg's charger followed the fenced road snaking through the starlit night, the stars sparkling like white pinpricks. The humidity was thinning and a slight breeze brushed his bearded face. He yawned, his weary lungs begging for more air. A march in the cool night could not quench the murderous fatigue and tormenting hunger. A fifteen-mile march to Gettysburg. Would they arrive in time for today's fight? *This is going to be a horrendous ride.* A chilling unease flowed deep inside him like an icy stream. John Reynolds dead. He was the best infantry general in the Army of the Potomac. Meade was new to such a senior command. Would he fight? Or retreat like the three previous army commanders?

Trotting horses' hooves heralded the arrival of Captains Meyer and Weir, but they needn't have bothered—the smell was enough to warn anyone of their presence.

"I'm delighted my two Henrys have rejoined the head of the column." Gregg sniffed and his breath snagged. "You two smell like rotting fish."

"I dozed off in a fish stall," Meyer said.

Gregg grinned and continued. "Ride close by. Perhaps your stench can keep me alert."

"As we rode up, several dismounted troopers were leading their fatigued mounts to save the animals' strength," Weir said. "The horses are worn out. The cavalrymen are not in much better shape."

Gregg uttered a deep sigh. He focused on keeping a reasonable marching speed. The sparsely populated countryside rose and fell like small waves on a glistening ocean.

A shout shattered the stillness. "Where is General Gregg?"

Gregg swiveled in his saddle and eyed the lone rider. "I'm General Gregg."

"General Gregg, I'm Dr. Theodore Tate, assistant surgeon in the Third Pennsylvania Cavalry Regiment. I'm a resident of Gettysburg and sometimes I make medical visits in Hanover. I know all the backroads. It's a much faster route if we travel on the Hanover Road through Bonneauville and on to Gettysburg."

"Are you sure you can find the way in the pitch dark?"

"Yes. I can lead you on a shortcut to hit the Hanover Road at McSherrystown. Then you will have a direct shot to Gettysburg."

"Lead the way, Doctor," Gregg said. He turned to Meyer and Thomas Gregg. "Henry and T.J., ride with the doctor." He smiled. "The column will follow your noxious smell."

The doctor spurred his steed and broke right across a flat field, followed by Meyer and T.J. The 2,600-trooper column forked and streamed across the countryside like a large, slithering black snake. After a few miles, Captain Meyer rode toward the head of the column.

Meyer pointed. "General Gregg, see that square castle-looking turret with the pointed cupola?"

"Yes, I see it."

"That's St. Joseph Academy in McSherrystown. Dr. Tate said when we pass St. Joseph, we will turn onto the Hanover Road. Bonneauville is five miles down the road and Gettysburg is five miles after that."

"Good."

A few minutes later, Gregg led his division past the Academy and turned onto the Hanover Road. It was a straight shot to Gettysburg.

26

Miller — Thursday, July 2

3:45 a.m.
Captain William E. Miller
Commander, Company D, Third Pennsylvania

Miller hunched in his saddle as he lumbered down the dark road. His head jerked up and his eyes jolted wide. *What was that?* His heart raced. He glanced forwards and backwards. Nothing but clopping horse hooves muffled the air. *Must have dozed off again.* He strained to keep his eyelids open. His mind felt like a collapsed cave, dark and empty; it was impossible to concentrate. He slipped his hand into his coat pocket and fished out a needle. This medieval torture was going to hurt. He jabbed downward like an ice pick stabbing a frozen pond. The slender spike pierced his trousers and twisted into his thigh. He shrieked a muffled cry and pulled the needle out. His fagged-out brain burst awake like an exploding shell. He inserted the torture device into his coat pocket. A violent prick every half hour was going to leave his thigh looking like an outbreak of the measles.

He glanced over at McIntosh's adjutant general, Captain Walter Newhall, riding next to him.

"Walter, you're bobbing and weaving like the town drunk. Do you want to borrow my needle?"

"I have my own needle," Newhall said. He slapped his face twice. "That should keep me awake for the next few minutes."

Miller shook his head. "Are you trying to knock yourself out?"

"I don't like needles."

Miller yelped. Damn calves cramped again. He yipped again and bolted upright in his stirrups, pressing down on the balls of his feet. The spasm cinched tighter, like the last wrings of a wet washcloth. He lurched forward against the pommel, stretching the knotted muscles.

"William, are trying to wake the dead?" Newhall said.

"My calves keep cramping up." Miller gritted his teeth. "That's better." The stretching was working. The knotted muscle loosened as if kneaded by a rolling pin. He eased down in his saddle.

"I think jabbing yourself with that needle is causing your cramps."

"The needle pricks are the only way I can stay awake."

Miller glanced forward and saw Colonel McIntosh crunch downward onto his mount's neck as if gut-shot. A shiver slithered up Miller's neck. He spurred his horse forward, pulled up to the left of the slumping colonel, and grabbed his arm.

"Colonel, are you alright? Colonel!"

McIntosh's eyes were shut, his jaw slack. Slobber dribbled out of his mouth. The colonel started to spiral to his right.

Miller yanked on McIntosh's arm. "Walter!" Newhall rode up on McIntosh's right side and grabbed him about the waist. "Walter, do you have him?"

"I have him, William," said Newhall.

"I'm letting go, Walter."

Newhall grunted. "I'm pulling off the road and laying the colonel down on his back."

"I'll locate Dr. Tate." Miller departed.

A chorus of "Halt" cascaded over the column.

3:47 a.m.
Dr. Theodore Tate
Side of the Hanover Road

Dr. Tate bent over Colonel McIntosh and placed his ear on his sternum. A shallow beating. He loosened the scarf around the colonel's neck. "Captain Miller, hand me your canteen."

"Here you go, Doc."

"Thanks." He drenched a rag with water and applied it to the colonel's head.

Pounding hooves approached and halted. Tate glanced up. Captain Weir dismounted and knelt. "Doc, how serious is Colonel McIntosh's injury?"

"He is suffering from heat exhaustion." Tate scanned the shadowy terrain. He turned to Miller. "William, we have reached the Geiselmans' woods. Their house is right over there. Before the war I was a Gettysburg physician and traveled to the Geiselmans' farm to make house calls. William and Walter, help me carry the colonel to the house."

4:00 a.m.
Dr. Theodore Tate
Geiselmans' house

Tate rested on the edge of the bed, patting the wet rag on McIntosh's head, which was resting on a small pillow. He had elevated the colonel's legs with two large pillows. The colonel opened his eyes and blinked several times, apparently confused.

"Colonel, it's Dr. Tate, with Captain Newhall and Captain Miller. You almost tumbled off your horse."

"Walter caught you before you hit the ground," Miller said.

"Where are we?" McIntosh said, trying to focus in the dim light.

"We are at the Geiselman house just off the Hanover Road," Dr. Tate told him. "You are suffering from heat exhaustion. You need to drink cool fluids." He placed a cup against McIntosh's lips. "Now, sip."

McIntosh took a couple of sips and laid his head back on the pillow. He glanced down. "Doc, you almost undressed me."

Tate smiled. "I just loosened your clothing."

Heavy footsteps trodded into the room. A deep, soft voice. "Dr. Tate, how is Colonel McIntosh doing?"

Tate glanced up to the towering figure sporting a chest-length beard. "General Gregg, Colonel McIntosh is suffering from heat exhaustion. He passed out on his horse, but Captain Miller and Captain Newhall caught him before he crashed to the ground."

"General Gregg, I'm feeling much better, sir," McIntosh insisted.

Gregg turned to Tate. "Doc, I've halted the column. I'm worried several other troopers are also suffering from heat exhaustion. Do you think Colonel McIntosh will be able to ride in twenty minutes?"

"I'll be ready, General," McIntosh said.

Gregg smiled. "Good. I have a feeling, John, I'm going to need my First Brigade commander today." Gregg departed.

"I want to thank you, Doc, and William and Walter. I'm most grateful," McIntosh said.

Tate nodded.

"You're welcome, sir," said Miller. Newhall smiled.

McIntosh said, "Walter, inform the regimental commanders we will start marching again in twenty minutes."

Newhall saluted and departed.

Tate turned to Miller. "Let's step outside, William, and give the colonel a few minutes to rest alone."

Tate stepped out of the bedroom and Miller followed him. Coffee scented the room.

"Dr. Tate, Captain Miller," Mrs. Geiselman said," I have hot coffee for you on the table."

"Thank you, Mrs. Geiselman," said Tate. "You're a godsend."

Tate sat down. Miller slumped into a chair across the table. They both sipped the dark brew.

"William, are you a West Point grad?" Tate asked. "You're one of the most respected officers in the regiment. The troopers have told me the story about your rescue of that Union battery at Antietam, and Colonel McIntosh values you."

"No, I'm not, I wish, but I haven't had any formal schooling. I'm the oldest of six children and my father was an invalid. I was a farmer until I turned twenty-three. When the war broke out, I left the farm to join the Union cavalry."

Tate pursed his lips and sipped the steaming coffee. "I like how you figure out what needs to be done and you do it. I guess that's a result of tilling the land."

Miller covered his mouth and yawned. "...ahhh-hhaaaaaa!" He shook his head. "I need at least a gallon of coffee."

Tate grinned. "I think you woke up the dead."

"And my brain too." Miller gripped the cup and gulped. His breath quickened. "The farmer's enemy is the weather. So, I guess I've been fighting either nature or the Rebels my whole life. A winning fighter relies on his instincts like a skilled boxer. And when the unexpected occurs, he has to react faster than his opponent."

Tate spotted McIntosh stepping into the dining room. The colonel halted and buttoned up his blouse, then glanced up and grinned. "Thank you, gentlemen, for letting me get some useful beauty sleep. Let's move out."

5:00 a.m. (Sunrise 4:48 a.m.)
General David Gregg
One mile from Bonneauville, Pennsylvania

Mile after mile the column lumbered over the dirt road. Gregg's breath hitched. McIntosh's medical emergency could easily happen to any of his troopers. His boys needed a few hours' rest when they reached Gettysburg. Gregg's starving stomach rumbled like a brimstone pit. He cringed. His troopers needed to eat. Him, too. They were fading fast. How well would his dog-tired troopers fight against a rested enemy? The monotonous chorus of hooves, rattling spurs, and clattering sabers split the air.

"General Gregg," Meyer said, "someone yelled 'halt.'"

"Halt!" Gregg shouted.

"Another dead-tired trooper slipped from his saddle and crashed to the ground."

Gregg grumbled. At this pace it would take eight more hours to reach the outskirts of Gettysburg. A deafening silence like a church funeral quelled the countryside. He pried his drooping eyelids open. He feared that if he closed them, he would slumber into a deep sleep, as if he had breathed chloroform.

He swiveled in the saddle. A sergeant dismounted and lifted the exhausted trooper back onto the saddle. The fallen trooper did not elicit the usual peals of laughter and side-splitting halloos. The weary division was too tired to muster the energy for mockery. Anyone could be next to tumble, including them.

"General, we're ready to march again."

Gregg shouted, "Forward, march."

The column eased forward again, resuming the rhythmic clop of horse hooves. He had pushed his dragoons to their own limits and beyond. Were they in any shape to fight when they arrived at Gettysburg? He would soon find out.

27

Custer — Thursday, July 2

5:00 a.m. (Sunrise 4:48 a.m.)
Private Norvell Churchill
Camp between East Berlin and Abbottstown

Private Churchill bounded toward General Custer's tent, gripping the note from Lieutenant Colerick. Fidgetiness rattled his insides. He had been Custer's orderly for only twelve hours, and this was his first task: delivering a message to the boy general. Custer was probably asleep.

He shook his head and frowned. He had delivered messages before to the nervous and fussy, white-haired, white-bearded General Mansfield, always a grouchy bear upon waking. What would the young boy general be like? Colerick had no advice on what to expect, as he had only been Custer's orderly for two days. Many Wolverines were still unsure about the boy general's tactical abilities, calling it martial madness to have a prancing peacock commanding the Michigan Brigade. But his performance yesterday during the Battle of Hanover had surprised many of the grizzled veterans of his old regiment. Although Custer had led the dismounted attack against Rice's Hill with poise and courage, many of the First Michigan thought he was still too young and believed Colonel Alger should be commanding the brigade. The common gripe was that Custer should be at least able to grow a beard.

His eyes riveted on a tall, lean guard gripping his Spencer rifle twenty yards ahead. His throat tightened as he angled toward Custer's tent. Custer had been cordial upon their brief introduction; the general had said, "it sounds like you have the dash to serve as my orderly." The warm feeling that had given him was quickly replaced by a cold chill when Custer said, "I just hope you're not bad luck and I end up like General Mansfield."

Those eerie words were haunting. Was he bad luck? More than anything he wanted Custer to trust him to do his duty. A short prayer slipped over his lips, swearing he would protect the general at all cost. He stopped and saluted.

"Corporal," Churchill said, "Lieutenant Colerick, General Custer's aide-de-camp, has requested I deliver a message to General Custer."

The guard cracked a half grin. "So how is the general's boyish orderly liking his new duty? Since yesterday, you've been scurrying around his headquarters like a scared rabbit."

Churchill frowned. "I might not be his orderly much longer if I don't deliver the message."

The guard stepped aside and opened the tent flap. "I'm not sure he is awake yet, but go on in."

Churchill gulped a breath, stepped inside the tent, and paused. Sunrays tunneled into the tent and arced over a body lying on the ground. Long, golden ringlets flowed down the figure's neck. Curled at his feet was his white pointer. Rose lifted her head and yawned. He reached down and stroked the dog's silky fur. "Sorry, girl," he whispered, "it's time to get up."

Rose stood and scratched her side.

He fidgeted and his eyes narrowed. "General Custer. It's Private Churchill. I have a message from Lieutenant Colerick, sir."

<hr />

5:05 a.m.
Custer
Camp between East Berlin and Abbottstown

Custer turned toward the voice. "Is that you, Norvell?"

"Yes, sir. Lieutenant Colerick said Division Staff received a message from General Pleasonton's headquarters. General Kilpatrick is to march his two brigades toward Gettysburg. General Custer's brigade is to take the lead."

Churchill handed him the note.

Custer's skin pebbled. "That's great news, Norvell. I love being first." He grinned. "I'll be right out."

Churchill saluted and stepped out of the tent. Custer pulled on his knee-high boots and slipped on his black, gold-laced jacket. He gripped his black velvet hat in one hand and his red scarf and the note in the other. He sprang out of the tent and spotted Churchill standing next to Johnny and Harry, his big black gelding, and Roanoke, his beautiful gray stallion.

"Johnny, I'm going to ride Harry this morning."

"Yes, General. I will get him ready."

Custer pulled the starred shirt collar up and wrapped the long red tie around his neck. As he knotted the tie, he glanced at Churchill, mounted on his steed. Did he look as young as Norvell? They were the same age. Well, he was six months older. He read the note, took the reins from Johnny and mounted Harry, then turned to Churchill.

"I've been thinking about your General Mansfield story." Custer smiled. "He was one of the oldest generals in the Union army and filled with pure cussedness when fighting the enemy."

Churchill grinned. "He looked as ancient as an Old Testament prophet."

"Ironically, you now have a chance to be an orderly for the youngest general in the army." He assumed a theatrical air. "I'm not a prophet of old, but as a burgeoning seer, I prophesize glorious success for the Wolverines." He paused and drew a breath. "But just like General Mansfield, I believe in leading from the front. That's why I chose you to be my orderly."

"I will be right there next to you, General." He smiled. "Just stay on my right side."

He nodded with a slight smile. "Lieutenant Colerick said that you were one of the best horsemen in the brigade and an excellent marksman."

"Well, thank you, General. I try."

"Maybe we will get a chance to laugh at death today."

Churchill grinned. "Just as long as death doesn't get the last laugh."

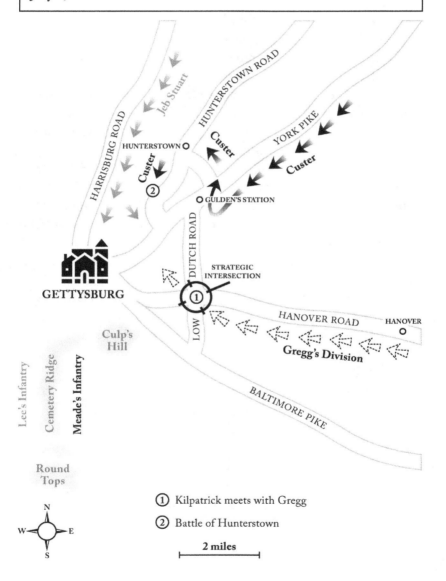

**Custer's Brigade Leading Kilpatrick's Division to Gulden's Station
Gregg's Division Marches West on Hanover Road
July 2, 1863**

HUNTERSTOWN ROAD

Jeb Stuart

HARRISBURG ROAD

YORK PIKE

HUNTERSTOWN

Custer

Custer

Custer

②

GULDEN'S STATION

DUTCH ROAD

STRATEGIC
INTERSECTION

GETTYSBURG

①

LOW

HANOVER ROAD

HANOVER

Culp's
Hill

Gregg's Division

Lee's Infantry

Cemetery Ridge

Meade's Infantry

BALTIMORE PIKE

Round
Tops

N
W — E
S

① Kilpatrick meets with Gregg

② Battle of Hunterstown

2 miles

244

28

Gregg — Thursday, July 2

11:30 a.m.
General David Gregg
Strategic intersection: Hanover Road and Low Dutch Road crossroad
Three miles east of the Gettysburg battlefield

Athick, boundless weariness draped Gregg's body. God, he was tired. Every muscle ached. Sweltering heat scorched the countryside, with its small farms dotting the dense woods like pieces in a patchwork quilt. Captain Weir approached down the Hanover Road from Gettysburg. Gripping his binoculars, Gregg browsed the looming crest one mile west of the strategic intersection. The ridgeline ran northward like the backbone of a great beast.

Captain Weir reined up. "General, the scouts report the crest ahead is named Brinkerhoff's Ridge. It runs at right angles across the Hanover Road. One mile west of the ridge is Culp's Hill. The several farmhouses you see up ahead off to your right are mostly owned by members of the Brinkerhoff families."

"Are they in their farms?"

"No, sir. With enemy activity a mile or so to the west, the Brinkerhoff clan vacated their homes and are staying with relatives near the village of Two Taverns on the Baltimore Pike."

"Any signs of enemy activity?"

"Yes, Union infantry pickets about a quarter mile west of Brinkerhoff's ridge are taking potshots at Rebel infantry skirmishers. Our scouts did not spot any enemy cavalry." Weir pointed. "The shallow valley east of the ridge is drained by Cress Run that flows from north to south."

Gregg gestured. "What's the wooded high ground north of Brinkerhoff's Ridge?"

"That's known as Cress Ridge. It is densely wooded. Beyond the woods is the Stallsmith farm, which we can't see because of the timber. The farm has open fields on which an entire cavalry division could mass without being detected from the Hanover Road."

Gregg pointed. "Is that house there, just south of the Cress Ridge wooded area, owned by the Brinkerhoffs?"

"No, that's the Rummel place, and the stream running south from the house is called Little Run. After Little Run crosses the Hanover Road it unites with Cress Run and continues about a mile and a half before crossing the Baltimore Pike. This is important because there is a small road that parallels the streams that places you about 2,500 yards in the rear of Meade's headquarters."

"I smell danger," Gregg said. "Enemy cavalry could mass in the woods north of Cress Ridge and then without warning burst through the woods like an avalanche and barrel down the Low Dutch Road and the road paralleling the Cress Run stream and end up in the rear area of the Union army. These two roads are ideal channels for the enemy to spill down and shatter Meade's right flank."

Weir said, "I agree, sir. These sheltered byways remind me of the masked ground on Hooker's right flank at Chancellorsville."

Gregg gestured to Captain Meyer. The captain rode up.

"Henry, you are going to accompany me to Meade's headquarters. Captain Weir, when the column reaches the intersection of the Low Dutch Road and Hanover, ahead, halt the division. Order the rail fences removed on the Hanover and Low Dutch Roads to give open fields for the mounted troops."

Weir said, "Does the division have permission to dismount and rest in the fields?"

Gregg said, "Yes. Order scouting and picket parties forward to Brinkerhoff's Ridge and northward into the woods of Cress Ridge. The remaining two brigades can dismount and unsaddle their horses. I will return as fast as I can."

12:00 p.m.
General David Gregg
Meade's headquarters, Leister house

Gregg and Captain Meyer pulled off the Taneytown Road into the yard of the Leister house, a shabby little white farmhouse. Gregg uttered a deep sigh. General Pleasonton stood on the covered front porch and waved. Gregg dismounted, wincing, his saddle-sore butt feeling like a huge boil. He handed the reins to a groom. "I don't plan on being here long, but if you have any oats and water for Pretty and Captain Meyer's mount, I would greatly appreciate it."

Gregg glanced up as Pleasonton strode toward him. He saluted. "Good afternoon, General Pleasonton."

Pleasonton returned the salute. "David, it's great to see you. It looks as if you have ridden to hell and back. I hope your division is ready to tangle with the enemy."

"Two of my brigades just arrived a few miles from here at the Hanover and Low Dutch Road crossroads and are resting from the all-night march." He grimaced. "Colonel Huey's brigade should have arrived at Westminster by now as you ordered."

"Good. Your orders are to protect the army's right flank. General Slocum's Twelfth Infantry Corps is occupying Culp's Hill."

Gregg nodded. "My division is about two miles east of Culp's Hill."

"I sent a courier ordering Colonel Gregg's brigade to march southwest toward the Baltimore Pike," Pleasonton said. "Meade is expecting General Sedgwick's Sixth Infantry Corps to be marching up the Baltimore Pike from Westminster. Meade is praying Sedgwick's corps arrives before the enemy attacks."

Gregg glared as Pleasonton's words spilled over him. Horrified alarm clawed at him. "What?" Gregg's throat tightened. "You're expecting me to cover the army's right flank with one brigade?"

"For now, yes."

Gregg shuddered. Warning bells clanged in his head.

Pleasonton gestured. "General Meade wants to see you." He turned and stepped toward the Leister house.

Gregg trodded behind Pleasonton. He stepped onto the small porch and peered through the open doorway into the house. Meade was bent over a dining room table. General Hunt, the commander of the army's artillery reserve, was pointing at the map.

"What's your assessment of Sickles's desire to move forward?" Meade asked.

Hunt replied, "Although the peach orchard has some advantages over the southern part of Cemetery Ridge, the disadvantages are profound."

"Explain," Meade said.

"Occupying the peach orchard would require twice as many soldiers, as the forward line is twice as long as the Cemetery Ridge line."

"Did you give Sickles permission to move forward?"

"No, sir."

"Good."

Gregg stepped back from the doorway and leaned on the porch railing to collect himself and wait for Meade to call for him. He closed his eyes, and gaped a protracted yawn. His legs wobbled.

Hunt stepped onto the porch. "David, it's good to see you, and we are thankful your cavalry division has arrived."

"Thanks, Henry." Gregg covered his mouth as he yawned again. "It seems my division is down to one brigade."

Hunt smiled and patted his shoulder. "Good luck this afternoon. Before long, Meade expects Lee to attack the Union's right flank." Hunt skittered toward his horse with long bounding strides.

Gregg drew a shivering breath and winced. His brain throbbed. One brigade to defend the army's right flank. Impossible.

Pleasonton stood in the doorway. "David, General Meade requests your presence."

Gregg stepped through the door, stopped, and saluted. "Reporting as ordered, General Meade."

Meade glanced through his thick glasses, grinned through his scraggly beard, and returned the salute. "Please sit, General Gregg. Looks as if you've had one hell of a march."

"Thank you, sir." Gregg plumped down in a chair. "My division departed Hanover Junction around 3:00 p.m. yesterday. We arrived in Hanover about 2:00 a.m. this morning. I saw the remnants of Kilpatrick's fight with Stuart."

"Kilpatrick reported both Custer and Farnsworth performed well in the fight." Meade turned to Pleasonton. "Alfred, I took a big chance promoting three captains to brigadier generals on your recommendation, but thus far that was a good recommendation."

"I agree, General Meade."

Meade pointed to the map lying on the dining room table. "Major Biddle. Please hold up the map for General Gregg." Biddle and another aide picked up the ends of the map and held it in front of Gregg. Meade pressed his finger on the map. "General Gregg, this is Culp's Hill. Your division is about two miles east from Culp's Hill. You're protecting the right flank of the army. Notice our defenses are in the shape of a fishhook."

"Whose enemy infantry are threatening Culp's Hill?" Gregg asked.

"General Edward Johnson's infantry division of Ewell's corps. General Walker's Virginia troops of the Stonewall Brigade are protecting Johnson's left flank. Johnson has skirmishers extending a mile east from the base of Brenner's Hill to Brinkerhoff's Ridge."

Gregg pointed. "My cavalry division is arriving at the intersection of Hanover Road and Low Dutch Road east of Brinkerhoff's Ridge. What Union troops are facing Walker's skirmishers on the ridge?"

"The Twenty-Seventh Indiana Regiment from Ruger's brigade of Twelve Corps. The Hoosiers have been exchanging shots with the enemy on Brinkerhoff's Ridge since daybreak." Meade paused and stroked his salt-and-pepper beard. "These two regiments are going to be relieved by a screening regiment from Fifth Corps that is traveling west on the Hanover Road and will cut off at White Run Road to Power's Hill. I believe the infantry regiment will be the Ninth Massachusetts."

An aide handed a note to the commanding general. Meade glanced at the note and nodded. "Okay, I will deal with this in a moment."

Meade pointed to the map. "General Gregg, once your division arrives and has deployed, you can expect an order from my headquarters to have your cavalry troopers relieve the Ninth Massachusetts so they can rejoin Fifth Corps."

Gregg nodded. "Yes, sir."

"See these three north–south roads here: White Run Road, Low Dutch Road, and Highland Road?" Meade pointed to the map. "They are critical access roads that lead to the Baltimore Pike. You're to protect these three access roads. The Baltimore Pike is the army's key logistics artery from Union Mills, fourteen miles southeast of Gettysburg. Currently marching on the Baltimore Pike are twenty thousand horses and mules pulling logistics, ambulance, and ordnance trains to Gettysburg."

Colonel George Sharpe stepped into the room and saluted. Meade glanced up. "Does the army's intelligence officer have anything to report to General Gregg?"

"Jeb Stuart's cavalry division is arriving piecemeal at Gettysburg from Carlisle," said Sharpe. "I'm unsure where Wade Hampton's cavalry brigade is now. But I believe he will be arriving at Gettysburg from the northeast, traveling down the York Pike. Once Hampton's brigade arrives, my guess is that they will relieve Walker's infantry brigade guarding the Rebels' left flank."

"David, stay sharp and protect the army's right flank." Meade advised. "My instinct says that you will be facing either enemy infantry or cavalry trying to get around our right flank."

Gregg nodded.

"General Pleasonton," Meade said, "do you have anything else to add to General Gregg?"

"Yes. I sent a courier to General Kilpatrick, directing he meet with you at the intersection of the Hanover Road and Low Dutch Road. Kilpatrick's division is arriving at Gulden's Station on the York Pike. The railroad stop is three miles north of the intersection. Kilpatrick will ride down the Low Dutch Road and meet you. As the senior cavalry division commander, you will direct Kilpatrick to move into position to guard the right flank of the army in conjunction with your division."

Meade faced him squarely. "David, you're the more experienced cavalry general and Kilpatrick was your former brigade commander. I want you to impress upon Kilpatrick the seriousness of the situation. Do you understand?"

Gregg nodded. "Yes, sir."

"Keep army headquarters informed of your situation. Do you have anything else for me?"

"No, sir." Gregg stood up and held his gaze for a moment as Meade adjusted his thick spectacles. "I should congratulate you on your promotion, General Meade."

Meade cracked a half smile. "See what can happen, David, when you despise both politicians and reporters? You will be promoted to command the army so both the snake-infested groups can sink their poisonous fangs into you at the same time."

Gregg grinned, saluted, and scurried outside, then aimed for Henry, who was faithfully holding Pretty's reins.

"Good luck, General Gregg," Pleasonton shouted.

Gregg smiled, tight-lipped. "Thank you, sir." He mounted Pretty. "As soon as you can order Colonel Gregg's brigade to rejoin my division, I would be most grateful." He turned to Captain Meyer. "Come on Henry, let's head back to the division."

Major General George Gordon Meade

29

Custer — Thursday, July 2

2:00 p.m.
Custer
Gulden's Station[7]

Custer's eyes swiveled left and right, scanning the fields as he rode at the head of Kilpatrick's column. Where were the Rebels? They couldn't be too far away. Sweat dripped down his brow, stinging his eyes. He wiped his gloved hand across his face. He blinked twice. Ahead, in blistering heat, he cast his gaze on the two-story red brick Gulden's Mill and nearby Gulden's Station, a whistle-stop along the Hanover and Gettysburg railroad line intersecting the York Pike. He twisted in his saddle and glanced at the ponderous, blue-coated cavalry column stretching for miles up the York Pike.

Private Churchill pointed ahead. "General Custer, there's Union pickets ahead straddling the York Pike."

He squinted and spotted Colerick galloping up the Pike.

Colerick reined up. "General, those pickets are General David Gregg's Second Cavalry Division. Gregg's pickets are patrolling the intersection of the York Pike and the Low Dutch Road. Their patrols run south on the Low Dutch Road for two and half miles where the Low Dutch Road intersects Hanover Road. That's where General Gregg is currently located."

A courier rode east through Gregg's picket line up the York Road. It was Captain George Yates. Yates pulled up, sweat dripping from his brow, and saluted. "Great to see you, General Custer. I spotted your red necktie a quarter mile away."

---

7 A whistle-stop along the Hanover Junction and Gettysburg Railroad where the tracks bisected the York Pike. Gulden's Station was four miles east of Gettysburg. Low Dutch Road connects Gulden's Station to Hanover Road.

Custer grinned. "I'm delighted no one else is wearing a red necktie."

Yates paused and wiped his face.

"Why is General Pleasonton's aide-de-camp riding so far from cavalry headquarters?"

"I have orders for General Kilpatrick."

Custer nodded. Glimmering excitement swirled in his mind. Maybe his brigade was being ordered to Gettysburg to participate in today's fight.

Hoofbeats pounded behind him. He twisted around, eyeing Kilpatrick and some of his staff approaching. The air hung hot and muggy. Kilpatrick pulled up.

Custer saluted. "Good afternoon, General."

Kilpatrick returned the salute.

Yates saluted. "Good afternoon, General Kilpatrick. I have written orders from General Pleasonton."

Yates reached into the satchel on his hip, produced an envelope, and handed it to Kilpatrick. The general opened the envelope and read the order.

Kilpatrick turned to Custer. "General Pleasonton wants a coordinated effort between Gregg's Second Division and my Third Division. I'm to report to General Gregg for additional orders. Gregg's headquarters is south about three miles down the Low Dutch Road where it intersects with the Hanover Road."

"Do you want me to continue to lead the division toward Gettysburg?" Custer asked.

Kilpatrick's nostrils flared like a charging bull. "No!" His voice resembled his unhinged cadet outbursts. "I don't want you to advance beyond Gulden's Station." A thundering boom burst across the sky. Kilpatrick turned his head and pointed down the York Pike. "If we face the enemy today, I want to be there in the lead for my division. Do you understand?"

Custer nodded.

Kilpatrick shouted, "Do you understand?"

Custer's face flared white-hot. "Yes, sir." A silent sigh left his lips. "I understand." Kill-Cavalry wanted all the glory and here was his chance.

"Good." Kilpatrick paused and scanned the terrain with his binoculars. "We are roughly four miles or so from Gettysburg. My two brigades stay here. But I do want you to send out scouts and advance pickets toward Gettysburg."

"What about scouting toward the north a couple of miles toward Hunterstown?"

Kilpatrick shook his head and pointed to Captain Estes. "I've ordered Llewellyn to lead Farnsworth's Company A from the Eighteenth Pennsylvania to scout the Hunterstown area. I will be back shortly."

"Yes, sir." Custer saluted.

Kilpatrick and eight members of his staff galloped southward on the Low Dutch Road. Captain Estes peeled off and rode back up the York Pike toward Farnsworth's brigade. Custer squinted and turned his red scarf around over his nose and mouth. Twenty yards behind Kilpatrick galloped a column of one hundred troopers of the Ohio First Regiment Headquarters Guard, kicking up a cloud of dust.

Custer gestured toward Churchill. The orderly rode up. "Norvell, have Second Lieutenant Charles Storrs, from Troop G, Sixth Michigan, report to me."

Churchill rode back up the York Pike. Custer turned to Colerick. "Inform the brigade that we are going to loiter here until Kilpatrick returns from visiting with Gregg. I want each regiment to send out advance pickets."

Colerick saluted and departed.

Private Joseph Fought pulled up. "How long do you think we will be here?"

"Kilpatrick should be back in a couple hours."

Storrs rode up and saluted. Custer smiled. The 30-year-old lieutenant sported a curly muttonchop beard. Storrs was a fierce fighter, perhaps the fiercest Wolverine in the Michigan Brigade.

"Charles, I want you to lead a patrol of twenty men from Troop G down to the intersection of the York Pike and Hunterstown Road. That should be about six or seven miles southwest down the Pike."

"Why do you think the Rebels would veer off the Harrisburg Pike to Hunterstown if they are headed to Gettysburg? The Pike is a direct shot into Gettysburg."

"Just a feeling." Custer tucked a golden lock behind his ear. "Hunterstown has plenty of watering holes, horses, and livestock. If I was Jeb Stuart and had a couple of brigades traveling south on the Harrisburg Road, I would have them veer off from Heidlersburg and ride through Hunterstown. It would be plum pickings and he could water and rest his horses a bit."

"Understood, sir. I will wait at the intersection to see if any Rebels are coming down the Hunterstown road. If I spot any enemy, I will ride back and report."

"Stay sharp. You're going to be only a few miles from Gettysburg and you're likely to run into enemy patrols trying to prevent us from flanking the Rebel army."

⚡ 30 ⚡

Gregg — Thursday, July 2

2:45 p.m.
General David Gregg
Abraham Reever house, Gregg's headquarters
Hanover Road and Low Dutch Road Crossroad

Gregg slumped in a chair in the Reever house, drinking coffee and munching on a sandwich.[8] Low voices droned in the next room. He dropped his head into his hands. His veins felt like ice. He had one brigade to defend the army's right flank. One brigade. Impossible. If Jeb Stuart launched an attack from the woods of Cress Ridge, his cavalry division of over 6,000 troopers would spill over McIntosh's brigade of 1,300 men and swallow them whole. God, he wished he had Colonel Huey's 1,400-man brigade and artillery battery.

A high-pitched voice screeched. "Tell General Gregg, General Kilpatrick is reporting as ordered."

Captain Meyer bolted into the room. "General Gregg, General Kilpatrick is here."

"Please show him in." Gregg stood up. A taunting thrill coursed through him. He enjoyed towering over the five-foot-five, fiery Irishman.

Kilpatrick lumbered into the dining room, swayed, and saluted. "Reporting as ordered, sir." He rubbed his lower back, plainly hurting.

Gregg paused for a moment, staring. "Judson, were you wounded?"

---

8 There is debate about General Gregg's headquarters being either the Reever house or the G. Howard house. I chose the Reever house based upon author Michael Phipps, Gettysburg Licensed Battlefield Guide at Gettysburg. See Michael Phipps, *"Come On, You Wolverines!": Custer at Gettysburg*, Farnsworth House Military Impressions, Gettysburg, PA, 1996, 42.

"Nope. My kidneys flamed up during my hell-bent gallop back to Hanover when Jeb's boys started firing artillery into the town. I arrived in time to achieve a glorious victory over Jeb's Invincibles."

Glorious victory? Gregg repressed a snigger. Kilpatrick had no more pursued Jeb Stuart after the Battle of Hanover than General Hooker had pursued Lee after the Confederates crossed the Potomac and streaked toward Pennsylvania. Judson was infamous for exaggerating his exploits.

"Judson, please sit down. This won't take long. I just returned from Meade's headquarters at Gettysburg. We've been ordered to protect Meade's right flank that is anchored on Culp's Hill." He paused. Out of courtesy, it was proper to praise Kilpatrick. "But first let me congratulate you on the victory at Hanover. General Meade and General Pleasonton were most pleased."

A devilish grin crossed Kilpatrick's face. "It was a terrific victory. I really whipped old Stuart's tail. It was touch and go until I rode back to Hanover and assumed command of Farnsworth's forces. But once there, I directed both Farnsworth and Custer's brigades to a great victory. Jeb's forces numbered 12,000. But I still licked him, and he skirted away in the night with his tail between his legs." Kilpatrick paused and puffed up like a peacock fanning its tail feathers. "I gave General Meade his first victory."

Gregg nodded as Judson reached into his pants pocket, retrieved a handkerchief, and wiped his sweaty brow. Gregg's mind raced. *If Kilpatrick whipped the Rebel cavalry, why did he let them escape?*

Kilpatrick prattled on. "My division is operating along the Gettysburg-York Pike. My scouts are investigating north of the York Pike. With your concurrence, I would like to move my division north of the York Pike and operate around Hunterstown. If I was Stuart, moving south from Carlisle area, I would send at least one brigade through Hunterstown because of its watering holes and large open fields for the horses to graze."

"I concur with you moving north toward Hunterstown. Maybe if you get there first you can surprise Jeb's boys. Good old

Jeb graduated a class ahead of me at West Point. I still remember the hazing he inflicted when I was a plebe."

"I heard he was a Bible class man."

Gregg chuckled. "When I was a plebe, Jeb was a big advocate of Old Testament fire and brimstone. You know, an eye for an eye, a tooth for a tooth."

"Well, maybe I will get a chance to deliver some Old Testament on Jeb's boys. I was pretty good at that at the Point."

"So, I've heard. Good luck, Judson. Keep me posted on your position."

Kilpatrick stood up slowly, saluted, and trundled out of the room, holding his back.

2:55 p.m.
General David Gregg
Hanover Road and Low Dutch Road Crossroad

Gregg stood in the yard of the Reever house, gripping his binoculars and scanning Brinkerhoff's Ridge. In front of it were two smaller ridges. The three rippling rises were like ocean waves separated by several hundred yards. The first ripple was the lowest ridgeline, 500 yards away; the third ripple wave was the highest ridgeline, 2,000 yards away. Scouts reported Cress Run stream flowing southward was just beyond the first ridge.

Thunder cracked. He glanced toward Culp's Hill. The sky was overcast, with a muzzling effort at rain.

Captain Weir pointed. "That was an artillery battery. There's the black tendril."

Gregg glanced toward Culp's Hill. "I see it."

"Will there be a battle today?" said Weir.

"Meade thinks Lee will attack before dusk. He almost whipped Meade yesterday. Fortunately, Hancock and Howard were able to hold on to Cemetery Hill and Culp's Hill last evening. Lee will try again, hoping all of Meade's forces have not arrived."

"Our scouts are reporting that General Sedgwick's Sixth Corps is arriving on the battlefield, so Meade should be at full strength."

"Good. That's Meade's largest infantry corps. I wish my division was at full strength."

Gregg lifted his binoculars a bit and scanned the second ripple, about 1,000 yards ahead. It was lined with trees running parallel to the ridge. Scouts reported a stone wall concealed by trees, running along a farm lane that crossed along the crest of the second ripple. He adjusted his binoculars and scanned 1,000 yards beyond the dense tree line. The Henry Brinkerhoff stone house and farm stood on the third highest ripple wave – Brinkerhoff's Ridge.

Captain Meyer reined up. "Look, General. A large cavalry force is approaching."

Gregg turned and peered south of the Hanover Road where Meyer was pointing and a cloud of fine white dust was rising. He smiled. His cousin was riding at the head of the cavalry column with Major Avery.

"Thank God, Henry." Gregg's heart hummed. "What a great sight."

Meyer said, "I guess Meade changed his mind about one cavalry brigade guarding his right flank."

"Not a minute too soon." Gregg shuddered with renewed hope. The odds of defending the army's right flank had increased twofold. "Tell Colonel Gregg to post his brigade south of Hanover Road across from Rank's artillery guns. And have Major Avery report to me."

Meyer saluted and galloped down the Low Dutch Road.

Gregg removed a handkerchief and wiped his brow, face, and neck. The sun's broiling flames were scorching his skin. He packed his pipe and lit it. Thank God his troopers were dismounted and resting, and the horses were being fed and watered. They had been in the saddle for four solid days. He yawned; perhaps he could get in a quick nap before the shooting started. He glanced skyward. *God be with you, General Meade, this afternoon. You're facing a furious General Lee who isn't used to a couple Union corps preventing the Confederates from taking the domineering heights east of Gettysburg.*

Major Avery rode up and saluted.

"Henry, don't you know this area?"

"Yes, this is familiar ground to the Tenth New York Cavalry. We spent the winter of 1861–1862 here." He pointed. "We camped on the Wolf farm, about seven hundred yards south of here."

"That's good news. When I met with General Meade at noon, he said that we should expect an order this afternoon to relieve the Ninth Massachusetts Regiment picketing close to Brinkerhoff's Ridge. What can you tell me about this area?"

Avery pointed west along Hanover Road. "See the ridgeline with the trees running along it?"

"Yes. That's where there's a stone wall."

"That's right. It's a natural defense for a jumping-off point to attack Brinkerhoff's Ridge where the enemy pickets are located."

"What's between the stone wall and the Rebels?"

"There is a large woodlot that our skirmishers could use to hide in and then spin out of to advance in the tall wheat and grass to a clump of trees just short of the ridge's crest. The enemy skirmishers are sitting on the crest."

"Henry, have a squadron of Tenth New Yorkers ready to move forward and relieve those Ninth Massachusetts boys."

"We'll be ready, sir."

3:05 p.m.
General David Gregg
Hanover Road and Low Dutch Road Crossroad

Gregg puffed on his pipe. If the fields flowing toward Brinkerhoff's Ridge were a chess board, how would he play his pieces? Opening moves should protect his king and position his pieces to press an attack and take advantage of his opponent's mistakes. He turned and glanced at the Hanover and Low Dutch Roads crossing. The strategic intersection was his king and had to be defended at all costs. He peered at Brinckerhoff Ridge held by the Confederates and looming like a castle in the sky. *Damn.* He was undermanned and missing several chess pieces. The best bet was a more passive, flexible style of play where he could set traps and wait for the enemy to make mistakes.

A courier rode up. "General Gregg. Colonel Guiney's Ninth Massachusetts Infantry Regiment guarding the army's right flank has received orders to return to Fifth Corps. They are to depart as soon as you relieve them."

"Very well. I will order Colonel Gregg to send troopers forward to relieve Colonel Guiney's men."

Crack, crack, crack. Gregg scanned the second ridgeline concealing the stone wall. Bullets sputtered and whined. *Crack, crack, crack.* This was more than skirmishers taking potshots. A clattering roar of hooves echoed from the south. Gregg twisted in his saddle and spotted Irvin and Major Henry Avery galloping toward him.

Irvin and Avery reined up. His cousin said, "General, the rattling fire is increasing. We may be facing a larger force than quarreling skirmishers."

"I agree." The general turned to Avery. "Major, send a Tenth New York squadron to relieve Colonel Guiney's skirmishers and picket the crest of Brinkerhoff's Ridge."

Avery saluted and departed.

General Gregg spurred his horse toward the ridge and halted at the Reever house, just north of the Hanover Road. Captain William Rank, commanding the Light Battery H of the Third Pennsylvania Artillery, rode up and saluted.

"Captain Rank," Gregg said, "to what Horse Artillery unit are you assigned?"

"I'm attached to Captain James Robertson's First Brigade of Horse Artillery, sir."

"I believe that General Hunt, commanding the Artillery Reserve, is using three batteries in Robertson's First Brigade, including yours, as fresh batteries to support the infantry."

"Yes, sir, I believe that to be true. I will learn this for sure when I report to Captain Robertson."

Gregg said, "I need your battery until I can sort out what the enemy is doing west of Brinkerhoff's Ridge. I'm requesting that you stay. I will write a note to General Hunt and Captain Robertson explaining my request."

"I'm standing by to support you, sir. What orders do you have?"

"How many fights has your battery been in?" said Gregg.

"Sir, we stood up on May Sixth as horse artillery, and today would be our first action."

Gregg smiled. "Captain Rank, you're going to get a chance to prove yourself. Unlimber your two artillery pieces on the elevated ground at the Reever house next to the Hanover Road and be prepared for battery fire against the enemy on Brinkerhoff's Ridge."

A grin creased Rank's cheeks. "My cannoneers will be up to the task, General."

"General Gregg," Weir said, "there is a courier galloping up the Low Dutch Road."

Gregg glanced up. A lone rider. He gripped his binoculars and scanned the ridge. Bullets popped and whined over Brinckerhoff Ridge. Gregg glanced toward Rank's artillery sergeants shouting as the limbers, attached caissons, and ordnance rifles rumbled into position. How would these cannoneers perform? A torrent of doubt swept through him. He didn't know Rank, having met him by accident three days ago. Rank was operating as an independent unit enroute to Captain Robertson's First Brigade of Horse Artillery and had nearly been captured by Stuart's column when he joined his cavalry division.

The courier reined up. "General Gregg. General Pleasonton orders you to provide a regiment to cover the army's left flank."

Gregg's brow froze in a scowl. "Wasn't Buford's division covering the left flank?"

"Yes, sir. They were but received orders to withdraw and refit."

"Why didn't Buford wait until he was relieved by another cavalry unit?"

"Sir, I'm not sure."

Gregg shook his head. His face flashed white-hot. "Very well. Inform General Pleasonton I have one brigade defending the army's far right flank. One brigade!" He turned to Captain Weir. "Order Colonel Gregg to send the Fourth Pennsylvania Cavalry Regiment to cover the army's left flank."

Captain Weir saluted and departed.

Artillery guns erupted with a thunderous roar. Gregg turned toward Wolf Hill as gun after gun reported. The bone-shaking explosions smote his ears. *The Confederates must be preparing to launch an infantry attack.*

3:10 p.m.
Major John Kemper
Commanding the Tenth New York Squadron of Companies H and L
Two hundred yards west of the Low Dutch Road

Major Kemper spied two riders approaching. Captain William Peck, commanding H company, and First Lieutenant Marshall Woodruff, commanding L company, reined up and saluted.

"William, Marshall," Kemper said, "we've been ordered to move forward to Brinkerhoff's Ridge and relieve Colonel Guiney's Ninth Massachusetts Regiment, protecting the right flank of the army."

He paused, eyeing both officers. The 42-year-old Peck glared, his nostrils flaring. Woodruff, eight years younger, broke eye contact and looked down. Both officers were plainly displeased with the task.

Kemper said, "The good news is that we've trained in this area, so we know the terrain."

Peck retorted, "The bad news is that my troopers are damn tired. Are we expecting reliefs in a couple of hours?"

"Major Avery said he would relieve us about six this evening." Kemper turned and pointed. "About one thousand yards ahead, next to the Hanover Road, is the W. Howard house. Just beyond the W. Howard house is the second ridgeline, concealing a dirt road and a high stone wall running north toward Cress Ridge. About four hundred yards west of the stone wall is the summit of the third ridge, where the Brinkerhoff house is located. The Rebels are occupying the area around the house."

"Are the Massachusetts skirmishers west of the stone wall?" Waters asked.

"Yes. Some of them are positioned in the trees and the wheat field about one hundred yards west from the second ridge. The enemy skirmishers are positioned on the crest. The rest of the

Massachusetts boys are acting as reserves, positioned east along the wall."

"Are we expecting much action?"

"No," said Kemper. "General Gregg told Major Avery that the Massachusetts boys have been exchanging shots sporadically with the Rebels throughout the morning and afternoon. I'm guessing we will be just throwing lead their way occasionally, like our infantry boys, to let them know we are here."

Popping cracks split the air like the start of a hailstorm.

Peck frowned. "It sounds like they're shooting a bit more regularly now."

"William, Company H will deploy next to the Hanover Road. Marshall, Company L will form up on the right flank of Company H. Both companies will spread out to the north. We will dismount and advance into two lines. We shall depart immediately. I will lead the advance. Any questions?"

Woodruff said, "Do you want the troopers to leave their sabers tethered to their horses?"

"Yes, leave the sabers behind. Have your carbines and pistols ready. Let's dismount and form up."

3:17 p.m.
Major John Kemper
Commanding the Tenth New York squadron of Companies H and L
Advancing westward on foot along the Hanover Road

Major Kemper peered at the dismounted cavalry squad from Companies H and L, formed in a single, 400-yard line, with 50 yards separating the two companies. The 120 troopers stood in tall, dust-covered black boots, spurs, light-blue trousers with yellow piping, dark-blue wool coats, high-crown blue kepi hats adorned with yellow crossed sabers, and holstered pistols. Each trooper stared straight ahead, gripping his carbine. They had left their Old Wristbreakers tethered to their horses.

Kemper spied Major Avery trotting toward the formation. Avery rode up to him and reined up.

"Are you ready, John?"

"Yes, sir." He pointed to his two squadrons. "My troopers are exhausted. I hope you'll relieve us soon."

Avery smiled. "Captain Benjamin Lownsbury will relieve you at six this evening with a squadron consisting of companies E and K." Avery turned and trotted toward the Hanover Road.

Kemper glanced at the squadron. A yawning and lip-biting epidemic had broken out. What a motley-looking bunch of troopers. The biggest challenge to this detail was going to be keeping the squadron awake and alert.

He dismounted, turned toward Brinkerhoff's Ridge, and shouted, "Forward, *March!*" He stepped off, using slow strides. Boot spurs jingled behind him like sleigh bells. The rolling field was a rising moorland dotted with shrubs and grasses clawed at by wind, stretching for a thousand yards uphill before hitting clumps of trees perched on top of the first crest marking Cress Run. The scent of heather filled his nose. Brow sweat stung his eyes. His wool uniform itched, cooking him like a roast in a stove pot in the relentless heat. Captain Peck was right. This was a lousy detail.

At the edge of his vision, Second Lieutenant Ira Allen was approaching. As he glanced in the lieutenant's direction, Allen pointed. "Major Kemper, there are families up ahead lingering along the Hanover Road near the Cress house."

"I see them. Tell Corporal William Potter and Corporal Abram Thompson to dart ahead and tell those families to scatter to someplace a bit safer."

"Yes, sir." Allen departed.

A cracking boom. He peered over Culp's Hill. A bursting thunderclap. Union and Confederate artillery at Gettysburg were taunting each other. A knot grew in his stomach. The two armies had stepped into the ring again and the fight would resume soon. He sprang up the gentle slope, skirted through the trees, traced through Cress Run, meandering through the undergrowth. The emerald creek rippled around speckled rocks. Flies flitted about as he leaped over the creek and strode through the trees. Water splashed behind him. He paused to watch the blue-clad troopers stepping into the water. Pointing, he cautioned, "Captain

Peck, when you cross the stream, halt at the Cress house and straighten out your line."

"Yes, sir."

Kemper yawned. What a miserable detail. The troopers crossed Cress Run, weaved through the clumps of trees, and emerged into an open meadow. Good. Everyone was keeping pace. He trod into the clearing and through an orchard toward the two-story Cress farmhouse. The family was scurrying from the house. The wife and older daughters carried pillows, blankets, and bedsheets. The father lugged heavy bags full of bread and meat. The children carried what they could—hats, bonnets, and shawls; boots and shoes—wrapped in their arms.

Kemper stopped the man. "Are you Mr. Cress? Is this your house?"

"Yes. I'm damn glad to see thousands of boys wearing Union blue." He dropped a couple of bags and pointed. "I'm worried those gray devils west of the ridge will ransack my house. Are you here to protect it?"

"I'll leave a handful of men here to guard your house and fields."

"Thank you, Major."

Kemper turned to Captain Peck. "William, pick ten troopers and a sergeant to stay round the property and act as a ready reserve."

"I'll have Sergeant Bonnell and his men do it."

"Companies H and L, forward march," Kemper shouted. His long skirmish line marched through the Cress orchard. Kemper scanned the rolling meadow beyond the orchard toward the second ridgeline. A field of tall, ripe wheat.

3:20 p.m.
Sergeant B. W. Bonnell, Company H
Cress farm

Bonnell clutched his carbine and stepped up to the farmhouse porch. "Private Jones and Private Smith. Go through the house and make sure there are no enemy sharpshooters lurking about.

Don't disturb anything. I'm going to walk around the outside of the house and survey the farm."

The privates entered the house. Bonnell ambled about the yard, wriggling between several strutting chickens fluffing their feathers and a cranky banty rooster who wasn't pleased Bonnell was there. He peeked into the woodshed. Empty. He strode toward the back of the house while keeping a sharp eye on the rooster. He whiffed a pungent, fishy odor and spotted a tub of water reeking like ammonia. He sauntered over and smiled.

He shouted. "Hey, boys, look what I found."

The two privates peeked out an open window. "Be right there, Sergeant." They flung themselves out of the house and stared into the tub. It was filled with several twelve-inch Boston mackerel. Private Jones shrilled a sharp whistle.

Bonnell said, "We will take some of these mackerel, but leave the chickens and the rooster."

Private Smith beamed. "Thank God. I'm starved."

Bonnell grinned as the privates scooped up the fish. His mouth watered. Those would taste great fried up. He gazed west. Kemper's line lumbered steadily toward the second ridgeline.

3:30 p.m.
Major John Kemper
Commanding the Tenth New York Squadron of Companies H and L
Advancing westward on foot toward the stone wall

Kemper panted as he trekked up the long, elevated rise through the tall wheat. His weary muscles ached as if his body had been skewered with a roasting spit and he was slowly rotating over a hot fire. God, he needed a few hours sleep—and a good meal. And so did his squadron. A couple hundred yards ahead, the W. Howard house anchored a grove of trees stretching north. The tree-lined ridge blocked his view of the ground on the far side. The thick trees rose skyward, their sun-dappled leaves creating a canopy of green clouds shading the afternoon sun. Beneath nature's leafy awning, the stone wall ran northward. He aimed toward a large hickory standing tall in the middle of the timber line.

The booming roar of hundreds of cannons erupted beyond Wolf Hill from the Union army's right flank. A few moments passed and artillery batteries from Culp's Hill poured out their thunder and iron. Shells hissed and crisscrossed over the tree line. The artillery's booming belted his body. He licked his lips and picked up the pace.

Skirmish fire rattled ahead. He turned to Second Lieutenant Ira Allen. "Ira, tell Captain Peck and Captain Waters to stay alert when we hit the tree line. It sounds like the skirmish fire is near the stone wall. If the enemy controls the stone wall, they will dominate Brinkerhoff's Ridge."

Allen saluted and scooted to the right where Woodruff was leading Company H. As Kemper approached the grove of trees, the booming din of cannon fire grew louder. Kemper's chest tightened. Would the Ninth Massachusetts wait for his New Yorkers to arrive before they rushed off to the infantry fight?

He turned, shouting, "Pick up the pace."

Angry voices grumbled behind him.

3:32 p.m.
General David Gregg
Hanover Road and Low Dutch Road Crossroad

Uneasiness crept into the tips of Gregg's fingers. Standing at the strategic intersection, his right flank was vulnerable. His forces were facing west toward Brinkerhoff's Ridge, occupied by Rebel infantry. He turned northward and scanned Cress Ridge. There was something ominous about this heavily forested brow, and it gnawed at him. Jeb Stuart's cavalry force could be lurking along the Ridge and threatening his exposed right flank. His scouts had not reported Rebels on Cress Ridge. But they could appear at any time. Uncertainty taunted him. His right flank was vulnerable, and he didn't have enough troops to protect it.

A messenger reined up. "General Gregg, General Pleasonton sends his respects and wishes to inform you that that General Sedgwick's Sixth Infantry Corps has arrived. Sixth Corps forced-marched all night from Manchester to Gettysburg, covering nearly 30 miles. Sixth Corps is acting as a reserve force for General Meade's fishhook defensive line."

"Very well." Gregg paused, stroking his beard. "What are General Meade's plans?"

"General Meade's plans are to stay on the defense today. He is waiting for the enemy to attack, which he believes will occur within the hour."

Gregg pointed. "That's Major Kemper's squadron darting forward toward the second ridgeline. Inform General Pleasonton that I plan to occupy and hold Brinkerhoff's Ridge until further notice."

The messenger departed.

McIntosh reined up.

"General Gregg, my regiments are deployed north of the Hanover Road. The Third Pennsylvania are closest to Little Run. The First New Jersey are closest to Low Dutch Road."

"Good." Gregg studied his First Brigade commander. "John, you're sure looking a lot better than you did early this morning. How are you feeling?"

"A lot better, sir. I appreciate you holding up the column for me for a bit. I caught my second wind."

Gregg continued, "We're positioned on a critical piece of real estate, especially where Low Dutch Road intersects Hanover Road."

"I agree, sir." McIntosh pointed westward, where Cress Ridge was covered by closely ranked, stocky trees. "The Cress house is standing in a shallow valley."

Gregg shook his head. An icy dread coursed his veins. "It's a natural spillway running south from the Cress Ridge. If the enemy launched a surprise cavalry attack down the dale, it would be like a dam burst. The Rebel floodwaters would surge through the hollow, breaching the Baltimore Pike and swamping the back of the Union's fishhook defense."

"I hope General Meade and General Pleasonton appreciate the importance of this strategic spot on the army's right flank," McIntosh said.

Gregg nodded. "I wish we had Colonel Huey's brigade of fourteen hundred. We need more troopers if we are to defend the army's right flank."

3:34 p.m.
Major John Kemper
Crest of Brinkerhoff's Ridge

Kemper skirted past the large hickory tree marking the middle of the timber line. His throat tightened. He gripped his pistol and peered through the far edge of the tree line. Sunrays glinted off metallic surfaces. Gun barrels. Graybacks or bluebacks? He crouched, picked his way up the embankment, and paused. Several blue-uniformed soldiers stood behind a chest-high stone wall, pointing their rifles toward the crest of Brinkerhoff's Ridge. A field of tall wheat just ripe for cutting flowed beyond the stone rampart.

"I'm Major Kemper," he shouted. "Where is Colonel Guiney?"

A second lieutenant whirled around, gaped, and pointed his pistol. "Halt." Several soldiers along the stone wall twisted around and aimed their rifles.

Kemper gulped in a lungful of air. His heart pounded in his ears. "Lieutenant! Tell your soldiers to lower their weapons. My men are here to relieve your regiment."

Captain Peck and several of his blue troopers bolted forward, pointing their carbines. Peck took a step toward the young officer. "Lieutenant," he shouted, "do as Major Kemper said and lower your rifles."

The lieutenant nodded and dropped his pistol. "Lower your rifles, men. These cavalry boys are here to relieve us."

Kemper's pounding heart stilled, and the blood pulsing in his ears dampened. A colonel snaked toward them, his face fiery red.

"I'm Colonel Guiney, commanding the Ninth Irish Massachusetts from the Fifth Infantry Corps," he declared in a thick brogue.

Kemper saluted. "I'm Major Kemper from the Tenth New York Cavalry Regiment. My squadron is here to relieve your skirmish line."

"Damn delighted to be relieved. I'm tired of my Irish boys protecting an idle cavalry large enough, and assuredly brave enough, to take care of your own front."

Kemper nodded.

Guiney scanned up and down Kemper's line of troopers. "Are these hundred or so cavalry troopers all you brought to relieve us?"

"Yes, I'm in command of two cavalry companies."

Guiney shook his head. "My Irish Ninth numbers four hundred seventy officers and men. I've been fretful all afternoon having the lone Union regiment on Brinkerhoff's Ridge with both flanks unconnected and exposed."

Kemper turned and pointed. "About a thousand yards eastward sits General Gregg's cavalry division. If we run into any problems, reinforcements are close by."

Guiney shook his head. "Very well." The colonel pointed westward. "That's the Henry Brinkerhoff farmhouse about two hundred fifty yards away. I have several companies up near the farm, exchanging shots with the Rebels. I will recall them, and you need to replace them, so the enemy won't rumble down the ridge and occupy this stone wall."

"I understand."

"You're not facing dismounted cavalry, Major. Those Rebels sitting up there are from Stonewall's old brigade. Brigadier General James Walker is commanding the brigade. They are part of General Ewell's corps. That's one of Lee's toughest infantry brigades."

"Is Walker's entire brigade sitting on Brinkerhoff's Ridge?"

"No, his brigade is spread out from Power's Hill to Brinkerhoff's Ridge."

"How aggressive are the enemy skirmishers?"

"The Rebel skirmishers have been content to lay on their backs, and occasionally roll over to their stomachs and shoot and then roll back onto their backs."

"Well, it seems my squadron can handle that sort of skirmishing."

"My guess is that after we depart, and the Rebel infantry boys see they are facing blue-trousered troopers with yellow pin stripes, they may become a bit feistier."

Kemper grimaced. "I'm ready to relieve you, Colonel."

"I stand relieved, Major. Good luck." To his Irish boys, Guiney shouted, "We're moving back to Fifth Corps."

The colonel turned to his aides. "Tell the forward skirmishers to fall back. We are moving out."

Kemper turned to Captain Peck and First Lieutenant Woodruff. "William. Marshall. Move your companies forward and replace the Ninth Irish skirmishers."

Woodruff pointed. "Major, I'm sure the Rebel infantry sitting up near the Brinkerhoff's Ridge spotted two blue infantry units being replaced by a squadron of dismounted cavalry. How long before they press us to see how strong we are?"

"I expect they'll be in our knickers before too long."

Kemper turned and leaped over the stone wall. Grunts and groans echoed from behind as the troopers leaped the stone wall. He stepped toward the Massachusetts soldiers falling back.

The Irish colonel shouted, "Good luck, cavalry boys!"

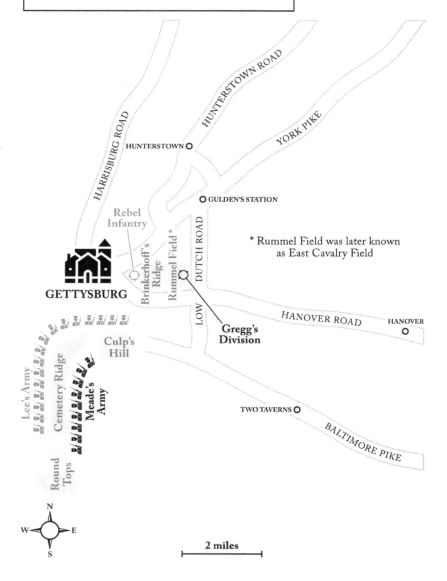

Gregg's Division Occupying Rummel Field
July 2, 1863
4:00 p.m.

HUNTERSTOWN ROAD

HARRISBURG ROAD

YORK PIKE

HUNTERSTOWN

GULDEN'S STATION

Rebel Infantry

Brinkerhoff's Ridge

Rummel Field *

DUTCH ROAD

* Rummel Field was later known as East Cavalry Field

GETTYSBURG

LOW

HANOVER ROAD

HANOVER

Gregg's Division

Lee's Army

Cemetery Ridge

Culp's Hill

Meade's Army

TWO TAVERNS

BALTIMORE PIKE

Round Tops

N
W · E
S

2 miles

31

Sixth Michigan — Thursday, July 2

3:30 p.m. (Four minutes earlier)
Second Lieutenant Charles Storrs
Intersection of the York Pike and Hunterstown Road

Storrs chewed on a long piece of straw grass, standing behind a clump of trees on the west side of the York Pike. He trained his binoculars thirty yards ahead on the intersection of the York and Hunterstown Roads. Most of his detachment of troopers were spread out and hiding at the intersection in a thicket of packed trees and large bushes. He eyed a sprawling dust cloud trundling down Hunterstown Road.

Storrs cocked his head toward Sergeant John Molloy. "John, my guess is a Rebel-size brigade is causing that swirling dust cloud."

Molloy peered up the Hunterstown Road. "It looks like the approaching dust storm is halting."

"You're right." Emerging from the dust cloud was a lone rider trotting on a beautiful black horse. "That sort of looks like Jeb Stuart riding toward us. The rider has a cavalier uniform. Here, take a look." He handed the binoculars to the sergeant.

"You're right, the rider is an officer sporting the Stuart cavalier getup. He's not wearing a red-lined gray cape, yellow sash, and a hat with an ostrich plume like Jeb Stuart would. But he does have a thick black beard and hair like Stuart."

Storr's throat caught, and his heart raced. "Then it must be General Wade Hampton and he is riding at the front of his brigade." Storrs gripped his binoculars. "Hampton just pulled off to the side of the road and stopped. He is drinking from his canteen."

The sergeant said, "Where are his guards?"

A rifle cracked and a bullet whined overhead. Hampton ducked, spurred his mount toward the thicket, and stopped about one hundred yards away.

"One of our boys standing on a tree stump took a shot at Hampton," Storrs said.

"Looks like he missed."

The air cracked twice as if two bull whips had snapped. Storrs squinted. "Hampton fired his pistol, and our trooper fired his carbine. They both missed. The private is holding up his hand. His weapon misfired. I'm charging."

He unsheathed his saber and spurred his horse into a flying gallop toward Hampton's back. His ears pounded in time with his heartbeats. Hampton paused, eyeing the private clearing his weapon. The private raised his rifle and they both fired again. Hampton clutched the side of his neck. Storrs's mount surged, his hooves pounding the ground. It appeared the general had been grazed. Hampton waited until the private reloaded.

God Almighty. Hampton is treating this like a gentleman's duel.

Storrs's eyes locked on the Rebel. *The general doesn't see me coming.* His heart pounded in his ears. Twenty yards to go. Hampton and the private fired. The private yelped and grabbed his wrist, scurrying into the thicket.

Storrs's jaw tightened. He raised his saber and sliced downward, aiming for Hampton's hat. He thrust downward as if splitting wood. A cracking thud and scream as the saber sliced into Hampton's hat and thick hair. His saber vibrated, stinging his hand like a batter hitting a pitch on the bat handle. Blood poured down Hampton's face.

Hampton turned his horse and aimed his revolver. *Click.* The gun misfired. Storrs's breath was ripped from his lungs. "You yellowbelly scoundrel," Hampton shouted.

Storrs hunched over his saddle and spurred his horse toward the thicket. His jaw muscles flinched. Hoofbeats pounded behind him. *Click.* Hampton's gun misfired again. Storrs raced past the tree stump and angled for a cluster of trees. He glanced over his shoulder. Hampton was not following. *Forget counterattacking. Must inform Custer.* He turned forward. *Slap!* A willow branch whipped across his cheek. A sharp pain like a razor cut stabbed his cheek and a warm wetness trickled down his face. *Keep galloping.* He thrashed through the thicket and spotted Sergeant John Molloy and the rest of the troopers sitting on the York Pike. Five troopers were dismounted and aiming their carbines.

"It's me," he shouted. "Don't shoot!" Panting, he pulled up next to Molloy.

"That's quite a slash across your face," Molloy said. "Is it a saber cut?"

"No," he gasped. "A tree branch got the worst of me."

"What happened between you and Hampton?"

"I saber-slashed his head and wounded him. He turned and fired his revolver and it misfired twice. I wasn't waiting around to see if it misfired a third time."

"Well, we know that Hampton's brigade is marching down Hunterstown Road and he probably still has a rear guard in the Hunterstown hamlet."

"Agreed." Storrs turned to the dismounted troopers. "Let's mount up and ride back to Custer."

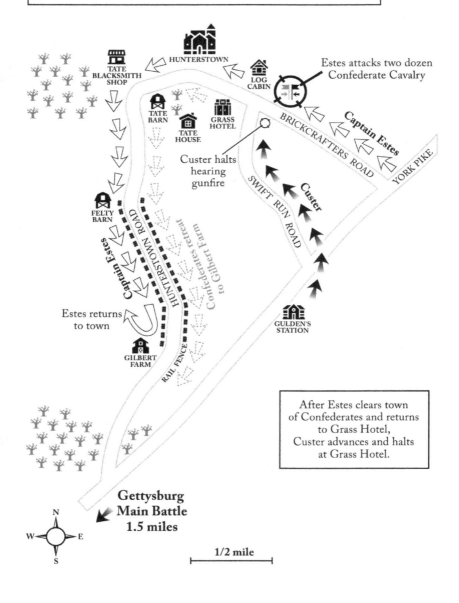

**Captain Estes Arriving First at Hunterstown, 4:05 p.m.
Custer Arrives and Halts at Edge of Town, 4:08 p.m.
July 2, 1863**

HUNTERSTOWN

TATE
BLACKSMITH
SHOP

LOG
CABIN

Estes attacks two dozen
Confederate Cavalry

TATE
BARN

GRASS
HOTEL

TATE
HOUSE

BRICKCRAFTERS ROAD

Captain Estes

YORK PIKE

Custer halts
hearing
gunfire

FELTY
BARN

SWIFT RUN ROAD

Custer

Captain Estes

HUNTERSTOWN ROAD

Confederates retreat
to Gilbert Farm

RAIL FENCE

Estes returns
to town

GULDEN'S
STATION

GILBERT
FARM

After Estes clears town
of Confederates and returns
to Grass Hotel,
Custer advances and halts
at Grass Hotel.

**Gettysburg
Main Battle
1.5 miles**

N
W E
S

1/2 mile

32

Kilpatrick — Thursday, July 2

4:00 p.m.
Kilpatrick
Gulden's Station

Kilpatrick gritted his teeth as he galloped north on the Low Dutch Road. He hadn't pissed all morning and his bladder was bursting at the seams. Booming artillery guns rumbled and poured out their muddled thunder. He glanced at the clustering white clouds, four miles to the west, raining fiery iron over the Gettysburg battlefield. A demonic hollowness wormed its way through his core. *Bugger the Devil.* He was missing the great battle.

His cavalcade crossed the York Pike and halted at Gulden's Station. Custer and Farnsworth were waiting.

"Gentlemen, I met with General Gregg. At 1:40 p.m. and 2:10 p.m. the Union signal station on top of Little Round Top spotted ten thousand confederate infantrymen marching northward.[9] Meade believes the Rebel force will advance to the Union's right flank on Culp's Hill. Our new orders are to screen the right flank of the army in a northerly direction from the York Pike. Gregg will screen the army in an easterly direction along Hanover Road."

"Does Meade believe the Confederates' main attack will be against our right flank?" Farnsworth said.

Kilpatrick grimaced. "Yes." He sipped from his canteen. "Have our scouting patrols and advance patrols spotted the enemy?"

---

9 The Union soldiers called Big Round Top and Little Round Top by other names during the battle. I used their common names we call them today for ease of telling the story for the reader.

Farnsworth shook his head. Custer said, "I sent Major Storrs to the intersection of York Pike and Hunterstown Road but have not heard back from him."

"Dispatch your aides and recall all advance patrols and pickets thrown out to the west along the Gettysburg-York Pike." He turned to Custer. "George, proceed northeast with your brigade up the York Pike and then turn north onto the Swift Run Road and ride to Hunterstown. Your mission is to see if that large Rebel infantry force marched to Hunterstown and then turned south on the Hunterstown road that leads into Culp's Hill and the Union right flank."

"Yes sir. My brigade will move out immediately."

Kilpatrick nodded. "Somewhere out there ten thousand Rebel infantry are roaming about. Let's find them and make sure they don't threaten Meade's right flank."

4:05 p.m.
Captain Llewellyn Estes
Leading Company A, Eighteenth Pennsylvania
Brickcrafters Road
Approaching the outskirts of Hunterstown from the southeast

Estes grinned. God, he loved independent missions. Hopefully, his small patrol would catch the Rebels dillydallying at Hunterstown and put a real twist on them. He rode northwest along the dirt road at the head of the fifty-man column from Troop A, Eighteenth Pennsylvania Cavalry. A pack of cloud fluffs sailed overhead, blocking the brutal sun. Ahead, greyish dust clouds billowed up to the west.

He turned to Sergeant Joseph Cooke, who was riding next to him. "What do you make of those dust clouds?"

"Several hundred infantry or cavalry troopers are kicking up dust."

"I agree." He squinted. "How far to Hunterstown?"

"About a quarter-mile."

Estes unsnapped his holster flap. Kilpatrick was smart in assigning troopers from the Keystone State. Some of these men should know the area.

"Sergeant, what do you know about Hunterstown?"

"It's a little town made up of mainly farmers and wagonmakers," said Cooke. "It has plenty of watering holes for horses. It's located on the intersections of Brickcrafters Road, Swift Run Road, and Hunterstown Road, which is one of the main arteries the Confederates must control if they want to hold Gettysburg."

"It seems like the dust swirls are moving down the Hunterstown Road toward Gettysburg."

Several sharp, thunderous cracks reverberated as if heralding a storm. Estes cocked his head toward Gettysburg. "That sounds like artillery fire, Sergeant."

"I bet it's the opening salvos of a big infantry fight."

"You might be right." Estes held up his hand and the column of horses slowed to a walk on the southern edge of Hunterstown. He pointed to a log house up ahead to the right.

"Whose house is that?"

"The McCreary house."

A shot shrilled overhead. Estes's heart froze. *Rebels.*

"Draw...*sabers!*" Estes shouted. He drew his saber and pointed the blade toward the town square. A lethal silence reigned, even as sabers rattled. He drew a deep breath.

"*Charge!*"

Estes spurred his horse. He bolted down the street, waving his saber. A muggy wind fluttered across his face. A chorus of yells followed him. *You're not alone. They're following you.*

"Rebels ahead," shouted Cooke.

Estes gripped his pistol and fired at the skedaddling enemy. A grayback plunged off his horse. They had caught the Rebels off guard. His chest heaved. "Come on boys, they're running."

Company A troopers pulled up, firing. Ahead, in the town square, the enemy halted and reformed. A Rebel officer pointed his sword and yelled, "*Charge!*"

Estes aimed for a Rebel outpacing his commander. His heart pounded. He closed at full speed and leaned to his right, extending his saber and slashing upward, slicing the razor-sharp blade through the Rebel's throat. Blood spurted like a hot spring. Estes sat upright, scanned the enemy, and located his next target.

A bullet whizzed past his cheek and thudded. He glanced to his left. Cooke shrieked and grabbed the side of his head as he tumbled to the ground. Estes's throat choked with rage.

He whirled on a Rebel and thrust his saber into the enemy's gut. The Rebel grunted and cast his pitiful eyes heavenward while slithering downward, dead. Estes breathed through his open mouth, his breath stinging his lungs. He swept forward, leading the storm surge. High, yelping cries filled the air. Dead and wounded Rebels littered the streets.

Estes's Pennsylvanians chased the enemy through the town square and a few hundred yards up Brickcrafters Road. At the intersection of Hunterstown Road, the Rebel colonel turned, leading his surviving troopers over a ridge covered with thick trees, racing down a long, narrow dirt road lined with fences.

Estes followed, chasing and firing at the retreating enemy. Seven hundred yards ahead, he saw the Rebels rounding a curving right bend in the road. He raised his hand and halted. His 49 troopers reined up behind him. Beyond the bend was a large, tree-covered ridge.

"Corporal, I'm not sure what the enemy strength is beyond the bend. I don't want to ride into a trap. The horses are winded, so let's move the detachment back into the center of Hunterstown."

Estes turned his patrol and rode back up Hunterstown Road and halted in the town square. Five blue troopers trotted around several townsfolk circled around a blue-clad soldier lying on the ground.

A sergeant from the cavalcade reined up and saluted. "Captain Estes, I'm First Sergeant Thomas Edie. We are the lead element from General Custer's Sixth Michigan Regiment. General Custer is riding at the head of the Sixth Michigan with Colonel Gray and should arrive in a few minutes."

"Is the surgeon riding with your regiment?"

"Yes," the sergeant said. "Assistant Surgeon David Spaulding is riding with the Sixth."

"That's good," said Estes. "Sergeant Cooke was shot in the head during a skirmish. Cooke was my detachment's only casualty."

Estes rode up to the group of civilians in the road and dismounted. He bent down next to Cooke. A bloody bandage wrapped his head. Cooke opened his eyes. "The damn Rebels shot me, and the bullet is lodged in the side of my head. The townsfolk are saying if I can talk, I should live."

"Hang on, Sergeant. The Sixth Michigan regimental surgeon will be here soon. In the meantime, we must get you off the street before Custer's brigade arrives."

An elderly man approached. "I'm Abraham King. That's my empty store. Let's move the sergeant there for safekeeping where the surgeon can treat him."

"Thank you, Mr. King. Please take good care of my sergeant." Estes turned to Cooke. "Joseph, the townsfolks are going to take good care of you. I have to inform General Custer that we have located the enemy."

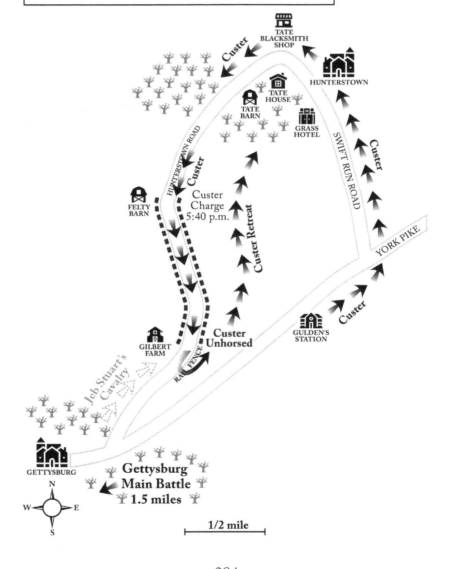

Custer's Charge from Felty Barn to Gilbert Farm
Battle of Hunterstown
July 2, 1863
5:40 p.m.

TATE BLACKSMITH SHOP

Custer

HUNTERSTOWN

TATE HOUSE

TATE BARN

GRASS HOTEL

SWIFT RUN ROAD

Custer

HUNTERSTOWN ROAD

Custer

Custer Charge 5:40 p.m.

Custer Retreat

FELTY BARN

YORK PIKE

Custer Unhorsed

RAIL FENCE

GILBERT FARM

GULDEN'S STATION

Custer

Jeb Stuart's Cavalry

GETTYSBURG

Gettysburg Main Battle 1.5 miles

N
W · E
S

1/2 mile

33

Custer — Thursday, July 2

The oppressive heat clung on as Custer galloped at the head of the Sixth Michigan. A feverish spirit tugged at his ambitious heartstrings. God, what a glorious feeling, commanding an entire brigade. Hopefully a battle would erupt and end with a magnificent victory—and a stepping stone to greatness.

Popping rifle and pistol shots cracked from Hunterstown. *Good. Estes must have found the enemy.* One-half mile ahead, he spotted the outline of the buildings in the Hunterstown square. He glanced at a log house up ahead to the right about one hundred yards. Shots rang out in the town square. He halted on the elevated ground and turned to Colerick. "William, have the regimental commanders and Captain Pennington report."

Custer stood up in his stirrups and peered with his binoculars toward the sputtering fire. No enemy. He scanned southward toward the Hunterstown Road leading to Gettysburg, billowing with rising dust clouds. Perhaps those were Rebel dust clouds.

The regimental commanders and Pennington arrived. Pointing to each location, Custer said, "Colonel Gray and Colonel Mann, I want you to deploy dismounted skirmishers in these elevated fields around these two farms. Captain Pennington, I want you to deploy your battery on the elevated ground in front of that log cabin farmhouse. Colonel Alger and Colonel Town, I want your regiments to stay mounted, acting as a reserve. Colonel Town, I want a squadron of your First Michigan to detach and cover the road into town from the east."

"I will task Captain Duggan for the rear-guard mission," Colonel Town said.

"Very well. Stay alert, gentlemen. This area appears to be infested with Rebels."

Peering at five mounted Union troopers on the side of the road in front of the log house, Custer reined up. Captain Henry Thompson, Commander of Troop A, pulled up next to him.

"General Custer, that's First Sergeant Thomas Edie, who led the advance patrol."

Edie saluted. "General Custer. We arrived at the tail end of a scrap between Captain Estes and his Pennsylvanians from Farnsworth's brigade and a Rebel patrol."

"I heard a spattering of gunfire as we approached Hunterstown." Custer wiped his face. "Is Captain Estes here?"

"Yes. His patrol's horses are spent, and he is waiting for you at the Grass Hotel in the center of the town. It's a two-story brick hotel on the southwest side of the town square. I talked with him briefly."

"What's the situation?"

"Estes said his fifty-man patrol arrived here at this log house and spotted about forty enemy troopers about one hundred yards ahead. Estes charged and pushed the enemy back into the town square. The enemy regrouped and countercharged. Estes's troopers held, and the enemy skedaddled down the Hunterstown road toward Gettysburg. Estes pursued until he came to a bend in the road and was unable to determine how large the enemy force was. So he pulled back into town and that's where we met him."

"Are the Rebels still holding the Hunterstown Road?"

"Yes, they reformed just around the bend where the Gilbert house is located."

"Are the enemy cavalry screening for several thousand Rebel infantry, or is it all enemy cavalry that Estes faced?"

"Estes did not report seeing any enemy infantry and we didn't see any, either. But that doesn't mean that there isn't enemy infantry moving south down the Hunterstown road."

4:27 p.m.
Custer
Arriving at the Grass Hotel, Center of Hunterstown

Custer pointed. "Colonel Gray. That's the Grass Hotel, and I see Captain Estes. Halt your regiment while I speak with Llewellyn."

"Yes, General." Gray raised his hand and shouted, "Halt!"

Custer reined up to Kilpatrick's acting assistant adjutant general. Grinning, he said, "Llewellyn, looks like you had an adventurous scrap. What happened?"

Estes saluted. "My patrol sprinted northwest toward Hunterstown on Brickcrafters Road. I spotted the Rebels' rear guard lollygagging on the outskirts of the town. I immediately charged and caught them with their pants down. They turned and skedaddled back into Hunterstown and reformed here at the Grass Hotel. I halted the patrol and reformed our lines for a charge. The Rebels shot forward and I charged them."

Custer's heart thumped. "My God, Llewellyn. I wish I had been with you for the charge."

Estes grinned. "It was a thing of beauty, General. We closed and used our sabers. We had us a good little scrap for a couple minutes and then the Rebels bolted back and skedaddled over Tate Ridge. I chased them over Tate Ridge onto a narrow fenced-in road until they rounded a blind bend at the Gilbert house. I didn't know how many Rebels were waiting around the bend. I didn't want to overextend myself or fall into a trap, so I returned to the Grass Hotel."

"How many Rebels were you fighting in the town?"

"About forty or so." Estes wiped his face. "I believe they were the rear guard of a Rebel brigade."

"A brigade?" Warmth filled his chest. "Lovely, that's just lovely. Maybe my Wolverines will get a chance to tangle with a Rebel brigade. I'm going to ride over the Tate Ridge to the Felty Barn and scout the area. Hopefully, General Kilpatrick will have arrived by then."

"Yes, sir. I'm going to wait here at the Grass Hotel for General Kilpatrick and tell him your plans. I'm also going to recommend that General Kilpatrick set up his headquarters at the Grass Hotel."

4:38 p.m.
Custer
At the Tate Ridgeline

Custer twinkled with a bubbling spirit. A glorious opportunity was at hand. He couldn't go back empty-handed without a cavalry charge. The Gettysburg battle could end this afternoon, one way or another. *Please, God, urge the Rebel cavalry to stay and fight. Leave the rest to me.* His dash, surprise, and swiftness would carry the day, enabling him to earn his preening rights as the Union's youngest general. He trotted next to First Sergeant Thomas Edie through Hunterstown.

Edie pointed to house on the left. "That's the Tate house. When we pass it, we are going to veer left onto the road that runs between his barn and blacksmith shop."

Custer peered at the small, square barn and the even smaller blacksmith shop. The dirt road angled between the barn and shop and then curved up to the left for a hundred yards to a tree-lined ridge. Custer and Edie turned onto the Tate Road, cutting between the barn and blacksmith shop. A four-rail fence lined the right side of the road and enclosed the blacksmith shop and an acre of corn. At the top of the ridge, the Tate cutoff road intersected Hunterstown Road.

Custer halted on top of the Tate ridgeline. He twisted in his saddle and gestured to Lieutenant Colerick. "William, post a reserve unit on Tate's Road. If the enemy breaks through on the Hunterstown Road, we can hold them here with a small rear guard."

"Yes sir," Colerick replied.

Custer gazed down the Hunterstown road leading to Gettysburg. One and half miles ahead, the road cut a gap through a ridgeline covered with trees on either side of the road.

Private Churchill pulled up. "General Custer, you need to be cautious moving forward. Those trees on the ridgeline are perfect cover for enemy sharpshooters."

"My guess is that the enemy scampered through this gap and hightailed it back a few miles. Let's see what's on the side of the gap."

Custer clapped his spurs and trotted forward, scouring the open fields. He reached down and unsnapped his holster flap. He picked up the pace. Hot blood pulsed through his veins with increased speed. *Careful. Norvell could be right about the sharp-shooters. Don't want to give the enemy an easy shot.* He emerged through the gap and tree line and halted on the low ridgeline.

Colonel Gray rode up. "I ordered the lead company commanders to clear the wood line behind us. I'm not expecting to find many of the enemy, but I want to make sure."

"Good." Custer scanned the terrain. All the trees had been cut down between a large two-story brick house and a huge barn on the right side of the road and another brick house about a half mile down on the same side. The cleared area was filled with tall wheat and corn, swaying in the slender breeze.

Custer turned to Gray. "The corn and wheat fields present a perfect field of fire for both rifles and artillery."

Gray uttered a sigh. "For both us and the enemy."

Norvell pointed. "General, there's a small group of enemy troopers who just rode around the bend on the right."

He lifted his glasses.

"See, about three hundred yards."

"I see them." The Rebels were loitering about, relaxed and unconcerned as if it was a Sunday picnic. Impatience nagged him. "They are not caged by any fear. That can change." He studied the narrow, rolling road. It was fenced in on both sides. He shook his head. There was room for just four horses abreast.

The clapping sound of several horses' hooves approached. He twisted in his saddle. His three other regimental commanders and Captain Pennington pulled up.

"Gentlemen," Custer said. "Sergeant Edie from the Sixth Michigan scout patrol said Captain Estes pushed the enemy down past the Felty house and barn up ahead." He pointed to the closest brick house. "We can't see it now, but if we rode up past the Felty house we could see the Gilbert house nearly a half mile ahead. That's where we believe the enemy have reformed."

"What're your intentions, sir?" Colonel Gray asked.

"I want the Seventh Michigan to deploy on the left side of the road. Behind them, the First Michigan will deploy." He pointed again. "I want the Sixth Michigan to deploy on the right side of the road and the Fifth Michigan to deploy behind them."

"Where do you want my battery to deploy?" Pennington asked.

"Alexander, I want you to deploy your battery on the right flank of the Sixth Michigan."

Custer paused and scanned the road with his binoculars. A headquarters aide arrived.

"General Custer. General Kilpatrick has established his head-quarters at the Jacob Grass Hotel. He requested your presence, sir."

"Very well." Custer turned to his commanders. "Let's deploy. I will tell you my plans after I meet with General Kilpatrick."

5:05 p.m.
Custer
Grass Hotel, Kilpatrick's Headquarters

Climbing the hotel steps, Custer fidgeted. What if Kilpatrick wouldn't let him attack? He strode into the hotel and found Kilpatrick talking with Captain Estes.

"The pickets and advance patrols are reporting that the woods about a mile south of town along the Hunterstown Road are swarming with Rebels," Llewellyn was saying.

Kilpatrick turned to Custer. "What do your scouts say?"

"The same. I spotted the Rebels forming up along a curve in the road near the Gilbert farm."

Kilpatrick pointed to the map table. "Hunterstown is five miles northeast of Gettysburg. General Gregg said that Meade is unsure where Jeb's cavalry is located."

"Maybe we've located Stuart's rear guard." Custer's mind was awhirl with attack plans. His finger traced the routes the Rebel cavalry would take from Carlisle to Gettysburg. "If we have located Jeb's boys, perhaps we can put a twist on them and attack them."

"Perhaps." Kilpatrick nodded. "Gregg also said that Meade's army is formed in a fishhook from Culp's Hill over to Cemetery Hill and the shaft of the fishhook runs along Cemetery Ridge. Sickles's Third Corps anchors the left, located on Little Round Top. General Sedgwick's large Sixth Corps arrived about an hour ago at Gettysburg after a forced march of thirty miles from Manchester."

"The artillery cannonading sounds like a prelude to Lee attacking. Where does Meade think Lee will attack?"

Kilpatrick pointed to the map. "General Ewell's Third Corps is across from Culp's Hill, and Meade believes that's where Lee will attack. Lee loves attacking the Union's right flank just like he did at Chancellorsville."

Booming thunder rocked the ground as flocks of shells crisscrossed Gettysburg, whistling and crashing. The hotel swayed; Custer gripped the table. It felt like an endless earthquake.

Custer shook his head. "How many artillery pieces does Lee have supporting an infantry assault?"

"Meade's head of intelligence, Colonel Sharpe, estimates Lee has 135 artillery pieces. Meade has 150 artillery pieces." Kilpatrick pointed to the map again. "George, here is the Felty farm. I want you to move a portion of your brigade down the Hunterstown Road and attack the enemy. Let's find out what the Rebels are up to."

Custer's teeth flashed a savage grin as a fierce and lethal animal instinct took hold. "I won't let you down, General Kilpatrick." He snapped a salute and rushed outside. A rip-roaring tingle pulsed through him. He craved this thrill. It surpassed even the daring excitement of riding in a spotting balloon, drifting over enemy lines during the Battle of Williamsburg.

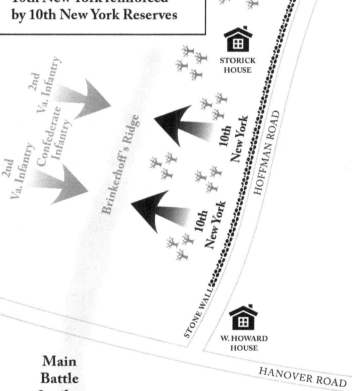

OPENING PHASE:
10th New York dismounted cavalry advance west beyond stone wall.

2nd Virginia infantry advance east to halt New York advance.

MIDDLE PHASE:
10th New York reinforced by 10th New York Reserves

STORICK HOUSE

2nd Va. Infantry

2nd Va. Infantry

Confederate Infantry

2nd Va. Infantry

Brinkerhoff's Ridge

10th New York

10th New York

HOFFMAN ROAD

STONE WALL

3rd Pa.

3rd Pa. Sits in Reserve

3rd Pa.

Cress Run Creek

W. HOWARD HOUSE

CRESS HOUSE

HANOVER ROAD

Main Battle 2 miles

N
W E
S

1/4 mile

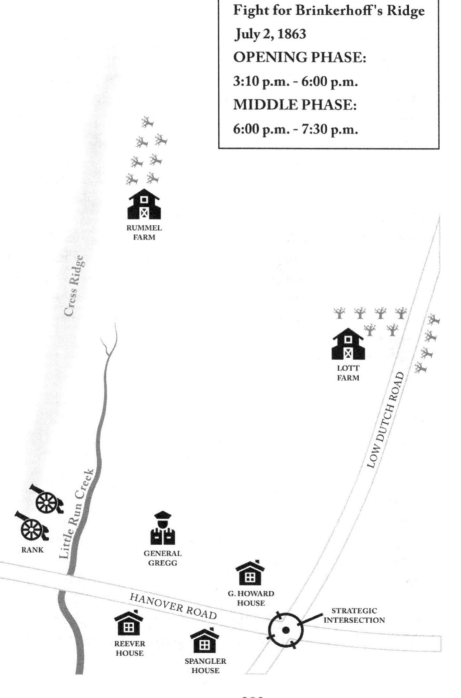

Fight for Brinkerhoff's Ridge
July 2, 1863
OPENING PHASE:
3:10 p.m. - 6:00 p.m.
MIDDLE PHASE:
6:00 p.m. - 7:30 p.m.

RUMMEL
FARM

Cress Ridge

LOTT
FARM

Little Run Creek

LOW DUTCH ROAD

RANK

GENERAL
GREGG

G. HOWARD
HOUSE

STRATEGIC
INTERSECTION

HANOVER ROAD

REEVER
HOUSE

SPANGLER
HOUSE

Astride his big, black gelding, Custer whisked toward his Wolverines, leather saddle squealing, bridle chains jingling, horse hooves scuffing. The familiar scent of wildness tweaked his nose. He pulled hard on Harry's reins and slid to a stop in front of Colonel Gray.

"Colonel Gray, General Kilpatrick has ordered me to attack the enemy south of us, along the road near the Gilbert house. Because the road is narrow and lined with fences, I'm going to order Troop A to conduct a mounted charge."

Gray glared. For a moment's pause, Gray's mouth twitched as if his mind was debating whether to disobey the order. He would give Gray a few more seconds before firing him. Gray was first to break the long silence, his furrowed brow plainly revealing his detestation. The colonel grumbled, undisguised bitterness in his voice. "I will inform Captain Henry Thompson of your attack order. He will lead the charge."

Custer nodded. Later, in private, he would discuss this near-insubordination. "Thompson's charge serves a couple of purposes. I don't want to wait until the brigade is positioned to conduct a general attack. I want to attack now with a smaller force to figure out what we are up against. Attacking now will also buy time for Pennington's battery to unlimber and be in position on your right flank." He paused and drew a breath. "Are we facing ten thousand infantry soldiers being screened by cavalry? Or are we facing only cavalry?" An electric tingle shivered him from hat to boot. "We shall soon find out."

"Are we expecting support from Farnsworth's brigade?" Gray asked.

"Yes, his brigade is going to deploy to the right of the Sixth and Fifth Michigan and Pennington's battery. Elder's battery will deploy west of Pennington's battery."

"Good."

"I also want you to deploy two more Spencer rifle companies on foot in the wheat field on the side of the road. They will be in a position to rake the road with fire."

5:28 p.m.
Captain James Kidd
One hundred yards from Felty barn

Kidd rolled his aching body around the saddle, scanning the Felty Barn one hundred yards ahead.

Colonel Gray galloped up. "James, I want you to dismount and move forward by foot to the Felty barn. Be ready for an enemy countercharge. I'm uncertain how many Rebels Captain Thompson will face when he charges up the fenced road."

"Colonel Gray," Kidd said. "With your permission, I will deploy some of the men in the hay loft."

Colonel Gray turned and glanced at the red brick barn. "Permission granted. The extra height will give you an excellent field of fire."

"Yes, sir."

"The other troops from the Sixth Michigan will remain mounted and in formation at the edge of the tree line on the ridge."

Kidd saluted and Gray trotted toward the Felty ridge. Kidd gestured to First Lieutenant Edward Craw.

"Edward, the company is going to move forward on foot. Have the troopers use the standard dismounted formation of one quarter of the troops holding the mounts in the rear. That will give us forty troopers going forward with Spencer rifles. I want some of those occupying the hay loft."

"Yes, sir."

Major Peter Weber reined up. "James, Colonel Gray wants you to be ready. He is worried about Thompson's charge being repelled. If they are, they will be sitting ducks, pinned in by the wooden fences along the road."

"It does appear to be a reckless charge." Kidd rubbed his chin. "I was impressed with our boy general leading the assaults against the Rebels on Rice's Hill in the Battle of Hanover. But I wonder if he is just another rash general like Kill-Cavalry, ordering troopers to strike out blindly on suicide missions for his own glory?"

"It sure looks that way now."

5:28 p.m.
Custer
Sixth Michigan Cavalry, Company A, mounted, at the Felty Barn

Custer veered off onto Tate Road. Ahead was a single-file limber and caisson pulled by six horses in a column of twos, with riders mounted on the left three horses. The iron muzzle jaws of one of Pennington's three-inch cannons stared at him as it bounced up the steep incline. He smiled. Pennington's battery had fought in every large battle in the East since First Bull Run, and Battery M had never lost a gun in battle.

A first sergeant at the head of the battery shouted, "Come on boys, pull!"

At the top of the Tate ridge, Custer pulled left on the reins. "Come on, Harry, let's pass him."

A gamecocky warmth bristled his limbs. He adjusted his saber so it stuck out Oriental-style from its eyelet rings, like a cockspur. He waved as he trotted past the battery like a chivalrous cavalier, grinning. Someone shouted, "It's General Custer!" A cheer pierced the air from the cannoneers.

Custer's insides tingled.

"They admire you, General Custer," Churchill said.

Custer smiled. "No Norvell, they love Harry."

He peered down the road. Across from the Felty barn, Captain Thompson was forming up Company A. Custer and Churchill rode up.

Thompson saluted. "General Custer, company A is ready to charge."

"Very well."

"General." Thompson paused, grimacing. "I have serious doubts about making this charge. The enemy force in our front is the same size as my company. We are attacking over a narrow road hemmed in by fences, so my troopers can't fan out during the attack. The Rebels could have dismounted troopers hiding in the tall wheat on either side of the road and in the trees on the ridge behind the enemy. I'm not sure we can defeat them."

Custer's heart leaped. Thompson was right about his troops being hemmed in during the charge. But dash and surprise would carry the day. It always did. "Captain, you will attack now, while the enemy is still forming up. I believe your force is larger than the Rebels'."

Thompson's brow furrowed and his face turned bright red, clearly suppressing rage. "I believe this is a suicidal attack. But I'm no coward. I will lead the charge."

Custer stared, concealing his growing rage. A couple heart-beats passed. "Very well. Conduct the charge."

Custer held his breath as he trotted onto center stage for all eyes of the Michigan Brigade to catch a glimpse of the Wolverines' new lead actor. The moment would be perfect, cantering toward the front of Company A as if a trumpet was playing "Garryowen." He tingled with excitement. Churchill rode slightly behind on his left. If only the famed General Philip Kearny, the Dashing Dragoon, could see him now. He aimed for Thompson, stifling a grin. Napoleon's Murat would have led this charge. Leaders led from the front. A sudden explosion of adrenaline erupted inside him like a pulsating geyser. *What a glorious moment.*

"Hold on, Captain," shouted Custer as he unsheathed his saber.

Thompson whipped his head around. "What?"

Custer dashed out in front of Company A and flashed his long Toledo blade. He stood up in his stirrups and scanned down the road. He slid back into his saddle and glanced at Thompson.

"I'll lead you this time, boys," he chortled. "Come on!"

Thompson's mouth fell open and his eyebrows arched.

Custer shouted, "Bugler Fought, 'Forward Walk.'"

Fought snapped the trumpet to his lips, shrilling the air with Custer's command.

Custer eased Harry forward. Thompson rode next to him on his right, and Churchill rode on his left, their sabers pointing forward. The clumping hooves of forty horses echoed behind them. About five miles behind the Rebel cavalry near Gettysburg, the sky was filled with a raging thunderstorm of bursting clouds cracking, rattling, and rumbling. *Must be the infantry fighting at Gettysburg.*

Custer pulled even with the Felty Barn on the right. He kicked his heels and Harry started trotting. Saber scabbards clanked and clattered behind. A shiver rushed through him, and his body lifted as if a strong wind had filled a sail. He loved leading men. Thirty yards past the Felty barn, his eyes stung. The trotting horses were kicking up puffs of dry gray dust that itched like talc powder. He wiped his gloved hand across his face and licked his lips.

Two hundred yards from the Gilbert house, the sun glinted off hundreds of sparkling Rebel sabers. A Confederate colonel sat in front of a large enemy force.

Custer turned to Thompson. "Are you ready, Captain?"

Thompson gave a steely but reluctant nod. "Yes, sir."

Custer glanced over his left shoulder, spotting Churchill. Good. "Bugler Fought," he shouted, "sound the charge."

Fought trumpeted the brash, shrilling notes.

Custer spurred Harry, and the steed lurched down the rolling road at a full gallop. Custer's skin prickled. A blinding dust blew into his face and his broad hat slid to the back of his head. A short yell echoed behind him. He glanced back; forty men raced four abreast, blurring past the fence posts. He snapped his head back around and drank in the beauty of the moment and the pounding of hooves on the dirt road.

Churchill pulled up even with him, grinning, his willowy body rippling like a wild beast poised for the kill.

"Come on, Norvell, let's show these Rebels what we are made of."

Churchill yelled and waved his saber.

Harry galloped at breakneck speed, a four-legged thunderbolt. *This is how you make a name for yourself.* God, he loved fighting. A guttural cluck erupted up his throat and his jaw tightened. *Damn.* The enclosed fenced lane was like riding down the confines of a bowling alley. Behind him the fence clattered as the frenzied horses banged and flailed up against the wooden rails.

He squinted with a vicious glee. *My God.* The Rebel colonel mounted on his stationary horse was his Georgia friend and West Point classmate Pierce Manning Butler Young. Young's departing prophetic words at the academy flashed in his memory: *And who knows but we may move against each other during the war.*

Twenty yards to go. His heart pounded with pure cussedness. The mounted Rebel skirmish line stretched thinly across the road. Countless flashes and cracking pops erupted from a Rebel volley. He ducked against Harry's long neck. A swarm of bullets hummed overhead like buzzing bumblebees. Custer shrieked, a wolf-like howl. A Rebel sergeant carrying a swallow-tailed red battle flag trotted his horse forward. Custer slashed his saber across the sergeant's face. The charging Union horses slammed into the stationary enemy with a bone-crushing thud. Screams erupted as sabers slashed and pistols fired. The enemy line was no match for the Wolverines' crushing first wave as the second and third Michigan waves rushed through the gaps in the enemy line.

The enemy skirmishers broke and raced back past the Gilbert farmhouse. Colonel Young had wheeled about and was bolting with his hat in hand. *Good.* He wanted to capture his West Point classmate and not kill him.

A shiver ran through Custer. *The Rebs are skedaddling.* "Let's go, boys!"

He spurred Harry and led his troopers around a bend. Thunder cracked against the flank of the charging Wolverines. Several troopers and horses screamed as they plunged to the ground. Dismounted enemy skirmishers hidden in the wheat field around the Gilbert house had fired a devasting broadside.

Company A returned fire. Custer glanced at Young as the Rebel's mount buckled and his classmate tumbled forward over the horse's head, hitting the ground and rolling. Young jumped to his feet, aimed his pistol, and fired. The bullet zipped past Custer's ear.

Custer shouted, "You cussed devil!"

The dismounted enemy fired another volley. A scream to his right. Thompson fell from his horse. *Damn.* A thud. Harry let out a screeching cry. The steed's front legs buckled and the mount spilled downward. He kicked out of his stirrups and hurled forward over Harry's nose, stomach fluttering, body freefalling. *Oh, no.* He tucked his chin, closed his eyes, hit on his right shoulder, and rolled once, throwing him flat on his chest. The air blasted out of his lungs. He gasped, unable to inhale. Fear gripped his dizzy brain. *What an inglorious way to die.* He forced himself to lie still and relax. After a few long seconds he was able to breathe slowly through his nose. He spit out the dust coating his mouth. His breathing quickened through his mouth. He opened his blurry eyes and saw Harry lying dead, with blood pouring from a bullet hole between his eyes. He stood up; his legs wobbled. His dazed brain was addled. *Can't focus.* Sweat crawled down his face. Pistols cracked, sabers slashed, piercing screams roared. Dust spiraled in the melee. He seemed to be in the eye of a whirling hurricane.

He picked up his saber and pointed it at a Confederate cavalryman charging on his horse with a raised sword. Custer started to raise his sword. But he was too late; the enemy sword flashed in the sun. He ducked and crouched. A horse pitched by, touching his jacket. Clashing metal rang like a clanging bell as the rider's saber deflected the enemy sword slicing down. *My God!* It was Churchill, his red face flashing with deviltry. Norvell pointed his pistol at the enemy's head. *Crack.* The bullet ripped through the Rebel's brow, blowing out blood and brains through the back of his head. Churchill twisted in his saddle and held out his hand.

"Grab my hand, General."

For a moment, silence was a stone wall between the two—a strained silence where he tried reaching out, but nothing moved. His body was frozen. The silence ran on, impossible to break. His mind screamed. *You're going to die.*

"So help me God, grab my hand, General!"

Churchill's voice was a distant echo, like a throaty whisper. His ruffled pride flamed, and Custer reached up with his right hand and gripped Norvell's hand. With his left hand, he gripped the saddle's cantle.

"Jump, General." With a huge grunt, Churchill pulled hard, and Custer sprang off his right foot while lifting his left leg over the saddle.

He flew upward, hit the saddle's croup, and kept sliding to his left. Churchill reached back with his left hand, catching Custer's side.

"Thank God you're as strong as an ox," Custer shouted.

"Thank God you're wearing a red scarf. Hold on tight."

Custer wrapped his arms around Norvell's waist. Churchill spurred his horse and they shot back toward the Felty farm. Custer glanced over his shoulder. Good. The remaining Union survivors were galloping behind them.

"Norvell, the Rebels are chasing us."

Churchill cocked his head. "They won't catch us." Norvell spurred his horse several times and the mount raced at breakneck speed like a wild mustang.

Custer gripped Norvell's waist and the mount veered to the right, kicking up white dust. Ahead, he spotted a dead blue-clad trooper sprawled in the middle of the road. As Churchill passed the body, the trooper's mangled head lay in a pool of dark red blood. A bullet had pierced his left eye and his face was smashed from scores of iron-shod hooves charging down the fenced-in lane. His trampled body suffered from cracked ribs through which his gray-colored lungs oozed, and sharp white bones protruded from his mangled legs.

Custer shuddered. This was not a good death. His heart quaked for the dead trooper's family.

6:05 p.m.
Captain James Kidd
Felty barn

Kidd scanned up and down the line of his dismounted troopers in the tall wheat. He shouted, "Hold your fire until Company A passes by."

He glanced down the road. A swirling dust cloud raced toward Company E like a spawning tornado. Kidd spotted Custer riding on the back of Churchill's horse as they raced past the Felty farm. Just behind Custer and Churchill, a Michigan trooper carried Captain Thompson behind on the saddle. Blood saturated Thompson's dust-covered uniform. A claw tore through Kidd's stomach. He hoped his fellow captain would make it.

Web approached. "How is it going, James?"

"I just saw both General Custer and Captain Thompson being ridden back from the fight."

"What's your guess of the casualties?"

"I've counted about thirty-three troopers returning, Web, so that means there are seven or so casualties not counting the wounded riding their horses back."

Web pointed. "Look, the Rebels are charging."

"They must believe that they completely routed Company A. They are going to be in for a big surprise when they race into Custer's brigade waiting for them."

Web nodded. "They're riding into a trap."

Kidd stared at the enemy rounding the slight curve in the road by the Felty house. He roared, "Fire!"

Spencer rifles unleashed a sheet of lead. Twenty enemy troopers fell from their horses. Searing rifle fire burst from the barn. Kidd glanced at the red-brick building. Every door and window blazed with streaking yellow flames.

A huge, thundering crack erupted behind Kidd. He turned. *Good.* Pennington's Battery M's magnificent cannons had started firing. Shells shrieked long and sharp, ripping through the enemy troopers.

7:11 p.m. (Sunset, 7:44 p.m.)
Custer
Felty Ridge, Hunterstown

Custer squinted toward the western sky blazing with orange fire beyond South Mountain. His mouth tightened as the shattered remnants of the enemy retreated toward the Gilbert house.

He turned to Churchill. "Well, Norvell. I think the cavalry battle is ending."

Enemy artillery erupted, sending screaming shells toward Pennington's battery. Pennington's batteries adjusted fire and started counterbattery fire against the growling cannons. Elder's batteries from Farnsworth's brigade joined the artillery duel. Flicking tongues of yellow light kissed the darkening sky like streaking comet tails.

"I'm most sorry about Harry being killed," Churchill said.

"Thank you." Custer wiped a tear from his eye. "I loved that horse."

Johnny came running up with Rose. Custer bent down and Rose licked his face, her tail wagging. "I missed you, Rose. We both owe a big debt of gratitude to Norvell."

Custer stood up. "Thank you, Norvell. You saved my life."

"Sir, that's my job, to protect you." Churchill grinned, a devilish smirk. "But you came close to being killed today. I barely got there in time to parry the Rebel's saber aimed for your head."

Custer smiled down from his four-inch advantage. "You're one hell of a gifted horseman, and I like your devil-may-care courage." He thought for a moment. "Would you consider being my special orderly?"

Churchill blushed. "That would be a great honor, sir. Just remember to keep unhorsing on the side of my good eye. I don't want to get a reputation for my generals dying on me."

Custer stuck out his hand. "I shall remember. But don't worry. The bullet has not yet been molded to kill me."

"That may be true, but what about a saber? That's what almost scalped you today."

"I'm possessed by Custer luck and that also covers being killed by a saber." They shook, sealing the agreement. "Norvell, I'm sure I can whip anything I meet as long as you are there with me."

"Thank you, General. It's an honor to serve you."

"Peter, you look grubstruck," Kidd observed, watching Web groom his horse. "Let's grab some supper."

Web glanced up. "In just a minute. I want to finish up."

"What did you think of General Custer's charge today?" Kidd said.

"It was a slapdash charge. After Custer was unhorsed, it was every Wolverine for himself, and Devil take the hindmost. Thank God for Private Norvell Churchill. He saved Custer's ass."

Kidd said, "I agree. The boy general's devil-may-care attack was nothing to crow about. In fact, the charge was harebrained cocksureness."

Web glanced up and grinned. "The daredevil Custer seems to defy death like the beggar Tom o' Bedlam."

"Custer is a shavetail general bent on living up to the *Harper's Weekly* sketch of him leading a cavalry charge at the Battle of Aldie."

"It was a great sketch." Web stopped brushing. "With his unkempt curls flying in the wind and his uplifted saber, Custer looked more like a Rebel than like one of ours."

Kidd said, "For me, the jury is still out. I'm not impressed with Custer's rakish air."

"I'll say one thing about the boy general. I was awed that he ordered the charge and then led it, knowing he was outnumbered. That takes raw courage, rare gallantry, and reckless heroism."

34

Tenth New York — Thursday, July 2

5:30 p.m. (Two and a half hours earlier)
Major John Kemper
Crest of Brinkerhoff's Ridge, 200 yards west of the stone wall

S tanding at the edge of a large, wooded lot, Kemper felt his heart accelerating. Ahead was a rolling field of tall, ripe wheat running west for 200 yards toward the crest of Brinkerhoff's Ridge. Yellow flashes and white puffs sprouted from the lacerated woods at the end of the wheat field; popping and cracking echoed above it. Bullets droned overhead.

He turned to First Lieutenant Woodruff. "Marshall, the Reb skirmishers are increasing their rate of fire. Their enfilade rifles have a greater range than our carbines. Let's move a bit closer and give them a taste of hot lead."

"Do you want me to advance in a line?"

"No. We're outnumbered, so I want to disguise how few skirmishers we have."

"How do you plan to do that?" Woodruff said with a ghostly smile.

"Break your company up into several small squads. They will depart at different times and operate independently." Kemper pointed. "See those detached clumps of woods dotting the wheat field?"

"I see them."

"I want your squads to weave toward the tree clumps like several slithering snakes. After they are in place, they will open fire at the enemy skirmishers hiding in those trees at the brow of the ridge."

"Yes, sir," said Woodruff.

Kemper turned to Captain Peck. "William, I want Company H to act as a reserve in case the enemy charges the clumps of trees. Any questions?"

Peck shook his head.

"Marshall, let's move out."

35

Gregg — Thursday, July 2

Gregg stood up in his stirrups and gripped his binoculars, scanning the southwestern sky above Wolf Hill and Cemetery Ridge. Late afternoon had worn out and given way to early evening. A creeping fear was rising from a hellish place. His troopers were dead tired from marching for the past twenty-four hours, and now the casual exchanges of cracking firing was reaching a crescendo. Hundreds of cannons blasted, and thousands of rifles rattled. Smoke rose from the trembling ground like a thick, low-lying fog. The clattering storm was punctuated with shrieking Rebel wolf cries. His pulse beat in his ears. Who was winning the Gettysburg fight?

He scanned Brinkerhoff's Ridge. The sputtering rifle fire had erupted into a steady rattling, like hard rain pelting a tin roof. An emptiness snaked through him. Would the enemy infantry launch an attack down the ridge?

Gregg turned to Captain Meyer. "Henry, order Colonel Gregg to reinforce Major Kemper's squad with fifty more troopers."

Meyer saluted and departed.

Gregg glanced at Rank's two unlimbered artillery pieces. He swallowed hard. Rank's battery had never fired against the enemy in battle. They might get their chance in the next hour or so if things kept heating up.

McIntosh rode up and saluted. "General Gregg, my brigade has deployed north of Rank's battery along Little Run."

"Thanks, John. I may need your brigade to reinforce the Tenth New York. It sounds as if the Confederates on Brinkerhoff's Ridge are becoming more peppery."

5:55 p.m.
Major John Kemper
Crest of Brinkerhoff's Ridge, 100 yards west of the stone wall

Kemper knelt in the middle of Captain Peck's concealed skirmish line. He slipped his hand into his jacket, pulled out a soiled handkerchief, and wiped his face. The blistering heat was sizzling his troopers as if they were in a cast-iron Dutch oven.

Conversations hummed around him. "How did we get stuck with this forward duty?" "Hell, the rest of the division is lounging under shade trees." "Why doesn't Sergeant Bonnell come up from the Cress house with his boys and relieve us?"

Beyond the southern hills of Gettysburg, thundering cannons and rifle fire split the air. The ground shook as the missiles tore and plowed it. Metal shards whistled. Kemper lifted his head to the top of the wheat and glanced southwest toward the Union lines. The sky was crisscrossed with black tendrils. Beneath the shrieking projectiles a murky, sulphur-laden smoke cloud belched above Wolf Hill and Culp's Hill. A big battle had begun.

Kemper stood. His eyes locked on Woodruff's L Company troopers whirling out of the tree line and zigzagging toward the tree islands floating in the sea of tall wheat. A silence broke over the ridge. An eerie silence, like a robber suddenly realizing his victim was armed.

Peck stood up next to him. "Major, it appears you have confused the Rebels with your scrambled skirmishing tactic."

Kemper smiled. "I just hope the enemy thinks our numbers are twice as large as they are."

"The detached clumps of woods are like frontier outposts," replied Peck.

Kemper studied rifle blasts from the tree outpost. Woodruff's troopers laid down a searing blanket of lead into the enemy tree line hugging the ridge. The blue troopers stopped firing and a creepy pause broke. He scanned the Rebel tree line through narrowed eyes. How would the enemy react? Unsettling moments passed, then yellow flashes and smoke puffs burst from the enemy tree line. A hailstorm of enemy bullets riddled the outposts. A musket ball whistled over his head. The onslaught was relentless. More yellow flashes were chased by several bullets zipping by, one whizzing by his cheek. A shiver spiraled through him. *That was close.*

Company L Sergeant David Rines shouted, "Major Kemper, this is more than skirmish fire. They are preparing to attack."

"I think you're right, Sergeant." *The Rebels saw our infantry skirmishers depart and know we are dismounted cavalry that is one-fourth the numbers of the Irish regiment.*

6:00 p.m.
Colonel Irvin Gregg
Little Run

Colonel Irvin Gregg galloped toward Major Avery's regiment loitering near Little Run. He reined up. Avery's binoculars were glued to his eyes, scanning Brinkerhoff's Ridge. Gregg spotted Captain Benjamin Lownsbury sitting on a tree stump, cleaning his pistol. Avery twisted in his saddle and saluted.

"I just spoke with General Gregg," Colonel Gregg said. "The general is worried about the enemy's incessant, harassing fire along Brinkerhoff's Ridge. I'm growing frustrated that Kemper's vedettes are facing increased fire from enemy sharpshooters."

"Do you think the enemy's boldness is related to the army's raging battle?" Avery said.

"I'm not sure. But I'm ordering you to send another squadron of fifty troopers to reinforce Major Kemper's troopers."

"Yes, sir. I was getting ready to send Captain Benjamin Lownsbury forward to relieve Major Kemper's squadron."

"Understood." Gregg swiveled in his saddle and gestured. "Captain Lownsbury, I want you to hear this."

Lownsbury jumped up, whirled over to Gregg and Avery, and saluted. "Yes, sir, Colonel."

Gregg said, "I want you to lead a squadron to reinforce Kemper's troopers. Don't relieve Kemper's forces just yet. They are to stay and support you. Once your troopers are in place, I want you to drive back those enemy sharpshooters on the ridge. When the enemy fire subsides, then you can relieve Kemper's men."

Avery added, "Benjamin, you will lead a squadron composed of Companies E and K. You will reinforce Kemper's troopers. If your combined forces are being pushed back, I will send another squadron of Companies B and D, commanded by Lieutenant Truman White, to support you."

"Yes sir," Lownsbury said, "I understand."

"Henry," Colonel Gregg said, "if you need further support, I will request General Gregg send reinforcements from Colonel McIntosh's brigade."

6:07 p.m.
Captain Benjamin Lownsbury
Approaching the tree line concealing the stone wall
Leading Companies E and K

Lownsbury scampered across Cress Run. He paused as his two-man column of twenty-seven dismounted troopers hopped the creek. When half the column had crossed the creek, he leapt forward to lead his squadron uphill toward the tree line concealing the stone wall.

He lowered his hat across his brow and eyed a rail fence cutting across the field one hundred yards from the stone wall.

He turned and shouted, "Troopers, we will halt at the rail fence."

He scampered forward and halted at the fence, squeezing his eyes shut against the blinding sunlight. Speckled spots glinted against his inner eyelids. The merciless rays slanting over the treed ridgeline rendered it hard to see anything ahead.

"Troopers," he shouted, "lay down for a few moments, until the trees in our front shade the sun."

6:09 p.m.
General David Gregg
Near Captain Rank's artillery battery

A courier reined up. "General Gregg, General Pleasonton sends his respects. This afternoon General Daniel Sickles, command-ing Third Infantry Corps, disobeyed orders and moved his corps one-half mile in front of the Union defensive line along Cemetery Ridge. The Rebels launched an echelon attack against Sickles's stranded corps. Meade has been rushing reinforce-ments to his left flank for the past two hours, trying to shore up Sickles's depleted corps and plug holes along Cemetery Ridge."

"Are we winning?"

"Too close to call now. There have been heavy losses on both sides. Sickles left Little Round Top undefended. Meade was fu-rious. General Gouverneur Warren rushed infantry and artillery to the top of Little Round Top just in time to set up a defense against the attacking Rebels. The fight for Little Round Top is still going on. The middle of the Union line is very thin, and Meade left only General George Greene's brigade defending Culp's Hill after he pulled the rest of General Henry Slocum's Twelve Corps away to bolster his left flank."

"What about Jeb Stuart's cavalry?"

"Colonel Sharpe believes the vanguard of Stuart's cavalry division is arriving in Gettysburg. He does not believe you will face any Rebel cavalry this evening."

"What about tomorrow? What are Meade's plans?"

"I know of no plans for tomorrow. Meade is just trying to survive today. But I did hear Colonel Sharpe say if there is a battle tomorrow, you may face Stuart's cavalry."

"Inform General Pleasonton that my division has been hold-ing off Confederate infantry attacks from Brinkerhoff's Ridge. I've had to throw more troopers up to the ridge than I expected. I will keep him informed of the situation as it develops this evening."

The courier saluted and departed.

General Gregg glanced up Hanover Road toward Brinkerhoff's Ridge. Hoofbeats were thundering down the road.

He snapped his hand across his brow and spotted a Union rider galloping down from the ridge. A cavalcade of graybacks were chasing the lone rider.

He turned to Colonel Gregg. "Irvin, what do you make of that?"

Irvin Gregg looked through his binoculars. "If I'm not mistaken, those Rebels are chasing Dr. Theodore Tate."

"I'll be damned. The same surgeon from the Third Pennsylvania who guided us on last night's shortcut?"

"Yes, sir."

"Well, let's see how accurate Captain Rank's artillery boys are. Have Rank send those Rebels a feeler."

Irvin grinned and rode over to Rank. General Gregg turned and stared at Tate's harrowing sprint. Tate's legs swished back and forth like a fledging bird flapping its wings. The length of his spurring stroke extended from his boots, touching the horse's shoulder, and sweeping to the back of the saddle.

Irvin shouted, "Captain Rank, the Rebels are gaining on Dr. Tate. Hurry and fire!"

General Gregg spotted an old woman emerging from a stone house down in the ravine. She leaned on her waist-high walking cane and began climbing the steep hill toward Rank's guns.

At the same moment, Rank shouted, "Fire!" A thundering blast erupted and streaming yellow flames tore from the iron jaws of Rank's two cannons. The shells streaked over the woman's head. She screamed, threw her cane into the air, and fell over backwards as if she had been shot. Gregg gasped. Had the blast crushed her?

He flicked his gaze toward the screeching shells wisping up the Hanover Road. The flying iron plunged down and burst amid the pursuing enemy cavalrymen. The Rebel cavalcade scattered like chaff in a windstorm.

"Superb shooting, Captain Rank," he shouted.

Rank tipped his cap. His gunners pointed and broke out laughing. Gregg glanced down the ravine and chuckled. The old woman was shrieking and sprinting without a cane toward her house, like a teenage girl trying to outrun a tornado.

"Irvin," he said, "Captain Rank's well-placed artillery rounds have temporarily cured the woman of her infirmities."

His cousin replied, "She is skedaddling almost as fast as those enemy troopers flying for their lives back up the hill."

Dr. Tate pulled up, panting, his knackered horse snorting.

"That was a narrow escape, Dr. Tate," said General Gregg.

Tate gasped, "I attempted to enter Gettysburg and visit my wife and children. I know a goat path between Hanover Road and York Pike that leads into the town. I got close enough to spot the Fahnestock building on the corner of Baltimore and Middle Street. The dry goods store is the tallest building in town and Confederate lookouts were standing on its observation deck."

"Did you observe any of the fighting south of the town?"

"I spotted thousands of graybacks massed south of town, facing Cemetery Hill. It looked as if they were preparing for an assault. The fighting was a mile or so south of the town along Cemetery Ridge."

"How did you manage to escape?"

"A Rebel cavalry party was scouting south of the York Pike. They approached and demanded I surrender. I spurred my horse and raced back here."

"You're lucky Rank's greenhorn artillerymen are such good shots. They saved your bacon."

Colonel John B. McIntosh

36

Tenth New York — Thursday, July 2

6:10 p.m.
Major Kemper
Southern edge of Brinkerhoff's Ridge wheat field

Kemper stood and watched enemy skirmishers advancing toward Waters's island outposts.

"Major," Peck said, "look several hundred yards behind the Rebel skirmishers."

Kemper glanced at the edge of the woodlot on Brinkerhoff's Ridge. A line of enemy infantry was forming. He spotted a shot-torn rebel flag. *Damn. That's a rebel infantry regiment.* The enemy line advanced at a walk. The enemy skirmishers leapfrogged toward Woodruff's outposts and fired. The rebels knelt as they reloaded their long-range enfilade rifles.

Kemper shouted, "First Lieutenant Woodruff, retreat!"

Carbine fire burst from the tree outposts. Woodruff's troopers turned and skedaddled toward Peck's line at the edge of the wheat field.

The enemy skirmishers stood and aimed. "Drop!" Kemper bellowed as he lurched down to one knee.

Woodruff's troopers dove to the ground, thudding like dropped flour sacks as the enemy skirmishers fired. Bullets cut through the wheat like a scythe.

Woodruff leaped up shouting, "Run!"

The blue-clad cavalrymen jumped up and raced toward the Peck's line. The Rebel infantry line halted one hundred yards from Company H's kneeling troopers and fired a broadside. Bullets zipped over the tops of the wheat stalks.

Captain Peck shouted, "Stand and fire."

Company H popped up like meerkats and fired a blanket of lead. Screams rent the air.

First Lieutenant Woodruff scrambled up and halted. Screeching and yelling echoed over the wheat stalks.

Kemper's eyes locked on Company L troopers dashing toward him.

Peck's H troopers cheered as the last of Woodruff's L troopers reached their line and crouched out of sight. Kemper's heart leaped and he stood, grinning at the skedaddling Confederates disappearing into the tree line.

Out of a momentary hush, mongrel cries erupted from the Rebel infantry line as they rushed forward. Yellow flashes and white smoke puffs drew Kemper's gaze to the enemy's left side of the line. A bullet breezed past his ear. He shivered. The Rebels were flanking them.

He shouted, "Captain Peck and First Lieutenant Woodruff. We're outnumbered and we're being flanked. Our line is too thin to hold the Rebels. Retreat diagonally toward the W. Howard house next to the Hanover Road."

Kemper's squadron sprang backwards and scrambled toward the Howard house. Bullets whizzed overhead as the Rebels bounded down the hill. He set his jaw and turned his head forward. A howling scream; a trooper tumbled forward. Kemper rushed over to the wounded man. Corporal William Potter gripped his bloody side. "Corporal Potter, can you walk? If you can't, you'll be a prisoner in a few moments."

Corporal Abram Thompson rushed forward, gripped Potter's back, and pulled him up. "William, I'll help you to safety."

Potter groaned. "Thank you, Abram. Let's go."

Kemper raced into the backyard of the W. Howard house. He turned and shouted, "Captain Peck and First Lieutenant Woodruff. Form a defensive line across the backyard."

Peck and Woodruff shouted out orders. The Union troopers stormed in, turned, knelt, and formed up a defensive line. Kemper glanced up the hill. The enemy regiment had halted one hundred yards away and was moving back up toward Brinkerhoff's Ridge.

Thank God.

6:20 p.m.
Captain Benjamin Lownsbury
Southern edge of Brinkerhoff's Ridge wheat field, leading Companies
E and K

Lownsbury raised his head off the ground and squinted toward the dipping sun behind the treetops. The welcoming long shadows edged toward the rail fence. *Almost time to scoot forward.*

Corporal Edmund Dow said, "Captain, look behind. Another squadron is scrambling toward us."

Lownsbury turned on his side and spotted several dismounted troopers clamoring up the slope. "Corporal, it's Lieutenant Truman White darting up the slope." His heart whirled like a pinwheel. *Reinforcements.*

Dow said, "Lieutenant White is leading companies B and D. I recommend they fall in on our right."

"Agreed." Lownsbury waved and shouted, "Truman, this way."

"I see you," White shouted, and pressed forward. "Benjamin, Major Avery ordered my squadron forward after Major Kemper's line was pushed back."

"As soon as your squadron is deployed to the right of mine," Lownsbury said, "let's move forward."

6:50 p.m.
Captain Benjamin Lownsbury, Leading Companies E and K and
supported by Lieutenant White's Companies B and D
Wheat field containing the tree outpost

Lownsbury lay in the wheat field. The enemy hid along the tree line on the crest of Brinkerhoff's Ridge. A shot whizzed a few inches over his head. His skin quivered like a frightened dog. He flattened himself a little more. The two Union squadrons pelted the tree line with a harassing fire. Hundreds of wolf cries screeched from the trees. He raised his head and glanced at three hundred Rebels rushing toward them.

"Corporal Dow, we can't hold this position." He pointed toward Lieutenant White's line of troopers. "Tell your men to leave and then then tell Lieutenant White to fall back."

Lownsbury stood up in the tall wheat and started backing up as he fired his revolver. He turned to Bugler William Doan. "Sound 'Recall.'"

A pang of urgency seized him. The rushing gray line spilled down the slope like water from a broken dam. A shiver traced its way down his spine. *I'm too late.*

He shouted, "Fall back, troopers! Fall back!"

The sharp bugle notes pierced the air. The troopers sprouted up through the wheat like alert prairie dogs.. They skittered backwards, firing their carbines. Lownsbury saw the enemy line swell and surge forward like a tidal wave.

He shouted, "Everyone skedaddle. Run!"

Lownsbury turned and tore toward a fence at the brow of the hill. He spotted the left side of the line reaching the fence first and leaping over it. His eyes flicked to Corporal Philip Bentzel halting at the fence ten yards ahead. Bentzel was trying to clear a section of the fence.

Lownsbury shouted, "Corporal Bentzel! Jump the fence!"

A wave of cracking rifle fire. Several bullets buzzed by like a swarm of wasps. Bentzel screamed and lurched forward across the fence railing. Lownsbury's right leg stung as if fanged by a sidewinder. He skirted up to Bentzel, the corporal's mangled back oozing blood through several bullet holes. *Poor Bentzel.* He placed his hand on the rail and started to leap.

A Southern voice shouted, "Halt, Captain. You're our prisoner."

Lownsbury stopped and glanced over his shoulder. A throng of Rebels crowded around him and Corporal Dow. A bayonet was pointed at his heart.

"I surrender," he said. He handed his revolver to a young lieutenant.

The Rebel lieutenant said, "Follow us."

7:10 p.m.
Captain Benjamin Lownsbury
Shriver farm, west of Brinkerhoff's Ridge
Confederate General James Walker's headquarters

Lownsbury limped toward the Shriver Barn, blood oozing down his right boot. His leg felt numb, as if he had soaked it in ice water. Ahead a Confederate general sitting on a rail fence was talking with a colonel. The Rebel lieutenant escorted him and Corporal Dow to the general.

The lieutenant said, "General, we captured Captain Lownsbury and Corporal Dow during our advance down the ridge."

The Rebel commander said, "Captain Lownsbury, I'm General James Walker, the commander of the Stonewall Brigade. It's my pleasure to make your acquaintance."

Lownsbury stared at Walker. The general spoke in a gentlemanly Virginia accent.

Walker asked, "What cavalry unit is my force facing?"

Lownsbury said, "General David Gregg's Second Cavalry Division."

"David Gregg." Walker nodded. "Gregg is a West Point graduate. I believe General Jeb Stuart and General Pender were at the academy at the same time. Stuart has high respect for General Gregg. He is perhaps the Union's best cavalry general." Walker pulled on his white mustache. "How large is Gregg's force?"

"I'm not at privilege to answer that question, but if you only have an infantry brigade sitting here on the Confederate flank, you're outnumbered three to one."

Walker stared, his icy-blue eyes holding a hint of sly amusement. "We've been outnumbered in every battle we've fought, and we haven't lost yet. I hear you have a new army commander, General George Meade. Your President Lincoln is an idiot for replacing General Hooker with Meade on the eve of this great battle. It's impossible for Meade to win this battle. His troops are tired from all the forced marches trying to find Lee's army foraging up here in Pennsylvania. After we defeat Meade at Gettysburg, the war will be over."

Lownsbury's jaw tightened, and his mind groaned. How could Meade win after being in command for five days?

"I see you're bleeding, Captain. I will have my surgeon attend to you. After the war ends here at Gettysburg and you have recovered from your wound, I invite you to visit me in Pulaski County, Virginia. That is where my law practice is. I have an old bottle of Scotch we can share. Good evening, sir."

6:55 p.m. (Fifteen minutes earlier)
Major Henry Avery
Cress farm

Avery scanned Brinkerhoff's Ridge. Scudding fright gripped his body. *On God's bones!* Lownsbury and White's squads were being pushed back.

He turned to Lieutenant James Matthews. "James, move your company F forward to support Lownsbury and White's squadrons."

Matthews's troopers dismounted and rushed up the ridge. Rank's batteries thundered as the two artillery guns threw shell after shell on top of the ridge. Avery spotted Matthews and his company reaching the ridge and then falling back and sheltering beneath the brow of the hill. A hot stream of anger coursed through him.

"What the hell is going on?" He mounted his horse, and rode toward Company F. "Who ordered Company F back from the ridge?"

Matthews said, "I did, Major."

Several rifles cracked a detonating roar and a swarm of bullets swept over him. He ducked. A wisp of wind feathered his cheek as bullets grazed his uniform.

Avery shouted, "Hell, you ought to have ordered the company back before. This is a Rebel rat's nest. I'm ordering all the Tenth New York squadrons back to Cress Run."

7:15 p.m. (Sunset 7:44 p.m.)
General David Gregg
East of Little Run

Wolf cries screeched from Brinkerhoff's Ridge. The Rebel Yell. Foreboding gripped Gregg by the throat. The Confederate infantry were attacking. He flipped his hat down his brow and squinted at the Tenth New Yorkers scurrying down Brinkerhoff's Ridge toward Cress Run. This was no longer a skirmish. He licked his lips. How large was the Rebel force? He turned to Colonel McIntosh.

"John, Kemper's New Yorkers are in trouble. Move your First Brigade forward to the Cress farm orchard and move enough units forward to control that ridge."

"Yes, sir," said McIntosh. "After First Brigade arrives in the woods on Cress Ridge, I will order two squadrons from the Third Pennsylvania to dismount and move up to the ridge."

"Very well," Gregg said. "Hurry! This could be serious."

McIntosh shouted, "To horse!"

Gregg watched the troopers of First Brigade mount their horses and trot up the Hanover Road, passing by Rank's thundering guns and crossing over Cress Run. McIntosh led his column off to the right toward the Cress house, forming them up in columns in the orchard.

Captain William E. Miller

37

Miller — Thursday, July 2

7:25 p.m. (Sunset 7:44 p.m.)
Captain William Miller
Cress farm orchard

Captain William Miller peered toward Brinkerhoff's Ridge. The spattering of popping fire swelled into a chorus of cracking fire, heralding a storm. New Yorkers were emerging from a belt of woods and scurrying down the slope like escaping fugitives. Rebel soldiers gripping gleaming rifles were square on their heels, screaming bloodcurdling wolf cries. *What a dreadful sight. Damn, this breaking storm was turning into a spirited little fight.*

Miller turned to Captain Frank Hess. "Without reinforcements, the enemy will sweep the field."

Lieutenant Colonel Edward Jones, the Third Regimental commander, reined up. "Captains, your squadrons will dismount, advance up the ridge, and hold it." Jones pointed. "Frank, your left flank will rest on the Hanover Road. William, your troopers will advance on Hess's right flank."

Miller saluted and cantered over to Companies D and H. He dismounted next to Lieutenant William Brooke-Rawle and First Sergeant Thomas Wier of Company D.

"First Sergeant Wier, dismount Companies D and H and ready the squadron to advance up the ridge." Miller turned to Brooke-Rawle. "William, we need to scamper up the ridge as quickly as we can and get into a good defensive position before sunset in about half an hour. Let's move out."

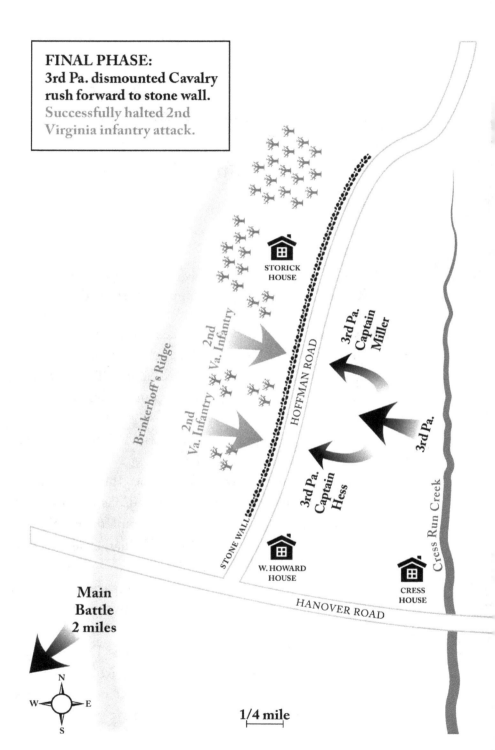

FINAL PHASE:
3rd Pa. dismounted Cavalry
rush forward to stone wall.
Successfully halted 2nd
Virginia infantry attack.

STORICK
HOUSE

Brinkerhoff's Ridge

2nd Va. Infantry

2nd Va. Infantry

2nd Va. Infantry

HOFFMAN ROAD

3rd Pa. Captain Miller

3rd Pa.

3rd Pa. Captain Hess

STONE WALL

W. HOWARD HOUSE

CRESS HOUSE

Cress Run Creek

HANOVER ROAD

Main Battle 2 miles

N
W — E
S

1/4 mile

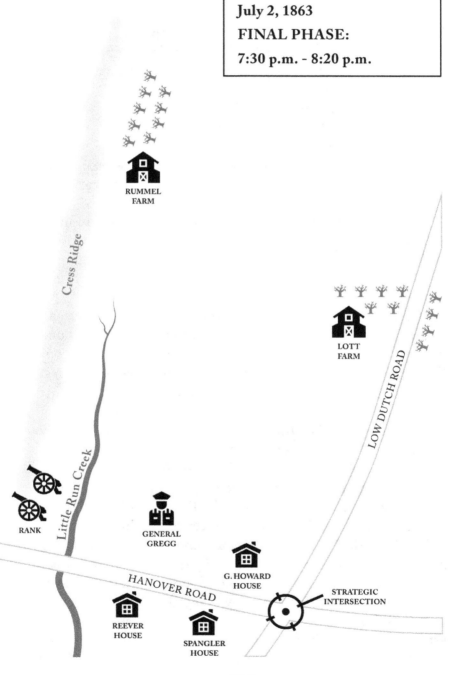

Fight for Brinkerhoff's Ridge
July 2, 1863
FINAL PHASE:
7:30 p.m. – 8:20 p.m.

RUMMEL
FARM

Cress Ridge

LOTT
FARM

LOW DUTCH ROAD

Little Run Creek

RANK

GENERAL
GREGG

G. HOWARD
HOUSE

STRATEGIC
INTERSECTION

HANOVER ROAD

REEVER
HOUSE

SPANGLER
HOUSE

Miller stood at the head of the D and H companies, which were formed in a single line. He glanced over at Captain Frank Hess standing in front of his squadron of two Third Pennsylvania companies.

"Are you ready, Captain Hess?" Miller shouted.

"We're ready," Hess shouted back.

Miller bellowed, "Squadrons, move out!" and strode forward. Hundreds of boot spurs clinked behind him like fine wineglasses. He narrowed his eyes, focusing on the woodlots marking Cress Run. In a matter of moments, the two squadrons crossed Cress Run and angled up the slope toward a long line of trees running northward. A lengthening shadow crept toward the squadrons as they climbed.

Sergeant Wier shouted, "Stay sharp, men. Enemy skirmishers are ahead in that tree line."

Miller's breathing quickened and he picked up the pace and lengthened his stride. As he stepped onto the elevated ground marking the tree line, he scanned underneath the tree canopy. Forty yards ahead was a tall stone fence running along the crest of the ridge. A jolt shot through him. Fifty yards on the other side of the stone fence, a line of Rebel infantry was advancing toward the wall. *Must reach the wall first.* The pit of his belly tightened as he belched a trumpeting breath.

"Double quick to the stone wall!" he shouted.

Miller's squadron surged forward, sprinting.

Sergeant Wier bellowed, "Beat the Rebels to the wall!"

Miller spotted a Confederate officer raising his sword. The Rebel shouted, "Charge!" The enemy line surged forward. The race was on. He shot a glance at Corporal Andrew Speese shooting past him. Right behind Speese, Private Nicholas Woods sprinted and burst past, winning the race to the stone wall. Woods rested his carbine on top of the wall and fired. Two artillery projectiles shrieked overhead and swooped down with a thundering crash among the front line of the advancing enemy.

Screams rent the air as several enemy fell to the ground dead and others hobbled, mangled by shrapnel.

Miller skidded into the stone wall. The enemy was twenty paces away. The hairs on his neck stood erect. He aimed and fired his revolver. An enemy soldier clutched his belly, screamed, and fell to the ground. Brooke-Rawle slid in next to him.

"Did you see the accuracy of Rank's artillery boys?" Brooke-Rawle said.

Miller nodded. "That was superb shooting. It delayed the Rebels just long enough to let us win the race to the stone wall."

Miller's squadron reached the wall and opened a murderous barrage with their carbines. The first line of the enemy tumbled to the ground. Miller's troopers cheered.

Sergeant Wier shouted, "Keep firing."

They aimed and fired repeatedly, tearing flesh and killing like ravening animals. He glanced northward along the wall. His blue troopers were pounding the wall with the butts of their carbines and punching holes through the wall, creating castle-like parapets.

Rifles rattled and bullets whizzed as the Pennsylvanians delivered point-blank fire. Rank's artillery shells screamed overhead. The Rebels were pinned between the stone wall and Rank's shells hitting behind them. A dense smoke cloud enveloped no-man's-land. The enemy repeatedly charged, and each time, Miller's troopers threw them back.

8:00 p.m. (Sunset 7:44 p.m.)
Captain William Miller
Stone wall

Miller stared into the darkness and could not spot any Rebels. An eerie silence draped the battlefield, the foreboding pause between the widow taking the podium and delivering her husband's eulogy. His heart thumped in his ears. Sweat trickled down his brow. He wiped it away with his hand.

"I can't see any of the enemy," Brooke-Rawle said. "Are they done attacking?"

"Perhaps," Miller answered.

A screeching yell pierced the air on Miller's right flank. He wheeled. Yellow flashes were erupting like fireflies. Twenty paces away, a host of demonic shadows sprinted toward them. The forces collided and his troopers on the flank fled back, some staggering, some sprinting. Terror gripped him by the throat.

"Stay together." Miller shouted. He fired his pistol at a screaming, ghostly figure, hitting the Rebel in the gut. The enemy hordes streaked past on either side like ravaging wolves. He twisted and fired, hitting a Rebel in the back.

Miller bellowed, "Sergeant Wier, our flank is collapsing. Order the men south of us to pivot their line like a swinging gate. I'm the pivot point."

Wier skittered back down the line. The Rebels shrieked like battle-lusted berserkers. Miller fired point-blank, blasting a demonic face, the head jerking back, the eye socket bursting blood. A shiver jolted through him.

Brooke-Rawle bounded next to him, firing his revolver. "William, Sergeant Wier's troopers are rushing forward."

"Good."

Blood pounded in Miller's ear. Wier's troopers were swinging into a transverse defensive line. "Sergeant, let me know when our troopers are behind the transverse line."

He turned and bellowed, "Lieutenant Brooke-Rawle, fall back behind Wier's line." His muscles tightened and he darted for the defensive line like a fleeing cottontail. The Rebels chased close behind, howling for blood. Brooke-Rawle beat him through the troopers' line.

Wier shouted, "All the troopers are behind the line."

Miller turned. "Open fire!"

Carbines cracked and bullets zipped thick and fast, ripping into flesh. The Rebels shrieked and halted. The Union troopers poured sheets of lead into the enemy. Screams of the dying and wounded filled the air.

"Captain Miller, we're holding them!" Wier shouted.

Long wolf-howls shrieked from the Rebels.

"I agree. Keep the troopers firing."

A second wave of blue troopers pulled up behind the kneeling transverse line and fired a blistering volley. Miller's ears cracked. His heart raced. He aimed toward a yellow flash and fired, and an enemy soldier screamed.

A Southern voice shouted, "Withdraw, boys, withdraw!"

The enemy flankers stopped firing and fled the melee into the darkness. A short silence, then a huge roar erupted from Miller's squadron. Miller's scuffed soul leaped. His troopers had held the ridge.

"Captain Miller," Wier said, "see those troopers standing behind the kneeling soldiers?"

Miller turned and nodded. "Yes, I do."

"Most of them are Tenth New Yorkers from Major Kemper's squadron—Companies H and L. They were the first squadron to arrive on the ridge at 3:00 p.m. They had fallen back to Cress Run, and when we crossed the creek, they joined us as we ascended the ridge."

The corners of Miller's lips quirked into a light smile. "I'm proud of those Tenth New Yorkers. They have had one hell of a day!"

A long-range Parrot rifled cannon commands the fields along today's
East Confederate Avenue, north of the Rummel Farm

38

Gregg — Thursday, July 2

8:30 p.m.
General David Gregg
Hanover and Low Dutch Road Intersection

Gregg puffed on his pipe as the growing darkness blanketed Cress Ridge. He turned to Captain Henry Meyer. "Damn't Henry, we were lucky today. If the Rebels had attacked in full force this afternoon, they would have clobbered us."

"The boys put up one hell of a fight after riding all night from Hanover Junction."

Gregg sniffed and chuckled. "Henry, you still smell like rotten fish."

A courier arrived and saluted. "General Gregg, General Pleasonton wishes to report that Meade's forces repulsed Lee's army this afternoon and evening."

A rush of joy swelled in Gregg's chest. He nodded his head. *Thank you, God.* Culp's Hill thundered with artillery and rifle fire like an erupting volcano. "What about the fighting on Culp's Hill? It sounds like a major battle."

"General Greene's lone brigade is defending Culp's Hill from entrenched positions. Greene is holding. The rest of Slocum's Twelfth Corps is darting back to Culp's Hill to reinforce Greene's forces."

"What happened to Sickles's Third Corps?"

"They were overrun and decimated. Sickles suffered a severe leg wound when a bouncing solid shot shattered his lower leg."

"Will he live?"

"Not sure. He lost a lot of blood and was removed to a rear hospital."

331

Gregg puffed on his pipe. *Sickles is a flaming idiot for disobeying Meade's orders and endangering the entire army. I hope Meade court-martials Sickles's ass.*

"What does Meade think Lee will do tomorrow?"

"Colonel Sharpe, Meade's intelligence officer, believes Lee will attack Meade's forces again tomorrow."

Gregg nodded. "Understood." He thought for a moment. "Please inform General Pleasonton that my division successfully defended Brinkerhoff's Ridge from a Confederate infantry assault." He pointed. "See that house on the third ridge?"

"I see it."

"Tell General Pleasanton and Colonel Sharpe I believe I spotted Jeb Stuart and his small cavalcade next to that house around 6:00 p.m. Old Jeb was wearing a cape and his plumed ostrich hat was cocked to the side."

The courier nodded.

"My guess is that his exhausted troops arrived late in the afternoon at Gettysburg, and he rode to Lee's left flank to assess the situation."

"How long was Jeb on the ridge?"

"Just long enough to survey the terrain and see how large a cavalry force was defending Meade's right flank." His breath stalled. "I have a gut feeling I may face Jeb Stuart's cavalry tomorrow."

The courier saluted and departed.

He turned to his brother Thomas Jackson Gregg. "T.J., I think I solved the great mystery of where Stuart is. That should be helpful news to Meade."

"What do you think he learned?" T.J. said.

Gregg packed his pipe. "Stuart spotted my divisional flag and knows he is facing me." He lit his pipe and blew smoke rings. "Jeb observed Major Kemper's Tenth New York squadron scrambling up through the wheat fields and threatening Brinkerhoff's Ridge. What concerns me is that Stuart learned that my division is missing at least a brigade. Stuart knows now that he outnumbers my forces."

T.J. frowned, shaking his head. "What do you think Stuart will do tomorrow?"

David Gregg stared northward toward the dark trees of Cress Ridge. "If I were Jeb, I would mass my cavalry north of Cress Ridge and then attack down the sloping field, break through our depleted defences, and race into Meade's rear."

T.J.'s eyes widened. "Stuart outnumbers your forces by three-fold. What are you going to do?"

"If and when Stuart shows up tomorrow, I'm going to do what any good chess player would do. I'm going to surprise him with an opening move that he won't expect."

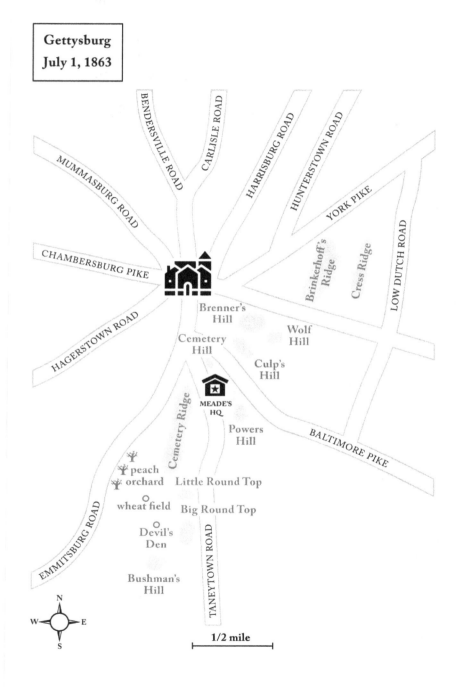

Gettysburg
July 1, 1863

BENDERSVILLE ROAD

CARLISLE ROAD

MUMMASBURG ROAD

HARRISBURG ROAD

HUNTERSTOWN ROAD

YORK PIKE

LOW DUTCH ROAD

CHAMBERSBURG PIKE

Brinkerhoff's Ridge

Cress Ridge

HAGERSTOWN ROAD

Brenner's Hill

Wolf Hill

Cemetery Hill

Culp's Hill

MEADE'S HQ

Cemetery Ridge

Powers Hill

BALTIMORE PIKE

peach orchard

Little Round Top

wheat field

Big Round Top

EMMITSBURG ROAD

Devil's Den

TANEYTOWN ROAD

Bushman's Hill

N
W   E
S

1/2 mile

334

39

Kilpatrick — Thursday, July 2

11:00 p.m.
Kilpatrick
Grass Hotel

Kilpatrick winced as coarse tremors wracked his lower back. *Damn kidneys.* He leaned forward in the chair, lowered the rectangular pillow, and leaned back against the down-and-feather batting. He gripped a shot glass of bourbon sitting on the map table and tipped the glass to his lips. The fumes tingled the roof of his mouth. He closed his eyes, letting the whiskey slip across his tongue. A warm burn settled in his throat. *Lovely.* The aching eased.

He glanced at Custer studying a map of the Gettysburg area. Devilish mischief danced across Fanny's face. *Damn glory hound, always craving the attention from reporters.* Custer may have hopscotched to general, but his days of gallivanting about, untethered like a cadet at West Point, were over. He would keep Fanny on a short leash.

Captain Estes stepped into the room. "Sir, General Farnsworth will arrive shortly."

Kilpatrick nodded. He turned to Custer. "I received the casualty report from the Battle of Hunterstown. Four officers were wounded. Four enlisted killed in action or mortally wounded in action. Two prisoners of war and nine missing in action for total casualties numbering nineteen."

Custer added, "Nine of those casualties are from Troop A, Sixth Michigan."

"George, I heard you were unhorsed and had a close call today."

"Yes, my Custer luck was working overtime today. I was most fortunate that my orderly Private Norvell Churchill was right

335

there to kill the Rebel officer trying to slash me after my horse was killed."

"You've always been one lucky son of a bitch, George. I can't remember all the times you got away with murder at the Academy."

Custer seethed.

"I have a different view of Custer luck," Kilpatrick went on. "Your good fortune is that war artist Alfred Waud wasn't present to draw your inglorious tumble and a lowly private saving your sorry ass. That's the sketch that should have appeared in *Harper's Weekly*. Not the one of you at the Battle of Aldie."

Custer's face flushed red.

"You see, George. I'm one of the few people who knows the real Custer. I was never impressed with your puckish charm at West Point. My biggest regret at the Academy was tolerating your antics instead of getting you dismissed as an undesirable."

Custer furrowed his brow, plainly angry.

"I'll tell you this just one time, George. I expect you to toe the line. No shenanigans. Do you understand?"

Custer nodded, tight-lipped. "Yes, sir."

Farnsworth walked into the room and saluted. "Reporting as ordered, sir."

Kilpatrick paused, eyeing both boy generals. "I'm proud of both of your aggressive actions yesterday and today. That's exactly what General Pleasonton was hoping for when he recommmended you both to become generals."

Both men nodded.

Custer said, "The officer leading the Rebel guard was my classmate at West Point...Pierce Young."

Kilpatrick pursed his lips and bottled an urge to swear. "I hope you shot that slave-owning Georgian."

Custer shook his head. "He almost shot my head off, that Benedict Arnold."

"Can you blame him? I would have done the same thing." Kilpatrick reached behind himself and grabbed his aching back. "George, I rode to the Felty Ridge just before sunset. Choosing to lead Company A down that narrow, hemmed-in road was one hell of a saber charge."

Custer smiled.

Kilpatrick paused for a moment, holding his breath as he rubbed his back, jaws clamped. Damn kidneys were flaming like a fiery ember. He turned and snarled at Farnsworth. "Elon, hopefully you will get a chance to outshine George in a saber charge."

Farnsworth stared, tight-jawed and clenched-fisted. Kilpatrick fought to control the gleeful thrill of goading Elon. *Good.* Farnsworth would bend like a reed in the wind if he blustered hard enough.

Elon dropped his eyes and turned to peer at Custer. "George, that was an impressive saber charge."

"Thank you, Elon. I was a little surprised by the number of enemy forces around the bend."

"I received Storrs's report and his encounter with General Wade Hampton," Kilpatrick said. "Storrs said he slashed Hampton in the head. I hope that Southern traitor bleeds to death."

"I also talked with Storrs," Custer said, " and it seems that Hampton's entire brigade was on Hunterstown Road when Storrs caught him. Hampton was being pretty cavalier, riding ahead of his brigade without security forces."

Farnsworth said, "My guess is that our actions today prevented Hampton's brigade from reinforcing Lee's flank against Culp's Hill.

"I agree," Kilpatrick said.

Captain Estes pelted into the room, escorting a captain. "General Pleasonton's courier has critical orders."

Captain George Yates saluted. "General Pleasonton orders you to move your division immediately to Two Taverns."

Kilpatrick said, "Point to it on the map."

Yates pointed. "Here it is. It's a small settlement along the Baltimore Pike."

"It's due south of Hunterstown. Why are we abandoning Hunterstown?"

"Meade's left flank has been without cavalry support since early in the afternoon."

"How in the hell did that happen?"

"There was a mix-up in orders and Buford departed the left flank without being properly relieved. He rode toward Westminster to provide security for army supplies at Westminster and to refit after fighting most of the first day of the battle."

Kilpatrick glowered. "Buford is always looking to skedaddle somewhere for a respite. You tell General Pleasonton that we had a great victory at Hanover and a great victory today at Hunterstown. Kilpatrick's boys don't run from a fight. We run toward the fight."

40

Custer — Friday, July 3

uster's mind pulsed with frothing anger. The incessant throbbing pounded against his skull. He had been ingloriously unhorsed and nearly killed, and damn Kilpatrick had insulted him like a school headmaster. No, there was no glory today. In fact, his unhorsing had sparked a gale of guffaws from his Wolverines. He rubbed his aching head.

Colerick was riding beside him. William was a good officer. He was lucky to have him as his aide-de-camp. Churchill trotted a horse length behind on his left. *And thank God for Private Churchill*. Norvell was fearless.

The Michigan Brigade trudged down the Low Dutch Road, lit by a waning full moon. The night's cold light shimmered off the road like glinting sabers. Thousands of echoing hooves pattered against the dirt road. Custer narrowed his eyes and stared ahead along the endless corridor of chirping crickets. A growing bitterness was eclipsing the dissolving euphoria of his first victory as a general. The approval he craved so desperately from his Wolverines was missing. Instead, he was being denounced with ridicule. Despite his dashing charge and daring grit at Hunterstown, the bearded Wolverines called him *boy general* and sneered in mocking amusement. He had yet to prove himself to the quippy veterans accusing him of being a madcap glory hunter.

He glanced to his left as Churchill pulled up, stirrup to stirrup. Did he look as boyishly young as Norvell? Was that the problem? Perhaps. But young or old, he loved being a swashbuckling dragoon and, like Napoleon's Murat, he believed in heroic leadership.

A cavalcade of scouts trotted up. A sergeant saluted. "General Custer, we rode down the Low Dutch Road, and when we hit the Baltimore Pike, we trotted down to Two Taverns. We didn't spot Rebels."

"Very well."

"We passed General Gregg's division on our way to Two Taverns. Gregg's brigades are bivouacked where White Run crosses the Baltimore Pike. I expect your brigade will arrive at the Two Taverns bivouac around four a.m."

He nodded. Hopefully his pounding headache would be gone by then.

"General Farnsworth's brigade is about half an hour behind your brigade. General Pleasonton is riding at the head."

"Thank you."

No sooner had the scouts departed than Colerick, whose head was drooping, snorted awake, gasping for air.

"William, are you trying to wake the dead?" Custer teased him.

"Sorry, General."

The night dragged on. The dark was a frustrating reminder of the bitterness swirling in his stormy mind. It wasn't his fault Hunterstown Road was fenced in. Kilpatrick told him to attack, and he did. His fuming face burned. He hated the withering sarcasm being uttered about him by his Wolverines.

His mind traveled back to yesterday's charge. Stuart's troopers had deployed in a massive line, blocking the Hunterstown Road heading to Gettysburg. They stared, defiant and cocksure, gripping their glittering carbines. He rode ahead of his sixty troopers, halted, and spied the Confederates through his field glasses. Some Rebels had pointed, and some laughed, clearly mocking his grand uniform and his small force. Bloodlust coursed through his veins. They were daring him to charge.

His Wolverines were muttering behind him. "Custer is a foolhardy hotspur if he charges. It's a trap waiting to spring."

"Our boy general is a clownlike peacock masquerading as a mud-lark." A deep voice echoed, "He needs his feathers plucked."

His overbearing pride had clanged inside his skull like a bouncing bell clapper. He twisted in his saddle and peered at his dragoons. A bitter taste whirled in his mouth. They were waiting like watchful theater critics, judging to see what Murat's glorious protégé in full costume would do. He drew his saber. The squadron stared with dropped jaws and open mouths, as if he were a harlequin. His Wolverines had not seen his glorious charge at the Battle of Aldie. Or his gallantry at Brandy Station. But he was only a supporting actor in those battles. He was now center stage and the lead actor. His credo guiding him at West Point and through the first two years of the war had pulsed in his mind. *Allow nothing to swerve me from my purpose, however perilous and uncertain.*

He had no choice. He believed in the proverb *audentes fortuna juvat* —fortune favors the bold. He had turned and glared at the cocky Rebels. A forceful urge pulsed through him, and he raised his saber and shouted "Charge!" He spurred his mount and raced ahead like a thunderbolt. His Wolverines yelled and screamed as a tidal wave of blue dragoons surged forward at full gallop.

It was a glorious charge. Sixty troopers attacking a Confederate regiment. Every man for himself, the Devil for all.

Risk is a hazard of the die, and it was worth rolling the cube. Despite nine Wolverine casualties in the Company A, Sixth Michigan charge, he would lead that charge again. But he had been unhorsed like a dethroned feudal baron. A low groan rumbled from his throat. His brigade had witnessed Private Churchill racing back to friendly lines with him mounted behind, holding on for dear life, amid a rain of Rebel rifle bullets. Pride poured from the cracked seams of his soul. Being carried back had sullied his glory.

He glanced at Churchill and uttered a deep sigh. If not for Norvell, he would be dead.

The stars glinted through the opaque shadows of darkness. He rubbed his stiff shoulder, aching with a sluggish throb. Luckily, his fall and near death had acted as bait that the Rebels swallowed. The enemy unwisely chased him back into the blazing jaws of Pennington's big guns and the lead storm of Michigan repeating rifles. The shocked Confederates were caught in a deadly crossfire, were cut up, and retreated.

It was his first heroic charge and his brigade's first victory as their commander. It wouldn't be his last. Luck was his guiding star, and Custer luck had prevailed. Warmth coursed through him. Despite being ridiculed in private, Kilpatrick had praised him in public and cited him for gallantry. He winced. But the cruel whispers about the *boy general* still swirled.

He turned to Churchill. "If Kilpatrick would have pursued Stuart after we bloodied his nose at Hanover, we wouldn't be worried tonight about Rebel phantoms appearing."

"We missed a great opportunity to fight Stuart's boys again," Churchill responded.

"Agreed." The rawboned bantam Kilpatrick was acting timid. Custer fought to control his raging anger. His brain flashed to Kilpatrick's brutal fistfight at West Point after Georgia cadet Pierce Young hung John Brown's body in effigy from a West Point barracks window. What happened to Kilpatrick after the Hanover battle, the firebrand who was willing to fight any Southern cadet sowing the seeds of sedition?

His mount's front leg crooked, thrusting him forward against the saddle's pommel and jolting his frozen shoulder. He winced. It felt like a hot poker stabbing into his arm joint and shearing the stiff tendons. He rubbed his throbbing shoulder, still smarting from tumbling from his mount during the Hunterstown melee.

"Is your shoulder feeling any better?" Churchill asked.

He grimaced and shook his head. No matter the odds, he would never pass up a chance to lead a saber charge. He loved being a daredevil, craving the giddy jolts of passion, the crunching collisions, the ducking and twisting, the thrusting and slashing, the scraping and clanging of steel. Afterwards, he relished the troopers' cheers, making him feel like a mythical hero. If given the chance today, he would prove his worth and capture the imaginations of his Flying Devils.

Churchill studied Custer rubbing his shoulder. The general's broad-brimmed hat draped over his left ear. Even though injured, Custer rode with a lively devil-may-care style. He had heard the Wolverines babbling after Custer's charge at Hunterstown. They called him reckless and impulsive. He confounds bravery with stupidity, they said. Others said it was a boyish stunt, leading a grand charge of sixty troopers against three hundred enemy cavalrymen. Custer's sheer folly resulted in Captain Thompson, a well-liked fighter and commander, being severely wounded.

Churchill wiped his brow. But there was a growing respect for the boy general from the younger Wolverines. No one now doubted his raw courage and daring gallantry. He charged fearlessly and heedlessly, wielding a great sword as if masquerading as one of the four horsemen of the Apocalypse. He could blind you with his brilliant bursts of charm and fiery excitement.

Churchill smiled. He would follow General George Armstrong Custer to the gates of hell.

Custer turned to Churchill. "Norvell, I want to thank you again for saving my life in yesterday's fight."

Churchill sat up a little straighter. "Sir, it is my duty as your special orderly to protect you. I'm lucky I was close enough to defend you. You were sprinting forward like you were racing a thoroughbred."

"When I was unhorsed and sprawled out on the ground, gasping for breath, I spotted the Rebel reining up, baring his fanged teeth and brandishing his saber. For a moment, the Rebel disappeared in the cloud of dust billowing up from the horse's hooves."

"That dust cloud saved you, sir. When you disappeared briefly, the Rebel paused before slashing at your arm. Before he could strike again, I spurred forward and parried his killing blow with my saber. Then I pulled my revolver and shot him."

"Fortunately, the Rebel only slashed my jacket sleeve. Next time I lead a charge, I will make sure of two things: You're right next to me, and we're not hemmed in by a fence."

"I will be right next to you, General Custer."

Custer rubbed his shoulder. He was damn lucky Churchill had chased him and was close enough to save his ass. He drew a deep breath and stretched his breast muscles. His mind warned, *Your Wolverines aren't invincible. Even the best troopers can be pushed too far.*

He shook his head and grinned. "Lieutenant Colerick says you're quite the gifted horseman. Perhaps the best in the Michigan Brigade."

Churchill nodded. "I'm not sure about that. But I know a few tricks."

"Let's see one."

Churchill reached into his coat pocket and held out a white handkerchief. "Take this, General, and ride ahead a couple rods and drop it."

Custer gripped the handkerchief and rode forward into the moonlit night. He twisted in his saddle and shouted, "I'm dropping it."

He released the handkerchief and it floated downward like a snowflake. Norvell spurred his mount and slid nearly out of his saddle as if catching a runaway steer. A foot above the ground, he snatched the handkerchief with his teeth and bolted back up.

Custer stared. "I've never seen anyone perform that trick. And you did it in the dead of night. You must have eyes like an owl and the agility of a circus rider."

Norvell removed the handkerchief from his mouth. "My daytime vision is also pretty good, like a red-tailed hawk. I think I will need it to keep up with you."

Custer smiled. The stiffness in his frozen shoulder started to thaw.

41

Gregg — Friday, July 3

3:30 a.m.
General David Gregg
White Run Creek and Baltimore Pike

Gregg stood over a barrel of flour, studying a map, his stomach growling. He turned the wick up on the oil lamp at the edge of the makeshift table. He fished out his watch. Half past three.

Sunup was in a couple hours. Meade had decided to stay in his fishhook defense today and wait to see if Lee would attack or retreat. He shivered. Pleasonton had ordered him to vacate the Hanover and Low Dutch Road strategic intersection. Did Meade know his right flank was undefended and hanging in the air?

His mind swirled like the smoke from his pipe. His orders yesterday were to protect the right flank of the army, which curved like a fishhook around Culp's Hill. His worn-out troopers had succeeded. Major Avery's Tenth New Yorkers and Captain William Miller's Third Pennsylvanians had performed exceptionally well, driving the enemy back from the stone wall and holding Brinkerhoff's Ridge. Rank's battery's accurate shooting had been a godsend. He smiled. Rank's gunners had even cured the old lady of using her cane.

He stroked his thick black beard as if milking a cow's teat. He glanced through the dark blanket covering his division, bivouacking next to White Run. His exhausted troopers lay as if dead, snoring like denning bears. Boot spurs jingled in the darkness, and his breath quickened. Captain Henry Weir emerged like a ghostly apparition. The captain set down a steaming cup of coffee on the map table.

345

"Thanks, Henry. You gave me a start." He sipped the steaming brew, letting its witchlike power jolt his fatigued body. He placed his finger on the map. "Henry, I'm concerned that General Pleasonton ordered us to vacate Brinkerhoff's Ridge last evening."

Weir pointed. "Apparently, General Pleasonton wanted us to occupy this area along the Baltimore Pike to protect the army's supply and reserve artillery trains."

"I smell danger." Gregg stroked his beard. "Remember yesterday, when that Confederate general and his cavalcade arrived on the brow of Brinkerhoff's Ridge?"

"Yes, they watched the Tenth New Yorkers defend the ridge from six p.m. to seven p.m."

"I noticed the cavalry general wearing a foot-long ostrich-plumed hat. I believe it was Stuart himself. Jeb saw what we observed. That wide, sloping plain stretching southward from the high-ground perch of Cress Ridge."

He pointed to the Rummel farm and the Cress Ridge defending the farm's northern border.

"These woodlots of tall hardwood trees cover the southern crown of Cress Ridge like a green quilt. The dense timber extends northward to the upper end of Cress Ridge and conceals the Stallsmith farm. Beyond the farm are large, open fields that could serve as a staging area for Stuart's cavalry division. The Cress Ridge woods could conceal Stuart's cavalry and enable them to advance under cover, down the ridge's brow onto the sloping Rummel fields under cover."

Weir nodded.

"I remember yesterday how the terrain funnels downhill from the top of the Cress Ridge past the Rummel farm into a valley and crosses the Hanover Road," Gregg continued. "The narrow part of the funnel flows into these two lanes, the White Creek and Low Dutch dirt roads. These two secluded byways are lined with patches of timber and afford direct access to the immediate rear of the Union army."

Weir said, "Cress Ridge reminds me of the masked country on General Howard's right flank at Chancellorsville."

"Agreed. Cress Ridge controls the wide plain of fields stretching toward our army's rear. I've been fighting Stuart long enough to know he can't pass up this opportunity to attack the army's right flank from the woods of Cress Ridge. It's what I would do if I were him."

"The Rummel land would be a perfect field for a grand cavalry charge if it wasn't for the stone and post-and-rail fences crisscrossing the fields," Weir said.

"Good point. But if Pleasonton chooses to leave the Rummel fields unoccupied, Stuart's cavalry will mosey down to the Hanover Road like a Sunday stroll and then spill into the rear of Meade's army like a storm surge."

4:00 a.m. (Dawn 4:16 a.m.)
General David Gregg
White Run Creek and Baltimore Pike

Clapping hooves pelted the white crushed-limestone road, heralding Weir's arrival.

"General, our scouts report Kilpatrick's division is moving down the Low Dutch Road." Weir pointed. "General Custer is the lead brigade, and they should be arriving on the Baltimore Pike momentarily."

Gregg smiled. "That's good news. Ride out and meet General Custer and request his presence at my headquarters."

Weir departed into the dying darkness.

4:10 a.m.
General David Gregg
White Run Creek and Baltimore Pike

Jingling spurs filled the air like a chorus of winter sleigh bells as Weir returned, bringing Custer with him. Dawn's gilded light radiated in Custer's golden locks as darkness continued its slow surrender.

Custer dismounted and saluted. "General Gregg, reporting as ordered, sir."

347

"George, I'm mighty glad the Michigan Brigade is arriving. General Pleasonton's courier reported late last night that you had quite a little fight at Hunterstown. Apparently, you ran into General Hampton's rear guard."

"That is right. The Wolverines fought well. General Kilpatrick received orders about eleven p.m. to march south to Two Taverns along the Baltimore Pike. Kilpatrick is riding with Farnsworth's brigade and should arrive in a half hour or so. What are you expecting today?"

"General Meade has survived two days of attacks in his fishhook defense." Gregg pointed towards the sun's yellow fingers stretching across the gray skies. "In that direction about two and a half miles is Culp's Hill, and that's the right flank and barb of the fishhook defense. Today, Meade is expecting Lee to attack the middle of the fishhook defense along Cemetery Ridge."

"What about Stuart's cavalry? What are you expecting?"

"Remember the intersection of Low Dutch Road and Hanover Road that you crossed early this morning?"

"Yes."

"Two miles to the west of that intersection is Brinkerhoff's Ridge, and my division spent most of the afternoon and early evening yesterday skirmishing with General Walker's Stonewall Brigade of Johnson's division. My gut tells me that General Stuart and his staff watched this fight."

"Are you expecting Stuart to mount an attack from Brinkerhoff's Ridge today?"

"Hell, Jeb doesn't even have to attack. He can just waltz right down the ridge because damn Pleasonton made me pull all my forces from the strategic intersection."

"My God, what are you going to do?"

"A few minutes ago, I sent a courier to Pleasanton requesting a third brigade."

A thread of sunlight lit Custer's face.

"If I get a third brigade, I will have them face Brinkerhoff's Ridge in case of a possible attack. That's where the Confederate infantry attacked from yesterday." He stroked his beard. "But

Stuart may try to attack from the northeastern part of Cress Ridge."

"Why Cress Ridge?"

"True, it would take Stuart a lot longer to get to Cress Ridge. He would have to ride up the York Pike and then turn south. But there is a large woodlot on the northern crown of Cress Ridge where Stuart can conceal his force. If he attacks from Cress Ridge into the valley below and crosses Hanover Road, he can surge down Low Dutch Road southwest into the rear of Meade's army."

He shook his head. "If Pleasonton orders Kilpatrick to send one of his brigades to the strategic intersection, I will order the brigade to face toward Brinkerhoff's Ridge because that's the shortest distance for Jeb to launch an attack."

Custer grinned. "I sure hope it's my brigade Pleasonton orders to the strategic intersection. If the opportunity arises, I would consider it an honor to have the Michigan Brigade support your division. With your leave, I will proceed to my Two Taverns bivouac."

"Permission granted. Also, congratulations on your promotion, George."

Custer saluted. "Thank you, sir."

6:00 a.m.
General David Gregg
White Run Creek and Baltimore Pike

Gregg peered down the Baltimore Pike at the sun blooming in a perfect flame on the horizon. He shook his head as the sky heated up. How many soldiers and troopers were witnessing their last sunrise? Too many! He gazed up the Pike, spotting a distant rider galloping toward his headquarters.

General Pleasonton's aide-de-camp, Captain George Yates, reined up and saluted.

"General Gregg, General Pleasonton orders you to move your division to a position between White Run and Cemetery Hill in the event of a change in the main Union line."

Gregg said, "What if the Union line remains the same?"

"You are to remain at White Run. This point is so important it must be held at all hazards."

His stomach tied into knots. "Captain Yates, if I execute this order, the Union right flank will be dangerously vulnerable to attack by Stuart's cavalry. The Low Dutch Road would be exposed and open for the enemy to race down it into the army's rear."

"What message do you want me to give to General Pleasanton?"

Gregg frowned. "I regard the situation on the right of our army as exceedingly perilous. I am familiar with the terrain east of Brinkerhoff's Ridge. It's open, and there are two roads leading from Hanover Road to the Baltimore Turnpike. If these two roads are not covered by a sufficient force of cavalry it would invite an attack upon our rear with possibly disastrous results."

"I will relay your concerns to General Pleasanton," Yates said.

"Please remind General Pleasonton that my division is depleted with Colonel Pennock Huey's brigade detached and guarding Westminster. I only have two brigades. If I am to guard both the intersection of White Run and Baltimore Pike and the intersection of the Hanover and Low Dutch Road, I will request one of General Kilpatrick's brigades, preferably General Custer's Wolverine Brigade."

"Understood, General Gregg." Yates departed.

6:58 a.m.
General David Gregg
White Run Creek and Baltimore Pike

Gregg ran his finger along the map roads on the army's right flank. He fought to contain the anger percolating up his throat. His instincts seesawed between obedience and defiance. Should he order Colonel Gregg's brigade to occupy the right flank if Pleasonton refused his request to bolster it?

"Captain Yates is galloping up," an aide shouted.

Gregg didn't take his eyes off Yates as the lieutenant reined up and remained mounted.

"General Gregg, I relayed your concerns to General Pleasonton. Your previous orders stand. But General Pleasonton gave you the discretion to detach one of General Kilpatrick's brigades to the Hanover Road and Low Dutch Road intersection if you're concerned covering the army's right flank."

"Very well." A knot loosened inside him. "I will coordinate with General Kilpatrick."

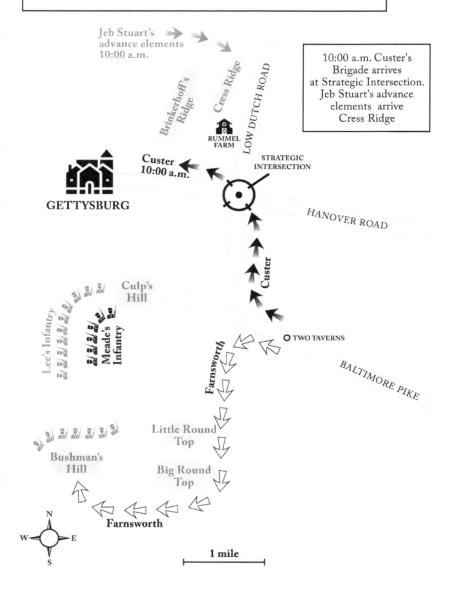

Farnsworth's Brigade Marches to Bushman's Hill, 8:00 a.m.

Custer's Brigade Marches toward Strategic Intersection, 8:30 a.m.

July 3, 1863

Jeb Stuart's advance elements 10:00 a.m.

10:00 a.m. Custer's Brigade arrives at Strategic Intersection. Jeb Stuart's advance elements arrive Cress Ridge

Brinkerhoff's Ridge

Cress Ridge

LOW DUTCH ROAD

RUMMEL FARM

Custer 10:00 a.m.

STRATEGIC INTERSECTION

GETTYSBURG

HANOVER ROAD

Custer

Culp's Hill

Lee's Infantry

Meade's Infantry

TWO TAVERNS

Farnsworth

BALTIMORE PIKE

Little Round Top

Bushman's Hill

Big Round Top

Farnsworth

N
W   E
S

1 mile

42

Kilpatrick — Friday, July 3

6:00 a.m. (58 minutes earlier)
Kilpatrick
Third Division Bivouac at Two Taverns

Kilpatrick's heart pounded as he trotted toward Custer's bivouac. Artillery fire thundered from Culp's Hill. What a glorious morning. For the past two days the two armies had mauled each other on the Gettysburg fields. Today the fate of the Union would be decided, and his cavalry division could play a heroic role. He could feel it in his bones. He smirked, catching two of Custer's senior officers curled up under the same rubber blanket. *Damn Custer. He'd let his troopers snooze all morning if he could get away with it. Only in command of his brigade for three days and already his officers are becoming slackers, just like Cinnamon was at West Point.*

"Major Noah Ferry and Major Luther Trowbridge," Kilpatrick shouted. "Come on, boys, turn out, turn out!"

Ferry sat up and yawned. He shook Trowbridge's shoulder. "Wake up, Luther. General Kilpatrick is calling us."

Kilpatrick glanced at Trowbridge lying flat on the ground and rubbing his eyes. "Major Trowbridge, turn out." Trowbridge rose up. "We are all going in today, and we are going to clean 'em out."

Both majors nodded. Kilpatrick glared at Trowbridge. "I couldn't find General Custer, so thought I'd just turn you out myself. Locate Custer and tell him to have his brigade ready to depart by eight a.m. My division is not going to miss this battle."

He pulled on the reins, clapped his spurs, and headed for General Farnsworth's bivouac. His departing comment hung in the air, glorious and clear. He would never rest until he received the nation's praise that he so well deserved. He shook his head.

353

Custer and Farnsworth, what a pair. *My two brigade commanders would sleep all day if I didn't rouse 'em up.*

7:00 a.m.
Kilpatrick
Two Taverns
Along the Baltimore Pike

Standing outside his tent, next to a grove of tall white oaks, Kilpatrick was enveloped in silence.

It was a brooding silence, like his jail cell in the Old Capitol Prison. Why in the hell was his division five miles away from the Gettysburg battlefield, twiddling its thumbs?

He fished out his watch. Seven a.m. His eyes narrowed at the map on the upturned flour barrel that was serving as a makeshift table, studying key roads and strategic intersections. A drop of sweat splattered the map. He glanced up at the dappled sun creeping higher through the leafy canopy. The soaring heat promised to be merciless. He bristled. The color of his fiery face probably matched the color of his long red sideburns. He wiped his brow.

His fame was rising like a shooting star. But General Pleasonton had stuck his cavalry division in the rear of Meade's army for the third day of the Battle of Gettysburg. He muttered a dark curse. He was playing third fiddle to Buford and Gregg's cavalry divisions. He gritted his teeth, suppressing the rage boiling in his gullet.

Hooves clip-clopped from the edge of the bivouac. He glanced up. Captain Llewellyn Estes reined up, dismounted, and trundled toward the map table. His cheeks were flushed, and his clothes were covered in dust.

Kilpatrick's nostrils flared. Wasn't he the hero of the Battle of Hanover a day before Buford's little scrap with Lee's army at Gettysburg? Hell, he had defeated Jeb Stuart, the so-called beau sabreur of the Confederacy, at Hanover. Then yesterday he had whipped one of Stuart's brigades at the Battle of Hunterstown.

Estes saluted.

He scowled and pointed at the map. "Llewellyn, look here at Two Taverns and the Baltimore Pike." His hands squeezed into fists. "Damn't. General Pleasonton has my cavalry division twiddling their thumbs five miles behind the Union lines. I refuse to sit back and miss the Gettysburg battle. This is my chance to appear again on the front page of the *New York Times* like I did after my gallant cavalry charge at Hampton, Virginia."

"Do you want me to ride to army headquarters and visit with General Pleasonton?"

"No, not yet. If I haven't heard anything before eight a.m. I'll send you."

Estes nodded. "What do you think Jeb Stuart is planning today?"

"My guess is that he will split his cavalry forces and deploy half to each of Lee's flanks."

Thundering hooves rattled down the Baltimore Pike's macadam surface, rapping the gloomy air. Kilpatrick spotted a courier galloping toward them at full speed, and an impulse of sudden hope emerged. "It's Yates, Pleasonton's aide-de-camp. Perhaps he has good news."

Yates reined up and saluted. "General Kilpatrick. General Pleasonton sends his respects and requests you move your division to the south of Big Round Top."

He grinned and stepped closer. A great gust of air gushed from his lungs. "That's good news."

Yates reached into his satchel hanging on his hip and removed a sealed envelope. "Here's the written order."

He reached up and gripped the order. His heart danced.

Yates pointed to the map. "Lee's right flank is positioned at the base of Big Round Top. Meade's left flank is anchored on the crest of Big Round Top."

Kilpatrick studied the terrain between Big Round Top and Emmitsburg Road. A pause ensued as he rubbed his back.

Yates continued, "When you arrive to the left of the Union line you will attack the enemy's right flank and rear with your cavalry division. General Pleasonton has ordered General Wesley Merritt's regular cavalry brigade to support your attack.

You will prevent any enemy movement around the left flank of the Army of the Potomac."

Kilpatrick nodded. "Where is General Merritt's brigade, and when do you expect him to arrive on the Union's left flank?"

"General Merritt's brigade spent the night at Emmitsburg, Maryland, eleven miles southwest of Big Round Top. They should arrive around noon."

Kilpatrick felt drenched in a cloudburst of cheer. He would have three cavalry brigades for the attack. He opened the envelope. General Pleasonton had signed the order. He glanced up and beamed.

"Please give my respects to General Pleasonton and tell him I'm moving my division out right away. Tell the general I won't let him down. At the first opportunity, I will attack the enemy." The familiar flame of brawling began to flicker inside.

"Yes, sir." Yates saluted and departed.

Kilpatrick turned to Captain Estes and handed him the envelope. "Llewellyn, this is the order I was waiting for. I'm riding ahead with my headquarters staff to Big Round Top. When I arrive at Farnsworth's bivouac, I will order his brigade to march immediately. I didn't see Custer this morning in the Michigan bivouac. Find Custer and tell him to follow Farnsworth's brigade. Then I want you to join me."

Estes saluted and departed.

Kilpatrick mounted his horse and galloped northwest up the Baltimore Pike. He spotted Farnsworth's brigade flag and reined up. Farnsworth was standing next to his horse, outside his headquarters tent. What was he doing there? Just standing?

"Elon, I just received orders from army headquarters. My division is to move out immediately and ride to the left flank of the army near the Big Round Top. I'm riding ahead to scout the enemy's right flank. I want you to proceed up the Baltimore Pike, cross Marsh Creek, and then head for the Taneytown Road and ride south. I will have my staff meet you east of Big Round Top and guide your brigade into position."

"Understood, General. Is Custer's brigade going to follow me?"

"Yes. Captain Estes is riding to Custer's bivouac to give him the order. He should be departing around eight a.m."

8:00 a.m.
Kilpatrick
En route to Big Round Top

Kilpatrick trotted south and studied the eastern slope of Big Round Top, covered with thick timber and big boulders. He shook his head. The steep slope and boulder-strewn terrain precluded placing artillery on the summit. Riding at the head of Farnsworth's brigade, he turned to the boy general.

"Elon, my orders are to ride to Big Round Top, which is Meade's left flank. Send scouts ahead to survey the terrain and determine where Lee's right flank is anchored.

"Yes, sir."

"Once Custer's brigade and Merritt's brigade arrive, I will attack the enemy."

"With those two brigades and mine," Farnsworth said, "we should be able to overwhelm the Rebels' right flank."

Kilpatrick gulped a quick breath as goosebumps erupted on his arms. "I agree. Perhaps we can even attack Lee's rear and destroy his trains."

General Custer and General Pleasonton

43

Custer — Friday, July 3

*D*amn Kilpatrick! Sending my brigade to plod behind *Farnsworth's brigade, heading for Big Round Top and Bushman's Hill. Making me the last to march, for fear that I might encounter Rebels first and show up my vainglorious divisional commander. Judson, you're an asshole.*

Boredom and uncertainty made Custer fidgety and his mind race. God, he hoped Gregg ordered him to Cress Ridge before Jeb Stuart launched a cavalry attack. This could be a glorious day, instead of standing in the wings while Kilpatrick took center stage. Hmph.

Reluctantly, he turned to Bugler Boehm. "Peter, let's move out."

Boehm drew a deep breath, snapped his copper bugle to his lips, and trumpeted a piercing, C-pitched "Boots and Saddles." The Wolverines swung up onto their mounts, and the long blue column started plodding up the Baltimore Pike.

Custer spied Gregg's adjutant general cantering down the Pike. He smiled as Captain Weir reined up. "Henry, what's the big hurry?"

Weir said, "I have orders for General Kilpatrick."

"General Kilpatrick departed around eight a.m. for Big Round Top, anchoring the army's left flank. What does the order say?"

"General Pleasonton has authorized General Gregg to request one of General Kilpatrick's brigades to move north three miles to the Rummel farm to protect the army's right flank from a possible enemy cavalry attack."

"Did General Gregg say which brigade he preferred?"

"General Gregg said his preference was the Michigan Brigade."

Custer's heart leaped. "My brigade will execute this order. I will march my brigade immediately to the Rummel farm."

Weir's brow furrowed. "Shouldn't General Kilpatrick approve General Gregg's appeal for one of his brigades?"

Custer shook his head. "General Gregg made a compelling argument for General Pleasonton to approve him requesting one of Kilpatrick's brigades. That's good enough for me."

Weir continued, "General Gregg directed me to deliver his order to General Kilpatrick."

Blinding rage shrieked across his nerves. "Gregg doesn't have time for this order to sift down to Kilpatrick and then to me. My brigade is the closest to executing General Pleasonton's orders. If I follow the chain of command, Pleasonton's order will fail to reach Kilpatrick in time for him to direct me to support General Gregg. By that time, Gregg's undersized force could be shattered."

Weir pressed his lips together and grimaced, plainly conflicted. "I'm just a courier delivering this order. I can't jump the chain of command."

Custer bristled. Sharply and coldly, he said, "This crisis demands I ignore the chain of command and take the initiative to fulfill Pleasonton's ordered mission. Between orders and duty, blind obedience and justified defiance hang in the balance. I refuse to let Gregg's outnumbered dragoons dangle on Meade's murky flank like raw meat in front of a bear. I take full responsibility for executing this order without being directed by Kilpatrick."

Weir licked his lips. "You're right about General Gregg being concerned about the right flank. It's vulnerable to attack."

Custer turned to Colerick. "William, inform the brigade we are riding immediately to the Rummel farm. I'm riding ahead with Captain Weir."

Custer trotted next to Weir up the Baltimore Pike toward the Low Dutch Road. He glanced back over his left shoulder, spotting Churchill following a horse length behind. Warmed by his special orderly's loyalty, he turned his head and followed Weir as they rode toward the intersection of White Run and the Baltimore Pike.

He suppressed a shudder at the opportunity to redeem himself for being unhorsed at Hunterstown. His thoughts scrambled to reject that unacceptable humiliation. *Don't doubt yourself. Be sure you're right and go ahead with what you know to be correct. You may have a chance to make a glorious charge today.*

8:30 a.m.
Sergeant George Patten
Baltimore Pike

Sergeant George Patten glanced at the yawning troopers of Company B, Sixth Michigan. Some of the horses were pitching a little. *Only two hours' sleep after an all-night ride. Puffy clouds drifting overhead. If only horses could sail on wind's river. Clattering hooves.* His mouth gaped, uttering a noisy *ahhhh-hhaaaaa.* Major Peter Weber reined up.

"Do you have news, Major?"

"We have new orders, George. General Gregg ordered the Michigan Brigade to ride to the far right of the Union army, at the crossroads of Hanover and Low Dutch Roads."

Patten grinned. "That's a stroke of luck. I feel a lot more secure under the thoughtful judgment of General Gregg than old 'Kill-Cavalry.' Kilpatrick's leadership gives me the chills!"

Weber cracked a smile. "I agree. General Gregg is a good tactician and isn't looking for glory at the expense of his troopers."

"But I am concerned about General Custer, Major. After his foolhardy charge yesterday afternoon outside Hunterstown, it appears he is cut from the same cloth as Kilpatrick. Weren't they in the same graduating class at West Point?"

"No, Kilpatrick was a class ahead of Custer. But they both graduated a month apart in 1861. Custer's class graduated a year early because the war broke out."

Patten nodded. "Maybe Custer needed another year of seasoning at The Point."

Weber smiled. "But as Custer demonstrated yesterday, when he orders a Wolverine regiment or company to conduct a mounted saber attack, he leads the charge. That's much different than Kilpatrick ordering his brigades to spill blood as he sits in the rear with reporters, claiming to be the hero."

Patten grinned. "That makes me feel a hell of a lot better, sir. Custer will be right next to me as blood is spilling."

44

Gregg — Friday, July 3

8:35 a.m.
General David Gregg
White Run Creek and Baltimore Pike

Gregg fretted. *How long will it take for one of Kilpatrick's brigades to arrive at Cress Ridge? That's assuming that Kilpatrick releases one of his brigades, based upon my written request. Well, Pleasonton approved the request, so Kilpatrick should obey the order. So far, my scouts patrolling the Rummel field haven't reported any enemy activity. But Jeb's boys could be hidden in the Cress Woods, just waiting.*

Captain Henry Meyer broke the silence. "General, how long is your headquarters going to remain here? We might as well be sitting in Washington, D.C., for all the good we are doing here."

"Hopefully not long. I'm working on moving the division back to Cress Ridge."

Dust began to stream up the Baltimore Pike. "Look, General," Meyer said, nodding in the direction of the dust cloud. "Captain Weir and General Custer."

Custer's red scarf was twirling in the wind, whipping his smiling face. The boy general had a fighter's heart. The pride that lay in the flesh of all men was thicker in Custer. He was the perfect brigade commander to be commanding from the front against Stuart—hugely spirited, tactically flexible, and boldly courageous.

Custer was also fiercely ambitious and lacked experience in commanding a full brigade in a battle, and the hunger for praise that all men also craved was greater in him as well. Gregg took a deep and unsettling breath as Custer and Weir reined up. Today was Custer's fifth day in command. He would have to keep the human lightning bolt on a short string like a marionette.

Custer saluted. "General Gregg, I received your order for General Kilpatrick, and I understand your predicament. My brigade is marching, and they should arrive in a half hour at the Hanover and Low Dutch Road intersection."

"George, I'm relieved your brigade is arriving. General Pleasonton still lauds your courage leading a pell-mell cavalry charge at the Battle of Aldie. I've heard that in the last three days you've kept up your flair for leading spirited mounted charges. If my instincts are right, I may need that same courage today."

"I've always loved a good fight, General."

Weir said, "General Kilpatrick had departed with General Farnsworth's brigade when I arrived at Two Taverns."

Custer said, "I read your message to General Kilpatrick. It would waste too much time for Captain Weir to locate him and then for Kilpatrick to order my brigade to support you. So, I took the initiative and rode here without Kilpatrick's knowledge."

"You made the right decision. We can deal with General Kilpatrick and any hurt feelings later."

"Judson can get pretty fired up." Custer grinned. "I had the honor of being the goat in our West Point class and witnessed his bestial thrill of hazing new cadets."

"I'm senior to Kilpatrick. I'm not worried about him."

"What about General Pleasonton? Should you tell him that I chose to fulfill his order without telling Kilpatrick?"

Gregg shook his head. "Never pass up the opportunity to keep your mouth shut."

Custer's eyes widened.

"Pleasonton doesn't understand the gravity of leaving the army's right flank dangling in the air," Gregg continued. "I barely squeezed your brigade out of him. I need a division, not a brigade. Fortunately, your Michigan Wolverines are equipped with Spencer rifles and are one of the toughest fighting units in the army. So, before Pleasonton changes his mind, ride forward and occupy the critical crossroads of Hanover and the Low Dutch Road."

Custer nodded.

"If Stuart's cavalry attacks, I will tell Pleasonton and ride forward to take command and reinforce you." He paused and studied Custer. "George, you're the right person to protect the right flank with one brigade. I know you won't let me down."

"The clash of sabers and the whine of bullets are a beautiful chorus to my ears. I won't let you down, General."

"Let's dismount and look at the map that Captain Meyer has laid out."

He dismounted and Custer slid off his mount and knelt beside him.

Gregg pointed to the map. "George, when your brigade arrives, I want you to deploy a portion along the Low Dutch Road, north of the Hanover Road toward the Lott house and Cress Ridge. Then form an *L* with the rest of your brigade, running west up the Hanover Road toward Brinkerhoff's Ridge. The fight I had yesterday was for Brinkerhoff's Ridge, so deploy your brigade facing west toward the ridge and Gettysburg."

"Yes, sir." Custer pointed toward Brinkerhoff's Ridge. "General Gregg, where has Colonel Gregg deployed his brigade?"

Gregg pointed. "See the crest of the Brinkerhoff's Ridge?"

"Yes."

"About five hundred yards to the south of Hanover Road is Gregg's brigade. His position runs west and connects with the infantry of General Sedgwick's Sixth Corps on Wolf Hill."

Custer moved his gloved finger north along Brinkerhoff's Ridge.

"George, I believe that if Stuart attacks today, it will be aimed at breaking the joint between Gregg's cavalrymen and Sedgwick's infantrymen. If Stuart can pierce that joint, he will have the shortest path to the Baltimore Pike and the rear of the Union army."

"If I start scrapping with Stuart's boys, will Colonel McIntosh's brigade remain at the intersection of White Run Road and the Baltimore Pike?"

"Yes, General Pleasonton ordered me to leave a brigade there. That's why having your Wolverines occupying this area south of the Rummel farm is critical to defending the army's right flank."

Custer grinned widely, like a schoolboy pulling a prank. "It's my pleasure, sir. I'm hoping Stuart will not disappoint me and fail to show up for a fight. I'm hoping for another cavalry charge like the Battle of Aldie."

"You may get your wish. When your brigade arrives, I want you to tuck them away in the patches of woods and behind stone walls. I don't want Stuart to learn how light our line is."

Custer nodded.

"By the way, George. I didn't get to admire your black velvet suit trimmed with gold lace in the dark this morning." He paused and chuckled. "It goes well with your blue navy shirt and brilliant crimson necktie."

Custer cracked a smile. "I didn't want you to mistake me for a Rebel on the battlefield."

"George, if there was a contest for the most picturesque figure on the battlefield, you would win. Your only competition is Confederate General George Pickett, and your cinnamon-scented hair smells better."

"Well, General Gregg, coming from you, that means a lot. I would appreciate it if you sent General Lee a note letting him know how George Armstrong Custer outshines General George Pickett."

"I would send a note, but I've heard General Meade doesn't have quite the sense of humor that Hooker did. Meade might relieve my ass."

Custer smiled. "If Meade did that, maybe I could convince him to give me your division."

Gregg's jaw tightened. Custer's arrogant pride rivaled the Devil's. The boy general needed to be moved like a chess piece.

The clanking of sabers filled the air as the lead elements of the Wolverine brigade began arriving.

"Good luck today, George. I'm remaining here at my headquarters along Baltimore Pike, at White Run. It's between you, Colonel McIntosh, and Colonel Gregg's brigades. Keep me informed of developing situations."

Custer smiled. "Will do, General."

"If Stuart's cavalry appears, I will relocate my headquarters to the strategic crossroads you are guarding. You must hold the crossroads at all hazards. Do you understand?"

Custer saluted. "I understand, General."

Cress Ridge and the Rummel Farm
as it is today

45

Custer — Friday, July 3

8:45 a.m.
Custer
Riding up the Low Dutch Road toward the Hanover Road

Custer beamed, his brain swirling with excitement and his skin tingling as if he were tipsy. God, what a moment. His brigade would be the lone defense on Meade's right flank.

He turned to Weir. "Lead the way, Captain."

Weir trotted up the Low Dutch Road, cutting through lush farmlands. Custer pulled up beside him. A slight breeze rolled soft and warm through the woods lining the road.

"The Rummel farm and Lott farm are about three miles ahead," Weir said.

"Do you think Stuart will attack the crossroads?"

"Yes. When you see the wide-open fields of the Rummel farm you will understand why General Gregg is so concerned about the area. It's a perfect field for a grand charge."

Custer shuddered with anticipation. "A grand charge. That's great news." His heart danced.

"When we arrive," said Weir, "I will point out the key terrain features and review yesterday's skirmishing. I will also point out where General Gregg wants you to deploy your brigade."

"Very well."

9:12 a.m.
Major Peter Weber
Approaching strategic crossroads: intersection of Hanover and Low Dutch Roads

Weber's mount was churning a torrent of dust. His face cracked into a half-amused glance, spotting Custer and Private Churchill sitting at the intersection of Hanover Road and Low Dutch Road. Custer's scarlet cravat was flapping about his neck like a general's swallow-tailed flag.

Weber turned to Sergeant George Patten, riding alongside him. "Sergeant, I've noticed that Private Churchill has been at General Custer's side since yesterday's battle."

Patten murmured, "Churchill told me this morning that Custer appointed him as his *special orderly.*"

"I bet Custer ordered his *good luck charm* to stay at his side for the rest of the war."

"Who is your good luck charm, Major?"

"It's you, Sergeant Patten." He turned his head and grinned. "That is, until I get shot, and then I'm trading you for Private Churchill."

They reined up and saluted.

Weber said, "General Custer, reporting as ordered, sir."

"Peter," Custer inquired, "I see you are still wearing Captain's bars."

His face flushed with heat. "Yes, sir."

"If you need someone to find and sew on your major's rank, I know the right man." He grinned and brushed his hands over his two large stars. "My bugler Joseph Fought fixed me up with this uniform worthy of my exalted new position."

"General, if Meade was promoting me from captain to brigadier general, I would definitely request Bugler Fought to rig me up a general's uniform just like yours." He grinned. "But since I'm only going up one rank, I will wait to sew on my new insignia after this battle." A shiver spiraled through him. "Truth be known, sir, I have the new insignia in my saddlebag."

Custer winked. "Good." He pointed up the Hanover Road. "Peter, we need to protect the brigade's flanks. I want two companies from the Sixth Regiment to act as scouting parties, carrying Spencer rifles. Send Lieutenant Charles Storrs and his Company G west along the Hanover Road. Take Company B and ride north up the Low Dutch Road. You and Storrs ride up each road about a mile and a half. Send five troopers up to the York Pike, which is about three miles north of here."

"Are you expecting the enemy to use the York Pike and then travel down the Low Dutch Road, instead of riding east on the Hanover Road over Brinkerhoff's Ridge?"

"I'm not sure. General Gregg seems to think the enemy will use the Hanover Road to attack us from the west as they did yesterday late afternoon." Custer paused and glanced north toward the Cress Ridge. "If I was General Stuart, I would ride northeast from Gettysburg on York Pike and then turn south toward the Cress Ridge and ride down the Low Dutch Road to the Union army's rear."

"Understood, sir."

"You're in command of both Lieutenant Storrs's company and your company. I don't want to get caught again with my boots off like yesterday on the road at Hunterstown. That's why I picked you, Peter, to lead the scouting teams. Stay sharp and report any activity, *Major*."

"Will do. Thank you, sir."

9:30 a.m.
Custer
Strategic crossroads

Custer chewed on his toothbrush. Despite the white, fleecy clouds floating over the bright sky to the west, an unsettling lull and sweltering sultriness hovered over Gettysburg and Cress Ridge. Would Lee stay and fight, or retreat? Had he had enough yesterday and would head towards the Potomac? Or would Lee make another grand effort to pierce Union lines and turn its flanks? A chill slid down his back. *If Lee stays and attacks again today, I might get a chance to lead a cavalry charge against Jeb's boys.* The excitement churning inside him was nearly unbearable.

Lieutenant T.J. Gregg reined up. "General Custer, General Gregg sends his respects and wishes to inform you that the Rebels are starting to mass their artillery batteries across from Meade's center along Cemetery Ridge."

"Are they preparing to conduct an infantry charge or are the batteries preparing to cover a retreat?"

"General Gregg believes the Confederates are preparing to attack the center of the Union line."

His nerves were tingling. "Any word on movement by Jeb Stuart's cavalry?"

"No word. By your leave, I will ride to inform Colonel McIntosh and Colonel Gregg of the situation."

"Permission granted."

Custer turned to Captain Weir. "Please inform General Gregg that, based upon yesterday's Brinkerhoff fight, I'm going to deploy my brigade in a line facing west toward Brinkerhoff's ridge and running northwest toward Cress Ridge."

"I concur with you that the main threat you may face will be the same as yesterday." Weir pointed. "My guess is that the enemy will come over Brinkerhoff's Ridge from Gettysburg and move east down the Hanover Road. When they reach the Low Dutch Road, the Rebels will turn south toward the rear of the Union line."

"I've ordered the Fifth and Sixth Michigan to dismount and align in a defensive position, protecting the strategic crossroads. I've told both regiments that the main threat is down the Hanover Road, but they should be prepared for an attack from Cress Ridge down the Low Dutch Road."

Weir nodded.

"Please inform General Gregg that I deployed Major Weber and fifty troopers from his Company B about a half mile north on the Low Dutch Road at the Lott house. Weber is to extend his patrol another mile beyond the Lott house up the Low Dutch Road. I consider the Lott woods a more immediate threat to the strategic intersection than the timbered crest of Cress Ridge, which is over a mile away. If the Rebels hide in the Lott woods, they could swiftly attack south and penetrate my lines."

"I agree," said Weir. "The Lott woods poses a threat because it's also higher ground than the crossroads."

"I also directed Major Weber to send five troopers as far north as the York Pike. They will hopefully detect Stuart's cavalry if they decide to ride that way."

"Good plan."

"I've ordered Lieutenant Charles Storrs to lead troopers west up the Hanover Road about a mile to the crest of Brinkerhoff's Ridge. My flanks are anchored by Weber and Storrs's troopers."

"Is Storrs the officer that had a saber duel with Wade Hampton at Hunterstown and slashed the Rebel general?"

"Yes, that was Storrs."

Weir smiled. "Do you have questions for General Gregg?"

"No. Tell General Gregg that I will hold the strategic crossroads at all hazards. I'm going to send skirmishers from the Fifth and Sixth Michigan to advance into the fields north of the crossroads. The Sixth Michigan skirmishers are to advance to the lengthy Rummel farm fences along Little Run. If I'm attacked, I request that General Gregg order Colonel McIntosh's brigade forward to support me."

"Will do, General Custer." Weir saluted and departed.

Custer scanned northward, eyeing the Rummel log home, large barn, blacksmith shop, and springhouse. The Rummel farm sprawled over a hundred acres of rolling hills and woodlots. The magnificent farmland made an ideal battlefield. His skin tingled. It was just too tempting for Stuart not to fight here. Custer scanned Brinkerhoff's Ridge and Cress Ridge.

Colerick reined up. "General Custer, Major Peter Weber reports all the scouting parties are in position. He also sent one scouting patrol ranging as far north as the York Pike."

Custer snickered. "Yesterday, I learned the value of knowing what we're facing. I'm not going blind into battle today."

Colerick pointed toward Brinkerhoff's Ridge. "General Custer, see that two-story red brick farmhouse about 250 yards and just south of the Hanover Road?"

"Yes."

"That's the Joseph Spangler farm. We've set up your headquarters at the house."

"Let's ride up there."

Brinkerhoff Ridge loomed ahead and he had ordered his brigade to face toward it. Why was Gregg so sure Stuart would attack from there? He swiveled about and glanced at Cress Ridge. He shook his head. *That's where I would launch an attack.*

An eerie hollowness clawed at his stomach. *Don't take any unnecessary chances.* Protecting the army's right flank was a huge responsibility. If he failed, the Army of the Potomac could be defeated. His stomach clenched. The Rebels could be hidden in the thick woods and high ground of the Lott farm and Cress Ridge.

9:35 a.m.
Sergeant George Thomas Patten
One-quarter-mile north of Lott house

Patten halted his horse next to Major Weber's horse, standing in a small ravine in a wooded lot north of the Lott house.

"Sergeant," Weber said, "pick four troopers and ride north up Low Dutch Road. About a mile and half up the road, take the left fork in the road. Follow the left fork for a mile and you should arrive at the York Pike. Ride down the York Road toward Gettysburg and watch for Stuart's cavalry moving our way."

Patten saluted. "Yes, sir."

9:45 a.m.
Custer
Spangler farm, Custer's headquarters

Custer relaxed at the dining room table, sipping a glass of water and studying a map. Gettysburg was a hub, resting in the middle of ten converging roads like spokes on a wagon wheel. What would Stuart do? His index finger traveled along the York Pike, running northeast. Three miles from Gettysburg, his finger followed a crossroad leading southeast toward the Stallsmith farm. He leaned closer. A few hundred yards below the Stallsmith farm was Cress Ridge that loomed above the Rummel farm. His breath rasped. He spun around.

"William, I figured it out." He pointed. "Here is the route that I would take to attack the Union's rear. This is what Stuart is going to do."

Colerick said, "You don't think Stuart will attack down the Hanover Road from Brinckerhoff Ridge?"

"No. Stuart will use Cress Ridge to conceal his cavalry and charge south through the Rummel farm.

"Do you want me to inform General Gregg of the situation?"

"I'll tell him myself."

10:15 a.m.
Custer
White Run Creek and Baltimore Pike
General David Gregg's headquarters

Custer arrived at Gregg's headquarters and reined up at the general's divisional flag flying next to a large tent. He dismounted and adjusted his wide-brimmed hat to a jaunty angle. Weir darted toward him and saluted.

Custer returned the salute. "Henry, I would like to provide General Gregg a situational report of my defensive position. Then I will return to my brigade."

"General Custer, just a moment. General Gregg is resting in his tent and is with the divisional surgeon. I will tell the general you're here."

Custer's fidgety nerves jumped. What was wrong with Old Steady? Muffled silence hung in the humid air. A disturbing silence signaling an ominous uncertainty. Gregg was the only senior officer who seemed to understand the importance of defending the right flank. Gregg emerged from the tent without his coat and halted. His trouser suspenders hung from his belt. A pasty sheen covered his face, and he stared with a tormented gaze, plainly in distress.

Custer stepped forward and saluted. "General, I'm here to give you a situational report."

Gregg nodded and pointed. "Let's move under the tree shade."

Gregg lumbered toward a large oak tree with a map table and several cracker boxes and plopped down at the map table. Custer sat down across from him.

"Are you well, sir?"

"I have been better. During our march to Gettysburg, I came down with a bowel illness. The doctor is treating me with the infamous blue mass."

"Oh, God. That's what the doctors gave me when I was sick at West Point. No pun intended, I could hardly stomach that mixture of mercury and chalk."

Gregg cracked a tight-lipped smile. "I'm delighted to see the blue mass worked for you. If it works for me, do I have to wear a red scarf?"

Custer winked. "I have deployed my brigade in a strong defensive position protecting the Hanover Road from Brinkerhoff's Ridge to the Low Dutch Road. Pennington's batteries are deployed along Hanover Road. Major Weber has troopers covering the Lott house along Low Dutch Road. I have patrols as far north as the York Pike. Dismounted troopers from the Sixth Michigan are acting as skirmishers and moving slowly north toward the Rummel farm."

Gregg snapped. "What's the purpose of the skirmishers? I don't want you to bring on a big fight until McIntosh's brigade has moved forward and I've relocated my headquarters near yours."

"I learned a valuable lesson yesterday leading the cavalry charge at Hunterstown."

Gregg raised his eyebrows.

"Before charging make sure you know the enemy's numbers and defensive position." He stopped and drew a breath. "The purpose of the skirmishers is to cover and protect the strategic intersection. I don't want to be surprised by a hidden enemy suddenly emerging from the woods and racing down the slope. So, I ordered my skirmishers to remain out of sight as much as possible, tucking away in patches of woods and behind stone walls."

Gregg nodded. "Did you spot any enemy activity?"

"It's all quiet. But I've seen some enemy skirmishers on the southern crown of Cress Ridge. I'm not sure if they are infantry pickets sniffing out where our right flank is or if they are the vanguard of Stuart's cavalry."

"Which way is your brigade facing?"

"With the exception of the Sixth Michigan skirmishers, who are facing north toward the Rummel house, the brigade is facing west to meet any enemy attacks from Brinkerhoff's Ridge.

My skirmishers are fanned out and moving north toward the Rummel farm, flushing out hidden Rebels lurking within wood-lots and ravines."

"Good, George. I'm fully satisfied with your tactical decisions and the disposition of your forces. Keep me posted if the situation changes."

"Will do, General."

"George, remember, you are in a defensive position, protecting the army's right. I don't want any cavalry charges. I will coordinate all offensive actions if Stuart shows up."

He bit his tongue in frustration. "Understood, General." He paused, scratching his chin. "After studying the terrain, I believe Stuart will attack from Cress Ridge. That's what I would do. If that's Stuart's plan, my forward deployed scouts should give us plenty of warning."

12:25 p.m.
General David Gregg
White Run Creek and Baltimore Pike

Under the flickering shade of a large white oak, Gregg squirmed on a cracker box and stared at a map. His stomach growled. He lifted his eyes toward Captain Weir.

"Henry, look here."

Weir took a step closer and stared down at the map. "I believe Custer is correct in his prediction. Stuart is going to ride out on the York Pike and then turn south toward Cress Ridge. He can hide his forces in the thick woods on the high ground until he swoops out of them and rushes down the slope toward the low ground around the crossroads."

An approaching clip-clippity-clip and a courier reined up, breathing hard. His horse was sweating and thick-winded. First Lieutenant Clifford Thompson, one of Pleasonton's aide-de-camps, dismounted.

Thompson took a deep breath, wiped his brow, and saluted. "General Gregg, General Howard, commanding Eleventh Infantry Corps and occupying Cemetery Hill, reported to

General Pleasonton a large enemy cavalry force riding east toward the York Pike."

Gregg said, "How large is the enemy force?"

"Howard estimates it is five thousand troopers. General Meade's intelligence officer, Colonel George Sharpe, states the force is General Stuart's cavalry division. The cavalry division consists of four brigades commanded by Chambliss, Hampton, Fitzhugh Lee, and Jenkins."

"What horse artillery is supporting Stuart?"

"Colonel Sharpe believes three or more batteries are supporting Stuart."

Gregg turned to Captain Weir. "Have a courier inform General Custer that Stuart's division has been spotted. My guess is that Stuart's division will depart the York Pike and head south toward Cress Ridge area."

Weir said, "Do you think we should move McIntosh's brigade forward to reinforce Custer and relocate your headquarters near the Michigan Brigade?"

"Not yet. Unless the Rebels are attacking Custer's brigade, I need General Pleasonton's damn permission to move McIntosh's brigade."

12:30 p.m.
Custer
Spangler house

Custer gulped down a glass of water, stepped outside of the Spangler house, and stood on the porch. The sweltering heat licked at his face. He strode toward his quartermaster staff, who were loading canteens of water into a wagon.

"First Lieutenant William North. Ensure the troopers have plenty of water."

"Yes, sir. The waggoners, teamsters, and quartermasters have been filling canteens from Cress Run and Little Run creeks."

Custer gripped his binoculars and scanned east down the Hanover Road. He spotted Colonel Town, commanding the First Michigan, at five hundred yards at the strategic crossroads. Warmth flowed through his veins. His best regiment was mounted and aligned in a column of squadrons, protecting the critical crossroads. They would act as his strategic reserve and could react to threats from the west and north.

Two hundred yards west, up the Hanover Road from the strategic intersection, Colonel Mann and his mounted Seventh Michigan were protecting two of Pennington's batteries. Thirty yards further up the Hanover Road was the dismounted Sixth Michigan, covering Pennington's remaining four artillery batteries.

He glanced north at Colonel Alger's dismounted blue skirmishers, armed with the fast-firing Spencer rifles. The Fifth Michigan were skirting north along Little Run toward the Rummel farm.

He turned to Colerick. "William, I have a feeling the Rebels are lurking in those dark woods above the Rummel house. Alger's skirmishers can flush out any Rebels prowling beyond the Rummel house."

"General, if I were the enemy, I would launch an attack from the Cress Woods."

"I agree. I don't like sitting at the bottom of this mount. But I've done everything possible to protect the crossroads. Captain Weber and Captain Storrs's forward patrols will provide us early warning of enemy advances. We shall soon learn if the Fifth Michigan skirmishers flush out any Rebels loitering around the Rummel farm. If so, I may also learn something about the Rebels' tactical plans."

"What are your plans?"

"To fight the enemy as far north from the crossroads as possible. Then hope that General Gregg can reinforce us before we are overrun."

Colerick pointed. "Look, General. Rebel skirmishers appearing just south of the Cress Ridge tree line."

Custer whirled his binoculars on Cress Ridge beyond the Rummel farm. His heart pounded in his ears. "I see them, William. Maybe fifty dismounted graybacks."

"It does not appear a considerable force."

A sharp crack pierced the lull blanketing the fields. Custer swiveled in his saddle and sighted a black tendril snaking toward Brinkerhoff's Ridge. The shell burst and bloomed into a white puff.

"Look where I'm pointing on the northern end of Cress Ridge," Colerick said. "Do you see the smoke from the artillery?"

Custer turned and located the smoke. "Yes, I see it."

The lull returned for several moments. Custer gripped his binoculars and scanned Cress Ridge. A burst of streaking yellow flames and a thunderous crack. A shell whistled over the Spangler house and burst a hundred yards south of Hanover Road.

"That's odd. That shell's trajectory was nearly 90 degrees from the first shell."

"Maybe the Rebels are trying to figure out where we are?" Colerick said.

"Perhaps."

Another tomb-like lull cloaked Rummel Field for several moments. A sharp crack. Custer spotted a shell's black tendril screaming toward the Lott woods bordering Low Dutch Road. He said, "That shell was nearly 90 degrees from the last shell. I think you're right, William. The Rebels are trying to figure out if we are here."

"Agreed, sir."

A storm gust of excitement rushed over him. "Let's let them know we are here with our artillery. William, order the brigade to face north."

Custer bolted toward his mount. The groom handed him the reins and he swung into the saddle and rode west on the Hanover Road. Two hundred yards ahead, Pennington stood next to his battery. Custer reined up.

"Alexander, it would give me great pleasure if Battery M would give that Rebel gun something to shoot at."

Pennington grinned. He turned and shouted, "Lieutenant Carle Woodruff. I would like for you to silence that enemy gun that fired those shots."

"Yes, sir," Woodruff said.

Custer watched him closely. Woodruff knelt behind the gun. "Five-degree elevation!" The big gun's barrel rose. Woodruff stood up. "Fire!"

The battery sergeant pulled the lanyard, and the ordnance rifle thundered and jerked back. Flames blazed from the muzzle, and sulphur-laden smoke filled the air. The missile shrieked, its black tendril arced like a base ball thrown from the outfield to home base.[10]

The shell swooped down and shattered the enemy gun.

"Alexander, that was a hell of a shot," Custer cheered. "Now Stuart knows we are here, and we mean business."

Pennington grinned and touched his cap.

Custer turned to First Lieutenant William Wheeler. "William, ride to General Gregg's headquarters and inform him of the enemy artillery fire apparently trying to figure out if we're here."

12:40 p.m.
Custer
Spangler house

Uncertainty crowded Custer's mind as he scanned the Rummel fields with his binoculars. *What are you up to, Jeb? The fat's in the fire.* Clapping horse hooves raced up Hanover Road. A courier came galloping into the Spangler yard.

Lieutenant T.J. Gregg reined up and saluted. "General Custer. General Gregg wishes to inform you that large columns of the enemy cavalry were observed moving toward the right of General Howard's position at the northern end of Cemetery Ridge. General Gregg believes the enemy cavalry are from General Stuart's division and are riding toward the rear of Cress Ridge."

"Thank you, Lieutenant. Please request General Gregg consider moving his headquarters and Colonel McIntosh's brigade forward to the Rummel farm and reinforcing my brigade."

---

10 In 1863, baseball was called base ball and home plate was called home base. Source: *The Laws of Base Ball* as created by the 1857 Convention of Baseball Players, Page 1.

Pennington injected, "Lieutenant, please inform General Gregg that we will need Captain Randol's battery from Colonel McIntosh's brigade as soon as possible. I believe the enemy will soon unlimber several more artillery guns."

Lieutenant Gregg departed.

"General Custer," Pennington said, "I believe as soon as all of Stuart's forces arrive, they will attack."

"Alexander, I agree. Make sure you have plenty of cannister ready if the Rebels breach our lines."

46

Gregg — Friday, July 3

12:42 p.m.
General David Gregg
White Run Creek and Baltimore Pike

A deafening silence hovered over Gregg, who was standing under the large oak tree, peering at one of General Pleasonton's couriers riding toward him. "Henry," he said, in a tone bordering on sarcasm, "I wonder what good news General Pleasonton has for us?"

"General Meade has promoted you to a major general?" Weir said.

Gregg smiled. "The way General Meade is promoting captains to brigadier general, it's more likely *you're* getting a star!"

Captain George Yates, General Pleasonton's aide-de-camp, arrived in cloud of dust. "General Pleasonton sends his respects and concurs with you regarding the necessity to protect the Hanover and Low Dutch Roads crossroads. You are to move Colonel McIntosh's brigade to the crossroads and relocate your headquarters there."

A blast of warmth and relief consumed him. "That is good news. I will depart immediately."

Yates said, "Also, you are to detach Custer's brigade and have him rejoin General Kilpatrick on the army's left flank."

Gregg glared as a violent silence exploded. Blood roared in his ears. His hands trembled for a few beats. "Captain, removing Custer's brigade is a horrific mistake. General Howard reported Stuart's force is 6,000 troopers. If Custer's brigade of 1,900 troopers departs, that leaves me with McIntosh's 1,300 men."

"General Gregg, you have Colonel Irvin Gregg's Third Brigade of 1,200 troopers."

"Damnation, Lieutenant, General Pleasonton ordered me to leave Colonel Gregg's brigade south of Brinkerhoff's Ridge, snugged up against Wolf Hill. Are you permitting me now to use Gregg's brigade to replace Custer's brigade?"

"No, sir. General Pleasonton wants Gregg's brigade to remain where it is."

Gregg shook his head. An ice-cold foreboding laced with pure anger coursed through his veins. He gulped down a breath through his taut throat and stepped toward Yates. "This is sheer madness. Does Pleasonton not grasp the grave threat posed by Stuart's cavalry against our right?"

"The Rebels are lining up all their artillery against the middle of the Union line. That is the greatest threat."

"God damn it, Captain. The greatest threat is Stuart piercing my thin line and attacking the army's rear. If Stuart succeeds, the army cannot escape down the Baltimore Pike and could possibly be destroyed."

"I shall report your concerns to General Pleasonton."

His heart roared as a rebuff charred on his tongue. "I consider the verbal order to release Custer and his brigade a grave mistake. I will need a written order signed by General Pleasonton before I release Custer."

Yates stiffened and stared. He shook his head as if searching for something to say. After a couple of moments, he saluted, and galloped back down the Low Dutch Road.

Gregg turned to Captain Weir. "I've stalled releasing Custer for about a half hour."

"You may face disciplinary action for requesting a written order."

"That's the least of my worries. If Stuart penetrates the army's right, we will lose this battle... Just a second." He clutched his cramping gut. It felt like it was churning curdled milk.

"General, are you yourself?"

He shook his head and gripped the bottle of blue mass in his jacket pocket and took a swig.

"Inform Colonel McIntosh that his brigade departs immediately at best speed for the strategic crossroads. I'm departing to inform General Custer of General Pleasonton's impending decision."

An unholy oath flamed in his mind. *Pleasonton is a buffooned imbecile.*

Captain Llewellyn Garrish Estes

47

Sixth Michigan — Friday, July 3

12:30 p.m. (Twelve minutes earlier)
Sergeant George Thomas Patten
One-quarter mile north of the Lott house

Patten hid in a small grove of trees off the York Pike. The clip-clop of thousands of hooves on the hard macadam road echoed overhead. Rebel cavalry. A galloping horse approached. He gripped his revolver and aimed. Private Charles Batson emerged from the wooded area.

Batson dismounted and wiped his brow. "Sergeant, I spotted General Stuart's lead brigades. They rode northeast on the York Pike about two and a half miles and then turned south on a crossroad, cutting through heavy woods toward the Stallsmith farm."

"I hear them," Patten said. "Stuart is going to be surprised we detected him. I will ride back and inform Major Weber. You stay here and keep scouting. Don't let the Rebels spot you."

12:40 p.m.
Sergeant George Thomas Patten
Riding Down Low Dutch Road

Patten galloped down Low Dutch Road. Two hundred yards ahead, he spotted the Lott house. A bright flash drew his gaze toward the Rummel house. He reined up and stared toward the dark woods dominating Cress Ridge. His jaw tightened. The sun was glinting off gun barrels like thousands of sparkling stars. He gripped his binoculars and spotted a brigade of dismounted Rebels and a Confederate battery filtering through the woods and massing on the south summit of Cress Ridge.

"Major Weber." Sergeant Patten paused, gulping for a breath. "Private Charles Batson observed Stuart's vanguard brigades arriving at the Stallsmith farm."

Patten panted and pointed.

"On the southern summit of Cress Ridge, a Rebel brigade and an artillery battery are emerging from the woods."

Weber grimaced. "I will report this to General Custer. Good job, Sergeant. Ride with me."

He mounted his horse and rode east toward the Low Dutch Road. Patten rode alongside him. The blazing midmorning sun had dried the dirt roads to a fine dust. He took a swig of water from his canteen, squinting as thundering hooves echoed up the road. He glanced over his shoulder. Five Union troopers were galloping down the Low Dutch Road toward the Lott house. Two hundred yards behind them, a blurring brown dust swirled. Dread clawed at his throat.

"The Rebels are chasing my scouting party," Patten shouted.

"Let's sprint south toward the intersection. The First Michigan are picketing there."

A pistol cracked. Weber ducked as a bullet whickered overhead. He spurred his horse and raced toward the First Michigan. He aimed for Colonel Town and his trumpeter, Milton Rice, and a company of dismounted troopers sitting on either side of the road pointing their carbine rifles. He raced past the picket line and skidded to a halt. The Rebels had stopped two hundred yards away and started riding back up the road.

Town rode up and grinned. "Peter, I didn't know you could ride that fast. Is that why you were promoted to major?"

Weber's heart pounded in his ears. He took a couple deep breaths. "I prefer charging into the enemy instead of hightailing away. I guess the Rebels now know we have scouting parties in the area."

"Has Stuart's cavalry division arrived yet?"

"No. They are arriving in spurts. My best guess is that one or two brigades have arrived. If they continue to trickle in like they have been, Stuart should be at full strength by 1:00 p.m."

Town nodded. "Then maybe you will get your chance to charge."

"Weber grinned. "It's a fine afternoon for it, Colonel." He turned to Sergeant Patten. "Let's ride to General Custer's headquarters and report our findings."

12:54 p.m.
Major Peter Weber
Hanover Road near Custer's headquarters

Weber spotted Lieutenant Storrs, fifty yards from Custer's headquarters, waiting on the side of the road. He arrived and pulled up.

Storrs saluted. "Major Weber, my scouting party rode over Brinkerhoff's Ridge toward Culp's Hill. We saw no Rebel cavalry advancing east on the Hanover Road."

He nodded. "That means that Stuart is massing all his forces north on Cress Ridge. I will inform General Custer."

12:55 p.m.
Custer
Spangler house

A lull had settled over the Rummel farm and the fields of Gettysburg. Custer leaned against a post support on the covered porch of the Spangler house, chewing on his toothbrush. His fidgeting boot tapped the wooden deck like a beating snare drum. He couldn't stop himself from staring at Alfred Waud's sketch of him leading the First Maine Cavalry at the Battle of Aldie. He was truly a creature of glory. He chuckled. In that picture he was a shabbily-dressed officer, looking more like a Yankee Rebel wearing his Confederate slouch hat. Today, he was in full costume, as if he were the lead actor of a Broadway play, and center stage was the Rummel field. His Charles I cavalier costume would have made Napoleon's flamboyant Prince Murat proud. Waud's sketch had captured how calm he was when sailing wind's river into the jaws of death. God, he loved being a ripsnorting daredevil. Cavalry charges were the Devil's own fun. He couldn't wait for the curtain to rise and the battle to begin. Today, he, the youngest general, would emerge as the beau sabreur of the Union army.

Colerick gestured. "It's way too quiet. Something is up."

"I agree, William. It's too quiet. It feels like we're between acts and the curtain will soon rise for the final act of the drama." He wiped his brow. "The Rebels are up to something."

"I thought the cannon fire from Culp's would never end this morning. I had just fallen asleep at Two Taverns when the thundering erupted."

Major Weber reined up. "General Custer, I saw one or two enemy brigades arriving." He pointed toward the north end of Cress Ridge. "Look over past the Rummel barn. The enemy are emerging above it. I've seen thousands of them over there and the country yonder is full of the enemy."

Custer's face tingled. "Are they getting ready to attack?"

"No, they are dismounting. They seem to be the vanguard of a larger force. I don't think the Rebels will attack until all their troopers have arrived." Weber drew a sharp breath. "Lieutenant Storrs reports no enemy activity on Brinkerhoff's Ridge."

Custer grinned. "Report your findings to General Gregg and then return to your squadron and provide me any new information on the enemy as soon as you get it."

Weber saluted and departed.

Colerick pointed. "General, the Michigan Brigade and Pennington's guns are still facing west toward Brinckerhoff Ridge. Should we have them face north toward the Rummel farm?"

"Yes. Order the brigade to face north. Also, have Colonel Alger report to my headquarters."

Colerick departed.

Custer leaped onto Roanoke and trotted over to Pennington's battery.

"Alexander, start firing on the enemy troops advancing on foot toward the Rummel farm."

Custer gripped his binoculars and scanned the Rummel farm, spotting graybacks starting to flow down toward the Rummel farm like a slow mudslide.

A thunderous crack shook the ground. Roanoke swayed as if riding a breaking wave. Custer twisted around; smoke bellowed from Pennington's six large artillery guns. He snapped his head back, and the corners of his mouth curled upward into a vile and cheery grin as the Union shells plunged down and exploded around the advancing enemy. The Rebels broke rank and scuttled, terror-stricken, for the cover of the large Rummel barn. The fiery jaws of Pennington's guns roared again, and rifled shells hissed toward Cress Ridge.

Custer spotted a Rebel battery of six guns unlimbering south of the one that Pennington had put out of commission.

"Alexander," he shouted, "do you see the enemy battery unlimbering?"

Pennington yelled back, "I see them, General. They won't be in action for long."

Pennington loped over to Lieutenant John Barlow and pointed. Barlow nodded and barked, and the gun crew fired. The percussion shell shrilled. A moment later it thundered, scattering whistling fragments, destroying the unlimbering Rebel gun.

Custer's skin prickled.

The smoke deepened and rolled as Pennington's batteries fired nonstop. The acrid reek of gunfire was sweet perfume to Custer's tingling nostrils. The Rebels started firing counterbattery. He smiled. The enemy shells fell harmlessly, two hundred yards in front of Pennington's guns.

Custer's face beamed as a devilish warmth flooded his insides. "Alexander, the Rebel guns can't reach you."

"We can sure reach them, General. My boys are going to give those jackanapes a twopenny dose of lead."

Colonel Alger reined up.

"Russell, Major Weber observed a couple enemy brigades arriving on Cress Ridge. It's clear to me that the threat is from the north along Cress Ridge and not west from Brinkerhoff's Ridge. I want you to move two more dismounted companies northward a few hundred yards toward the Rummel farm to act as a defensive shield. Have them move cautiously. I'm not trying to have Stuart believe we are attacking. They are serving as an extra layer of defense, like a buffer zone for the crossroads."

48

Gregg — Friday, July 3

12:58 p.m.
General David Gregg
Approaching strategic crossroads

Gregg let out a low growl as he trotted up the Low Dutch Road leading McIntosh's Brigade. God, he felt like someone had clapper-clawed his bowels. He gripped the canteen against his cracked lips and took a small swig, swirling the tepid water against his parched throat before gulping. Pounding iron horseshoes and clattering steel scabbards hanging from saddle rings echoed behind him in the sweltering heat. What was Stuart planning today? He glanced over his shoulder; Colonel McIntosh and his brigade's vanguard were meandering behind him like a blue mountain stream. The bulk of the brigade was shrouded in white dust.

"Sir," said Captain Weir, "Major Weber is approaching."

Weber saluted. "General Gregg, I saw several hundred dismounted enemy troopers in the woods beyond the Rummel farm. Custer ordered Pennington's batteries to fire upon Stuart's skirmishers."

"How long have the Rebel skirmishers been here?"

"They just emerged a few minutes ago. But half an hour ago a Rebel artillery gun fired three times in different directions."

"Why?"

"It appears Stuart was probing to see what he was up against. The first shot of one of Pennington's guns dismantled the Rebel artillery gun."

Gregg frowned, heat surging into his face. *Damn you Pleasonton!*

"Return to your forward outpost and let me know when Stuart's mounted troopers start to emerge."

Gregg spotted a red scarf through the billowing black smoke of Pennington's batteries. *Custer.* He made his way toward the red scarf.

Custer saluted. "Pennington's guns are doing a superb job, General."

Gregg grimaced. "George, I just met with General Pleasonton's courier. Pleasonton verbally ordered you to pull out your brigade and ride over to the army's left flank and report to General Kilpatrick."

"That's a ridiculous order, sir. Doesn't Pleasonton realize that Stuart and his six thousand mounted Rebels are getting ready to attack our right flank?"

"I made that point, George, but apparently Kilpatrick is furious that you supported me, and you didn't inform him of your actions." He clutched his rumbling stomach and took a deep breath. "I tried to buy some time and told the courier that I would not execute the order unless it was a written order signed by Pleasonton."

Custer's face turned bright red and he shook his fist. "General, the Rebel skirmishers are spread out in a strong line. From the sharp bark of their weapons, we are facing seasoned dismounted Rebels armed with Enfield rifles, which are their infantry's favorite weapon. The enemy's .577-caliber are accurate in a long-range firefight. These Rebel skirmishers I'm facing are deadly shots. Once they push our skirmishers back, Stuart is going to launch a cavalry attack and slice through you like a butcher carving meat."

"Agreed." He stared at Custer, who was writhing in his saddle like a worm on a fishhook. Anger boiled beneath his breastbone. *Damn you, Pleasonton. You can't start a chess match missing several pieces.* "I expect Pleasonton's courier to arrive within the half hour with the written order for you to depart. I ordered Colonel

McIntosh's brigade up to replace your forces. I told John to get a turnover from you on your situation."

Custer looked down for a moment, holding his breath and his temper, then looked up again. His face beamed bright red, plainly raging about the withdrawal order. He saluted. "Yes, sir. I will start to pull out my brigade. The First and Seventh Regiments will depart first for Little Round Top. The Fifth and Sixth Regiments will remain in place, fighting, until Colonel McIntosh's units can relieve them. I will order Pennington to keep firing until McIntosh's artillery battery arrives."

Gregg nodded. He shuddered. Panic stabbed through him.

1:03 p.m.
Colonel John McIntosh
En route to strategic crossroads

McIntosh pulled off the Low Dutch Road as Captain Walter Newhall, brigade adjutant, reined up. "Walter, where in the hell is Major Beaumont and his First New Jersey Regiment? I ordered Beaumont to move up the Low Dutch Road and replace General Custer's forward pickets positioned around the Lott house."

Newhall frowned. "Apparently, Colonel, Major Beaumont has come down with a sudden illness and has not moved the First New Jersey forward."

"Damn that man. Every time a battle is looming, Beaumont contracts a mysterious illness."

Newhall nodded.

McIntosh jabbed a finger toward the First New Jersey bivouac. "Tell Beaumont to bring his regiment up at a gallop or I'm going to shoot his ass." He fumed as Newhall tore off down the road, muttered a few choice epithets once the captain disappeared from view, and glared at him when he returned with Major Hugh Janeway behind him, galloping at the front of the First New Jersey. "Where is Beaumont?" he shouted.

"Major Beaumont was indisposed," Major Janeway replied, "and I will lead the regiment to the Lott house."

McIntosh growled, blazing rage scorching his throat. "Very well. I will deal with Beaumont after this is over."

49

Custer — Friday, July 3

1:06 p.m.
Captain Alexander Pennington
Near Spangler house

Pride's rugged heat flushed Pennington's face as he surveyed the different sections of Battery M preparing to fire. His breathing lifted. His war hounds were the best artillerymen in the Union army. Lieutenant John Barlow commanded one of his battery sections. Barlow had been recommended for a Medal of Honor for actions a year ago at Hanover Court House.

"John, didn't you graduate ahead of General Custer in the West Point June class of 1861?"

Barlow grinned. "Yes, I graduated fourteenth in my class, and Custer graduated the goat, dead last."

Pennington smirked. "How is it that he is now a general and you're still a lieutenant?"

Barlow paused. "With all due respect, Captain, you graduated a year ahead of Custer and me. Why aren't you a general?"

Pennington cracked a wry smile. "I graduated eighteenth in my class. I see a trend here. The lower you graduated in your class, the faster you get promoted to general." He pointed. "Show Custer why you graduated ahead of him and take out that Rebel battery."

"Will do, sir."

Barlow stepped between his cannons and shouted, "Load."

Cannoneers covered each breech vent with a leather-wrapped thumb. Privates rushed forward, jammed long staffs with pieces of sheep fleece into the muzzle faces, and sponged the bronze barrels. Crew members inserted a charge and projectile down the muzzle and then rammed the round down the bore. Gunners stepped up to the breech, placed the Hausse Sight in its seat, gripped the elevating screw under the breech, and adjusted the aim. The gunners nodded, removed the Hausse Sight, stepped back, and raised their hands. The cannoneers removed their thumbstalls and inserted a lanyard hook into the ring of a priming tube, dropped the tube into the breech vent, and stepped back as far as they could while keeping slack in the lanyard.

Barlow turned to Pennington. "The guns are ready, sir."

Pennington gripped his binoculars and scanned toward the Rummel farm. "Commence sustained counterbattery until you've destroyed that enemy battery."

Barlow shouted, "Fire!"

The cannoneers yanked the lanyards and the four artillery cannons cracked, spewing out yellow flames and iron northward. The thunder smote Pennington's ears, and the ground under his mount rolled and growled. He glanced northward, eyeing the demonic shells hissing and screaming toward the enemy. He whiffed the cannons' sulphur-laden breath rolling around along the ground. A tearing crash of thunder roared, and the projectiles flashed like lightning and vanished into puffy white clouds. The Rebel battery exploded into smithereens.

Pennington's war hounds shrilled and waved their arms, whooping like banshees.

Their sheer, outrageous precision flooded his soul with pride. He would pit Battery M against any other Union battery for accuracy.

1:07 p.m.
Custer
Visiting McIntosh at the strategic crossroads

Without warning, the skies over Gettysburg burst forth like a massive thunderstorm, with the sky vomiting lead shells and the ground shaking like an earthquake. *It's begun. The two armies' artillery batteries are dueling.* Custer's ears pulsed as he approached Colonel McIntosh.

McIntosh saluted. "General Custer. I want to compliment you on your fine body of men."

"Thank you, John. I'm proud of my Wolverines."

"General Gregg ordered my brigade to relieve your brigade."

Custer's jaw tightened. "John, General Pleasonton doesn't have a clue of what's going on here. Pulling my brigade out with a fight impending with Stuart's superior forces is idiotic."

McIntosh shook his head. "I wish your Wolverines were staying, General."

Custer pointed. "What regiment is that moving up the Low Dutch Road?"

"That's the First New Jersey. I ordered them to deploy in a skirmish line at the Lott house."

"As soon as they arrive at the Lott house, I will pull back the Fifth and Sixth Michigan Regiments and they will ride with the First and Seventh Regiments to Little Round Top on the army's left flank. When the Sixth Regiment departs, Pennington's guns will limber up and follow them."

"Where is the enemy positioned?"

"My forward outposts have seen only a few hundred dismounted Rebels." Custer gestured. "See that large white barn?

McIntosh nodded.

"That's part of the Rummel farm. Major Weber was manning an outpost near the Lott house and believes the dismounted Rebels may be moving forward to occupy the Rummel Farm.. Beyond the white barn is the Cress Ridge." Custer chuckled. "I think you will find the woods out there full of them as they continue to arrive in droves."

"What's the size of the enemy force?"

"Not sure. I would consider ordering the First New Jersey to form a skirmish line west of the Lott house and advance toward the Rummel house. That might stir up the Rebels and give you an idea of what you're up against."

"Understood, sir. It's definitely time to find out."

"Good luck, John. I will leave Pennington's guns firing as long as possible to cover the First New Jersey. That will give Captain Randol's batteries a chance to unlimber and be ready for action. I hate departing like this."

Captain Henry C. Meyer

50

Gregg — Friday, July 3

1:08 p.m.
General David Gregg
Strategic crossroads

Primal thunder bellowed across the sky, and Gregg's horse pitched. He gripped the reins. "Steady, boy, steady."

He glanced toward Gettysburg, where a multitude of artillery guns roared, splitting the air like a chain of thundering volcanoes. His eardrums popped and crackled. He twisted in his saddle and stared at the sky over Meade's headquarters as a blast of molten air slapped his face and pulsed his jacket. The ground shook as if it were straddling a splitting fault line. He gripped the saddle's pommel. The rumbling was terrifying, a thousand rogue waves hitting in succession. *This must be the Confederate artillery barrage before their infantry attack. Christ Almighty. Stuart will begin his cavalry attack soon to penetrate the Union rear.*

He turned to Captain Meyer. "Henry, order Colonel McIntosh to reinforce the First New Jersey skirmishers pressing toward the Rummel farm." Meyer saluted and galloped up the Low Dutch Road toward the Lott house.

Gregg's heart punched against his ribcage. The great chess game had begun, and Lee would soon move Stuart's knights against him.

1:20 p.m.
Major Hugh Janeway
Rummel farm stone fence

Major Hugh Janeway led the skirmish line with Sergeant Major Thomas Cox by his side. Janeway halted and glanced up and down the skirmish line at the one hundred and fifty dismounted troopers striding forward to the Rummel farm. He wheeled his mount and aimed toward a neck of woods. Through the tree line a fallow field undulated upward to the white Rummel barn.

"There, Major." Cox pointed. "Rebel skirmishers are emerging from behind the barn."

"I see them, Sergeant Major."

He gulped down a breath. Through a grove of trees circling the farm, some three hundred gray-clad, dismounted troopers emerged and sprang down the dale. *Crack.* A bullet hissed by his cheek, rippling the air like a gust of wind.

"They know we're here, Major! I recommend you dismount."

"Not yet. It looks as if the Rebels are stopping at that long rock fence closest to the barn. Let's move up to the first stone fence about twenty rods away and blast them."

Cox dismounted and handed his reins to Private Francis Brown, Company K. "Francis, pull back behind the skirmish line a good distance. If Major Janeway chooses to dismount I will have someone bring his mount back to you."

"Will do, Sergeant Major," Brown said and led the horse away.

"Sergeant Major," Janeway said, "are you ready to advance the line?"

Cox scanned up and down the line. "We're ready, sir."

Janeway's heart raced, thumping in his ears. He gulped a big breath and shouted, "Forward, march." He snapped the reins and his mount stepped forward.

A great, roaring cheer rose up from one hundred and fifty throats. The dismounted skirmishers thrust forward, staying even with his horse. A hail of enemy bullets whistled overhead; the wind of one minié ball buffeted his cheek. He gasped. *That was close.*

Cox stepped next to him. "Major, you should dismount," he shouted. "They are going to pick you off."

An icy calm flooded him. "The Rebs are always trying to pick me off." He narrowed his eyes and spotted a shallow dip in the ground like a wide furrow. "Sergeant, let's pause at the shallow gulch and fire a broadside."

Cox sprang forward. "Follow me!"

The troopers scrambled forward like bouncing rabbits and knelt in the gully. Janeway rode up behind the troopers and halted.

"Fire!" Cox shouted.

A blistering crack resounded from one hundred and fifty Burnside carbines, and a long, fiery sheet of lead whistled toward the enemy.

Janeway shouted, "Forward, men! Double-quick to the stone fence."

The blue-clad troopers cheered and leaped over the lip of the trough, sprinting forward. Janeway gripped his binoculars, scanning the howling gray ranks spreading out along the longer fence, kneeling and aiming. *You better not dally*. He spurred his mount. Rebel rifles blasted and bullets zipped through the air like whining cicadas. He rode behind his men as they sprinted forward, jockeyed behind the tall fence, and aimed their carbines.

"Fire!" he shouted.

The New Jersey troopers unleashed a booming barrage, spawning caterwauling from the enemy line.

Cox stood and screamed, "Keep firing!"

The Rebels replied with a storm of bullets whistling overhead. Janeway rode behind the Federal line to the right flank of his skirmishers. He scanned the fields to the north. No enemy. He let out a breath he hadn't even realized he was holding. He turned and rode south behind the troopers manning the stone fence.

"Keep firing, boys," Janeway shouted. "You're holding your own."

1:22 p.m.
General David Gregg
Strategic crossroads

Gregg trembled like a wounded animal. Ragged breaths tore at his lungs. Custer was forming up his brigade and soon departing for the Round Tops. Damn Pleasonton to hell for forcing him to defend the right flank with only McIntosh's brigade. Pleasonton was a pompous, vain, and incompetent commander, continually incapable of understanding the tactical situation and consistently issuing flawed orders. At Hanover Junction, Pleasonton sent him three contradictory orders minutes apart, and he had followed each one and marched up and down the same damn road for an hour. Should he have ignored these conflicting orders?

Panic and revulsion pulled at his heart. He gripped the reins with tight fists. Could willful insubordination be justified by circumstances? Since Pleasonton was incompetent and didn't understand he couldn't defend the right flank of the army with one brigade, was he justified in disobeying the order to release Custer? If he did order Custer to stay, he could be court-martialed.

God almighty, what a nutcracker. I'm damn certain the right flank will be destroyed if I release Custer's brigade and Stuart attacks.

He scanned the field in front of the advancing First New Jersey skirmishers. Dismounted enemy were tramping down from the Rummel farm and stopping behind a stone fence. The enemy paused and aimed. Cracking rifles blazed and streaking sheets flamed. The First New Jersey troopers knelt and fired. A devastating hailstorm of lead rattled and whizzed, heralding a fierce fight. His nerves tightened and his muscles twitched. *My God, this is the beginning of Stuart's probing attacks.*

He clapped his spurs and pitched toward Custer, leading his brigade off the Hanover Road and down the Low Dutch Road, his yellow curls bouncing beneath his black-brimmed hat. Gregg reined up next to the boy general.

"George, the First New Jersey have stumbled into a Rebel wolf pack up by the Rummel farm."

Custer furrowed his brow. "Once the enemy gets their dander up, they are going to burst forward like rabid beasts and swarm all over McIntosh's brigade."

Hundreds of cannons thundered south of Gettysburg town, belching billowy white clouds.

"It also appears that Lee has started his artillery barrage, trying to soften up the Union lines before his infantry charges."

"I agree, General Gregg. I believe you're going to have a spirited fight of your own before too long. I think you will find the woods beyond the Rummel farm full of Confederates with greater numbers than McIntosh's lone brigade."

Gregg grunted low in his throat. A riptide of fear slammed its way down to his stirrups. "McIntosh has 1,300 troopers deployed to face a tidal wave of 6,600 Rebel cavalrymen. That's a disaster."

"What do you suggest, General Gregg?"

He stared at Custer. "Just say you never got the message. I need you here."

Custer's smile crinkled the corners of his twinkling eyes. "I will only be too glad to stay if you will give the order."

Gregg prattled a devilish sigh. "General Custer, I order you to stay."

Custer's eyes alighted with a feverish twinkle. "Yes, sir. I will obey the order. Where do you want me to deploy my brigade?"

"I want you to deploy your brigade along the Hanover Road, facing north toward the Rummel farm. Order one regiment to anchor the strategic crossroads. Deploy the remaining three regiments westward up the Hanover Road toward Brinkerhoff's Ridge. I recommend you reestablish your headquarters at the Spangler house."

"Where would you like Pennington's six guns?"

"I want four of his guns to be west of the Spangler house. Position two of his guns east of the Spangler farm."

Custer rocked back in his saddle, snatched off his hat, and whooped.

"George, thank you for staying." A flame of hope spread through his body and warmed his heart. "This battle could be crucial to saving the Union army."

"General Gregg, thank you for ordering me to stay." Custer cracked a playful grin. "I love a good fight, especially when we're outnumbered."

"I've called for Colonel McIntosh to meet us here. After you give your orders, let's regroup at the crossroads in a few minutes."

Gregg chewed on the inside of his cheek. Custer's electrifying fervor and magnetizing valor was infectious. The boy general made him feel like he could cross the Rubicon and conquer Rome. Custer was not yet a master strategist, having been just promoted to general. But he was the supreme tactical instrument, possessing absolute fearlessness and a remarkable ability to execute. If Custer could spread his contagion of daring and fortitude to his Wolverines and McIntosh's brigade, the undersized forces on Meade's right flank had a chance to turn the tide against Stuart's Invincibles.

Gregg fired up his pipe, puffing smoke like a steam locomotive. McIntosh's brigade was fanning out north along the Low Dutch Road. Six hundred yards up the road stood Jacob Lott's two-story, white-framed house, with a single story jutting out from behind and butting up against a small barn. Woodlots bordered the eastern portion of the farm along the Low Dutch Road. A warmth of hope flickered in him. *Some of McIntosh's troopers could hide in these woods.*

He turned toward Brinkerhoff's Ridge. Beyond the ridge, toward General Meade's headquarters, a great cannonade roared and rumbled like a summer storm—crashing thunder, shrieking wind, clattering hailstones— dueling with blind fury. White banks of swift, convolving smoke billowed upwards as if a great forest fire were raging. The ground rolled gently, like a multitude of small, wind-driven waves.

A courier crested Brinkerhoff's Ridge and galloped down Hanover Road. *Was he delivering written orders for Custer to ride to the Round Tops?* His breath tripped in his throat.

Lieutenant James Wade reined up and saluted. "General Pleasonton sends his respects and wishes to report that the Confederate artillery is shelling the middle of General Meade's defensive line. Our Union artillery batteries replied, and they are conducting counterbattery fire against the Rebel guns."

"What's the purpose of the Confederate bombardment?"

"General Meade believes after the bombardment the Rebels will conduct an infantry attack."

Gregg puffed on his pipe. "What damage is Meade's infantry suffering?"

"Very little. The Rebel gunners are cutting their shell fuses too long and their artillery shells are sailing over our front lines and landing near Meade's headquarters."

"Is General Meade going to move his headquarters?"

"General Pleasonton requested General Meade move his headquarters to a safer position."

"I request that if General Meade moves his headquarters, you inform me." He paused. "Is that all that you have for me?"

Wade nodded and departed.

Gregg uttered a deep sigh. *Thank God.* No written orders for Custer to depart. He gripped his binoculars and scanned the open fields sprawling west of the Lott farm and rolling upward to the Rummel farm about half a mile to the northwest. His brow furrowed. He had to prevent Stuart's troopers from flowing down this vale like a devastating avalanche. Beyond the billowing smoke past Brinkerhoff's Ridge, where the relentless lead storm thundered, the bursting shells boomed like a thousand bass drums. Would the cannonading ever end? Then what?

Custer and McIntosh reined up.

"Gentlemen," Gregg said, "as soon as the enemy troopers that General Howard reported arrive, Stuart will have superior numbers. My guess is two or three thousand more troopers than we do. But I believe Stuart's first attacks will be dismounted and piecemeal, as he is doing against the First New Jersey."

"Why do you believe that?" Custer said. "If it were me, I would order one grand charge with all my troopers."

Gregg smiled. "I'm sure you would, George. But Stuart doesn't know the size of our force and isn't looking for another twelve-hour cavalry fight along a wide front like Brandy Station."

McIntosh spoke up. "What is Stuart's plan?"

"Stuart's goal is to attack the rear of our army. We are sitting in his way. He is not interested in fighting a drawn-out battle and us raising a white flag. Instead, he desires to pierce through our lines on a narrow front like a lightning bolt."

"How will he accomplish this?" Custer asked.

Gregg pulled on his beard. "He will try to bait us into exposing our positions. My guess is that he will thrust a large, dismounted skirmish force out of the woods off the Cress ridgeline and take a position behind the Rummel farm buildings. His sharpshooters will start peppering our skirmishers like pesky hornets in the hopes we will rush our entire force out into the open so they can squash us."

Custer said, "So Stuart's using dismounted skirmishers as bait?"

"Yes. Once he has us out in the open, he will locate a soft spot and launch a massive cavalry attack, piercing our lines as if thrusting a spear. Then he will flood his forces through this fleeting gap like a broken dam and race to our army's rear."

McIntosh wagged a finger toward his New Jersey troopers. "Maybe we should continue matching his dismounted skirmishers one to one with our skirmishers and not launch a major attack, since Stuart's success hinges on probing our lines."

Gregg paused and drew a breath. "Agreed. I want to play pawn against pawn as long as possible. So, let's match Stuart's dismounted forces with our dismounted forces. My guess is that Stuart does not want a dismounted fight. He wants to find a weakness quickly and then exploit it with a grand cavalry charge."

Custer said, "The Fifth and Sixth Michigan, armed with Spencer rifles, are ideal for fighting dismounted. My guess is that Stuart hasn't experienced the rapid firepower of the Spencer."

"Let me show you my plan." Gregg dismounted, and the two brigade commanders followed suit. He picked up a stick and drew lines in the dirt. "Gentlemen, I'm employing a layered defense like a medieval castle with its multi-tiered fortifications. This defense in depth is designed to delay rather than prevent Stuart from advancing. By slowly yielding territory, we will use land to stretch out Stuart's forces, and when he loses momentum, I will counterattack."

A tremendous explosion detonated in the direction of Cemetery Ridge, as if a limber's artillery chest had been hit. Gregg snapped his head toward a cloud of rolling black smoke rising in the shape of a deadly tornado.

"This is the longest-lasting artillery barrage I've witnessed," Custer declared.

Gregg nodded. "Me, too." He turned back to his two brigade commanders, using his stick to follow the lines in the dirt. "The castle's ramparts will be the Hanover and Low Dutch Roads. Along these two roads we will place Pennington's six-gun battery and Randol's four-gun battery. These rifled artillery pieces outrange the enemy's artillery."

Gregg turned to Custer. "After watching Pennington duel with the Rebel artillery guns, I realized we also have the advantage of being more accurate. I was impressed with Randol's batteries' accuracy, as well. His deadly guns saved one of McIntosh's surgeons and helped Captain Miller's Third Pennsylvania's successful assault against the Brinkerhoff stone wall."

Custer grinned. "Pennington's first shot landed this afternoon in the muzzle of the enemy cannon, ripping it up."

"That was impressive shooting." Gregg wiped his brow. "George, I want the Seventh Michigan protecting Pennington's guns." He glanced at McIntosh. "The First Maryland will protect Randol's guns."

Custer and McIntosh nodded agreement.

"I want to make this clear. We will stand firm in our layered defense. We will not fall for Stuart's bait." He paused and stared at Custer. "Do not attack until I give the order. Understood?"

Custer and McIntosh nodded again.

Gregg stroked his beard. He pointed his stick at the dirt lines again.

"John, I want your brigade positioned around the Lott farm. I also want you to send two companies from the Third Pennsylvania north along the Low Dutch Road. Position them in a woodlot across the field from the Rummel farm. Order that squadron not to participate in the fight. They are to stay hidden and defend against the enemy trying to reach the Low Dutch Road and rushing south."

McIntosh said, "Understood. I will detach Captain William Miller and he will command the squadron of the two Pennsylvania companies."

He dipped a quick nod. "Captain Miller is the right choice to hold the road. His squadron did a great job last evening along Brinkerhoff's Ridge." Gregg pointed to his improvised map. "I want the rest of your brigade to form a north–south line beyond the Lott farm."

He took a deep breath. "Who is leading the First New Jersey fight at the Rummel farm?"

"Major Hugh Janeway."

He frowned. "Did Major Myron Beaumont's mysterious pre-battlefield illness emerge again?"

"Yes. I will fix this problem after the fight."

"Very well. My intent is that Janeway's skirmishing will act as a berm and divert the enemy's efforts eastward toward the Lott house and away from attacking directly south toward the Hanover Road. If Janeway needs reinforcements, advance the Third Pennsylvania, minus Miller's two squadrons."

Gregg turned to Custer. "George, I want the Fifth Michigan Regiment to dismount and stand by to move forward toward the First New Jersey and extend their skirmish line. The rest of your brigade will position along the Hanover Road."

"Yes, sir."

Gregg's jaw tightened. "The First New Jersey and Fifth Michigan will act as our forward line of defense and do their best to control the Rummel farm area."

Custer and McIntosh nodded.

"If there are no questions, I would like to have a word with General Custer in private."

McIntosh saluted, mounted his horse, and departed.

Gregg glared into Custer's eyes. "General, there will be no pre-emptive heroics today. Don't get your blood up and take their bait when the Rebels start to push our skirmishers back.

You must hold your flanks and the center of your position until the right moment! I will determine when the moment is right. Have I made myself clear?"

Custer shifted his feet; his cheeks turned crimson. "Yes, sir."

"George, time is on our side. The longer we can keep Stuart from penetrating our lines and attacking the army's rear, the better. I would love playing a skirmisher chess game with Stuart all day."

"I understand, sir." Custer saluted, mounted his horse, and departed.

He stared at Custer riding away. A roiling darkness pervaded him, portending doom. Would Custer disobey orders and launch an impulsive cavalry charge? He wavered, swallowing back his uncertainty. *Not sure.*

1:45 p.m.
Major Hugh Janeway, First New Jersey
Rummel farm fence

Watching over his troopers firing behind a stone fence, Major Janeway was gripped by a persistently stronger surge of alarm. Fifty yards away, the enemy crouched behind a longer fence that ran beyond the left flank of Janeway's fence and his men. He reined up next to Sergeant Major Cox and pulled his hat down against the heavy sun, squinting. "Sergeant Major, how is the ammunition holding out?"

"The carbine ammunition has almost run out. When it does, we will have to face the Rebels with our revolvers."

A chill shot across his shoulders and spiked down his arms. "I'll ride back to the Lott house and report to Major Beaumont and request more ammunition and reserves."

Cox shot a sly smile. "I hope Major Beaumont made a quick recovery."

"Me, too!"

1:52 p.m.
Major Hugh Janeway
Approaching the Lott Farm

Janeway found Major Beaumont resting on his mount near the Lott house, observing the action. Beaumont's dark, drooping mustache and his bushy black eyebrows matched his wilted mettle.

"Myron, we're holding the enemy. But we are running low on ammunition, and we need reinforcements."

"I will inform Colonel McIntosh," responded Beaumont. "Return to the skirmish line and hold it. Ammunition and reinforcements will arrive shortly."

"Yes, sir." His bones rattled as he galloped back to the fence. Would that skittish Beaumont deliver?

1:54 p.m.
Colonel John McIntosh
Lott house

McIntosh plunged past the Lott barn and aimed for Major Beaumont. His heart pounded in his ears.

"Major Beaumont, what's the situation with Major Janeway's skirmishers?"

"They are holding their own. But they need ammunition and another regiment to come forward and reinforce them."

"The First New Jersey needs to fall back, regroup, and replenish their carbine ammunition. I will order the Third Pennsylvania to replace the First New Jersey troopers."

McIntosh galloped toward Lieutenant Colonel Edward Jones, commanding the Third Pennsylvanians.

"Edward, deploy two squadrons commanded by Captain Charles Treichel and Captain William Rogers and relieve Major Janeway's First New Jersey skirmishers. Take extra ammunition with you. I'm also going to order Captain Robert Duval's Company A from Purnell's Legion to provide support."

"Yes, sir."

2:00 p.m.
General David Gregg
Strategic crossroads

Gregg's hands were slick with sweat. The thundering roar of hundreds of bursting cannons filling the air with hot lead along Cemetery Ridge and the twenty or so cannons booming around Rummel farm overwhelmed any other sounds. He gripped the saddle's pommel as the ground rocked and his mount swayed beneath him. He felt like he was standing on a trembling timber trestle supporting a rumbling freight train, racing by but never ending. All he could do was hold on and watch.

He wiped his brow and gripped his binoculars. The Third Pennsylvanians were darting forward, making good progress. *Good.*

Captain Meyer shouted, "General, enemy reinforcements are advancing to support the Rebels firing at the First New Jersey."

Gregg peered toward Cress Ridge. A creeping hollowness was working its way through him. If the Third Pennsylvania didn't advance in time, the First New Jersey would falter and be overrun.

"Henry," he said, "Stuart is using his dismounted troopers as pawns and trying to get me to commit all my pieces."

"Do you want to move up the Fifth Michigan?"

"Yes, order General Custer to move up the Fifth Michigan. Also, tell him that I want the First Michigan and Seventh Michigan ready to counter an enemy-mounted charge."

Spangler House as it is today

51

Fifth Michigan — Friday, July 3

2:05 p.m.
Colonel Russell Alger, commanding Fifth Michigan
Custer's headquarters at the Spangler house

Alger's pulse thudded in his ears. The Rebels were scrambling down the slope like hordes of angry red ants. He sucked air between his teeth and a lump formed under his ribs. Panic surged through him.

"Colonel Alger!"

He whirled and eyed Custer. "Yes, General."

"Colonel Alger, see the Rebels emerging from Cress Ridge and darting toward the New Jersey troopers?"

"I do, General."

"Deploy the dismounted Fifth Michigan forward to support the New Jersey and Pennsylvania boys," Custer shouted.

"Yes, sir."

Alger spurred across Hanover Road and rode two hundred yards north toward Cress Ridge, halting in front of two lines of mounted Wolverines. He pointed at Major Ferry and Major Trowbridge and shouted, "Dismount to fight."

Six hundred forty-five troopers each gathered their reins in their left hand and held them above their horse's withers while they gripped the front of the saddle with their right hand. In unison, each trooper removed their right foot from the stirrup and swung their right leg over the horse's croup while slipping their left foot from its stirrup. They slid down along the horse's side and thumped the ground. The troopers handed their reins to every fourth man and stepped forward, forming two long lines of battle.

Alger shouted, "Now, Wolverines, be steady—be men! Tomorrow will be the fourth of July, and we must begin our celebration this day. Let no man forget the State of Michigan, his own manhood, the loved ones at home, and always keep one load in your long arm and revolver."

He glanced up and down the line. The troopers stared, stern-faced.

"Major Ferry, take charge of the right." He twisted in his saddle. "Major Trowbridge, take the left."

Ferry and Trowbridge sprang forward in front of their two squadrons.

2:06 p.m.
Major Noah Ferry
Wheat field near Little Run

A glaring sun poured down at a slight pitch from straight overhead. Ferry lowered his field glasses onto his chest. An intrepid spirit calmed his muscles. Narrowing his eyes, he scanned his Fifth Michigan squadron of two hundred forty troopers forming up into one long line. Sergeant Edwin Bigelow, Troop B, standing beside him, stepped forward.

Bigelow bellowed, "Dress up the lines, men. Snap it up." The sergeant looked up and down and the line. "Check your Spencers, make sure you've inserted a cartridge in the magazine."

The sergeant stared at Private Lewis Gardner. "Gardner, how many bullets are in the cartridge?"

"Seven, Sergeant," said Private Gardner.

"Good." Bigelow scanned the squadron. "Now, men, lock the spring-loaded follower tube in place. Half-cock the hammer, lower the lever, and then raise the lever. You should have a chambered round ready to fire."

A chorus of metallic clicking filled the air like calling cicadas. Ferry stepped forward and strode along the line.

"Now, boys," Major Ferry said, "if any of you are unwilling to go forward, you may stay here."

A cheer erupted from the Wolverines. "Ferry, Ferry, Ferry!"

His heart danced a jig.

Ferry stepped toward Colonel Alger, sitting on his mount. "Colonel Alger, my squadron is ready to advance."

"Very well." Alger turned to Major Trowbridge.

Trowbridge said, "My squadron is ready, sir."

Alger bellowed, "Forward!"

Ferry sucked in a deep breath and stepped into the waist-high wheat. He pointed and said, "Sergeant Bigelow, head for the left flank of McIntosh's troopers at the stone wall."

Major Noah Ferry

52

Custer — Friday, July 3

Custer's heartbeat sped up as four hundred seventy-nine Wolverines sprang forward, cradling their seven-shot Spencer rifles. Their .44-caliber revolvers were holstered.

He turned to Colerick. "William, three dismounted Rebel regiments are whirling around McIntosh's troopers' left flank. Major Ferry and Major Trowbridge's troopers are going to give the Rebels the surprise of their life when they unleash those Spencers."

"General, I see more Rebels emerging from behind the Rummel farm. Do you think you should order the Sixth Michigan forward to support the Fifth?"

A tempest churned inside him. He hated watching a fight. He bit his tongue to keep the epithets seething in his mind from escaping.

"Not yet. General Gregg gave me strict orders not to deploy any other regiments until he says so." He paused, studying Alger's two advancing squadrons. "Except for some Rebels at the Battles of Hanover and Hunterstown, most of the enemy have not experienced the deadly firepower of the repeating rifles. Hopefully, Colonel Alger's troopers' firepower will confuse the enemy into believing they are facing a much larger force."

He squinted, watching Ferry lead the Fifth Michigan's right squadron through the wheat field, moving back and forth across his line, chatting with troopers, gesturing toward the enemy line. His troopers erupted into a cheer as they strode forward.

"William," Custer said, "I've been impressed with Major Noah Ferry."

Pennington's battery sounded a thundering crack, the shells whistling over Ferry's ducking troopers toward an enemy battery on Cress Hill. Ferry turned toward his men and broke out in a large grin as he brandished his saber.

"I like the way he leads his men from the front." Custer pointed. "I also like that it is easy to spot Ferry because of his beaver-like beard."

"Ferry is the most beloved man in the Fifth Michigan and one hell of a fighter," Colerick said.

Custer nodded. "After this battle, I'm going to submit him for a promotion to Lieutenant Colonel."

53

First New Jersey — Friday, July 3

2:08 p.m.
Major Hugh Janeway
Rummel farm fence

Janeway pressed toward the shorter stone fence. Thirty yards behind the First New Jersey troopers, he slowed his horse to a jarring walk. Sergeant Major Cox skirted behind the kneeling First New Jersey firing their revolvers. *Damn, they must be almost out of ammunition.* He spotted a couple hundred dismounted Rebels emerging from the Rummel barn, hurtling toward the enemy's right flank. His heart pitched forward, clawing at his ribcage. The enemy fence on his left flank was longer than his troopers' fence. Once the advancing Confederates occupied it, they would be able to curl around the New Jersey's left flank.

He reined up behind Cox. "Sergeant Major, what's the situation?"

Cox shouted, "All the carbines are out of ammunition. We are down to about ten rounds per man for their revolvers. Is Colonel McIntosh sending reinforcements?"

"Yes, he ordered the Third Pennsylvania and Company A from Purnell's Legion forward to support us."

Cox pointed toward the Hanover Road and grinned. "Look, Major—dismounted Wolverines with Spencer rifles are storming toward us."

Janeway twisted in his saddle and drank in the sight of Colonel Alger's Fifth Michigan advancing. A tingle feathered the hairs on his neck. *Thank God.* "I see them."

The charging Rebels arrived, extending their line along the rock fence. Several hundred rifles cracked, and bullets ripped overhead. His hat flipped back, floating to the ground. He shuddered.

"Dammit, Major, dismount!" Cox shouted. "The graybacks are aiming for you."

The gray, rattling storm scurried down the rock fence, its blazing volleys raking the blue line. His frightened steed winnowed and reared. He clung to the poor animal's neck. When she landed on all fours, he scissored his legs off the saddle and landed on his feet. The mare ripped the reins from his gloved hand and tore for the Lott house. He knelt and picked up his blue slouch hat, a hole the size of a copperhead token through the gold cross-sword insignia.

He glanced toward the rear and saw his frantic mare dashing through a stalled reinforcement line. He drew in a shivering breath. What the hell? The Third Pennsylvanians had halted about one hundred yards to the rear of the Jerseymen.

Cox knelt beside him. Beads of sweat dripped down his red face. He gasped hard, struggling for breath. "What the hell is going on, Major? We're almost out of ammunition."

"Colonel McIntosh will push some forward. Wait and see."

"I hope so, Major. The boys won't abandon the line until the reserves come up."

Janeway glanced up to the right flank as Captain Robert Duvall's company of Marylanders was arriving. Hope shot through his body. He pointed. "Sergeant Major, the Marylanders are arriving."

Cox turned his head and scanned northward. "They are taking an L-shaped position, half facing north and the rest extending our line."

Janeway gulped. "I see mounted Rebel troops emerging from the trees on the northern Cress Ridge."

"Oh," said Cox, "that's why the Marylanders formed an L-shape."

Janeway turned and glanced south toward Hanover Road. His breath hitched in his throat. "Here come the dismounted Wolverines with their repeating rifles. We must hold on until Colonel McIntosh pushes up the reserves."

2:10 p.m.
Colonel John McIntosh
Twenty yards behind the Third Pennsylvania reserve line

McIntosh fumed as he neared Beaumont. "Major, where is your regiment?"

Beaumont said, "On the skirmish line, sir."

"Damn it, Major. I ordered them to be relieved."

"The Third Pennsylvania Regiment cannot move forward to relieve the First New Jersey."

"Why the hell not?" Gesturing, McIntosh demanded, "Recall Major Janeway and his men."

"I have recalled them," said Beaumont, "and they won't come."

A searing fury erupted, heating his blood. McIntosh spurred and dashed to the rear of the Third Pennsylvania line. Captain Charles Treichel and Captain William Rogers were dismounted, chatting.

The captains saluted.

"Why haven't you advanced, you damn whelps, and relieved the First New Jersey squadron?"

Captain Treichel stared up beneath his floppy hat, sweat dripping from his lambchop beard. "Colonel, the enemy fire is too intense to move forward."

McIntosh glanced at the First New Jersey troopers firing their revolvers at a long row of Rebels. Graybacks stood behind the long fence, spewing flaky streams of yellow fire. Sulphury smoke billowed up between the two fences like a field of geysers sending up shards of steam.

He bristled. "Captains, the First New Jersey can't hold out much longer. If the enemy overruns them, Stuart will lead a grand cavalry charge past Rummel farm and crush Custer's brigade." With a sharp toss of his chin, he twisted around and stared hard at the line of kneeling reserves. He jerked his head back and glared. In a cold, snarling tone, he punched each word. "Either you lead your troopers forward or I will."

The captains glanced at each other and glared back at the colonel. "We will lead them forward," Treichel growled. He stepped through the Pennsylvania line, followed by Rogers, and shouted, "Charge!"

A great cheer erupted from the line, and troopers rushed forward. McIntosh replaced his disgust for the recalcitrant captains with grateful awe for their troopers. They looked like a pack of starving wolves, leaping and bounding with fangs bared.

As they neared the New Jersey line, the Third Pennsylvanian captains split their force thirty yards from the stone fence and rushed to both flanks.

2:13 p.m.
Major Hugh Janeway
Rummel farm fence

Janeway plunged, breathless, toward the fence. He wiped his wet brow, aimed, and fired his revolver. A steady crackle of gunfire rang in his ears. Boot spurs jingled behind him, and he shot a glance sideways, where Captain Treichel was darting up.

"Hugh, I'm ready to relieve your squadron," Treichel declared.

"Charles, I'm damn glad you advanced. We're out of ammunition."

"You pull back and William Rogers and my squadrons will fill in."

Janeway's mouth twisted into a harsh sneer. "No, we're not going to leave. The enemy keeps pushing troops into their line. Give us ammunition and we will stay and fight."

"Are you sure?" Treichel paused, his mouth gaping. "Colonel McIntosh gave us a direct order to relieve you."

"We're staying. I will deal with McIntosh later."

2:14 p.m.
Colonel John McIntosh
En route to General David Gregg's headquarters at the strategic crossroads

McIntosh galloped toward Gregg's divisional flag planted at the intersection of the Hanover and Low Dutch Roads. He cast a strained eye toward where Gregg was chatting with an aide. He swung his horse around and pointed.

"General Gregg. I want to provide you a situation report and request reinforcements."

Gregg nodded. "Report."

He pointed toward the Lott house. "I've established a thin defensive line that is anchored north of the Lott house in a strip of woods. The line extends west toward the Rummel springhouse, then south along the stone fence toward the Hanover Road."

Gregg scanned the defensive line, using his binoculars. "Good. I see Custer's Fifth Michigan moving across Little Run toward your left flank. That should help shore up your defenses."

"With all due respect, sir, my line running from the Lott woods to the Rummel spring house is as thin as greased paper windows. I'm facing a numerically superior force holding a commanding ridge that dominates a wide plain of cultivated fields stretching towards the Hanover Road. I respectfully request reinforcements from Irvin Gregg's brigade."

Gregg frowned and shook his head. "General Pleasonton ordered Colonel Gregg's brigade to remain in place. But I will move Captain Alanson Randol's batteries E and G forward to protect your brigade."

McIntosh's heart quaked. He was not sure if Randol's battery would suffice.

Captain Alexander C. M. Pennington

54

Fifth Michigan — Friday, July 3

2:20 p.m.
Major Noah Ferry
Wheat field near Little Run

Ferry slithered through the tall wheat, his head just above golden stalks. No enemy fire was directed toward the Fifth Michigan. His heart skipped a beat. The tall, golden grain was enabling them to creep like hunting cougars. Sergeant Edwin Bigelow came crouch-walking toward him.

"Major, one of our flankers reports the Rebels are in a strong line just beyond the wheat field," Bigelow reported. "He believes the Rebels know we are coming and will start shooting soon."

"Okay Sergeant, let's keep crawling forward."

An ominous lull engulfed the creeping Wolverines—like the stillness following shattered snow spilling down a slope. Ferry paused and wiped his brow. *Where are the Rebels?* There was a ghostly shriek, then rifles cracked and blind bullets whizzed, harvesting wheat and death like a swinging scythe. Wolverines screamed.

A guttural thrill swept through him. "Fire and rush forward," he shouted. "The Rebels must reload."

The Wolverines poked their heads above the stalks and fired their Spencers in true hunter style.

Ferry popped his head above the golden stalks and scanned the Rummel farm about 300 rods ahead. He glanced to the northwest. Graybacks were rushing from the wooded screen of Cress Ridge.

He pointed. "Sergeant Edwin Bigelow, those Rebs emerging from the ridge are trying to flank the First New Jersey and Third Pennsylvania, hunkered behind the stone wall, firing their weapons."

"I see them."

"We need to swing our line well forward and Major Trowbridge needs to refuse his line."

"I will tell Major Trowbridge." Bigelow hurtled off.

Ferry shouted, "Swing our line to the left."

The line started rotating left, like a fence gate opening. He glanced down the line toward Trowbridge's squadron swinging the left end of their line back, like a door pivoting on a hinge. He peeked ahead at the First New Jersey and Third Pennsylvania holding their own behind the stone fence as the enemy poured fire at them. *Got to hurry.* He scrambled forward, pushing up the slope toward the left flank of McIntosh's hard-pressed troopers.

He gripped the trigger on his Spencer and stood and shouted, "Fire."

The Wolverines unleashed a fiery blaze of lead. A chorus of metallic clicking filled the air as the troopers cocked the Spencer levers and hammers and fired again. Volley after volley spewed, creating a deadly lead blanket. The enemy line buckled like a boxer hit with a knockout punch. The Wolverines slid forward like a slow-moving mudslide, firing, cocking, and firing. The Rebel fire slackened to a drizzle across no-man's-land.

Ferry turned to Bigelow. "The Rebels are faltering."

"I think they are running out of ammunition."

"Let's press forward." Ferry turned and brandished his saber. "'Charge!'"

A bugle blew sharp, piercing notes. The blue troopers leaped forward, firing, cocking, firing. Their lines blazed like a wildfire sweeping toward the enemy lines. Ferry leaped forward, keeping pace with the chorus of roars surrounding him. His boots flew over the ground as if he had winged heels. He screamed louder. His throat was scraped rawhide.

From the northern slope of Cress Ridge, tearing thunder exploded, leaving a dazed hollowness echoing through him. Four black tendrils arced from broad-mouthed Rebel Napoleons toward the Fifth Michigan. He drew in a shivering breath. Screaming shells swooped to the ground and burst into blinding, wintery light among the blue troopers. Hot lead fragments swept over the Wolverines in pelting, crazed torrents. He dropped to the ground, shaking his addled head. All sound was obliterated except the ringing in his ears.

Bigelow grabbed his shoulder. A distant, muddled voice said, "Major, are you hit?"

He shook his head again and glanced down at his uniform. *No blood. No pain.* He glanced back at the Wolverines. Flying fragments had torn through soft flesh, and screams echoed throughout the ranks. Without warning, enemy rifle fire burst like clattering rain. The Rebel jaws of iron thundered again, heralding prolonged hissing like a pit of fanged vipers as the shells plunged into the Wolverines.

Ferry glanced up. A swarm of dismounted graybacks slithered from the wooded crest and spilled toward the bluecoats' left flank.

"We're being flanked," Bigelow shouted. "Our troopers are running out of ammunition."

Sheets of flame leaped out from the flanking graybacks. The Rebels screamed a bloodcurdling yell. Muzzle flashes burst through the smoke.

Bigelow shouted, "Major, we have to fall back, sir."

"Agreed. Tell Major Trowbridge we have to fall back."

2:30 p.m.
Major Luther Trowbridge
Wheat field near Little Run

Trowbridge fired his rifle, wiped his brow, and glanced to his right. An emerging uncertainty began to nag at him as Sergeant Bigelow scudded down the line. The sergeant halted, gasping for a breath, his eyes twitching with panic.

"Major Ferry said we have to fall back," Bigelow wheezed. "We are being flanked."

A bullet whistled overhead, and Trowbridge ducked. "Concur. We shall fall back." He stepped toward Sergeant Major Charles Osborne.

"Sergeant Major," shouted Trowbridge, "Let's fall back with Major Ferry's troopers."

Trowbridge turned and stepped back toward Hanover Road. The line undulated backwards like a sidewinding diamondback. "Don't worry about keeping the line straight, Sergeant Major!"

A mounted colonel rode up. Trowbridge didn't recognize the officer. *Must be from McIntosh's brigade.*

"This is blasphemous behavior," the colonel shouted. "Why are you skedaddling, Major?"

Rage clawed his gut. "We are not skedaddling, Colonel. We are not beaten. We are falling back because our ammunition is gone."

The colonel frowned. "Very well. Let's show the Rebels our spirit. Stop your retreat and give a cheer."

Trowbridge hesitated. *That's crazy.* "Yes, sir." He turned to Sergeant Major Osborne. "Order the troopers to about face and march back a few rods and give three ringing cheers."

Osborne glared, plainly confused.

Trowbridge shouted, "Damn it, Sergeant. Order the cheer!"

Osborne shook his head and belted out the order; the troopers halted and reverse-marched. After covering twenty yards he shouted, "Three cheers for the Union." A roaring shout erupted. "Hip hip hurrah! Hip hip hurrah! Hip hip hurrah!"

2:33 p.m.
Major Noah Ferry
Wheat field near Little Run

Major Ferry skittered along the forward lines. Why were Trowbridge's Wolverines cheering? There was a large, flat-sawn stump ahead; he burst forward and leaped onto it. The enemy's left line was advancing. Thirty yards away. "Come on, boys. Use your revolvers. Keep firing. You're doing great."

A pelting shower of bullets splattered around him like a spring rain.

"Get down, Major!" Osborne shouted.

A hand gripped his saber belt and yanked. He hit the ground with a bone-jarring jolt.

"Major, this is the Devil's absurdity." Osborne gestured. "You can't expose yourself like that. The Rebels are deadly shots at this range."

"Sergeant Major, the Rebels are pressing our left flank."

"Major, you must fall back with the troopers."

He whirled and glared at Osborne. "I'm falling back, Sergeant Major!" He turned and stepped down the sloping wheat field. Sweat poured down off his brow like melting snow. He paused and wiped his jacket sleeve across his face. The stinging eased. He squinted at the retreating troopers.

A gasping moan. "Please, Major, over here." It was a private, sprawled out on the ground.

"Major, I feel faint; I am going to die."

He tore toward the trooper and bent down. "Let me take a look."

"It's my arm."

Major Ferry gripped the private's hand and moved it away from the wound. The private winced. The injured arm was slick with dark red blood, oozing from a flesh wound.

He smiled. "I have good news, Private. You're not going to die."

"Are you sure, Major? It hurts like hell."

He grinned. "You're just lucky these dismounted Rebels can't shoot worth a darn."

The private nodded.

"I'm going to take your Spencer repeater and your cartridges. I'll give the Rebels a surprise." He reached into the private's ammunition box, grabbed several bullets, and filled his jacket pockets. He grabbed another handful and removed the magazine and filled it with seven bullets, nose first, and inserted the magazine into the Spencer.

2:35 p.m.
Major Noah Ferry
Wheat field near Little Run

Ferry's finger covered the trigger. He scooted toward the enemy. Ahead was a large boulder thirty yards from the Rebel line. A sudden impulse overcame him. He smiled. *The Rebels can taste my Spencer.* He lurched toward the rounded rock and leaped onto it. He gazed at the enemy line. The left and right Rebel flanks were retreating toward the Rummel farm. His smile broadened into a grin. The Wolverine firepower had proved too much for the skedaddlers.

Standing tall, he glared at the middle of the Rebel line. *If we advance, they will retreat.* He aimed and fired at the traitorous red flag anchoring the middle of the Rebel line. He cocked and raised the lever seven times. Kneeling, he removed the fired cartridge case and reloaded it. He stood, aimed, and fired.

Crack. A lead sheet of Enfield rifle .58-caliber minié balls whizzed past, two feathering each side of his face. *Damn, that was close.*

"Get down, Major!" Sergeant Major Osborne was gripping the side of his trousers. Osborne pulled and he plunged sideways. He extended his right arm and broke the fall.

"Damn it, Major, you're going to get yourself killed standing up like that."

"The Rebel flanks are retreating. If we charge their middle, we can break their line."

"Dammit, Major, *get down.*"

Ferry waved and shouted, "Follow me!" A cheer broke out behind him. "Come on, boys, we can do it. Rally, boys! Rally for the fence!"

Crack. His skull exploded as all thoughts flashed into blackness.

2:36 p.m.
Sergeant Major John Osborne
Wheat field

Osborne's gaze flickered toward the tumbling major. *Oh, my God.* Ferry hit with a thud. Osborne bolted forward and bent down.

He screamed, "Major, are you hit?"

Osborne swallowed, his heart hammering. Ferry lay face down, lifeless. He bent down and gripped the major's bloody skull and turned him over, laying him face upward.

"No!"

He dry heaved, sour stomach acids geysering into his mouth. He spit them out. A bullet had grooved through Ferry's skull. The major's grayish brain protruded in lumps like stringy biscuits, ebbing down his face in a red sea of blood, staining the ground crimson.

Osborne looked up, searching for help from nearby troopers. "The Major is dead," he panted. Carry him back to our lines."

Four troopers rushed forward, each grabbing an arm and a leg, picked up the major, and trundled back a few yards toward Pennington's booming cannons.

Nearly five hundred Rebel wolf cries bayed. Osborne turned to see the dismounted enemy advancing. The Rebels paused and aimed. "Down, everyone down," he shouted. Countless flashes and cracking erupted as long, fiery sheets of musket lead stormed toward the Wolverines.

"Sergeant Major, we are out of ammunition."

Osborne ordered, "Leave the major's body on the field. Retreat! Retreat!"

The troopers laid Major Ferry's body gently on the ground, turned, and sprinted toward Pennington's battery.

Tears stung his eyes as he stared at Ferry's body. "We will come back for you, Major," he whispered.

He turned and raced toward the rear. His lungs spasmed as he gasped for more air. An icy cold seized him. *Don't falter.* It seemed impossible. Their gallant leader was dead. A deep gloom covered the retreating regiment like a death shroud.

2:40 p.m.
Captain Alexander Pennington
Just north of Spangler house and Hanover Road

Pennington stood in the thunderous hell of his six batteries, pummeling the dismounted Rebels. The rising brimstone clouds belching from their iron jaws nearly cloaked the big guns. A fearless delight swept over his soul. The precision of his pitchforked devils throwing hails of iron was remarkable. He drifted over toward Lieutenant Carle Woodruff's battery.

433

"Carle," he shouted over the deafening roar of artillery, "the dismounted Rebels are retreating to the woods of Cress Ridge and the Rummel farm buildings. Keep pounding their heels and scatter them."

"Yes, sir," Woodruff yelled.

Pennington felt a growing confidence bubbling. Although Jeb Stuart's force might be twice as large as General Gregg's cavalry, the blue-clad boys held the edge in several ways. The Union batteries were more accurate and had a greater range than the Rebel cannons, and the Spencer rifles were faster to load and fire than the enemy's muzzle-loaded Enfield rifles. He guffawed. And most importantly, Custer's outfit was more flamboyant than any of the Rebels'. That should count for something.

2:41 p.m.
Major Peter Weber
Spangler farm

Weber's heart pounded and the wind buffeted his cheeks as he leaned into the gallop and clapped his spurs against the steed's ribs. As he approached the strategic intersection he let up on the right rein. His horse's hooves sent clods of dirt flying as the mount dipped into a swinging turn up the Hanover Road and into the Spangler yard. Panic clawed at his stomach. He reined up and saluted.

"General Custer. My outpost on the Low Dutch Road was overrun by superior enemy forces. I've posted my two companies next to the four Sixth Michigan companies supporting Pennington's guns."

Custer's face blossomed with a daredevilish sparkle, like a boy skipping chores and running with his rod to his secret fishing hole. "What's the situation beyond the Rummel farm?"

Weber pointed. "I have seen thousands of mounted Rebels over yonder. The wooded country over there is full of them."

Custer beamed. "Maybe Stuart will finally order a mounted charge. My Wolverines will respond in kind."

"On my ride down the Low Dutch Road, I saw the enemy pulling back toward the Rummel farm as Pennington and Randol's artillery blasted the hell out of their dismounted troops."

"I've ordered Colonel Alger to resupply the Fifth Michigan's ammunition and advance to support Colonel McIntosh's troops." Custer leaned forward in his saddle, his voice booming like Pennington's big guns. "It looks like McIntosh's troopers are chasing the enemy and clearing the Rummel farm of enemy soldiers."

"My guess is that the mounted Rebel troops I spotted in the Cress Ridge woods will be coming our way soon in a full mounted cavalry charge."

Custer slapped his thigh. "God, I hope so. I truly hope so." His pitched voice shot out the words in a rapid burst. "Inform General Gregg."

Major Peter A. Weber

55

Gregg — Friday, July 3

2:45 p.m.
General David Gregg
Strategic crossroads

In the quiet lull of the hushed cannonading at both Cemetery Ridge and the Rummel farm, a lone messenger galloped through the lingering mist and pulled up.

"General Gregg. General Pleasonton sends his respects and wishes to inform you that the Confederates are emerging from the woods along Seminary Ridge. Regiment after regiment and brigade after brigade are taking their places in three lines, forming for an assault. The second line is a short interval behind the first line and the third line is a short interval behind the second line. The enemy lines extend over a thousand yards, man touching man, rank pressing rank, from across Cemetery Hill south to across the Trostle farm, which is a thousand yards south of Meade's headquarters at the Leister house. The general estimates eighteen thousand men are forming up, with their barrels and bayonets gleaming in the sun. It looks like a forest of flashing steel."

"What damage did the Confederate artillery inflict?"

"It appeared the enemy guns were focused on a copse of trees occupied by General Hancock's Second Corps. The Rebel gunners seemed to have cut their fuses too long and most of the shells were too high and flew over Cemetery Ridge, occupied by our infantry. The shells hit near the Leister house, which General Meade was using as his headquarters."

"Did Meade move his headquarters?"

437

"Yes, he moved about five hundred yards south down the Taneytown Road. That's where General Pleasonton is."

"Inform General Pleasonton that most of Jeb Stuart's cavalry has arrived on Cress Ridge and I expect them to attack soon. I believe Stuart's goal is to simultaneously attack the rear of Meade's defensive line. My guess is that while the Rebel infantry is attacking the front of Meade's defensive line, Stuart's cavalry will be attacking the rear of Meade's defensive line."

The messenger departed.

A sharpshooter's rifle cracked, and a bullet droned overhead.

Weber reined up. "General Gregg, I saw thousands of mounted Rebels in the woods on the northern slope of Cress Ridge."

"Very well. When do you expect them to attack?

"In the next fifteen or twenty minutes."

"Tell General Custer to have the First and Seventh Michigan ready for a mounted charge."

"General Custer is chomping at the bit for a saber fight."

Gregg furrowed his brow. "I'm sure General Custer is more than anxious to lead a daredevil charge." He pointed his finger. "Tell General Custer that all mounted charges will be given on my command. Make sure he understands this order."

"Yes, sir." Weber spurred his horse up the Hanover Road toward the Spangler house.

Gregg turned to Captain Henry Weir. "Well, Henry, what do you think?"

"I think we are in for a hell of a fight in the next half hour."

"I know that. What do you think of Custer champing at the bit to lead a cavalry charge?"

Weir paused. "I'm pretty sure he is going to get his chance."

Gregg nodded. "We are playing a tactical chess game this afternoon with Old Beauty."

"Old Beauty?"

"At West Point, Jeb's classmates jokingly called him Beauty because of his China-Blue eyes and rugged features."

Weir smiled. "Did you ever call him Old Beauty?"

"Hell, no. Stuart was a class ahead of me." He pointed toward the Rummel farm. "We can beat Old Beauty this afternoon if we move our chess pieces at the right time. That is if Custer's romantic notion of being a cavalry hero like Napoleon's Murat doesn't get the best of him and he recklessly moves without permission."

"Custer has followed orders so far."

"So far. But I heard about his reckless cavalry charge at Hunterstown. Custer needs to be like a puppet this afternoon, while I pull the strings."

2:54 p.m.
General David Gregg
Strategic crossroads

Rolling volleys of cannon fire erupted, thundering southwest beyond Brinkerhoff's Ridge. Gregg felt a pang and swallowed hard. So much for the lull in the cannonading. That was a mere pause along Cemetery Ridge.

He raised his binoculars and scanned the Rummel field, blanketed in smoke, silent as a dark graveyard. Drifts of bluish-white smoke dotted the meadows. Burnt sulphur and saltpeter singed his nostrils and stung his eyes. What did the lull in the fighting at the Rummel field mean? What was Stuart's next move?

His chest muscles stirred his blue cavalry jacket.

Above the dying din of the cannons' booming, the screams of clashing soldiers burst forth in a terrifying fury. His stomach knotted. Meade and Lee's infantries were in a warring death grip. Hard to tell who would survive the raging storm.

<hr />

2:54 p.m.
Custer
Approaching strategic crossroads

Custer was in the grip of a feverish frenzy. His breath rasped, and his mind raced like a jittery squirrel. Gregg must let him lead a charge. He trotted toward the strategic crossroads, aiming for

Gregg's mounted guidon. The pennant bearer stood like a lone sentinel, gripping a lance flying a huge red-and-white, swallow-tailed headquarters flag with a gold-embroidered *2* and crossed sabers.

He pulled up, quaking. "General Gregg, the Rebels in front of the Fifth Michigan are falling back to the top of Cress Ridge. The enemy has run low on ammunition. The Wolverines are staying on their heels."

Gregg stared through his field glasses. "It looks like your troopers are clearing the fields."

Colerick rode up. "General Custer. Colonel Alger reports that his troopers taking possession of the Rummel farm report a line of mounted enemy atop Cress Ridge. The ridge is bristling with cavalry and artillery."

"Very well," Custer said. He gripped his field glasses and scanned the enemy positions. Mounted Rebel troopers were tumbling out of the woods skirting Cress Ridge. Twenty yards down the ridge's brow they halted and started to form up into long lines.

He squirmed in his saddle. "General Gregg, if we dismount and advance the Sixth Michigan to support the Fifth Michigan's success, we could split the Rebels' line of battle. Pennington and Randol's guns would cover the Sixth's advance."

Gregg nodded and stroked his beavertail beard.

Custer paused. Gregg's expression remained frozen. He continued, "After the Sixth advances and creates a gap in the Rebel line, I would like your permission to lead the Seventh in a cavalry charge into the gap. Stuart won't be expecting us to charge him."

Gregg furrowed his brow and shook his head. "Be patient, George. It's no occasion for haste. Stuart's force is much larger than mine."

Gregg fished for his pipe and his tobacco pouch as if he were preparing to read a novel. He sprinkled loose tobacco into the bowl until it overflowed. After tamping down the bowl, he lit his pipe.

After several puffs, he said, "Stuart is troll fishing and dangling a couple mounted regiments on the ridge as bait, hoping

I'll bite. He wants me to commit a strong force toward Cress Ridge, and once we are strung out, he would attack and overwhelm us." Gregg paused, puffing on his pipe. "We hold the strategic crossroads. It's his move in this chess game."

Custer gritted his teeth, trying to choke down the rage surging into his throat. His face grew hot and the hairs on his neck prickled. He wormed about in his saddle, casting a long glance at Old Steady puffing on his reddish-orange meerschaum pipe. Pleasonton and Kilpatrick would let him charge. His airy hopes for glory and surpassing Murat's great Napoleonic charges were dwindling.

His jaw tightened and the silence grew. The frustrating kind of silence that has no effect on changing minds. He glared at Gregg's furrowed brow and heavy blue eyes. Gregg was missing a great opportunity. He was acting warily, just as he did at Brandy Station, sending his cavalry in piecemeal, resulting in their repulse. He ground his teeth. Gregg was holding fast and wasn't going to change his mind.

He fumed. "Yes, sir," he said, his tone a degree above insubordination. He reined his mount about and rode back toward his headquarters. His throat seized up, and he spit as a sour taste filled his mouth. "The Devil be damned."

2:55 p.m.
Lieutenant William Brooke-Rawle
Third Pennsylvania squadron on the eastern edge of Lott's woods

Brooke-Rawle pointed. "Captain Miller, see the Fifth Michigan and First New Jersey, three hundred yards west of the Lott house near the stone fence? They have stopped advancing and are falling back."

Miller stared through his binoculars. "The dismounted Confederates are dogging the steps of the retreating Yankees."

"I pray the advancing Rebels don't overrun our boys." Brooke-Rawle scanned Cress Ridge and pointed again. "The plumed hats of the First Virginia are cantering forth from the Cress Ridge tree line toward our position along the Low Dutch Road."

Miller nodded. "It appears Stuart is going to try to rout us with a charge."

3:05 p.m.
General David Gregg
Reever house, divisional headquarters, with Custer

An icy chill ran across Gregg's shoulders. *Damn.*

"George, the Fifth Michigan are falling back. They must be getting low on ammunition."

"The dismounted Rebels are going to take the Rummel farm again," Custer said. "I believe Stuart will try to exploit this success by charging down the slope at the retreating Fifth Michigan."

"Agreed. Look. The dismounted enemy is also pushing McIntosh's troopers back toward the Lott house and Low Dutch Road."

Custer pointed. "General, several hundred mounted Rebels have emerged from the Cress Ridge woods."

Gregg fretted. The gray horsemen cantered slowly down the gentle slope in rippling waves. *Stuart is finally making his castling chess play, trying to checkmate me by deploying his cavalry in the center of the field.*

"George, I am awed. I expected Stuart's cavalry would attack down the Low Dutch Road. But it looks as if they're going to attack over open ground."

"It appears they're headed for my headquarters at the Spangler house."

"I agree, George." He glared, weighing his options. *Must turn the tide.* He had to order a surprise countercharge against the dismounted enemy before the First Virginia conducted a mounted attack and scattered the Fifth Michigan like debris in a windstorm. Scrambling for a solution, he remembered his favorite opening chess move. He loved the age-old Queen's Gambit tactic of sacrificing a pawn to secure control of the center of the board. But these were not chess pieces. He steeled the shudder trying to race up his spine. *I cannot lose thousands of men.*

Custer's two saber regiments were the First Michigan and the Seventh Michigan. The First was a much larger and more experienced regiment, acting as his reserve, defending the crossroads. He glanced over to the greenhorn Seventh Michigan, the smallest of Custer's four regiments, mustering only twenty-seven commissioned officers and four hundred forty-seven enlisted, and having only ten rather than the usual twelve mounted companies. They had been in existence for only six months and had seen limited combat action, fighting in no major battles. At the Battle of Hanover, they had guarded the Union batteries on Bunker Hill. Three days ago, three of the enlisted men and one noncommissioned officer had deserted.

He shook his head and took a deep breath, weighing his options. The untried and untested Seventh were mostly young boys. They had never experienced the gruesome reality of battle before. A countercharge was imperative and would take a dreadful toll. But the Seventh was ignorant of the dangers—and would be, until it was too late to turn back. *God, please forgive me! It's now or never to strike.* His Queen's Gambit pawn would be Colonel Mann's regiment.

"Follow me, George."

He spurred his horse and rode toward the Wolverines occupying the ground between the Reever and Spangler houses and supporting Pennington's six thundering guns. He and Custer reined up next to Colonel Mann at the front of the Seventh Michigan. Gregg glared at the growing gray swell rolling down the hill. He sucked in a deep breath and held it. His heart raced, arguing frantically with his mind. Were there any other options? He shook his head and set his jaw. *Turn the Seventh Michigan loose.*

He whirled and pointed at Cress Ridge. "Colonel Mann. The Seventh Michigan has to buy time for the retreating Fifth Michigan." He paused, letting the words sink in as he removed his sword. He thrust the saber skyward. "Charge that enemy cavalry emerging from the Cress Ridge!"

Mann cocked his head toward the Rummel farm. His galloping heart thundered in his chest. My God, how could his regiment survive this rolling gray wave spilling down the slope? He snapped his head back, staring at Gregg. The general grimaced, plainly knowing the charge was a forlorn hope. Mann glared for a moment as reality set in. He finally nodded and saluted. "Yes, sir."

Mann reined about and trotted back toward the main body of the Seventh Michigan. Halting, he shouted, "Regiment, form up in a close column of squadrons."

Gregg turned toward the column of mounted blue troopers, colors gaily fluttering in the breeze, advancing beyond Pennington's guns like a bonny blue brook. He turned his eyes toward the smoke-laden fields of the Rummel farm. The dismounted Rebel vanguard was 2,000 yards from the Seventh Michigan and Hanover Road and moving down the slope like a creeping lava flow. A large, mounted Rebel force trotted 700 yards behind the dismounted vanguard. He twisted in his saddle and wiped his upper lip swimming in sweat. What a sight. Four hundred fifty troopers of the Seventh Michigan advancing in front of Pennington's batteries. A cheer resounded from one hundred hat-waving artillerymen. A shiver spiraled through him.

"General Gregg," Custer said, "the Seventh Michigan has not fought in a major action yet. It's the youngest regiment, average age eighteen. I have the greatest confidence in Colonel Mann and his leadership abilities. But as the Wolverine brigade commander, it is my solemn duty to lead this saber charge."

Gregg stared at the boy general, his golden curls flowing beneath his tilted, wide-brimmed hat. Custer's face beamed like a schoolboy preparing to bolt out to recess. If any daredevil could succeed in stopping the Rebel advance, it was Custer. He sucked in a deep breath, letting the hot air stretch his lungs. After a moment, he nodded. "Good luck, George. Make this a hard-hitting counterattack like Aldie. If ever, this is the time for fearless audacity."

Custer flashed a jaunty smile and touched his hat. "Understood. Bold recklessness."

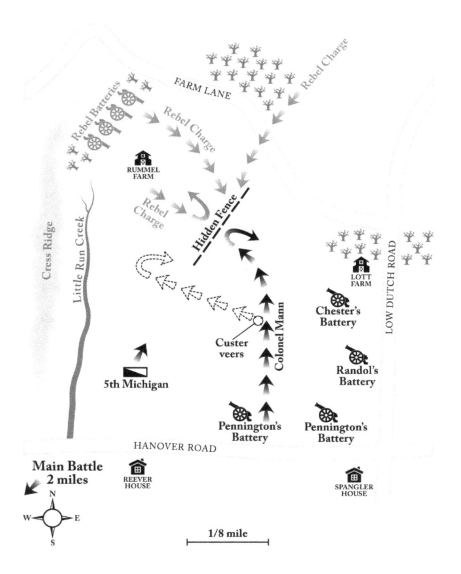

Custer Leading 7th Michigan Charge
July 3, 1863
3:00 p.m. - 3:30 p.m.

Rebel Charge

FARM LANE

Rebel Batteries

Rebel Charge

Rebel Charge

RUMMEL FARM

Hidden Fence

Cress Ridge

Little Run Creek

LOW DUTCH ROAD

LOTT FARM

Chester's Battery

Custer veers

Colonel Mann

Randol's Battery

5th Michigan

Pennington's Battery

Pennington's Battery

HANOVER ROAD

Main Battle 2 miles

REEVER HOUSE

SPANGLER HOUSE

N
W — E
S

1/8 mile

56

Custer — Friday, July 3

Custer's quick and restless nerves relaxed as if he were soaking in a hot spring. His blind faith in the dauntless spirit of Custer luck was finally paying off. All day, Gregg had leashed him like a pit bull, forcing him to curb his nearly ungovernable devil-may-care impulses. Now his glorious moment had come. Fortune favored the bold.

He glanced at Churchill riding alongside. He took a deep breath and held it. A voice whispered in his head. *It's time to make things right with the Almighty.* He swallowed. *Lord, I commend myself to thy keeping and ask thee to forgive my past sins, and to watch over me in danger while leading this attack.* A thrilling, calm, yet stirring spirit swirled through him like white water weaving in a rain-swelled stream.

He grinned. "Norvell, I'm going to lead this charge. I need you to stick close, and if I get unhorsed or something else happens, I need you to save my ass again."

"I'll be right next to you, General. I will also say a quick prayer for both of us."

"Good. Make it short, but good."

Norvell closed his eyes and moved his silent lips. His eyes opened. "Let's go, General."

Custer pulled up stirrup to stirrup with Colonel Mann, riding in front of the Seventh Michigan. Mann's face was tight, his breathing almost an imperceptible, high-pitched warbling, like a wolf on a string.

Custer touched his hat. "I am well aware, William, that rousing words by a brigade general cannot always inspire valor. But

I know a brave and resolute spirit resides in the heart of each of your glorious Wolverines. What stirs that spirit is a general who has the mettle to lead them into danger."

He paused and grinned. "I am that general."

Mann's eyes widened.

"William, I would consider it a great privilege to lead this saber charge."

The colonel hedged a moment, staring. After a moment, a tight-lipped smile broke and he saluted. "General Custer, the Seventh Michigan would be honored."

Custer shivered with unbridled excitement. He gripped his sheathed saber and pulled. The blade swished from its metal scabbard with the sleekness of a swooping hawk. He whisked the burnished Toledo over his head, swirling it like a lasso. A great cheer erupted from Mann's Wolverines. A jolt of glory pulsed through him, prickling his skin.

Mann raised his saber and the yelling stopped. "Draw!" he shouted.

Each trooper turned his head to the left and glanced down at his saber. Each one's left hand grasped the scabbard at the upper ring, unhooked the scabbard from the belt, and brought the hilt to the front. Using their right hand, they each gripped the saber knot and drew the blade six inches out of the scabbard. They faced back to the front, eyes focused on Colonel Mann.

"Saber!" Mann shouted.

The troopers drew their sabers fully out of the scabbard, each extending the right arm, holding their saber up at a 45-degree angle in front of their right shoulder. Custer drank in the beauty of these dragoons. *What a glorious sight*. He had never seen a finer regiment to wield the Napoleonic weapon of glory.

Mann shouted, "Carry!"

The troopers each lowered their right hand and placed the grip on the upper part of the right thigh, letting the back of the blade rest against the hollow of the right shoulder with the edge to the front. Custer glanced up and down the long blue column. The sparkling sabers tilted like a field of windblown cornstalks.

Mann turned, raised his saber, and shouted, "Bugler, blow 'Walk, March'!"

The bugler trumpeted, signaling the regiment's forward march.

Custer turned his head. "Norvell, let's give 'em hell."

Churchill grinned. "I'm ready, General."

Custer pointed the Toledo toward the advancing dismounted Rebels and eased Roanoke into a canter. Horse hooves plodded behind him like hundreds of clip-clopping heartbeats, "printing their proud hooves i' th' receiving earth," as they had for Shakespeare's *Henry V*. Custer cast his gaze toward the Rummel farm. His heart swelled with savage glee. This wide stretch of open ground was perfect for a Napoleonic mounted charge. He spurred Roanoke a length ahead of Mann and the Seventh Michigan guidon flying the stars and stripes. His red scarf flapped in the breeze like a luffing sail. He narrowed his eyes and stared at death yawning before him. His heart roared, pounding in his ears. What a plucky moment for the Union's beau sabreur.

He trotted up the sloping ground toward the dismounted Rebels. For a moment he was an Irish Dragoon, recalling his favorite Charles O'Malley quote:

> *The pace increased at every stride, the ranks grew closer, and like the dread force of some mighty engine, we fell upon the foe.*

3:12 p.m.
Captain William Miller
The eastern edge of Lott's woods

From the edge of the woods, Miller gazed west across the Rummel fields. He turned to Lieutenant Brooke-Rawle. "William, who are those attacking mounted Rebels?"

Brooke-Rawle gripped his field glasses and scanned the Confederates slipping down the slope. "Based on Captain Weber's assessment, I believe the mounted enemy regiment are the First Virginia, the Invincibles, from General Fitz Lee's brigade."

Miller trembled. "That's Stuart's best regiment." Fear flared in his stomach. "Custer is about to charge into a bear's cave right after the winter thaw."

3:12 p.m.
Custer
Leading the Seventh Michigan
In the middle of the Rummel field, about one thousand yards south-east of the Rummel house

Two hundred yards to the enemy. Custer beamed. The corners of his lips quirked into a slight smile. His fatalistic mind flashed. *Unless destiny wills me to die, Custer luck will prevail.*

He shouted, "Here we go, Norvell!"

His legs nudged Roanoke into a limited gallop. His eyes skated left, and Churchill was a half horse-length away, flying with him. His soul leaped. His lucky charm rode with the gracefulness of one of Charles O'Malley's rousing Irish dragoons.

"I'm right here, General!" Churchill shouted.

Custer's heart thumped against his breastbone. His face tingled with the thirst for battle. He waved his black hat over his head and shouted, "Now! Come on, you Wolverines!" He tucked his black slouch hat into his coat pocket.

Bugler Joseph Fought, riding at his heels, split the air with his piercing notes. Custer spurred his warhorse into a full gallop, heading straight north and parallel to Little Run. A torrent of joy swept through him. Over a thousand horse hooves burst forward and kept pace, pounding a thundering bass beat. His golden hair blew in the wind as the howling Wolverines raced over the open field with sabers gleaming and colors blowing defiantly in the breeze. His mind flashed to the romantic annals of dragoon charges over a sprawling plain like the Rummel fields. *What an unbelievable moment.*

He glanced over his shoulder. He was four lengths ahead of Colonel Mann and the Seventh Michigan. His body relaxed as if swinging in a hammock, and his vision sharpened as if aiming a hunting rifle. Boldness flushed out all fears. He grinned. The Father Almighty had given him this moment to prove he was the First Horseman of the Union. His eyes drank in the beauty of the charge. *I will ride them down and crush them. Thank you, Lord.*

3:12 p.m.
Colonel John McIntosh
Near the Lott house

The plumed hats of the legendary First Virginia Cavalry flowed down the hill like the shimmering plumage of a long peacock tail. McIntosh swallowed as a nightmarish realization crept down his spine. *My God, the Rebels are headed for the strategic intersection.* Trying to maintain a grip on his voice, he turned to Captain Walter Newhall, determined to deliver a confident but perilous order.

"Walter, it looks as if Stuart is intending to crush us with a mounted cavalry attack. It's time to throw in our reserves. Find Lieutenant Colonel James Deem and have the Maryland Cavalry ride forward to the Lott house."

Newhall saluted and departed.

McIntosh's pulse stalled as terror clawed his insides, and he let out the ragged breath he had been holding in. Staring at the oncoming tide of the enemy, he let himself feel for one moment the somber reality of what they were up against.

My God. The Virginians look invincible.

3:13 p.m.
Captain William Miller
Eastern edge of Lott's woods

Trepidation seared Miller's throat. Custer was leading a suicide charge against an overwhelming force determined to swamp the Seventh Michigan like churning snow barreling down a mountain. God willing the Union artillery would provide a temporal shield for the charging Wolverines. Pennington and Randol's big guns blasted yellow tongues of fire across the Rummel field. Rolling thunder forked below the brow of Cress Ridge and iron shards pelted the charging graybacks like a blinding hailstorm. Back toward Little Run, Custer's Wolverines were sailing fearlessly up the slope on a raging river of wind. The dismounted Fifth Michigan, standing in a line parallel to the Hanover Road and one hundred yards ahead on the left flank of Seventh Michigan, swung about the trooper on the far west end to the right like a picket fence gate, allowing a clear path for Custer's charging troopers.

Brooke-Rawle shook his head. "Custer is screaming at the top of his lungs as if he's yelling at the Gods of War. He's a fearless daredevil. He seems to cherish these moments."

Miller grinned. "The madcap harlequin. He looks exactly like the *Harper's Weekly* sketch of him leading a cavalry charge at the Battle of Aldie."

"I'm not sure Custer and the Seventh are going to survive this daredevil charge unless they are supported by flanking fire into the charging Rebels."

"I agree." An ominous silence filled Miller's mind. Over a thousand enemy sabers glinted in the sun like rattlesnake eyes. His stomach twisted. This was the most determined and vigorous Rebel charge he had ever seen. But both enemy flanks were exposed.

He stared at the charging dismounted Rebels and his retreating Company H pickets. Bullets struck the trees, cracking branches like pistol shots, and his squadron was aiming their carbines.

"Don't fire!" he shouted. "Wait until the pickets clear our line!"

Someone shouted, "We can't wait too long, Captain!"

He gripped his pistol. Two pickets were helping Private James Smith, wounded in the leg. "Hurry, Private Smith!" he shouted.

Smith wobbled and lunged forward the last five steps with the help of his comrades. They trundled into the Lott woods. The charging First Virginians' left flank was even with his squadron.

"Fire!" Miller shouted.

Hundreds of flashes spewed from the rattling volley of carbines. Rebels spilled from their horses like rag dolls.

"Keep firing!"

The Rebel left flank shredded like grain in a mill.

3:13 p.m.
Custer
Leading the Seventh Michigan

Custer's high-spirited heart pounded in his ears and pumped savagery through his veins. Roanoke was Pegasus, flying up the slope. Pure cussedness coursed through him. The air rocked with bursting shells and shouting men. A hail of bullets cracked, spilling Wolverines and their horses to the ground.

Churchill pointed left. "See smoke over the fence running along Little Run? Rebels behind the fence fired a volley into the left flank of the Seventh."

"Keep charging!" Custer shouted. "Speed is our weapon!"

He aimed for the unprotected Rebels in the open field. Pennington's shells screamed overhead, tearing wide gaps through the Rebel ranks. Dense smoke billowed up. Roanoke bowled over a dismounted Confederate, knocking him to the ground. Custer bounced in his saddle, raised his saber, and slashed a grayback across the neck.

"Norvell, they cannot check us!"

He galloped at breakneck speed toward dismounted Confederates beyond Little Run creek. "Norvell, stay close. We are going to barrel through these Rebels."

"Let's bust through them, General." Churchill pulled up and rode stirrup-to-stirrup with Roanoke.

Thundering hooves shook the ground like a violent earthquake. Custer glanced backwards. The flying Wolverines were screaming and brandishing their gleaming swords. A glowing warmth flooded his face. They were retaining formation. The Seventh were going to crash into the Rebels in one solid mass, like an avalanche bursting through the trees. He spied a gray-clad trooper struggling to reload his rifle.

Churchill screamed and bolted ahead, waving his sword. The Rebel glanced up and flinched. Norvell swung his saber downward, slicing the back of the enemy's shoulder.

Custer spotted a Rebel ten yards ahead, aiming his rifle at Churchill. He swung his raised blade downward to a near horizontal, resting on the right of Roanoke's head. He thrust his elbow away from his black velvet jacket and shot his arm forward, forming one straight line with the saber. His left hand slid forward on the reins, near the base on Roanoke's neck. He pulled slightly on the straps, feeling the mount's mouth. He swiveled the blade slightly to the right and pointed at the Rebel's breast. Bloodlust raged through his veins.

The Confederate glanced up, his mouth gaping like the opening of a dark cave. Custer gritted his teeth, anchored his boots firmly in the stirrups, and lunged forward. The saber pierced the Confederate's rib cage, and the Rebel let out an unearthly shriek, coughing blood from his mouth. Custer pulled back on the reins and yanked the blood-slick blade free. The dying Rebel tumbled to the ground.

He glanced ahead and a gray trooper knelt and pointed his rifle. His throat constricted. In a heartbeat, his body bent and twisted simultaneously, like a scorpion's tail, as the bullet whizzed past his head. Churchill surged past him and scuttled the Confederate with a savage slash of his saber. Norvell turned in his saddle and shouted, "Are you wounded?"

"No, keep charging!"

Churchill stormed ahead, sweeping his sharp-edged saber left and right like a pendulum. Custer spurred Roanoke and followed in his orderly's wake. Norvell was Death's scythe, reaping the Rebel horde like an autumn harvest. He had never seen a trooper more fit to wield the weapon.

The Wolverines were halfway across the sprawling field. He glanced northwest toward the Rummel farm. Two dismounted enemy brigades were positioned in front of the farmhouse. A large gap separated the two brigades. Beyond the gap, five enemy artillery batteries straddled the high ground of the Cress Ridge, firing at the Seventh. His heart leaped.

He pointed his saber. "Norvell, head for that gap and the far-left enemy battery."

"Yes, sir!"

He pulled on the reins and veered left, aiming for the gap. Churchill rode next to him. They rode in a sweeping gallop for one hundred yards.

Churchill shouted, "General, only a fourth of the regiment followed you! Colonel Mann is leading the rest of the regiment straight north."

He glanced behind him. "I swear to God! Mann, can't you follow my red scarf?" Splitting the regiment into two groups against a large force was disastrous.

Churchill pointed his saber. "Watch out for the worm fence."

He glanced ahead fifty yards and saw a worm fence constructed of split wooden rails stacked across one another at an angle, like a long, squirming snake.

"Rebels are behind and beyond the fence," Churchill shouted.

The enemy fired a volley, and he flinched as a hail of bullets zipped past his head, tearing into the Wolverines. Screams erupted behind him. The ground rumbled as troopers and horses thudded over the ground. A horse raced by with an empty saddle. His breathing was quick and ragged.

He charged toward the dismounted Rebels that had hopped the fence and were streaming toward the Wolverines. He aimed for a Rebel firing an Enfield rifle. The Rebel twisted and thrust his bayonet toward Roanoke's chest.

He ripped back on the reins and Roanoke reared. The bayonet thrust shivered past the horse.

"Damn you!" Bloodlust boiled in his veins. He slashed the saber across the Rebel's back, the blade slicing deep. Blood sprayed like a light rain. A bullet breezed by his neck. He glanced at a Rebel kneeling, reloading his rifle. He thrust the reins between his teeth and unholstered his revolver with his left hand. He aimed and fired. The kneeling Rebel shrieked and tumbled, a corpse before hitting the ground.

He glanced up. The fence was twenty yards ahead. He snapped the reins and jabbed his spurs into Roanoke's flanks. The ping of a ball whipped by. He flinched. Enemy fire from the right of the fence ripped holes in his detachment.

He shouted, "All in for it now, Roanoke!"

Yards from the fence, Roanoke rounded his back and brought his hind legs farther underneath as he ran. Custer leaned forward and Roanoke shifted his balance backward as if coiling a spring. The warhorse slammed his front legs into the ground and then lifted them as his hind legs thrusted upward. Roanoke sailed over the fence and galloped forward.

His mind flashed. Norvell should be coming up on his left. He twisted in his saddle. Norvell leapt over the fence like a mountain lion and raced alongside.

"Now, General, for a bit of fun!"

Custer grinned and plunged into the gap between two Rebel regiments. He cleared the narrow corridor and glanced over his shoulder, spotting a squadron of Wolverines galloping behind him, waving their flashing sabers. Pride pounded in his ears. *Now let's destroy that Rebel battery pummeling my Wolverines.*

57

McIntosh — Friday, July 3

3:16 p.m.
Colonel John McIntosh
Near the Lott house

His face ashen, Captain Weir slowed his galloping mount. "Colonel McIntosh, Captain Newhall informed General Gregg that you ordered the Marylanders forward. The Maryland Regiment won't be coming."

"What?"

"General Gregg ordered the Marylanders to dismount along a line of stone walls southeast of the Lott woods. They are acting as the general's tactical reserve that he will use if the Rebels break through and threaten the strategic intersection. "

An artillery shell shrieked overhead. Weir's foaming mare reared on her back legs and pedaled her front legs, lashing at the air. The captain leaned forward and put the reins over the horse's ears, settling the beast down. Weir's chest was pulsing like a charging bobcat and his breaths were short and violent. His trembling face was stained red and drenched in sweat.

McIntosh gritted his teeth, anguish gripping at his heart. He shook a finger toward the intersection. "Damn't, Captain. Custer's First Michigan are sitting on the strategic intersection, and they are General Gregg's tactical reserve. I'm ordering the Marylanders forward to support my brigade."

Weir shook his head. "General Gregg ordered Lieutenant Colonel James Deems to move only on his orders. The Marylanders are not available, sir."

McIntosh's face flared hot, and a lump lodged in his throat. "My God. The Marylanders are my only reserve. This is lunacy." His blood pulsed in his ears. "Damn't, Captain! Why didn't General Gregg concur with me? My position is hopeless without

457

reserves coming forward." Rage surged through his veins as he glared at Weir. For a moment, his heart teetered on the edge of justified defiance, begging him to disobey Gregg's orders. Artillery whickered overhead. He glanced at the enemy cavalry flowing down from Cress Ridge, disaster galloping toward his men. His stomach pitched and rolled. Frustration welled behind his eyes and erupted like a levee break, tears cascading down his flushed cheeks. "Blood and damnation!"

Weir pointed. "Colonel McIntosh, I spotted General Custer and his red scarf at the head of the Seventh Michigan, darting forward."

McIntosh wheeled toward where Weir was pointing. Custer was galloping ahead of the Wolverines as if he were riding in a victory parade. The hatless boy general was a circus rider gone mad, screaming and brandishing his saber, his hair streaming like a fluttering pennant. The air seething between the charging Wolverines and Rebels was alive with flying lead.

He snorted. "Custer is going to be ripped to shreds without supporting flank attacks against the mounted Rebels." He turned toward Weir, letting the silence grow uncomfortable. Perhaps Weir would rescind Gregg's order if he glared long enough. Despair and fury swept over him.

"Damn't, Captain, I need the Maryland Regiment to come forward so I can support Custer. Don't you understand?"

Weir shook his head. "I can't override the order."

McIntosh let out an anguished growl. "Son of a bitch!"

58

McIntosh — Friday, July 3

3:16 p.m.
Colonel William Mann
Leading a portion of his regiment straight north toward a far-right
Confederate battery

Mann galloped north as fast as the dense, drifting smoke would allow. He spotted Custer, thirty yards to the northwest and four horse-lengths ahead of everyone, brandishing his blade. Custer was bareheaded, his golden locks flowing in the breeze, and his red scarf flapping around his neck. To Mann's right, riding stirrup to stirrup, was Captain Heman Moore, commanding Company K. Mann narrowed his stinging eyes; through the gray, misty smoke he could make out dismounted enemy, four hundred yards ahead and advancing.

"Colonel," Moore shouted, "Custer is veering to the left!"

Mann shot a glance toward Custer and recoiled in horror. Sure enough, the general had peeled away, followed by a squadron of a hundred troopers, galloping directly toward the Rummel house. A blast of fear commandeered his stomach; the regimental attack was doomed without a full force attacking together. *What the devil. We are outnumbered and Custer is splitting the regiment.* Instead of commanding a brigade and ordering his colonels to charge, the rash boy general was acting like a colonel, which he never was, and leading charges himself. Didn't Custer learn anything from his near-disastrous charge at Hunterstown?

"Keep riding straight north!" Mann shouted.

"Custer must be going for the enemy batteries on the far left," Moore yelled into the wind.

"So are we, but we are going for the guns on the far right!"

His brain pulsed as he raced up the rise. Scores of thundering hooves trampled behind him. He lowered his saber to waist high, gripping it firmly in his right hand, leading the storm surge.

"For the Union!" he cried.

They rode one hundred yards, scattering dismounted enemy skirmishers. Without warning, a dreadful volley of rifles blasted to his front. Bullets whined like buzzing mosquitoes. Screams erupted behind. Through the battle smoke he spotted a long gray line of dismounted Rebels, forty yards ahead, reloading.

"Turn left!"

He reined his mount nearly ninety degrees and galloped ahead. A trooper on his left spurred ahead and topped the rise. The trooper raised his saber sky high and screamed, "Fence!"

Mann cleared the berm and glared down into a shallow gully fortified with a high post fence with lengthy rails, mounted upon a stone fence stretching across the open field. *Oh, my God!* Terror lurched into his throat. He yanked the reins and thrust backwards as he kicked his stirrups above the horse's shoulders. The mount slid on all four hooves, its muzzle cracking into the wooden rails like a summer thunderstorm.

Shouting "Dismount!" he swung to the ground. *Damn you, Custer. I'm missing a fourth of my regiment because of your reckless leadership and actions.* Dismounted enemy were twenty yards away, rushing for the fence. He slammed the saber into its scabbard and grabbed his revolver from its holster. A screaming Rebel thrust a bayonet through the fence. He sidestepped, jerked his revolver up, and fired. The Rebel screamed, clutching his middle as he fell across the bottom rail.

A horse and rider swept his arm as they bolted into the fence with a thunderclap. The rider's saber flew over the fence toward the advancing Rebels as he tumbled to the ground. He leaped up like a bobcat, cussing the Devil.

"Colonel Mann, where in the hell did that damned fence come from?" Sergeant Edwin Havens yelled.

"Are you wounded, Sergeant?"

"No, sir, but I lost my damned saber over the fence." Havens unholstered his revolver and fired at an oncoming Rebel across the fence. "Colonel, why didn't you catch my blade?"

Mann shot Havens a tight smile. "We'll get it after we get out of this jam."

Another horse flew into the railing and the rider flew over the fence, nearly knocking a Rebel down. The gray-clad private gutted the Wolverine with his bayonet. A soul-haunting coyote scream echoed over the gush of blood.

"You son of a whore!" Havens bellowed. He fired his revolver, hitting the Rebel between the eyes.

Mann emptied his revolver and bent down on one knee, his heart stuttering, hoping his regiment would survive the slaughter. He cursed Custer again and loaded the last of his ammunition. Bullets whizzed and clattered like hail hitting glass. The blackness in his brain told him to hurry and fire. He glanced up to see a rangy Rebel aiming his rifle. He cocked his revolver and fired, hitting the attacker before he could shoot.

All along the fence, Wolverines continued to race over the berm and crash into the stone wall. In his mind he was screaming, "This is madness!"

Bullets flew thick. The air was filled with the shouts of men, the cries of the wounded, and the commands of the officers on both sides. On both sides, the dead and the wounded were dropping. *Devil be damned.* The lurid site was an abattoir of horror, haunting in its violent savagery. The two demonic forces were ripping and tearing flesh, killing and murdering without mercy, like starving sewer rats. The ground was awash with tides of blood and steaming entrails. The slaughter was beyond imagination. *Damn you, Custer. Damn you for splitting my regiment and feeding it to the flames of hell.*

"Rebels are climbing the fence," Havens shrieked.

Through the billowing smoke, Mann could see figures clearing the fence. He emptied his revolver, firing at enemy troopers close enough to reach out and touch. He holstered the weapon and unsheathed his saber, then raised his blade and swooped down on the butternut like a hurtling hawk. He sliced the blade across the Rebel's back; blood sprayed forth. Through the swirling smoke, a woofing growl roared like a bear. A large Rebel scudded from the smoke, flashing his tobacco-stained fangs and swinging his clubbed musket. Mann parried the arm-jarring blow with his saber. The Rebel tumbled to the ground, and he struck him across the throat, hacking through the flesh.

"Sergeant Haven, this is madness!" Mann shouted. "I'm going to the rear and try to force the trailing squadrons to form a line on our right and left flanks along the fence."

He bounded up the berm, halting on the crest and waving his saber. He shouted, "Fence ahead! Don't bunch up!"

Fear clawed his stomach. The sky darkened with scores of Wolverines cresting the ridge and dashing down toward the high stake-and-rail fence. Troopers screamed and horses squealed as they crashed into the fence and tumbled to the ground. They struggled to stand but were knocked down as trailing squadrons broke on them like ocean waves smashing upon a rocky shore.

3:18 p.m.
Major Luther Trowbridge
Five hundred yards north of the Reever house, along Little Run

Pennington's guns thundered, the flying round shots shrieking as they sailed toward Cress Ridge. Major Trowbridge squinted at Colonel Mann leading the Seventh Michigan charge. Abruptly, Mann's Wolverines veered sharply left. What was happening? The enemy cannons were straight ahead.

"Major, why are the Seventh veering left?" Orderly William Dunn asked.

"I'm not sure." Trowbridge swallowed hard. "Oh, my God." Dark panic gripped him. Colonel Mann and several troopers raced up a berm and crashed into a high stake-and-rail fence. Squadron after squadron broke upon the struggling mass in front, like colliding trains, until all were mixed in one confused and tangled mass.

"For God's sake, change direction!"

Gawking, Dunn muttered, "The Seventh Michigan are a herd of lemmings, jumping off a cliff to their death."

3:18 p.m.
Captain George (Geo) Armstrong, Seventh Michigan, Commanding Company D
Following Colonel Mann's charge into the hidden stone-wall fence

The column broke, mangled and crushed. Captain Geo Armstrong's skewbald horse charged up the berm at a breakneck dash. He cleared the crest and gaped into hell's pit of death.

"Fence!" he screamed. He rocked back and pulled hard on the reins, spilling down into the sucking whirlpool filled with shattered bodies and crushed horses. Men screamed and horses whinnied, lying twisted and broken in clumps against the high railed fence. Armstrong jumped off his mount and pulled it away from the pit. At the top of the berm, squadron after squadron rushed pell-mell over the ridge, their mounts sliding on iron horseshoes, gliding over the turf as if pulled downward by an anchor. The impassable stone wall was breaking the columns into jelly and mixing the regiment up like a mass of pulp.

Rebels on the far side of the fence fired just yards away, killing and wounding scores of Wolverines.

"Throw down the fence!" Armstrong shouted.

Seventh Michigan Acting Adjutant George Briggs and Captain Heman Moore, commanding company K, slid down into the pit and began to tear down a portion of the fence. Other troopers, seeing what they were doing, braved Rebel fire and leaped down, joining them, tearing down the rails from atop the deadly stone wall.

3:18 p.m.
Colonel William Mann
The hidden fence

A white flash of panic overwhelmed Mann, standing on the top of the berm. "Sergeant Havens," he shouted, "keep forcing the troopers to spread out along the fence."

Havens turned, waving his arms at the approaching squadrons. "Spread out along the fence. Spread out!"

The Rebel Yell erupted, and Mann whirled around toward the fence. Dismounted Rebel troopers swarmed down the hill, racing for the fence, screaming in high-pitched shrills like a skulk of red foxes. His heart raced. Could his troopers breach the growing gap before the Rebels hit the fence?

"Captain Moore, hurry! The Rebels are trying to plug the fence!"

Moore kicked his boot onto a stone post and tugged on a wooden rail.

The bravery of his troopers was inspiring. Up beyond the fence, several yards behind the running Rebels, mounted enemy troopers were forming in a column, preparing to charge. Bullets whirled. Mann glanced down at the pit; his heart leaped. Several of the Wolverines had clambered out of hell's boiling cauldron and were standing behind the long rails, firing. How long could they hold?

The Wolverines roared as their pistols flashed.

"Steady, men," Mann rallied them. "Keep firing."

His face was drenched in sweat. His ears rang with the screams of close combat. Rifles and revolvers cracked like thousands of bursting firecrackers. The jostling, swaying lines on either side of the fence raged, thick with flashes like the fiery spray of a boiling ocean. White banks of convolving smoke hung like a pall over a torched town.

Sergeant Havens shouted. "Look, Colonel! The boys have nearly breached the fence!"

A pack of Wolverines were trying to tear down a section of fence rails. The post and intersecting eleven-foot oak beams were stacked six rails high and laid at an angle of 120 degrees to the next panel of rails and posts. Usually, a company would melt along the fence, dividing to the right and left. The troopers would grip the top rail and with one firm tug the whole section of rails would tumble in a heap. But not today. A chill zigzagged down his back, a chill of anger and frustration tensing his body. The posts and rails were nailed together, and the posts were anchored onto a low stone fence instead of resting on flat field boulders.

He shouted, "Sergeant Havens, tell the boys to lift out the posts and then move several lengths at once!"

Havens nodded and rushed into the pit.

The troopers pulled and heaved and finally lifted out three posts and removed two rail sections, creating a twenty-two-foot gap above the low stone fence.

Mann ordered, "Each company break off by fours from the right and form into a column. Captain Moore, your center company will lead the charge!"

"Yes, sir!" Moore yelled.

3:18 p.m.
Captain Heman Moore
Leading Company K through the gap

Blue and gray corpses were staggered along the fence. Captain Heman Moore's heart raced as the Wolverines threw the final timbers atop the stone wall to the ground. Company K was the center squadron behind the emerging gap.

Moore twisted in his saddle. "Sergeant Andrew Cline, form the company. We are going to charge through the gap!"

"Yes, sir," Cline yelled. "We're ready!"

Moore raised his saber. "Charge!"

He spurred his mount and leaped the small stone wall, minus the wood rails and post. He fired his pistol, hitting a Rebel in the head. Cline rode up even with him and fired his pistol into the back of a retreating grayback. Moore glanced over his shoulder. Company K gushed through the gap like water pouring out a spout. Two other squadrons spilled through the gap, racing after Captain Moore, galloping across a plowed field. The remaining squadrons remained behind the fence, firing their weapons.

Moore roared forward, cutting a corridor through the dismounted enemy, and sped toward the Rebel artillery batteries on Cress Ridge.

Mann spied the Confederates surging forward toward the fence. What a deadly donnybrook. His very core shuddered.

"Kill all you can!" he shouted, desperate.

Pistols clashed with rifles in a blind fury. The two rogue waves thrashed against each other and sank into a sea of hand-to-hand fighting. Growling and cursing replaced cheering and shouting. The green fields beneath the mingling combatants turned crimson; blood oozed in pools like oil in a tar pit. The enemy recoiled and withdrew as the bluecoats cut and shot them down. Wounded Wolverines crawled up the berm, dazed and exhausted. They paused to gather themselves and started trudging back toward the Lott house.

3:19 p.m.
Major James Carpenter
Charge through the hidden fence

Tarrying at the rear of the charging column, Major Carpenter spotted several troopers halted on the berm, shouting and waving their sabers. Something was wrong. He pulled on the reins and veered out of the column. Trotting to the top of the ridge, he glanced down into a medieval relic of hell. The pit of death. His stomach writhed and forced bile up into his throat. Twisted and broken troopers and horses lay crushed against the stone-and-rail fence, wailing like demons.

Sergeant Andrew Buck of Company F reined up, wide-eyed and breathing hard. Buck's face was contorted, plainly shocked by the horror. The sergeant wiped his brow and struggled to collect himself. "Major Carpenter, the boys are working to make a second gap through the fence. The Johnnies are rushing down to the fence and firing at point-blank range. This is Dante's hell!"

From his saddle, Carpenter studied the boys tearing down the fence rails. The acrid smoke of gunpowder swirled along the pit, cloaking the air and providing some protection for the troopers. If they could create a second gap and charge through it, they could turn the tide of battle.

"Order the remaining column to spread out right and left from the pit along the fence."

Buck saluted and rode back toward the rear of the column.

Carpenter gripped his carbine and rode down to the berm to the right of the pit. Aiming at a Rebel sprinting toward the fence, he fired, dropping the grayback like a sprinting stag in its prime. Troopers from Company F rode up next to him and unleashed a murderous volley.

Carpenter shouted, "Keep firing!" The cracking carbines and pistols were deafening. It was like swirling in a kettle of popping corn. Gray and blue, the assailants stood face to face, screaming across the fence, singeing each others' faces and beards with the flashing of their pistols. Several Wolverines dismounted, jumped the fence, and fought hand-to-hand.

"There's a gap in the fence!" shouted Sergeant Buck. "We are going to charge by column!"

"Form Company F up by fours," Carpenter ordered.

A screeching, massive yell erupted, and he spotted Captain Moore leading a charge of Company K through the first gap, with two other companies close on their heels.

"Sergeant Buck," Carpenter shouted, "charge!"

Sergeant Buck lunged ahead and streaked for the second gap. Carpenter galloped fifteen yards behind. Buck's horse leaped over the low stone wall and galloped ahead a few yards. Suddenly, the Rebels on the right volleyed. Buck's horse tumbled, and a piercing pain like an arrow ripped through Carpenter's left side. He reined his mount and skidded to a halt before the gap.

He grabbed his side. It felt as if someone had jabbed him with a spear. His shirt was bloodied. Damn. He moved his left arm in a circle. No pain. Good. His arm and shoulder were not broken. He touched his mount with spurs, and she jumped through the opening and passed Buck, lying on the ground. He galloped with the column over the grassy field.

Adjutant James Birney rode up. He shouted, "Major Carpenter, you're bleeding like a stuck pig. You should pull out of the column, sir."

He shook his head. "I can make it."

He galloped in line with the column for two hundred yards. His left side started cramping and his legs began quaking. His breath shortened and his stomach heaved. Bitter bile rose in his throat like a flood tide. He pulled out of the column and dismounted. He gripped the reins and bent over and retched. A sharp claw of pain ripped his side. He grabbed his wound; blood drenched his glove as if he were painting a house. *Must make it back to the fence.* He reached up and grabbed the pommel.

his gloved right hand and gripped the reins with his left, leaning on his mount as he walked back. Thundering hooves approached.

He glanced up and muttered, "Oh, no."

The riderless horse crashed into him, jamming his body between the two horses. Both mounts bolted. Somehow, he didn't fall, but his legs shook. He glanced toward the fatal fence and started tottering. His mind was whirling and addled. *Must find a safe place to lay down.*

A horse cantered up and halted. He glanced up; his heart sank.

A gentlemanly Rebel said, "Sir, may I have your pistol?"

Bugger the Devil. He grasped his revolver and handed it to the officer.

"Major, you are wounded. Hang on to my stirrup straps and come on."

He gripped the stirrup straps with both hands and trundled a few rods, lumbering like a drunk. Sweat poured down his face as fast as the blood poured out of his wound.

"Mother of Jesus," he muttered.

The fear of death was gone. He heaved and pitched to the ground. He clutched his side, blood spurting out with each beat of his heart. *I'm going to die, either from loss of blood or from the scorching pain.* He glanced up at his captor, eyeing him closely. The Rebel reached into his jacket pocket, retrieved a pocket-sized derringer, half-cocked it, and aimed. An evil grin cracked his ʼe as he tried to fully cock the hammer. The gun wouldn't cock.

Rebel cussed, trying to manipulate the hammer. Wounded ʼn the ground, nevertheless, Carpenter had to smile at the awkwardness. What irony. He would gladly have the him out of his tortuous retching.

ʼur lucky day, Major," the grayback drawled. "The ʼes not want me to kill you." He tipped his hat and

down. The battle would be over soon, and then ʼk to his battalion. But for now, he'd just rest ʼrotection.

59

Custer — Friday, July 3

3:17 p.m. (Two minutes earlier)
Custer
Charging an enemy artillery battery on Cress Ridge

The clack-clack of rifle fire and bullets overhead were the percussion in the orchestra pit, beating the rhythm of his charge. A snappy snare drum tapped in Custer's brain. The Rummel field raced beneath Roanoke's hooves as he jutted parallel to Cress Ridge off to his left. Portions of Cress Ridge glittered as the sun glinted off the sabers of thousands of concealed, mounted Rebel troopers. Norvell pounded alongside. Custer twisted in his saddle and glanced at the hundred troopers galloping close behind. *Good.* He spun back around, spotting his target: the four-gun Rebel battery ahead. He aimed for the far left battery on a row of several thundering enemy cannons. His mind was racing. *Speed is our weapon. If we rush those four cannons on the far left like a storm surge, we can swamp them before they know what hit them.*

Churchill shouted, "General, Mann's troopers are bunching up behind a sturdy fence."

What! Custer looked over his right shoulder. Sure enough, Mann's Wolverines were crashing into a stone-wall-and-wood fence that had been hidden behind a ridge. Frustration swept through him. *Damn the Devil.* If Mann would have followed him, the storm surge of his one hundred troopers would be a tsunami of four hundred Wolverines. He could have possibly captured perhaps two or three enemy batteries.

An idea jolted through him. This might be a blessing in disguise, if his troopers could continue the hell-bent charge. Perhaps Mann's troopers would act as a diversion, forcing the

Rebels to thin their lines ahead of him to provide reinforcements to the fence.

A glorious craving hungered in his bones. He smiled, tight-lipped, aiming for a gap between two enemy brigades. A Rebel battery sat in the gap on the northern spur of Cress Ridge, four hundred yards northwest of the Rummel House, firing at his dragoons fighting along the fence. Howling Wolverines and hundreds of thundering hooves rattled the air.

He waved his saber and led his detachment of the Wolverines toward the Rummel farm. Ahead three hundred yards along Cress Ridge preened five beautiful, unprotected Rebel batteries.

"Capture the Rebel battery on our left! Let us rout them!" He spurred Roanoke and raced across the open field.

Churchill pointed. "General, some of Colonel Mann's squadrons have leaped the deadly hidden fence and are gallop-ing northward."

His heart roared, pounding in his ears. *Keep charging, boys.*

3:19 p.m.
Captain Heman Moore
Racing toward the second fence

The pitch of the slope steepened as Moore led the charge upward. His mount grunted and snorted. *Come on, boy.* The pace quick-ened and Moore's excitement surged.

Sergeant Cline pointed with his pistol. "There's Custer and his detachment."

Moore glanced toward the Rummel house and spotted Custer's red scarf and one hundred Wolverines racing helter-skelter after him. Custer was galloping toward a row of five Rebel batteries on Cress Ridge. It appeared as if Custer was going to attack the Rebel battery on the general's far left.

"Sergeant," Moore said, "let's aim for the Rebel battery on our far right."

"Yes, sir."

Moore and Company K veered slightly right and rumbled over the plowed field, darting past the right of the Rummel barn. Three hundred yards ahead, the far-right Rebel battery fired a shell. Its bursting canister hurled cast-iron balls through charging Wolverines like a shotgun blast. Screams erupted and an empty-saddled horse bolted past. As he crested the berm, a strong fence zigzagging across their advance came suddenly into view. "Oh, my God," he muttered. "This is a disaster. Where did this second fence come from?"

"Worm fence ahead!" Cline bellowed.

Damn. Moore reined up and halted at the fence. The troopers of Company K pulled up on either side of him and started firing across it. Two troopers bolted ahead, leaped the fence, and raced toward the battery.

"Sergeant," he called, "who are those two troopers making that daredevil charge?"

"Private Joseph Powers and Private Eber Ingelede."

The two privates closed their distance to within two hundred yards of the cannon. A thundering blast of cannister rippled the air. Ingelede tumbled from his horse. Powers halted and helped Ingelede onto the back of his saddle and raced back, leaping the second worm fence.

Cline pointed. "Captain, the Rebels wearing plumed hats are about to charge."

Moore glanced toward the Wolverines' right flank. His heart pounded faster. "That's the First Virginia."

Several bright yellow flashes drew his eyes left toward Custer's detachment. Rebel batteries were blasting the general's forward troopers with cannister. Custer had halted and was scanning the Cress Ridge with his field glasses. Wolverine wounded were limping and crawling back.

"Keep firing!" Moore shouted.

"Their ammunition is nearly expended," Cline said. "We won't be able to breach this second fence before the enemy cavalry arrives. We're outnumbered. You should consider falling back."

He set his jaw. "I'm not falling back until General Custer orders a retreat."

In rapid succession, artillery shells hissed and plunged down, exploding all around the Wolverines. The ground trembled as flying iron tore through flesh and bone. He glanced up toward

Cress Ridge and spotted five artillery guns blazing with smoky tongues of living fire. The cannonading roar was ceaseless, pounding his ears. The Rebs were racing to encircle Custer and his boys. Custer was in a bad place.

3:19 p.m.
Custer
Leading charge toward the Rebel batteries

Custer's heart shrank. Hundreds of dismounted Rebels were rushing down the slope from the Confederate batteries toward a stone fence leading east from the Rummel barn. He recoiled in horror. His Wolverines were completely exposed in the open field. Two hundred yards ahead, the iron barrel of the left enemy battery thundered. Cannister balls sliced through his dragoons. He reined up, his heart pounding, and halted the detachment.

Churchill pulled up, shouting, "The boys in your detachment are being shot up. They're dropping out of their saddles like flies."

Son of a bitch. If Mann had only followed me. Custer gripped his binoculars and scanned Cress Ridge. Three hundred yards to the right, he spotted several Wolverine companies. Two troopers leaped a fence and charged the Rebel on the right.

"Keep charging!" he yelled. "Run over them like sheep!" A cannon thundered and one of the troopers dropped from his mount. *"Damn!"*

Churchill warned, "A brigade of mounted cavalry are emerging from the trees above Colonel Mann's forward troopers at the second fence."

Custer's eyes narrowed and he shuddered. The Seventh Michigan had advanced too far north, beyond the protection of Pennington's batteries. Disaster loomed. Stuart was getting ready to launch a massive cavalry charge.

"I see them," he said. "It's an ambuscade. Ride over there and order the Wolverines to retreat to the first fence. Follow them back and I will meet you there. I'm ordering my detachment to retreat."

Churchill departed.

Custer ordered, "Private Boehm, blow 'Retreat.'"

The bugler blew the piercing notes of "Retreat."

"Follow me!" Custer said. He turned Roanoke and started galloping for the first fence.

3:20 p.m.
Captain Heman Moore
At the second fence

Moore's faced flushed hot. The charge had petered out. But he wasn't withdrawing until Custer gave the order. A private galloped toward him from Custer's detachment. The rider pulled up, sweat dripping from his face as if he had dunked his head in a pond.

The rider said, "I am Private Churchill, General Custer's special orderly. General Custer said our forward lines are over-extended and we lack enough troopers to take the enemy guns." Churchill pointed. "The enemy to our right is throwing down fences and forming a column for a charge. Our front and right flank are exposed."

"What are General Custer's orders?" Moore said.

"You are to fall back to the gap in the first fence and General Custer's detachment will follow you."

"Understood, Private. I will order my troopers to fall back. Sixteen horses from my company have been killed. I'm going to retreat slowly so the charging Rebels don't cut down my dismounted troopers before they reach the fence."

Churchill saluted. "I will lead your detachment, sir."

Moore turned. "Sergeant Cline, General Custer ordered all companies to pull back to the first fence! Company K will retreat slowly to protect our dismounted men."

Cline gave the order. "Company K, stand fast! Bugler, blow 'Retreat'!"

A bugle trumpeted and the mounted Wolverines galloped toward the first fence. The dismounted troopers sprinted behind their galloping comrades.

Moore shouted, "Company K, fall back slowly and cover the retreating dismounted troopers. Private Churchill will lead the retreat."

Moore's Wolverines started pulling back, firing as they re-treated. He spied Custer's detachment; Custer was in the lead, racing down the sloping field toward the first fence. The Rebel batteries opened a thundering barrage on the retreating regi-ment. Shells rained from the sky. Smoke blanketed the plowed field.

60

Custer — Friday, July 3

Aracketing roll of big guns and the thudding of hooves filled the air as Custer and company raced the several hundred yards toward the Union flag fluttering behind the first fence. He cast his gaze left and spotted Captain Moore's detachment. His heart leaped and he let out a screaming whoop. *Holy God, what a beautiful sight.* Churchill was leading Moore's detachment. The Churchill Wolverines were barreling toward the hidden fence like a cracked slab of hardened snow spilling down a steep slope. Those Rebels wouldn't catch them.

Custer flashed a devilish grin. Churchill was a superb horseman. Joy and pride bubbled up inside him like warm geysers. He was growing fond of his special orderly, who was becoming more indispensable by the moment. It was as if Churchill had magical powers to keep him alive. With Custer luck within him and Churchill by his side, nothing could harm him.

"Immortal," he whispered into the wind, then roared, "Ride like the Devil, Norvell!"

Orderly Joseph Fought pulled up next to Roanoke, shouting, "General Custer, the plumed-hat Rebels are beginning their charge."

Custer spotted a forest of glittering sabers in the smoke-filled field, sailing downward like a scudding cloud. A few hundred yards below the mounted Rebels, a horde of dismounted Wolverines churned behind Churchill's galloping Wolverines. "Run like hell, you Wolverines!" he thundered.

Custer's cavalcade scurried toward the gap in the hidden fence. Wolverines manning the fence erupted into a huge cheer and started waving their hats. He spied the gap marked by the Union flag.

"Joseph," he bellowed, "aim for the flag!"

The column swept forward. Roanoke approached the gap at an extended gallop. Custer's breath stilled; Roanoke leaped over the low stone fence and through the gap littered with dead troopers and mangled horses. He rode up the berm, turned northward, skittered to the right end of the fence, and reined up.

He scanned up and down the Michigan line. *Where is Colonel Mann?* Glancing sideways, he saw Lieutenant Colonel Allyne Litchfield trudging through the gap and climbing the berm.

"Colonel Litchfield, where is Colonel Mann? Is he wounded or dead?"

Litchfield shook his head. "I don't believe he is wounded or dead, but probably lingering in the rear of the regiment somewhere."

Hearing the word *lingering*, Custer's face heated like a hot skillet. No one lingered in his brigade. "What?"

Litchfield continued, "When Colonel Mann led us into the hidden fence, he fired his pistol a few times. He spun about, his face crumpled, and he bolted back over the berm. That's the last I saw of him. I charged through the gap and was shot off my horse. I picked up a discarded carbine and fought with the other dismounted troopers."

"Very well. You're the acting commander of the regiment. I will give you orders."

Litchfield saluted. "Yes, sir."

Custer gripped his field glasses and peered toward the Cress Ridge. His mind was a whirling dervish. Litchfield's tone was sharp and disrespectful toward Mann. He was unaware of any tension between the two officers. But something had happened, and he didn't know either officer well enough to make a judgment. He shook his head. He would sort out the possible feud between Mann and Litchfield later. *Must focus on Stuart's Invincibles charging from the north.*

Captain Armstrong pulled up. "General Custer, the Rebel cavalry regiment are swinging into view on our left, and they are charging."

"Yes, I know it, and we must get back under our guns," Custer replied.

"The last of the dismounted Wolverines are clearing the gap," Armstrong reported.

His mind fluxed with worry and his nerves tightened. *Damn't. Need to get the Wolverines out of here.* "Colonel Litchfield, order the dismounted troopers to keep racing to the Lott house and Low Dutch Road. I will order the mounted Wolverines to fire a few volleys before riding back."

Churchill rode up, sweat pouring from his brow. Custer glowed with pride. "Nice job, Norvell, leading the Wolverines to the fence gap. Now stay close."

They rode along the fence, and Custer shouted, "Fire, boys!"

The Wolverines unleashed a deadly volley. The charging Rebel vanguard tumbled from their horses. "Keep firing!" he ordered.

Churchill said, "The dismounted troopers are sprinting for the Lott house."

His scalp hair prickled. The Lott house was two hundred yards from the racing troopers. *Must protect them.*

"Pull back, Wolverines!"

He whirled Roanoke about and spurred the warhorse. He leaned forward and shouted into Roanoke's ear. "Twirl your whirligig hooves swiftly back to our lines!"

Churchill pulled up spur to spur. Pounding hooves filled the air. "Do you want to race?" Norvell shouted.

He cracked a grin and roared, "I thought we *were* racing!"

Churchill clapped his spurs and shot ahead half a horse length.

Custer brightened with a vicious sort of glee. *My God, Norvell is one hell of a horseman, fast as a Wyoming pronghorn.* He silenced his pelting mind and offered a rare prayer. *Please, Lord, keep Norvell safe as he follows me to the gates of hell. I pray that death won't define either of our lives.* God answered instantly with the same gushing warmth he'd felt when he prayed he would graduate from West Point.

He glanced up into the swirling blue sky. *Thank you. I won't let you down.*

3:23 p.m.
Captain Heman Moore
Riding toward the hidden fence

Moore squinted through the thickening smoke rolling up in dense clouds and spotted two dismounted Wolverines angling left as they darted down the sloping field. A blood-curdling shriek erupted from Cress Ridge. The Rebel Yell. The First Virginia cavalry were charging.

"Damn," Moore hissed. Dark fear gripped him. The two Wolverines were in perilous danger, like hikers on a mountain scurrying to outpace an avalanche. A whooshing like the wind of a great storm echoed as the barreling Rebels gained speed and threatened to swallow the blue troopers.

Moore's stomach knotted and his heart raced. He spurred and veered his cantering mount to the left. *Must protect these troopers from the mounted Rebels.* The thundering hooves of the Rebel cavalry pounded the ground. The field rolled in waves like an earthquake. He glanced to his left, spying glinting sabers through the rolling smoke. He clapped his spurs again and again, tearing flesh. Twenty yards ahead, he spotted the hidden fence. Where was the gap? He searched to the right; the gap was a hundred yards away. His heart sank as an icy chill coursed through him. *My God, I'm doomed.* Bullets whizzed past his head. His pulse thudded in his ears.

A thundering stampede echoed behind him. He swallowed down a lump in his throat and glanced over his shoulder. He caught the gleam of a saber, thrust from the arm of a howling Rebel. He ducked. Too late. The blade point sliced the back of his head. He muffled a scream.

A pistol cracked. His charger's skull exploded, the steed tumbling down in a heap. He let go of the reins and kicked his boots out of the stirrups, whirling through the air, crashing to the ground like a frenzied wave on the shore, screaming as the crushing weight of the horse penned his right leg. The animal's brains gushed out of a bullet hole. He gripped his pistol and spotted the Confederate returning, brandishing his sword. He fired. The Rebel fell at his side, a bullet hole through his brow. He aimed his revolver at another Confederate and pulled the trigger. *Click.*

Devil be Damned. He had fired his last bullet.

A Rebel major wearing a plumed hat said, "Drop your pistol, Captain. You are my prisoner."

He glared and let the silence of a few heartbeats prevail. The silence grew into a threatening crescendo. The Rebel Major cracked a devilish grin and cocked his pistol.

"This is your last chance, Captain. Drop your pistol."

Moore scrunched his brows and curled his lips into a sneer. He let one more heartbeat of silence pass and dropped his revolver. Two Rebels dismounted and pulled him from under the dead horse. He stood, testing his throbbing leg. *Not broken. Good.*

With a Virginia accent, soft and polite, the Confederate major asked, "What regiment are you from?"

"We are Wolverines."

"What Union daredevil dressed like Prince Murat with a red scarf led your attack toward Cress Ridge?"

"General Armstrong Custer."

The Rebel major shook his head and grinned. "So, you now have boy generals leading your brigades?"

Moore stared. His breath lurched in his throat and his face grew hot. This arrogant prick couldn't hold a candle to his boy general. "Major, I would follow General Custer to the gates of hell."

He surprised himself with his rancorous tone. In a matter of five days, Custer had gone from a buffooned jester to a beloved hero. There was an irresistible thrill about following a fearless leader who loved gaming Fate.

The Rebel grinned. "Since this is probably the last battle of the war, I would like to meet your General Custer. Perhaps you can arrange an introduction. I've heard many tales about Fanny from his Southern West Point schoolmates."

Moore snarled.

"Now, Captain, let us march back to my lines."

3:24 p.m.
Major James Carpenter
Lying on the field during the First Virginia charge

Carpenter's addled mind fought to clear the cobwebs. A thundering column of cavalry roared down the slope. He opened his eyes and spotted an enemy column four abreast charging toward him.

His mind screamed, "I'm going to be trampled." He rolled over several times and stopped as they whizzed by like a swooping raptor. That was close. He took short breaths. Footsteps echoed, and he glanced up at a soldier in blue carrying a Burnside carbine.

"You're going to die, Rebel," the Union trooper declared.

"What the hell? I'm a Wolverine officer. Let me crawl away."

"Grayback, the only place you're crawling to is hell."

The trooper dropped on one knee and took deliberate aim.

"I'm a Wolverine, you crazy idiot," he screamed, his voice high and hysterical. "What's wrong with you? Are you suffering from Soldier's Heart?"[11] He couldn't move. His mother's kind face flashed in his mind. Would he ever see her again? Would his regiment give him a decent burial?

He stared down the gun barrel and eyed the ball. The gun snapped. His heart punched against his ribs.

---

11 Gary Paulsen, *Soldier's Heart,* Dell Laurel-Leaf, New York, 1998, xiii-xv. PTSD is a modern term to describe the mental injury from combat. In WW I it was called Shell Shock and WW II it was called Battle Fatigue. At the end of the Civil War it was called Soldier's Heart. Doctors thought that combat stress caused a physiological change in which heart dynamics and blood pressure and pulse rate were altered. I took the liberty to use Soldier's Heart to describe Post-Traumatic Stress Disorder (PSTD) during the Battle of Gettysburg.

"Son of a whore." The Union trooper rapped his hand against the carbine and took aim again. *Snap.* Carpenter's breath caught in his throat.

The Union trooper glared at the carbine and shouted, "You son of a bitch." He turned and walked away, shaking his head.

Pennington's artillery shells started exploding above the plowed field. The bursting shells rained iron, striking the ground, and throwing dirt on him. "I'm going to die," his blurry mind said. Blackness.

3:24 p.m.
Colonel John McIntosh
Near the Lott house

Shells rained lead over the Rummel field. Acrid smoke clouds lingered like a morning mist that stung McIntosh's nose. He peered toward Custer's Wolverines fighting at the hidden fence. He gasped hard, gathering a deep breath. Plumed Rebel cavalry pointing gleaming sabers were roaring down from Cress Ridge. The funnel-shaped slope squeezed the charging enemy toward the Seventh Michigan Regiment. The Wolverines behind the hidden fence broke and started skedaddling toward the Lott house.

"Custer's Wolverines are running back like sheep," Captain Newhall observed.

McIntosh shuddered. The Wolverines were retreating helter-skelter. Spirited hope had dissolved to cheerless shock. "Custer is being routed."

He hurtled to the Lott backyard, waving his saber, and bellowed, "For God's sake, men, if you are ever going to stand, stand now, for you are on free soil!"

The blue-jacketed horsemen skedaddled past, ignoring his pleas. Fear's icicle dangled in his throat, freezing his breath as a mix of alarm and rage coursed through his veins. His mind reeled. Impossible to stop the avalanche of spilling Wolverines barreling toward the Low Dutch Road. *Disaster. What can stop Stuart's Invincibles?*

3:24 p.m.
Major Luther Trowbridge
Counterattacking the right flank of the Rebels along Cress Ridge

Trowbridge's gasps cut the hot air as his legs whirled like a paddle wheel toward the Spangler house, heaving chest pulsing like an accordion, parched mouth huffing like a blacksmith's bellow. Squinting, he spotted a Fifth Michigan trooper holding the reins of his mount and three others for the dismounted troopers. He rushed up, grabbed the pommel, and mounted his horse. His dismounted First Battalion were bounding toward him like a herd of white-tailed deer.

A private dashed up, gripping several Spencer ammunition pouches. "Here you go, Major."

Trowbridge took the pouch filled with forty or so shells, removed the spring-loaded tubular magazine in the repeater's buttstock, and inserted seven shells.[12]

"I will resupply the others in your battalion, sir," the private said.

He nodded. "Good."

Colonel Alger rode up. "Luther, as soon as your First Battalion has reloaded their Spencers, conduct a mounted charge into the two Rebel regiments threatening the Seventh Michigan's right flank."

"Yes, sir."

Trowbridge gestured to his orderly, Private William Dunn. "William, as soon as the troopers reload, form them into a column, four abreast." Dunn rushed away toward the battalion, returning only after what seemed ages.

"Major, the column is ready."

Trowbridge unsheathed his saber and turned to his bugler. "'Charge!'"

---

12 At the Battle of Gettysburg, troopers reloaded the Spencer magazine (cartridge) tube by inserting seven bullets individually. Late in 1864 the Blakeslee cartridge box that held ten preloaded Spencer 7-shot cartridges was first used.

Trumpet notes split the air and Trowbridge surged forward, waving his saber. The air reverberated with a thrilling shout. "For Michigan!"

Trowbridge's battalion galloped forward like hounds unleashed. The air was thick and wet, and the hot sun poured down on his neck. The pitch of the sloping field lessened as they closed the Rebel flank. The wounded earth clacked beneath the pounding hooves. Rage roiled in the back of his throat. Ferry was dead. *Damn Rebel bastards.* He veered slightly to the right, swinging the charging Wolverines toward a Rebel officer riding a great black horse outside the Confederate right flank. The gloom and sourness of the earlier fight gave way to surging adrenaline. The hunger for vengeance was thicker in him than ever before. All semblance of balance had dissipated, and his thirst for revenge could not be quenched. This charge was less about rescuing Custer's charging Seventh Michigan than exacting blood for Ferry. *As God is my witness, I will avenge Ferry's death.*

He screamed as his battalion sliced through the right flank of the dismounted Rebels. The shocked Rebs stopped firing at the Seventh; instead, they turned and fought. A slashing saber fight broke out in the middle of the Rummel field. The Wolverines swapped their sabers for Spencers and covered the Rebels with a storm of lead, dropping many of the enemy dead in their tracks. In a few moments, the dismounted Confederates were running like lamplighters toward Cress Ridge.

Private Dunn shouted, "I see Custer's red scarf leading the Seventh back to the Lott house. Our counterattack worked."

Trowbridge spied Custer waving his hat. A popping crack transcended the tumult of battle, and he soared through the air, his mind screaming what his voice could not. He crashed, landing on his side. He glanced at his mount lying next to him, blood gushing from a head wound. *Damn. Must have been shot by a Confederate sharpshooter.* A Wolverine screamed and plunged from his saddle, crashing a few yards away, dead. A bullet had pierced his neck.

Am I wounded? No pain. He gripped his Spencer and stood. His column broke forward like a fan, sweeping through the Rebel right flank.

"Major Trowbridge!"

He turned and spotted Private Dunn riding up with a spare horse.

"Thank God!" he shouted, and gripped the horse pummel and scudded onto the new mount. He scanned the middle of the field. His troopers did quick work with their sabers and Spencers. The plumed Invincibles turned and raced back up Cress Ridge.

A vicious glee invaded him, and he welcomed it. His battalion had exacted revenge for Major Ferry and helped turn the tide against the charging Rebels. It was a damned good day's work.

"'Retreat,'" Trowbridge shouted.

The bugler blew "Retreat." The Fifth turned and galloped back toward Hanover Road.

3:30 p.m.
Custer
Spangler house

Custer broke into a big grin, bouncing on Roanoke as he approached the Spangler house. His skin tingled with brilliant bursts of energy and his veins throbbed with a fevered spirit. Leading the Seventh Michigan was just like the breathless exuberance of leading the charge at the Battle of Aldie. His eyes riveted on his staff waiting in the Spangler yard. He swallowed; small traces of the fear he dreaded most hovered nearby like a growing shadow. The thrill coursing inside him was like fading sunlight and would soon vanish. How soon could he lead another charge? His restless nerves craved more excitement and feared lifeless boredom. His daredevil impulses had no solid bottom.

"Easy boy, we're almost there." He reached down, rubbing Roanoke's neck. "You did great, my Iron Gray. I'm proud of you."

He pulled on the reins and halted in front of the Spangler house. He reached into his grimy velvet jacket, retrieved a handkerchief, and wiped his eyes and his drenched brow.

He grinned and dismounted. Acrid smoke from Pennington's artillery stung his eyes. He stared out across Rummel field. Both Union and Confederate batteries were resting their iron jaws. Tiny droplets of silence hung in the air as a hushed lull formed over the Rummel fields like a morning mist.

Churchill reined up, breathing hard.

Custer grinned boyishly. "Norvell, that was the most exciting sport I've ever engaged in."

"General, you rode hell-bent up the slope. I had to ride at a breakneck gallop to keep up with you."

"You performed gallantly again, Norvell."

"Thanks for not falling off Roanoke. That makes my job a lot easier."

Johnny scooted up, carrying a bucket of water. He gripped Roanoke's reins. "General Custer, I saw you lead the cavalry charge. You were four lengths ahead of the column. You were just a ripsnorter."

He grinned. "It was every inch a glorious cavalry charge."

"I thought for sure you'd get yourself blowed chock-full o' holes. But here you are."

"I call it Custer luck."

Johnny sat the bucket in front of Roanoke and started wiping the warhorse down.

Custer gripped the handle of his sheathed saber and shook his head, reluctant to let go of the waning joy of this day, when General Gregg rode up and dismounted.

"George, that was one hell of a mounted charge!"

Custer grinned. "We shocked the hell out of Stuart's boys. If the Seventh hadn't smashed into that hidden fence, I would have captured those Rebel batteries."

Gregg lit his pipe. "So far in this chess game I'm playing with old Jeb, I am winning. My guess is that Stuart wanted to bait me into advancing my entire division north past the Rummel farm. Then, with my division stretched out over three thousand yards of open field, Stuart would have ordered his best brigade commander, General Hampton, to launch a surprise attack."

"It was the First Virginia Cavalry from Fitz Lee's brigade that charged me," Custer said. "Not General Hampton's boys."

"Precisely. Stuart doesn't want a long, large cavalry fight. He wanted to slip past my division in a short, quick fight and then attack Meade's rear."

Custer nodded. "I didn't win the field, but the Seventh Michigan ate up a lot of time."

Gregg smiled. "You surprised Jeb with your dauntless charge and rode right up to his boys and ruffled their feathers." He puffed on his pipe. "Then, most importantly, you pulled back to regroup. You didn't stay strung out over the field, which is what Stuart wanted."

"I'm hoping General Hampton and his brigade will emerge from the Cress Ridge woods. I would love the chance to tangle with him."

"I'm sure you would, George. My hope is that Jeb has had enough and retreats to the York Road and then back to Gettysburg. But if he attacks, my goal is not to defeat him but to play for a stalemate and prevent him from slipping past me."

Custer nodded, but his heart sank. Hadn't he just proved he was First Horseman of the Union? He could beat any of Stuart's boys. He took a deep breath as he grappled with the passing, feral thrill of leading a magnificent Napoleonic charge. Would he get another chance for glory?

61

Farnsworth — Friday, July 3

Farnsworth studied the backside of Little Round Top, the smaller of the two rocky hills three miles south of Gettysburg. The summit and the eastern and southern slopes were lightly wooded. A Union battle flag flew on the crest alongside signal flags.

Pleasonton's courier last evening had said a fierce fight for Little Round Top had occurred in late afternoon. General Meade had ordered General Sickles's Third Corp to occupy Little Round Top, but Sickles disobeyed orders, left it undefended, and moved his corps a half mile in front of the mound. Just before the Confederates launched an attack against Meade's left flank, General Gouverneur Warren rode to the summit of Little Round Top and rallied enough soldiers to hold the Rebels off.

The final act of defending Little Round Top, the courier said, came from Colonel Joshua Chamberlain, commanding the Twentieth Maine. His regiment had run out of ammunition, and when the Confederates attacked, he ordered a bayonet charge and routed the enemy.

Farnsworth smirked. Chamberlain's daredevil feat sounded a lot like what Custer would do. Did Chamberlain dress in a gaudy uniform like Custer?

Kilpatrick's aide, Lieutenant Eli Holden, pulled up. "General Farnsworth, please follow me. I will escort you to Bushman's Hill, located southwest of Big Round Top."

He nodded. "Lead the way."

On the south side of Big Round Top, Farnsworth crossed the narrow valley and headed for Bushman's Hill, less than one thousand yards away. He followed a horse length behind his guide, Lieutenant Holden, trotting in the sweltering heat.

Holden halted behind the southern slope of the rising mount and pointed. "Ahead, that's Bushman's Hill."

Farnsworth scowled. Bushman's Hill wasn't favorable terrain for cavalry to operate. The low hill was heavily wooded, and the slopes were covered with immense granite boulders. He hoped to hell Kilpatrick wasn't going to make him hold Bushman's Hill.

Holden bolted into a trot and raced up the southern slope. Farnsworth touched his horse's flanks and the mount pitched and grunted as it loped up the steamy slope of Bushman's Hill. Dotted with big boulders, sticker bushes, and fallen trees, the difficult path upward wove through thick timbers whose branches intermingled into a dense canopy. The bright sky ended, and the inky earth began. It felt like he had entered a shadowy cave devoid of sharp yellow sunlight.

At the crest, he emerged from the thick canopy, halted, and wiped his sweaty face. The woods on the summit had thinned and shards of dappled light splayed through the covering like a kaleidoscope. He glanced east and spotted Kilpatrick's division flag on a small knoll twenty yards away. Kilpatrick and Captain Llewellyn Estes were peering northward through their field glasses toward Gettysburg. He rode toward the knoll.

"General Kilpatrick," Farnsworth announced. "My brigade is arriving on the field."

Kilpatrick's eyes bored into him. The empty silence that ensued did nothing to relieve the growing tension. Kilpatrick's body coiled as he bared his fangs, making him look even more irritable than usual. Perhaps his kidneys were giving him fits again.

Kilpatrick snarled. "Did you run into problems?"

"We would have been here a half hour earlier, but we mistakenly attempted to go through the gap between Big Round

Top and Little Round Top. We trudged through open, scrubby timber and around large boulders for forty rods or more. The area was sprinkled with dead men from both sides from the fight the day before. We halted when we ran into Colonel William Tilton's Infantry Brigade from Fifth Corps occupying the gap between the two round tops."

"Did you talk with Colonel Tilton?"

"No. His men said he was scouting the top of Little Round Top. I learned General Evander Law's Alabama brigade was on the western side of the Round Tops, guarding Lee's right flank. I countermarched and skirted around the southern base of Big Round Top."

Kilpatrick's brow furrowed.

"I also learned from Tilton's soldiers that General Law is commanding General Hood's infantry division. Hood was seriously wounded in yesterday's assault of the Round Tops. Besides commanding his Alabama brigade, Law is now commanding the Texas and Georgia brigades. Law has deployed the First Texas Regiment in a skirmish line stretching from the southwestern base of Big Round Top west toward the Emmitsburg Road. The Ninth Georgia Regiment is protecting the Rebel batteries on Warfield Ridge that runs parallel to Emmitsburg Road."

"Was Colonel's Tilton's brigade anchoring the Union's left flank?"

"No. Colonel Joseph Fisher's brigade from Fifth Corps is guarding the far left flank."

A rifle cracked. Farnsworth squinted down the northern slope. A white smoke tendril wormed its way up through the body of timbers. "Are those the First Texas skirmishers popping off shots?"

"Yes."

"Where is the enemy cavalry guarding Lee's flank?"

Kilpatrick smiled. "There is no Rebel cavalry in our front, only infantry. I believe Lee's right flank is vulnerable. I want to attack as soon as Merritt's and Custer's brigades arrive."

Farnsworth pulled on the corner of his mustache and scanned the rugged terrain, contemplating how much he might safely say.

After a few heartbeats he glanced down at Kilpatrick. "It's dicey conducting a cavalry attack against infantry protected by thick woods, stone breastworks, and long-range artillery. It's as fool-hardy as attacking a medieval castle without ladders, catapults, and battering rams."

Kilpatrick's face flamed red and his eyes narrowed like the slits of a viper. "I don't believe in siege warfare. By God, I have orders to attack the Rebel flank and that's what I'm going to do. Lee's right flank is his Achilles' heel." Kilpatrick lurched forward and puffed out his chest.

Farnsworth stood perfectly still, taking care to show an absolutely neutral expression, but on full alert. Had he overplayed his hand? Was Kilpatrick about to strike him?

"Once we break through the Texas line of defense," Kilpatrick hissed, "there is no Rebel cavalry stopping us from attacking Lee's unprotected rear. My cavalry division will destroy the enemy's vulnerable supply trains and force Lee to surrender or retreat back across the Potomac."

Kilpatrick paused, wiping the spittle from his wet lips. "I've changed my mind. As soon as the Michigan Brigade arrives, I will order an attack. I'm not going to wait on Merritt's brigade."

Kilpatrick turned to Captain Estes. "Did Custer's vanguard catch up with you?"

"No, I did not see any of Custer's Wolverines."

Kilpatrick's jaw clamped tight and his nostrils flared. His hands tightened into fists and his head snapped toward Estes. "Well, damnit?" Venom dripped from every word.

Estes drew a sharp breath. "At eight a.m. I told General Custer that the division was moving to the left flank of the army, and he was to follow General Farnsworth's brigade."

Kilpatrick sprayed spit like a cobra. "God damn you, Custer!" He pointed and scowled. "Elon, put your brigade in along Bushman's Hill and commence skirmishing till Custer comes up. Unlimber First Lieutenant Samuel Elder's Battery E on this knoll. I want your Fifth New York Regiment to protect Elder's battery. Deploy the Eighteenth Pennsylvania to the left of Elder's battery and the First West Virginia and the First Vermont to the right of the battery."

Farnsworth froze, heart pounding. Skirmishing against infantry concealed behind stone fences? His mind raced. What was Kilpatrick thinking? "Where do you plan to position Custer's brigade when he arrives?"

"Custer's brigade will fall in on the left of the Eighteenth Pennsylvania. His brigade will stretch out in a line to the west and cross Emmitsburg Road. If General Merritt's brigade arrives in time for the attack, they will form up west of Custer's brigade."

Farnsworth gritted his teeth and nodded. A pang of fear seized him. What if Custer didn't show up? Would Kilpatrick order his brigade to charge without Custer's brigade over this wretched ground?

Kilpatrick grinned and clapped his hands. "Once my two brigades are in line, I will order an attack."

Kilpatrick turned to Estes. "Llewellyn, let's ride over to the Emmitsburg Road." He reined his mount around and trotted west.

Turning to his aide-de-camp, Captain Andrew Cunningham, Farnsworth grumbled, "Andrew, ride to the regimental commanders and have them deploy on an east-west line as ordered by General Kilpatrick. The Fifth New York will protect Elder's battery."

"Yes, sir."

Farnsworth cut one hundred yards across the brow of Bushman's Hill toward Big Round Top and halted at the edge of an opening in the oak forest that covered Bushman's Hill. He gripped his field glasses, scanning the ground northwest of the two round tops. Fury pulsed in his veins. This was terrible terrain for a cavalry attack. *My brigade should move left near the Emmitsburg Road and attack with Custer's brigade when he arrives. Both brigades would have an open ride in rolling fields toward the rear of Lee's army.* He pursed his lips, damming the rage roaring up his throat. Several hundred clip-clopping horses echoed from behind. He whirled and spotted Lieutenant Colonel Addison Preston and Major John Bennett riding at the head of the 675 troopers of the First Vermont.

He raised his arm and beckoned. "Lieutenant Colonel Preston, Major Bennett."

Preston and Bennett reined up and saluted.

He returned the salute and pointed northward. "General Kilpatrick has ordered the brigade to occupy this line." He pointed ten degrees to the northeast. "See that two-story stone house, wooden barn, and shops about one thousand yards away?"

They both nodded.

"That's the John Slyder house. His property runs eastward to the western slope of Big Round Top. Plum Run runs north–south at the bottom of Big Round Top."

"General," Preston said, "this hilly, thickly wooded ground between here and Slyder's farm is unsuitable for mounted operations."

Bennett concurred. "The enemy could easily be waiting behind the stone fences, boulders, and thick trees. A charging cavalry wouldn't see them until they were right on them."

"I agree, gentlemen." His stomach churned. He shook his head as apprehension turned to agony. "John, I want you to deploy four Vermont companies as dismounted skirmishers. Drive the enemy skirmishers back and try to ascertain the enemy's strength. I'm going to set up my headquarters near Elder's guns and General Kilpatrick's headquarters."

He reined about. This was absurd. He fought to shut down the anger trying to rush up his throat, lest it come tumbling out in words. Kilpatrick was eyeing Elder's artilleryman unlimbering the battery.

Farnsworth reined up. "General, I'm deploying four dismounted companies from the First Vermont led by Major Bennett. Two mounted companies are backing them up."

Kilpatrick cracked his knuckles and flashed a devilish grin. "Good. As soon as Major Bennett reports on the enemy strength, let me know."

He paused, tight-lipped, glaring at Kilpatrick. Was the man seriously considering a charge through this timber? He nodded. "Will do, sir."

Lieutenant Eli Holden of Kilpatrick's staff reined up. "General Kilpatrick, I've located General Custer and his brigade. They are four miles northeast of last night's bivouac at Two Taverns, occupying the Hanover and Low Dutch Crossroads."

"Devil be damned. What the hell are they doing there?"

Holden wiped his face. "Custer believes he was ordered by General Gregg to occupy these crossroads."

Kilpatrick clenched his fist, plainly furious. "Damn Custer. Lieutenant Holden, ride to General Pleasonton and have him rescind General Gregg's order and have Custer report here immediately."

Holden saluted and departed.

Kilpatrick's face had turned beet red, and queasiness gripped Farnsworth's stomach. His lone cavalry brigade was facing a Rebel infantry brigade alone—an infantry brigade that was protected by trees and stone fences. He shuddered at the mortal danger that would likely result from Custer disobeying orders. His blood pulsed faster. "General Kilpatrick, I think you should reprimand Custer severely."

Kilpatrick's face contorted into a furious scowl as his face flushed crimson and his lips trembled. It appeared that he was struggling to collect himself. "Damn Custer still thinks he's a cadet, choosing which orders to follow." He paused and stared toward the Slyder house. "I hope a reprimand may not be necessary."

Frustration or utter disbelief left him befuddled. Why was Kilpatrick not going to discipline Custer? Foggy, he gestured west toward Emmitsburg Road. "Any word when Merritt's brigade will arrive?"

"Merritt's courier said his brigade should be here about 1:30 p.m."

Farnsworth swallowed hard.

Kilpatrick's face grew taut. "Without Custer's brigade, Merritt's brigade is necessary if we are to launch a major attack against the Rebel right flank. I need at least two brigades."

Relief swept over him. Kilpatrick was going to wait for either Custer's or Merritt's brigades to arrive before launching an attack. "I'm confident Custer will be arriving soon after General Pleasonton rescinds General Gregg's orders."

Kilpatrick glared. "You don't know Custer like I do. The brash daredevil craves national fame. Custer will go where he thinks he can best impress the reporters."

Elder's four big guns belched a thundering blast. Farnsworth jumped and jerked his head, spotting long, fiery tendrils spouting from the iron jaws. The snake-like tendrils scraped the top of the thick trees as they raced northward. What in the hell was Elder aiming at? He couldn't see a damn thing through the thick tree covering. The roaring battery fired in rapid succession, thumping his ears. The ground rolled like bouncing tumbleweeds. Elder skittered toward them and pointed.

"General Kilpatrick, I'm firing blindly. I'm elevating as high as I can to shoot over the trees, but I don't know if we are hitting the enemy."

Kilpatrick cracked a smile. "Just keep firing."

Fury coursed through Farnsworth. How long was damn Kilpatrick going to make Elder keep firing, blindly wasting shells? A whistling enemy shell arced through the sky. He glanced up and saw that the shell's spiraling smoke stream was slicing toward the dismounted Fifth New York troopers. The shell plunged and burst. Hot iron fragments clattered into the ground like a hailstorm. Screams rent the deafening roar of the explosion.

Elder shouted, "Now I know where the Rebel batteries are." He tore toward his battery and pointed over the trees. His gunners re-aimed the four big guns and fired.

Farnsworth gripped his binoculars and scanned over the trees. A furious explosion rocked the air as dark smoke shot upward like a volcanic plume. A cheer erupted from Elder's battery. Their guns must have hit a Rebel artillery limber. Three Rebel shells screamed back over the tall trees and burst, peppering the New Yorkers with hot shrapnel. A chorus of swearing burst out as the New Yorkers scrambled for cover. He rode toward Major John Hammond, commanding the regiment.

"John," he shouted, "dismount your regiment and move forward to the ravine at the base of Bushman's Hill. You can support Elder's battery from there and not be in a direct line with this artillery duel."

"Yes, sir." He turned and shouted, "Regiment, dismount." The New Yorkers leaped from their mounts. "Regiment, forward to the ravine!"

The New Yorkers yelled and stampeded down the slope like fleeing sheep sensing an impending danger.

Kilpatrick chuckled. "Elon, I don't think I've ever seen troopers race forward like that. I'm not sure they need horses."

Farnsworth bit his lip. What the hell was Kilpatrick doing? He started to say something, but the words caught in his gullet. This was the most miserable ground imaginable for mounted cavalry operations.

12:00 p.m.
Farnsworth
Bushman's Hill

The murderous heat was swelling on Bushman's Hill. Farnsworth wiped his wet face. "It feels like I'm sitting in a Finnish sauna," he muttered. Clapping hooves approached. Major John Bennett galloped out of the thick foliage.

Bennett saluted. "General Farnsworth, our skirmishers pushed out about two hundred yards. We ran into Rebel skirmishers and easily pushed them back another hundred yards. Then we ran into a strongly defended stone fence. The Rebels started hammering us with their long-range Enfield rifles and we pulled back fifty yards."

"What's the enemy's estimated strength?"

"My guess is at least an infantry regiment."

"Did you see any Rebel cavalry?"

"No."

"That's unusual. Kilpatrick's right. There are no enemy cavalry covering Lee's right flank."

Captain Samuel Sherer Elder

62

Kilpatrick — Friday, July 3

The sky was bright, with white, fleecy clouds floating in from the west. A sulky heat baked Kilpatrick's skin beneath his blue general's jacket. He scratched his itchy forearm. *Damn cruel sun.*

Five hundred yards up the Emmitsburg Road a Rebel battery and supporting enemy infantry were positioned in front of the Bushman house. The late-morning artillery duel between Elder's battery and the Rebel cannons had ceased. Now, a sweeping hush bristled against the long blue and gray lines. The quiet moment swirled eerily, as if a horde of twisters were preparing to spawn from brimstone clouds and unleash hell's vengeance.

Captain Estes pointed. "I'm not sure this lull is going to last long. Do you see the hundreds of Confederate cannons lining up?"

Kilpatrick scanned Lee's line. "Something's up." A mile and a half up the Emmitsburg Road there were heaps of enemy activity. Starting at the Sherfy peach orchard, the Rebels were methodically posting their dazzling brass Napoleons northward in a two-mile, concave line that hugged Seminary Ridge. He squinted. The Confederate batteries perched on two wooden wheels looked like a string of long-bodied mantises. They all seemed aimed at a copse of trees defended by General Hancock's Second Corps.

"Do you think the Rebels will give us battle today?" said Estes. "Or are their artillery batteries lining up to cover Lee's army as it heads towards the Potomac with their tails between their legs?"

"My God, I hope the Rebels stay and fight. This is the moment I've been waiting for my entire life." Kilpatrick retorted. "General Pleasonton promoted me to division commander because I'm an aggressive fighter." Smoldering bitterness singed his words. "But because damn Custer disobeyed orders, I'm just an idle spectator to this upcoming fight at the moment."

"What's your plan if Custer doesn't show up?"

"My orders are to threaten and strike the right and rear of Lee's army. I'm not going to wait all afternoon for an opportunity. If one doesn't happen, I will create one."

"Are you going to wait for Custer's brigade to arrive?'

"No. But I will wait for Merritt's brigade to arrive. That will give me two cavalry brigades against at least one or maybe two enemy infantry brigades."

"Where will you place Merritt's brigade?"

"West of the Emmitsburg road. Then I plan to attack in echelon. Merritt's brigade will open the attack by charging on foot. The Rebels will be forced to shift their infantry forces to the right to counter Merritt's brigade. That shift will create a gap. I will then order Farnsworth to charge through the gap with his mounted brigade. And I will order the rest of Merritt's brigade to conduct a cavalry attack. If Custer's brigade has arrived by then, they will act as reserve, and if Farnsworth achieves success, I will order Custer's brigade forward to exploit the success."

He wiped his face; the sultriness and silence of the afternoon reigned supreme. His scalp hair prickled. The sticky silence was growing in intensity as the muggy air threatened to erupt into thunder showers. He scanned the terrain. Open, flat ground along the Emmitsburg Road was perfect for Merritt's cavalry attack hitting the enemy's right flank. His jaw tightened and his blood boiled in his veins. He had orders to attack but was missing half his division.

"Damn you, Custer," he muttered. Fanny was fueling the fire in his throat with his insubordination. His showboat schoolmate didn't care about following orders at the academy and still didn't care about following them now. Custer was preventing him from achieving glory.

1:05 p.m.
Kilpatrick
Emmitsburg Road

Up and down Elder's battery on Bushman's Hill, artillerymen scurried about, staging shells and cannister and hauling buckets of water. Kilpatrick fretted, his stomach knotting tighter as his impatience grew. If Custer's brigade was here, he would have Pennington's battery positioned near the Emmitsburg Road. With the firepower from Elder's and Pennington's batteries he would overwhelm the Rebel batteries in his front.

"Son of a bitch," he muttered. Hadn't he warned Pleasonton that Custer was an impulsive jackanape seeking glory and stealing everyone's thunder? Because of Custer, he was missing the opportunity to attack and achieve the glory he so well deserved. He was being dragooned by that harebrained peacock!

Estes pointed. "General Kilpatrick, a courier is riding up the road from Emmitsburg."

A blue-clad officer reined up.

"General Kilpatrick, I'm Captain Isaac Dunkelberger, from the U.S. Cavalry. General Merritt sends his respects. His reserve brigade will arrive on the field in about twenty minutes. He requests to know where you want his brigade to deploy as well as Captain William Graham's Battery K, U.S. Artillery, six three-inch rifles."

Warmth swelled through Kilpatrick. "Please give my regards to General Merritt, as I'm anxiously awaiting his brigade's arrival." He pointed. "That's Captain Elder's battery atop of Bushman's Hill. I want Captain Graham's battery to deploy just west of the Emmitsburg Road and in line with Captain Elder's battery. I want General Merritt's brigade to deploy west of Captain Graham's battery."

"Yes, sir." Dunkelberger departed.

"General Kilpatrick," Estes mused, "I thought General Merritt graduated a year ahead of you at the academy."

"He did. But I got my general's star before him." His chest swelled. "That's why I'm the senior cavalry officer on the Union left flank."

A booming crack interrupted. No mistake: it was the sharp thunder of an artillery gun. Kilpatrick glanced northward. The cotton-ball smoke of a bursting enemy shell hovered over the copse of trees. He stiffened and his chin rose, suddenly alert. Was it a signal gun? In an instant, an earsplitting barrage of several hundred Rebel guns thundered to life like a reawakened volcano pouring out liquid fire and molten rock. Hundreds of enemy shells burst beyond Cemetery Ridge, flashing bright lightning from small, white, puffy clouds. The Union batteries retorted, blasting the air with wailing shells. Bursting thunderclaps battered his ears. Breeze from the blasts fluttered against his face like a hand-held fan waving back and forth. He gripped the reins hard and leaned forward in the saddle. The ground rolled like a great earthquake as all hell broke loose.

Estes leaned close to his ear, speaking loud enough to be heard over the din. "We will soon learn if the Rebels will attack or retreat."

He nodded as the opposing lines filled with flaky streams of yellow fire, piercing white banks of convolving smoke. An opportunity was developing. His eyes followed the line of the Emmitsburg Road north to Gettysburg. The rolling fields west of the road were ideal for a cavalry charge into Lee's rear. If Lee launched an infantry attack after the cannonade, he would order a Napoleonic attack into the Rebel flank and rear. A cold shiver tickled the back of his neck. This was his chance for eternal glory. The hero of the Battle of Gettysburg.

2:45 p.m.
Kilpatrick
Seventy-five yards west of Bushman's Hill

Kilpatrick groaned and rubbed his lower back. *Damn kidneys.* The cannonading was tapering. Thousands of Rebel soldiers were forming up. The gray lines were long, slithering snakes worming side by side. The lines were spiked with hundreds of treasonous, flaunting rags. His heart raced to a thundering gallop. As soon as Custer's Brigade arrived he would attack. What a glorious moment. Clapping hooves echoed behind; Captain Estes pulled up, galloping even with him.

"Llewellyn, any sign of Custer's brigade?"

"No, sir."

"Damn Custer! This was the perfect chance to launch a surprise attack." A raging river of anger kept time with the rapid rhythm of the two horses. He would court-martial Custer's ass when this was done.

"You don't need Custer's brigade," Estes said, wiping his mouth. "You can easily slice through these Rebels with Farnsworth and Merritt's brigades. You would be the hero of Gettysburg."

He drew a ragged breath. Estes was right. He could win without Custer. He swiped at a bug buzzing in his ear. If he attacked now, he wouldn't have to share the spoils of victory with that glory hound. He beamed as his gleefulness returned. He could see the newspaper headlines. *Judson Kilpatrick's Daring and Courage Saves the Union.*

"Let's visit Merritt." He spurred his mount toward Merritt's brigade pennant. No more of this lily-livered cowering. It was time. They reined up next to Merritt.

Merritt saluted. "I'm awaiting your orders, sir."

"General Merritt, I'm ordering you to attack." He pointed. "I want you to conduct a dismounted attack west of the Emmitsburg Road. You will attack north."

"Yes, sir."

"Your dismounted attack is designed to force the enemy to move reserves to blunt you. Once the Rebel reserves are moving, I will order Farnsworth to attack in the gap created by the enemy movements. Then I will order you to conduct a cavalry attack with the rest of your brigade."

"Understood, sir."

Emboldened by having delivered today's first set of attack orders, Kilpatrick scudded up Bushman's Hill and found Farnsworth next to Elder's battery. "Elon, have your brigade ready to launch a cavalry attack. As soon as the enemy rushes over to counter Merritt's attack, I will order you to charge."

Farnsworth pursed his lips and scowled, plainly upset about attacking. There was a brief, awkward silence, the kind of silence that lingers between dueling gentlemen aiming their cocked pistols.

"Yes, sir," Elon seethed.

63

Farnsworth — Friday, July 3

3:45 p.m.
Farnsworth
Eighty yards southwest from Elder's battery
Atop of Bushman's Hill

Farnsworth peered at Merritt's retreating dismounted troopers. He drew in a shivering breath and turned to Captain Cunningham. "Andrew, Merritt's attack failed. The Rebels are pushing back his troopers to their starting point. Rebel infantry with their long-range Enfield rifles have the advantage over the dismounted trooper's carbines."

Cunningham swore. "Merritt's attack failed to force the Rebels to shift men from your brigade's front. There is no gap for our cavalry to ride through."

Farnsworth's nostrils flared as his anger mounted. "Son of a bitch! Doesn't Kilpatrick realize that attacking through this godforsaken ground is suicide?"

4:00 p.m.
Farnsworth
Eighty yards southwest from Elder's battery
Atop of Bushman's Hill

My God, what a fight. The Union breastworks atop of Bushman's Hill blazed with ceaselessly rolling volleys. It was as if a summer cloud filled with incessant lightning flashes had descended over the copse of trees. It was impossible to tell who was winning.

Like a fidgeting gamecock, Kilpatrick reined up and barked out rapidly, his voice high-pitched and tight, "I just received word that Meade's center repulsed a large infantry attack. If

Meade counterattacks with his infantry and my Third Cavalry Division crushes Lee's right flank, we can decimate the Army of Northern Virginia. I'm ordering you to conduct a mounted attack with the left wing of your brigade."

Farnsworth's jaw tightened; his pulse pounded in his temples. "Merritt's dismounted echelon attack failed to create a gap, General. Instead, the Rebels have shifted their infantry units to repulse a mounted attack by my brigade. My troopers would be riding into the teeth of the enemy defense."

Kilpatrick glared and furrowed his brow. "I disagree. I'm commanding 4,000 troopers. My aggressive probes show the Rebel lines are overstretched. A mounted, quick strike will easily penetrate the enemy's defenses."

"General," Farnsworth fumed, "as you can plainly see, the terrain is densely wooded and littered with boulders and stone fences. It's not conducive to a cavalry attack. It's a trap."

Kilpatrick snarled. "Lee's army is on the brink of being routed," he shrieked. "I'm ordering the West Virginia to conduct a cavalry attack directly north."

Farnsworth fought to control the anger raging through his body. "General, would you consider ordering Merritt's troopers back to their mounts to support my attack?"

"No. That would take too long. I have confidence you can break the enemy line. You must attack now. There is no time to coordinate another attack with Merritt." Kilpatrick's face lit up, consumed with a dark giddiness. His lips pulled down into a scornful sneer and his eyes slitted like an infernal devil thirsting for battle. "Now order the mounted charge."

Farnsworth stared for a few heartbeats, his blood turning to ice in his bones. Kilpatrick's cocksure ignorance was on full display. Elon's brain swirled with a horde of clashing thoughts, and sweat slid down his neck. Didn't Kilpatrick understand the situation?

Dare he disobey the order?

Full of uncertainty, riddled with memories, he let a couple heavier heartbeats pass. The University of Michigan. One student dead. And now he was responsible for the lives of hundreds of men. Another memory rose up—much more recent, though it seemed ages ago—a conversation with Custer ... was it only on the eve of this battle?

"Elon, please take this to heart. Kilpatrick will bully you if you disagree with a bad decision. Defend yourself."

"George, thank you for sharing your experiences with Kilpatrick. Since my expulsion from the University of Michigan, I've tried hard to follow all the rules, and that means I will follow Kilpatrick's orders."

Never again. He had vowed to obey every rule. Every order.

Even if ...?

Death's chilling breath quivered in the still air.

Hundreds of men would be slaughtered like stockyard animals.

Damn! It was hopeless. He couldn't muster the will to disobey. He chewed at the inside of his cheek and inwardly wailed. *You don't have much to say about when and where you die.* Perhaps blind chance would protect his troopers from the hooded Grim Reaper. Eyes unfocused, he heaved a sigh and answered. "Yes, sir. I will order the Mountaineers to attack." He saluted and reined his horse about. A searing heat flushed his cheeks. Didn't that lunatic Kilpatrick understand that a cavalry attack against infantry defending strong defensive positions in a heavily wooded area was impossible?

Grimly, he trotted up to Colonel Nathaniel P. Richmond, commanding the West Virginia Cavalry. He drew a tight, ragged breath. "Nathaniel, General Kilpatrick has ordered your regiment to attack directly north. Good luck."

"That's an absurd order, General." He stared in sullen defiance and gestured north. "You want my regiment to attack over this ground?"

He nodded. "Yes, I do. I understand your concern. If you're successful, there's a chance Kilpatrick's division can rout the Rebels' rear. Now attack!"

He narrowed his eyes as the West Virginians drew sabers. His stomach churned, spraying acid up his throat. *God damn Kilpatrick. This charge should never be made.* His troopers thrust forward, thrashing through thick woods and weaving around huge boulders. On both ends of the stone wall, sturdy rail fences extended to the Emmitsburg Road and to the base of Big Round Top. The cheering blue troopers cleared the woods and raced toward a stone wall two hundred yards ahead.

Enemy artillery batteries near the Bushman house erupted. The ground trembled and the air thundered with shot and shell sailing over the West Virginians and scarring the earth with massive holes. The Mountaineers surged forward, riding down the Rebel skirmishers and slashing them with sabers. As the troopers neared the stone fence, the Rebels popped up behind it like woodchucks and delivered a devasting fire. Hundreds of yellow flashes streaked; screams echoed from wounded blue troopers.

As the Rebels reloaded, the Mountaineers plunged forward, hitting the fence, determined to overpower the enemy. Sabers and bayonets parried and clanked; pistols and muskets cracked. Riderless horses bolted to the rear. Some of the Mountaineers tugged at the stakes and rails, but the fence remained intact. The sheltered Rebels reloaded and fired a blazing barrage. The rattling storm spread along the stone wall as several blue troopers screamed and dropped.

Kilpatrick spurred up. "Elon, see that isolated Confederate battery about two hundred yards north of the Texas defensive line?"

"Yes, that's the battery that's been dueling with Elder's battery."

"It seems vulnerable to being captured. If we can eliminate that battery, we have a clear shot at attacking Lee's rear."

"Sir, my troopers cannot reach those guns because they are on a ridge protected by infantry and a high stone wall. Attacking the stone curtain would be like attacking a Norman castle."

Kilpatrick's eyes narrowed with rage, like an attacking pit viper. He snapped. "Elon, I disagree. Your brigade has been sitting around here on Bushman's Hill since we arrived at noon. It's time to be aggressive and take the fight to the enemy."

Farnsworth glared, his face growing hot and red. *Devil be damned.* "With all due respect, General, my skirmishers and Elder's battery have been hotly engaging the Rebels since we arrived."

Captain Andrew Cunningham's shout interrupted them. "The Mountaineers are falling back, General Farnsworth."

Kilpatrick wheeled and charged toward the brigade's left flank.

Farnsworth cringed, muttering, *"Damn you, Kilpatrick."* When the West Virginians reached his lines, he would have them regroup.

Cunningham pointed. "General Kilpatrick is racing toward the Eighteenth Pennsylvania."

Farnsworth glanced up, spotting Kilpatrick riding with a rolling gait. A hellish anger pulsed in his ears. The reckless damn fool was determined to destroy his entire brigade. He spurred his mount and galloped toward the Eighteenth Pennsylvania. He arrived next to Kilpatrick as they were forming up for a charge in a clearing at the western edge of Bushman's Hill woods.

Kilpatrick shouted, "Colonel William Brinton, why in hell and damnation don't you move those troops out?"

Brinton withdrew his saber and shouted, "Charge!"

A bugler blasted "'Charge.'" The Pennsylvanians surged forward, howling.

Farnsworth stared. Rage from a deep, primitive source overtook him. "General Kilpatrick, this is the second time in three days you've bypassed me and given orders directly to my regimental commanders. When this battle is over, I'm requesting an audience with General Pleasonton to address these extreme violations of the chain of command."

Kilpatrick's fist wrapped around the reins, tugging as if he wanted to strangle the horse. "Damn you, Farnsworth, you should be more worried about attacking the enemy instead of me."

"General Kilpatrick, this attack will falter. The stone wall is too heavily defended and supported by enemy artillery."

"Damn, Farnsworth, I'm sick and tired of your excuses for not throwing your regiments forward."

He bit his lip as if he were being scolded by a headmaster. He gripped his binoculars and glared at the Pennsylvanians racing full tilt toward the stone wall, sabers drawn. The charging troopers weaved through thick underbrush and large boulders. A sheet of flames shot out from behind the stone wall and the crack of several hundred Enfield rifles filled the air. The first enemy volley was too high. Something warm and hopeful skittered through him. *Keep charging, boys.* The troopers smashed into the stone wall, inciting a rattling of fire.

The second enemy volley was on the mark.

By God's bones, this is madness.

The troopers flung off their mounts with every fourth man retiring back thirty yards, holding the horses. The dismounted troopers dove behind trees and boulders and began firing their revolvers.

Cunningham shouted, "Rebels anchoring the bottom of Big Round Top are sprinting to reinforce the Texans." The enemy volleys along the stone wall intensified. The Pennsylvanians milled out from the front and began falling back.

4:40 p.m.
Farnsworth
Eighty yards southwest from Elder's battery

The terrible tempest storming near the copse of trees was ebbing. The cries and moans of the wounded cluttering the battlefield were drowning out the rattling storm of cannons and rifles. Sweat crawled down Farnsworth's face. His brain was hissing like a cracked steam pipe. *Do something besides staring at Elder's thundering gun. Damn Kilpatrick is butchering your regiments one by one.*

Kilpatrick trod up like a banty rooster flapping its wings. He pointed at the Rebel battery firing with great spirit and shouted in a pitchy voice, "Damn, Elon, you need to attack that isolated Rebel battery."

Grit leached from him. "Sir, charging that position is worse than folly. It is certain destruction."

Kilpatrick's face flared red. "General Farnsworth, I disagree. We have a great opportunity here to rout the retreating Rebels. They are whipped. We must be aggressive and bust through their lines and attack their rear."

Farnsworth's pulse rate catapulted, pounding in his ears. He took a deep breath and choked down his anger, letting the heat lick his face. After a moment of violent silence, he said, quietly but forcefully, "General Kilpatrick, let me consult with Major John Hammond, commanding the Fifth New York cavalry."

Kilpatrick narrowed his black, boiling eyes, plainly seething with rage and contempt. A biting chill filled the muffled silence, rich with discord. After a few seconds, Kilpatrick nodded.

Farnsworth strode toward Hammond. "John, please walk with me. I want to see what chance there is for a successful cavalry charge against that enemy battery near the Bushman farm."

They lumbered twenty yards forward and halted. "Well, John?"

Hammond stared north and rubbed the back of his neck. "On our side of Plum Run is a stone fence, some of it having a few rails on top. On the opposite side of the fence is swampy ground that is heavily timbered. On the other side of Plum Run is an appalling range of boulders and rocks."

"I see the same obstacles." Farnsworth bristled. "My God, John, Kilpatrick is going to force a cavalry charge. It is too awful to think of." He wiped his face. "A charge through this terrain will slaughter the boys. They won't have a chance."

Major John Bennett glided behind his battalion holding the skirmish line in the oak covered woods. The Federal and Rebel skirmish lines popped with rifle and carbine fire.

Must talk with Bennett. He inhaled deeply, inserted his index fingers into his mouth, and shrilled a whistle. Bennett whipped around. Farnsworth waved his arm. Bennett nodded and darted up the slope of Bushman's Hill, scurrying from tree to tree like a stag chased by a pack of hounds. He pulled up and put his hands on his knees, gasping, sweat dripping from his face, and glanced up. "Please give me a moment, General."

"Sure."

Hammond pointed. "Here comes Kilpatrick."

Kilpatrick pulled up, fangs bared, looking to tear some flesh like a vindictive vulture. "God damn't, what the hell is going on?"

Bennett stood up and saluted. "Generals."

"Major Bennett," Farnsworth began, "General Kilpatrick thinks that there is a fair chance to make a successful charge. You have been up in front all day. What do you think?"

Bennett opened his mouth and gaped.

Kilpatrick leapt forward like a fighting cock outfitted with metal spurs. "The whole Rebel army is in retreat," he shrilled. "I have just heard from the right, and our cavalry there is gobbling them up by the thousands. All we must do is charge, and the enemy will throw down their arms and surrender."

Bennett flinched, plainly surprised with Kilpatrick's assertion. "Sir, I don't know about the situation on the right, but the enemy in our front is not retreating."

Kilpatrick scowled, shaking his fist. "Dammit, they would be retreating if we attacked them in force."

Farnsworth said, "Sir, General Hood's Texans are defending a stone fence on our side of Plum Run. Beyond the fence the ground is heavily timbered and swampy, filled with giant boulders and rocks."

Kilpatrick's lips tightened and his face turned bright red.

Bennett pointed. "The Texans have a strong defensive position. Any concentrated cavalry charge would be broken up by the big boulders and thick trees in front of the wall." He paused and wiped his face. "General Kilpatrick, in my opinion, no successful charge can be made against the enemy in my front."

Kilpatrick bristled and his breath rasped like a hissing cottonmouth.

Farnsworth stared at Kilpatrick's reddening face, plainly ready to explode. "General Kilpatrick, I will mount up and ride with Major Bennett and reconnoiter the ground."

Kilpatrick snarled. "Very well. Report back to me with your assessment." He stormed toward his headquarters, muttering.

"John, let's ride forward and take a look at the ground."

They rode several yards behind Bennett's skirmish line and halted. Through his binoculars he spied the repulsed West Virginians regrouping and the Pennsylvanians on their heels racing back to the Union skirmish line. His stomach knotted.

"Major, I don't see the slightest chance for a successful charge."

"I agree, General."

"Let's ride back and report to Kilpatrick."

4:50 p.m.
Farnsworth
Arriving at Kilpatrick's headquarters

A bullet whipped overhead. Cold spite welled up in Farnsworth's throat. Rebel skirmishers were hiding behind the stone fences, baiting Kilpatrick. The man was a damn fool with as much sense as a bloodsucking leech.

He nudged his horse around a boulder and trotted toward Kilpatrick, who was waving his hands like a drowning man.

"General, I reconnoitered the ground with Major Bennett and we both agreed that there is little chance for a successful charge."

Kilpatrick bellowed like a poisonous dwarf. "General Farnsworth, I'm ordering you to make another charge."

A cruel, primitive instinct flooded Farnsworth's senses. "Sir, the only regiment I have left is the First Vermont. They have but four hundred and eighty men left in the regiment." He squared his shoulders. "I regard it as simple murder to charge a regiment of infantry armed with Enfield rifles and supported by batteries with that number of men."

Kilpatrick's nostrils flared. He screeched, "The charge must be made!"

Farnsworth glared. Hell's molten fires spewed up his throat. "General, do you mean it, sir?" he shouted. "Shall I throw my handful of men over rough ground, through timber, against a brigade of infantry? The First Vermont has already been cut half to pieces skirmishing this afternoon. These men are too good to kill."

Kilpatrick's face contorted, spearing Farnsworth with a venomous glare. The glowering silence lasted a few moments—the type of vindictive silence when a superior fires a subordinate for dereliction of duty. The long-hardened line of Kilpatrick's mouth cracked slightly open, baring his teeth. He shouted, "Do you refuse to obey my orders? If you are afraid to lead this charge, I will lead it."

Farnsworth bristled with rage. He rose in his stirrups. "Take that back! I ask no man to lead my troops forward." Every hair on his head stood erect.

Kilpatrick's glance, full of bitter disdain and feverish contempt, shot through Farnsworth's noble heart. This was a point of honor. Kilpatrick was calling him a coward, and no man called him a yellowbelly. The general's spiteful words were dishonoring—skewering, pit-viper slights that demanded satisfaction, even while his sinister smile grew wider. Farnsworth gripped his saber handle.

Kilpatrick's face gleamed with a fickle sneer. "I did not mean it." Unmistakable insincerity and a vexed little laugh laced his razor tone.

Farnsworth glared into the savage silence. His heart pounded in his ears, ticking off the moments. After several heartbeats, his voice hoarse with angry scorn, he said, "General, if you order the charge, I will lead it, but you must take the awful responsibility."

Kilpatrick nudged his mount closer. He whispered, "This is the moment my division can seal the fate of the Rebels. I'm not going to let it pass."

"I was not thinking of myself, sir! I was thinking of my troopers." His throat tightened, his eyes raking Kilpatrick. A silence fell, as if he had committed treason and a jury had imposed the death sentence. Fueled by Kilpatrick's smug smirk, the damning silence lingered until Farnsworth threw down the gauntlet. "I will obey your order."

Kilpatrick bared his teeth. "By thunder!" he shouted, petulant. "I take the responsibility." He half swung in his saddle and pointed. "Captain Estes will charge with you."

4:56 p.m.
Farnsworth
Addressing the First Vermont Battalion commanders
West side of Bushman's Hill

Farnsworth blinked, swallowing back tears. His mind was spinning. How many Vermonters would be murdered in a few moments because of Kilpatrick's vanity? By God's bones, Kilpatrick was not worth a turd. He dismounted in front of the First Vermont Regiment. He glanced at Lieutenant Colonel Addison Preston, Major William Wells, Major John Bennett, Captain Henry Parsons, and Captain Llewellyn Estes, standing in a semi-circle. They stared with a cold steadiness.

"Gentlemen, General Kilpatrick has ordered the First Vermont to charge and take the enemy battery near the Bushman farm."

"General, I would rather charge into hell than in there!" Wells objected. "The terrain is not suitable for a cavalry charge. The Texans have thrown back both the West Virginians and the Pennsylvanians. Do you expect a different outcome with our charge?"

He shook his head. "I objected. Kilpatrick and I had a heated exchange. But I could not change his mind. He gave me a lawful order that I must obey. He is taking full responsibility for this attack."

Preston asked sharply, "What are your orders for the attack?"

"We will use the same battalions as we did at the Battle of Hanover. Captain Parsons will lead First Battalion, Major Wells will lead Second Battalion, and Major Bennett will command

Third Battalion. Third Battalion will be dismounted and act as a reserve."

Preston said, "I will remain with the dismounted Third Battalion." He pointed. "I will position the battalion behind that stone wall. If you're repulsed, I will support the retreat or I will mount a charge if there's an opportunity to exploit success."

Farnsworth nodded. "Very well. I will ride with Major Wells's battalion."

"May I ride with you, General?" asked Captain Estes.

"Yes." Farnsworth paused and scanned the five officers. He inhaled a deep breath, letting his ribcage swell with pride. "I'm proud that you are in my brigade, and I bid each of you good luck and farewell." His breathing quickened as he stepped forward and shook each officer's hand. He stepped back and studied each face, searing the image into his mind. How many would survive this suicidal attack? Would he? A vise tightened around his chest. "Let's mount up."

He strode toward his mount, took the reins from Captain Cunningham, and slung himself into the saddle. He swallowed hard and retied his white neckerchief. His pulse quickened. "Stay close, Andrew, and hopefully we can make it through this charge."

He twisted in his saddle and spotted Parson's battalion forming up behind him. A lump formed in his throat. He nudged his mount into a trot and followed Major Wells, riding westward along the crest.

4:48 p.m. (Eight minutes earlier)
Captain Henry Parsons
Lower brow of Bushman's Hill

Parsons leaned forward on his Morgan's withers and whispered, "You're going to do great, Firefly. Morgans are the princes among horses, a fearless breed built for strength, speed, and endurance. I'm proud of you, girl."

Sergeant George Duncan reined up. "The four companies of battalion are formed up." Duncan grinned. "Have you seen Captain Oliver Cushman's white duck jacket?"

"No, but here he comes now." Cushman pulled up, hatless and wearing a white duck jacket trimmed in yellow braid.

Parsons pointed. "Oliver, what the damn hell are you wearing?"

Cushman grinned crookedly. "It's my fighting jacket."

"Rubbish. You look like a two-penny actor in that garb."

Cushman laughed. "A lady sent this to me, and said it was made with her own hands, and no Rebel bullet could pierce it. It may be a good day to try my magic chain mail."

Parsons frowned. "You're making yourself a conspicuous target. I strongly encourage you not to wear it into battle."

Duncan chuckled. "Captain Cushman, I respectfully request the honor of riding next to you during the charge. Staying close to you, I won't be a target. If that is a magical jacket, then neither one of us will catch a bullet."

"By all means," Cushman replied. "Please ride next to me."

"Oliver," Parsons said, "where is your cap?"

"Here it is." Cushman reached into his white jacket and removed a blue kepi cap that had a white handkerchief attached to the back of it. "I turned it into a Havelock. I want to keep the sun off my neck." He clapped it on his head and the white handkerchief flapped down upon his neck and shoulders.

Parsons shook his head. "It's clear you're going with your dashing Dartmouth swagger today."

5:00 p.m.
Farnsworth
Riding toward Major Wells's Second Battalion
West side of Bushman's Hill

Farnsworth's heart slugged against his ribs as he trotted up in front of Major Wells and the Second Battalion. Sixty yards to the east were Captain Parsons and his battalion. Behind Major Wells the Green Mountain troopers were snapping their headbands under their chins and winding their saber knots around their wrists.

Major Wells shouted, "Columns of four!"

The troopers lined up in columns and lifted their glittering blades until the flat edges rested against their right shoulders.

The flashing blades glittered like snow sparkle in the green canopy cover.

"William," Farnsworth said, "are you ready to give them the devil?"

Major Wells's blue eyes shined. "We're ready, General."

Farnsworth unsheathed his saber and pointed it toward the Texans. His heart raced. Despite the sun hovering over him like a hot shroud, he shivered with the same fearful chill he had felt when Kilpatrick ordered the First Vermont to attack. Was he justified in disobeying Kilpatrick's order? Perhaps. A suicide charge made tactical sense if there were no other options. But dying for the sake of dying for a pompous and vain fool whose tactical sense was in the shitter was beyond idiotic. It was criminal.

But being called a coward tugged at his checkered heartstrings. Outrage flooded through him like a dam break. *Damn that son of a bitch.* He would lead the charge and then afterwards file charges against Kill-Cavalry.

A trembling shudder shot through him and he shouted, "Give 'em hell, Vermonters!"

He nudged his mare forward into a walk, onto a wooded path cutting through the thick trees. Behind him branches bent and snapped, and trees groaned and creaked as if a brisk wind were blowing through. Out of the corner of his eyes he spied Major Wells riding a fourth of a horse length behind. On his other side rode Bugler Gilbert Buckman. A thick horizontal branch lay ahead and he lowered his saber and dropped his head as he whisked underneath it. This terrain was no place for a mounted charge.

He shot a sharp glance to his right where a great blue serpent sporting hundreds of flickering steel dorsal fins snaked down the hill through the thick woods. Parsons's battalion erupted in a resounding cheer. Parsons screamed and brandished his saber as he burst ahead of the charging Vermonters. An unexpected touch of warmth—and something that felt almost like hope—stirred in Farnsworth's agonized soul. *Best of luck, Captain Parsons.*

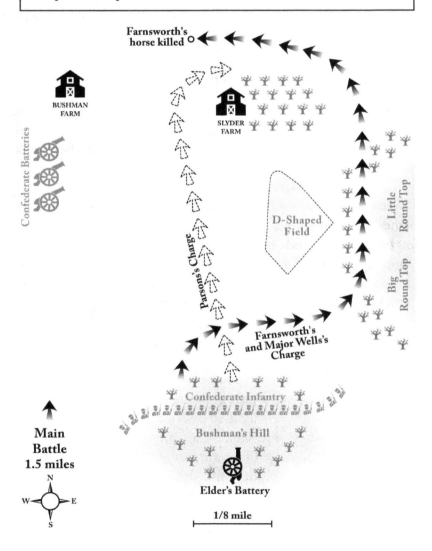

South Cavalry Field

Initial Charge: Parsons Goes First/Wells and Farnsworth Go Second

July 3, 1863

5:03 p.m. - 5:27 p.m.

Farnsworth's horse killed

BUSHMAN FARM

SLYDER FARM

Confederate Batteries

Parsons's Charge

D-Shaped Field

Little Round Top

Big Round Top

Farnsworth's and Major Wells's Charge

Confederate Infantry

Bushman's Hill

Main Battle 1.5 miles

N
W — E
S

Elder's Battery

1/8 mile

5:03 p.m.
Captain Henry Parsons[13] leading the battalion charge
Bushman's Hill

Parsons raced at the head of First Battalion through the thick trees of Bushman's Hill, eyeing the dismounted Rebel skirmishers ahead. The Confederates aimed their rifles. *Crack*. Bullets whipped by and thudded into the large oaks. The enemy skirmishers started skedaddling. The slower Rebels turned and shouted, "Halt, don't trample us. Halt."

Parsons pointed his saber. "Throw down your rifles."

The Rebel skirmishers dropped their rifles and raised their hands.

He whirled about and shouted, "Lieutenant Stephan Clark. Have Sergeant Willard Farrington from Company L round up the enemy skirmishers and turn them over to Major Bennett's dismounted Third Battalion."

Lieutenant Clark said, "Yes, sir."

Parsons spurred his Morgan past the surrendering skirmishers and swung past the timberline into the blistering sun. Sergeant Duncan rode beside him. On the other side of Duncan galloped Captain Cushman, adorned in his biblical garb. The blinding light made his white coat shimmer like an angelic host, a touch of wonderment gracing the gates of hell.

Duncan shouted, "Stone wall. It's low. We can leap it." The sergeant surged ahead, waving his saber. Cushman kept pace, screaming.

Parson's vision narrowed and he sawed at the reins. Countless rifles cracked, flashing flaming sheets of lead. Bullets ripped overhead. Thick smoke engulfed the stone wall, cloaking the charging Vermonters. He slapped his mount's neck. "Come on, Firefly. Fly." Firefly surged forward, extended her neck, brought her forelegs up, and exploded into the air, sailing high over the stone wall. She landed smoothly and surged forward. Hot lead breathed by, singing death's song.

"A beautiful jump, Firefly," he muttered.

---

13 See Appendix A

His eyes riveted on the white buildings of the Slyder farm, three hundred yards northward. *That's the goal.* He charged straight ahead toward the white house and barn. Duncan rode stirrup to stirrup next to him, brandishing his saber. All senses vanished except for sight.

Rebel artillery at the Bushman farm rumbled and shuddered as the roar of flying shells arched toward Elder's battery. Parsons's body was sweat-drenched. His mind was whirling with images of a plan. When they arrived at the Slyder farm, he would halt the charge and reform the battalion. He spurred Firefly, gliding gracefully across the field. The self-made wind buffeted his cheeks and whistled an upbeat tempo in his ears. Maybe Kilpatrick was right. The Vermonters could gallop all the way to Gettysburg and roll up the enemy's right flank. He turned his head. The battalion was retaining its formation. Hope swelled in his chest like a storm surge. If they clashed with the Confederates at this speed, they could crash through them in one solid mass and sweep them away. His eyes narrowed. Where was the Rebel infantry?

A thunderous crack. Artillery. He ducked and his heart fisted. Screaming shells exploded and whizzing fragments sailed. Troopers shrieked from behind and thudded to the ground like harvested trees. He glanced left toward the Bushman farm. Smoke bellowed southwest from six broad-mouthed Napoleons positioned two hundred yards away. The discharges had torn wide gaps through the ranks. He spurred Firefly again and again, tearing her flanks as a riderless Morgan raced by. Dread threatened to turn to despair. He couldn't let it. The big guns would reload and fire again in thirty seconds or so.

Parsons screamed, "Come on, boys!"

He galloped past the Slyder farm, turned east, and followed a split-rail fence running behind the stone house. He reined up north of the Slyder barn. Captain Cushman and Sergeant Duncan pulled up beside him.

"That was a hell of a charge," Duncan said, and pointed. "Captain Cushman, your sweat stains are turning your white jacket yellow." He laughed. "You're not turning into a yellow streaking skedaddler?"

Cushman flashed a smile. "Look, no bullet holes in my magical jacket."

Parsons twisted in his saddle as the rest of the First Battalion arrived. "Sergeant Duncan, how many men did we lose?"

"My guess is that we are missing about ten troopers," Duncan answered.

His spirit seethed, burning with anger for his men. "Let the battalion rest here for a moment as they form up."

Parsons pointed southeast. "Sergeant Duncan, that's Little Round Top and its crest is occupied by Union infantry." He pointed further southeast. "That's Big Round Top and the summit is also occupied by Union infantry. My guess is that Rebel infantry are positioned about three hundred yards up from the base of the two slopes, facing the Union infantry."

Duncan pointed westward toward Emmitsburg Road. "General Kilpatrick wants us to take those Rebel artillery batteries on the Bushman farm. What's the plan, Captain?"

He swung in the saddle and gazed. A ruffling chill sliced down his spine. One thousand yards of open fields to his west. He counted ten Rebel Napoleons and one dismounted infantry regiment protecting the enemy big guns. His heart quaked. A cannister cannonade could shred his entire battalion.

Cushman said, "Kilpatrick's order is as disastrous as Lord Cardigan ordering the notorious charge of the Light Brigade against well-defended Russian artillery batteries."

Parsons bristled. "Both Kilpatrick and Lord Cardigan have as much brains as my boot." He turned to Cushman. "No, Oliver. I will not replicate the disastrous British charge into the mouths of the Rebel cannons."

"I appreciate that, Henry."

"Even if we don't charge the Rebel cannons, we have the same problem as the Light Brigade," Cushman said. "After the British charged, they retreated through a gauntlet of enemy fire."

Duncan said, "If we retrace our path, the Rebel artillery and infantry to our west near the Bushman farm will decimate our flank."

Anger wedged itself in his throat. "Let's ride southeast along this farm road and hug the base of the Round Tops and hopefully avoid the flanking fire from the Bushman farm."

"What about the Rebel infantry sitting on the lower slopes of the Round Tops?" Cushman asked.

"My hope is that they stay there until we have ridden past." Parsons glanced down the farm road cutting through trees and leading toward the Big Round Top. *Good, no Rebels.* "Let's move out. No bugle calls."

Duncan said, "We're ready to move out, sir."

Parsons made a violent grimace and turned to Cushman. "Oliver, I want you to ride with the rear companies in case we get ambushed."

Oliver saluted and wheeled toward the rear.

Parsons waved his saber forward and started trotting down the farm lane. Harnesses jingled and hooves pattered on the dirt. A shivery sigh escaped him. They crossed Plum Run with a furtive splash of hoof-deep water swirling lazily around hand-sized rocks. Ahead was a slight wooded bend in the road, curving to the right around a copse of trees. A low stone wall wrapped around the trees. He nudged his mount, cleared the stone wall, and skirted out of the timber.

Duncan shouted, "Captain Parsons. Rebels on our left!"

At the edge of his vision, thirty paces away, a Rebel infantry regiment was darting pell-mell down the slope of Little Round Top. They aimed and fired a random volley. He held his breath. Bullets zipped overhead. *No screams. They fired too high.* Smoke covered the Rebels as they reloaded.

"Forward, men!" he shouted.

He leaned forward and hugged Firefly's neck. Another rattling volley erupted. *Pat. Pat. Pat.* Vermonters screamed as bullets pierced their uniforms. He rounded the bend and halted in the cover of thick trees.

Duncan reined up. "Captain Parsons, the troopers broke open like a woman's hand fan. Captain Cushman and the rear companies are not with us. They fell back when we were ambushed."

He gripped his binoculars and scanned southward. "Sergeant, I've spotted Farnsworth and Wells's Second Battalion crossing our track and riding eastward toward Big Round Top."

"My guess is that General Farnsworth didn't want to ride along our track to the Slyder farm." Duncan pointed. "The enemy artillery and infantry regiment supporting the batteries would have racked their left flank with a murderous fire."

5:15 p.m.
Captain Oliver Cushman
Riding with the rear companies

Panic crept up through the base of Cushman's skull. Grinding his teeth, he led the rear companies of Parson's battalion around a wooded bend. Cracking fire greeted them.

"An ambuscade!" he shouted. "Pull up!"

He spotted several glinting graybacks darting down Big Round Top toward the billowing smoke. Rebels were rushing toward the middle of Parsons's column. Every hair on his neck stood erect. *No way we can follow Parson's forward companies.* He turned his horse and waved his saber.

"Vermonters, follow me!"

He wheeled his Morgan about and galloped back up the farm road. Cracking pistol and rifle fire echoed from behind. His heart pounded in his ears. Sounded like Parsons's companies were in a hot fight. At the edge of the timber, he spotted a cross fence. A great place to reform the rear companies. He reined up at the cross fence and waved his saber. Two companies of the First Battalion rode up and halted.

"We will reform here," he shouted. "Stay alert; the Rebels are rushing down Big Round Top like angry red ants."

5:05 p.m. (Ten minutes earlier)
Farnsworth
Leading the Second Battalion

Farnsworth nudged his mount off the crest of Bushman's Hill and dribbled down a winding path tunneling through a shady canopy of trees. He cringed. The goat path was a meandering swath created by a torrent of pent-up water pouring through a breach and swirling around fallen logs and large boulders. Rebel vedettes could be hiding anywhere. Why, for God's sake, had Kilpatrick ordered his troopers to charge through this rugged terrain?

A beam of sunlight sliced through the forest glades, glinting off Wells's saber. He caught a flash of Captain Andrew Cunningham riding nearly stirrup to stirrup with Wells.

"The woods are thinning," Wells said. "Let's trot and get out of this hell hole."

Wells edged forward and Farnsworth snapped the reins and kept pace. *Crack.* He ducked and his spine seized up. Enemy bullets ripped through the trees, snapping branches and scattering leaves over the troopers like carnival confetti. His mount neighed and pulled at the bit.

"The Rebels aimed too high," Cunningham said. "No casualties."

"Let's dash forward before the Rebels find their aim." Farnsworth pointed his sword. "William, is your battalion ready to charge?"

"We're ready, General."

Farnsworth nudged his horse and trotted through the parting oaks and the cover of the woods. The brutal sun was blinding him. He squinted and lowered his hat, spotting an opening in a stone fence leading to the open ground.

He twisted toward his bugler. "Corporal Buckman, 'Charge!'"

Buckman snapped his horn to his lips and blew the piercing notes. The four company buglers of Second Battalion blew their horns, matching Buckman's shrilling notes.

Farnsworth spurred his horse and the mare snorted as she thumped the ground. Blood pounded in his ears. Was the gap in the stone fence wide enough for two horses?

Wells pulled even and shouted, "It's wide enough for us."

Perhaps. He held his breath and they shot through the fence gap together. He pulled up and halted beyond the gap.

Wells shouted, "Another stone wall."

He stared at the second stone wall protecting the Texans. Major Wells yelled and surged forward. A bursting crack and flashing yellow sheets of musket fire erupted from the second stone wall, connecting to a barricade of piled-up logs and rocks. A pelting storm of minié balls zipped overhead. Wells's mount jumped the fence and raced northward, followed by the lead elements of the battalion. Musket smoke engulfed the stone wall.

Farnsworth wheeled his horse around to face the charging Vermonters. A crazed horse rocketed by and leaped the fence. He waved his sword and shouted, "Stone wall. Stone wall."

The troopers raced forward and sailed over the wall. The Rebel musket fire slowed; the smoke cloaking the stone fence was clearing. Ahead of them, a roaring wail echoed. The Vermonters had pierced the Rebel line and the Texans were scattering. Farnsworth's pulse quickened. Half of the Second Battalion had cleared the fence. Time to catch up with Major Wells. He trotted south for fifteen yards and turned his horse toward the stone wall.

He patted the mare's neck. "Here we go." He leaned forward and the mount leapt over the stone wall. The mare landed stiff-legged, jolting him airborne momentarily. He and the horse bounced up and down for twenty yards before regaining a semblance of a smoother gait as they galloped forward into the open field. Seven hundred yards to the northwest, near the Bushman farm, the enemy's artillery guns thundered, blasting canister at Major Wells and the forward elements of the battalion. Rebel infantry guarding the artillery fired their long-range Enfield rifles. Wells's column swerved to the right, crossing Parsons's track and racing toward the safety of Big Round Top.

Farnsworth veered and raced at an oblique angle toward Wells, heading for the base of Big Round Top. The wind rushed past, and the ground blew by beneath the racketing roll of his horse's hooves. *Got to catch Wells before he enters the woods.* His chest heaved like a fireplace bellows, blowing rasping breaths out of his parched throat.

He narrowed his eyes and spotted Plum Run ahead. "William!"

Major Wells looked over his shoulder and slowed to a canter.

He pulled up even with Wells.

"General," Wells said, "I was worried about you."

"I wanted to make sure the remaining troopers behind me could spot the second stone fence that was shrouded in smoke." He wiped his face. "What's your plan?"

"Ride to the base of Big Round Top to escape the Rebel artillery batteries and rifle fire on our left flank. Then turn north and skirt along its base, behind the enemy battleline facing toward the Round Tops, and head for the Slyder farm and beyond. And then we can conduct a flanking attack against the Rebel batteries near the Bushman farm."

"Sounds good."

He and Wells pitched over Plum Run and raced two hundred yards eastward near the base of Big Round Top. Hundreds of horses thundered behind them. He glanced over his shoulder. The battalion galloped in a wrinkled line as if following a meandering creek. Wells shouted, "Let's turn north."

Wells wheeled to the left and Farnsworth followed him. He cast his eyes sideways, heart fluttering. Rebel infantry had turned about and were scampering down Big Round Top.

"William, Rebel soldiers on our right!"

Wells twisted in his saddle. "We can outrun them!" Wells leaned forward on his mount as if racing a quarter horse. Wells shot ahead two horse lengths and Farnsworth hugged his mount's mane, keeping pace.

Rebel fire cracked and bullets split the air. He followed Wells northward for five hundred yards. Ahead was Devil's Den and Rebel infantry sitting on top of the giant rocks, firing their muskets.

He shouted, "William, turn left."

Wells turned to the left and they galloped westward. Ahead was Plum Run; they splashed through it. One hundred yards south was the Slyder farm. Enemy cannons thundered from the Bushman house. Several shells shrieked, sputtered, and swooped down, splattering the ground. It was as if lightning smote the Vermonters. His horse screeched and tumbled. His stomach constricted and he arched skyward. For a moment he was suspended in midair. He gritted his teeth and crashed headfirst into the ground. A numbing blackness swallowed his brain like a violent windshear.

Grogginess surrounded him. He was floating in a dense fog. A strong hand gripped his shoulder and shook him. A distant voice was shouting. "General, are you alright? General, can you move?"

He gasped in half breaths and fought to open his eyelids toward the voice. A blurry Major Wells was shaking his curled body. Sour puke retched up his throat. His head pounded, his ears rang, and his foggy brain felt as if a morning mist swirled inside his skull.

Wells put a canteen to his lips. "General, take a sip of water."

He took a swig of warm water, swished it over his parched tongue, and spit.

"General, we have to get you up or you will be captured."

He shook his head and remembered. He was leading the Vermonters in a cavalry charge. He whispered, "William, please help me up."

"Corporal David Truman, help me," Wells shouted. Truman dismounted and grabbed Farnsworth's right shoulder. Wells grabbed the left one and they lifted him up. A razor-sharp claw tore through him.

"Corporal Truman, let's put the general on your horse."

Truman lifted Farnsworth's left boot into the stirrup. A sharp hammering beat at the base of his skull. The major gripped his holster belt. "General, mount the horse."

He pressed his left boot down and Wells heaved from behind. He lurched upwards and landed hard in the saddle. His heart pounded against his ribs, and his breath rasped.

"General, I'm going to have a small detachment accompany you back the way we came. I'm going to continue the attack westward against the enemy batteries. If I'm unsuccessful, I'm going to ride back on the track we took to get here."

He nodded as solace flooded his mind. The attack would continue. He muttered, "Good luck, Major Wells."

A squadron of galloping horses approached from the Slyder house. He twisted in his saddle and spotted a trooper wearing a white coat leading several Vermonters. The officer reined up.

Captain Cushman saluted. "General Farnsworth and Major Wells. I'm leading the rear squadron of the First Battalion, consisting of companies E and F."

"Oliver, what the hell is the white jacket all about?" Wells said.

"It's a magical jacket a lady friend made for me."

Wells shook his head. "How did you find us?"

"I spotted you riding along the base of Big Round Top. I was reforming my squadron in the woods to your left when you rode by.

"Where is Captain Parsons and the rest of First Battalion?"

"Captain Parsons ordered me to ride with the rear troopers of the battalion. He led the front troopers after we crossed behind the Slyder house, trying to make our way to the base of Big Round Top. We rode into an ambush and my rear squadron was separated from Parsons's forward squadron."

"Okay. I'm glad your jacket is magical because I want you and your squadron to escort General Farnsworth back to the base of Little Round Top and then ride south to our lines. General Farnsworth's horse was killed, and he hit his head during the fall."

Farnsworth shook his head. "I'm fine. I feel a little groggy and my head is pounding, but I can ride and fight."

Captain Llewellyn Estes reined up.

Farnsworth said, "Llewellyn, Captain Cushman and his squadron are going to escort me back the way we came. I want you to ride with us."

"Will do, sir."

He turned to Major Wells. "Good luck, William, charging those Rebel batteries." He twisted his saddle. "Let's ride, Captain Cushman."

They rode eastward back on the track they had taken earlier. He sucked shallow gulps of air, fighting to ease the stabbing pain below his breastbone. *Must have cracked some ribs.* He blinked twice and stared at Big Round Top, blurry like a cloudy moon.

64

First Vermont — Friday, July 3

5:27 p.m.
Major William Wells
North of the Slyder farm
Charging the Rebel batteries on the Bushman farm

The early evening sun was sliding toward South Mountain. Its stubborn heat refused to abate, and Wells felt like he was roasting inside a blazing Dutch oven. Bullets whined at the base of Big Round Top. *God, I hope General Farnsworth makes it back safely to Bushman's Hill.* He winced. Departing with Captain Cushman's escort squadron, the general appeared dazed and uncoordinated. Wells squinted into the western sun hovering over South Mountain. The hooves of his detachment clattered behind him. Confederate artillery batteries were positioned five hundred yards southwest on Warfield Ridge, near the Bushman farm.

Wells pointed his saber. "Sergeant Samuel Dowling. Let's circle northwest and then turn south and charge the left flank of the Rebel batteries."

"Yes, sir."

"When we turn south, we will charge at a full gallop before the Rebel infantry regiment straddling Emmitsburg Road has time to turn on us."

He rode northwest, letting the mare's swinging shoulders slide against his knees. He flicked his gaze toward Emmitsburg Road, and a thorny vine knotted around his throat. The enemy infantry straddling the road were sprinting toward the Rebel batteries. *Damn.* About eighty glimmering Confederate bayonets swayed like a rippling wave.

Dowling shouted, "At one hundred yards, let's slow and re-form from a marching column to an attack formation."

"Agreed." Wells led the Vermonters south for several rods, and nearing the charge line he raised his sword straight up and slowed to a canter.

Dowling wheeled in his saddle. "Form up for the charge."

Wells gripped his binoculars and scanned the meadow leading to the batteries. It was uphill and uneven ground. Dread swept over him. *Don't have time to reload the revolvers.*

"Sergeant Dowling, I'm tired of being a target in a shooting gallery. Let's drive 'em in."

Dowling turned to the troopers. "Let's bloody our swords!" he bellowed.

The Vermonters formed up on either side of him into a long line, waving their swords and yelling.

Wells shouted, "Bugler, 'Charge.'"

Metallic notes shrilled. His blood boiled as he gripped his saber. He gritted his teeth and surged forward. Sergeants shouted and the attack line pitched forward, troopers spurring and rolling in their saddles. He spotted a red battle flag and eighty Rebel infantry soldiers, halting beyond the batteries, forming in a straight line, aiming their Enfield rifles. His heart was racing. He glanced left and right, and the galloping Vermonters' line remained straight, charging like a pack of ravenous wolves. No one had faltered. Pride for his men came rushing over him.

Rifles cracked and flames leaped from the enemy line. Screams erupted on either side of him. Anger seared his throat. A riderless horse raced past him and galloped into the Rebel line. The enemy fire in this second charge was more deadly than the first charge against the Texans. The rifle volley had sliced the Vermont line into several small factions. A few troopers sabered their way through the enemy line and hurtled toward the big guns. His faction swept him up and he flowed to the right. The remaining factions split to the left and some scampered toward a skirt of timbers two hundred yards away.

"Sergeant Dowling, these attacks are suicide. We've been riding and charging for forty-five minutes. Let's get the hell out of here and stop slaughtering our boys."

"I agree, Major."

He shouted, "Bugler, 'Retreat.'"

A piercing retreat echoed across the meadow. He wheeled and rode southeast. Several flashes drew his gaze toward the second stone fence the Texans had defended during the first charge. He spotted several graybacks rushing from Big Round Top toward the Texans. His breath caught in his throat. The Texans' thin skirmish line during the breakout charge was being reinforced. *No escape to the south through the Texans.*

"Sergeant Dowling, let's ride east and angle for the corner where Plum Run runs between Big Round Top and Bushman's Hill."

"Right behind you, Major. And beware of Rebel skirmishers at the bottom of Big Round Top when we enter the woods."

Wells aimed for the southern meadow of the Slyder farm, where they had crossed eastward toward Big Round Top during the first assault.

A screeching wolf cry erupted ahead in the woods, and rifles cracked and flashed. He spotted a forest of steel as the Vermonters dashed through the trees, yelling and slashing.

Dowling shouted, "I spotted Major Bennett. Rebel skirmishers are tangling with the Vermonters' reserve battalion."

Thank God for Bennett ordering Third Battalion forward.

Dowling screamed and bolted ahead. Wells spurred his mount and galloped toward the sergeant, racing through trees. Twenty yards ahead, a mounted Rebel held a pistol to the head of Private Harry Sheldon of Company M. Wells pulled hard on the reins and rocked backward. His horse slid to a stop.

"You traitorous devil!" Dowling bellowed, shrilling with blood lust. He extended his saber skyward and lunged downward, slicing the Rebel from neck to gut. The Confederate screamed as his bowels tumbled out. Dowling wheeled and charged a dismounted Rebel. The grayback turned and sprinted toward a big oak. Dowling stood in his stirrups and raised his saber, slick with blood, high overhead. He swore and swung the saber down like a medieval battle axe and split the Rebel from his skull through his face and into his shoulder.

Wells's mouth gaped. *My God.* Dowling had halved the Rebel.

Dowling wheeled about and shouted, "Are you hurt, Harry?"
Private Sheldon shook his head. "No, I don't think so."

Major Wells rode up to Sheldon and Dowling. Dowling dismounted and wiped his blade across the trouser of one of the dead Rebels. The sergeant had arrived in the nick of time to save Private Sheldon.

Dowling glanced up. "Major Wells, Harry is my best friend. I couldn't stand the thought of his death."

"Sergeant Dowling, that was quite a display of savage swordsmanship," Wells remarked. Let's keep moving toward Big Round Top. Private Sheldon, you ride with my troopers."

"Yes, sir," Sheldon said.

65

Farnsworth — Friday, July 3

5:27 p.m.
General Farnsworth's splinter detachment
Racing from Slyder farm toward Big Round Top

Cobwebs floated inside Farnsworth's head, and a fever seared his face. His breathing was heavy, his eyes blurry. A tremor of fear drummed through his body. He felt like he was near the edge of rashness. Impulses controlled his addled brain. Damn, if he made it through this charge, he was going to brain Kilpatrick.

Jolting pain unsteadied him as he led the splinter detachment east on the Slyder farm lane. On his left, Captain Cushman's spoony white jacket flapped in the breeze, like sheets drying on a clothesline. He was sucking wind and his head pounded as if a bell clapper swung side to side, clanging against the inside of his skull. They crossed Plum Run and followed the dirt road into a thick wood. Big, blurry oaks rippled like heat waves as they rounded a bend.

"General," Cushman said, "on your right about one hundred yards is where we were ambushed by the Fourth Alabama infantry. The Rebels were positioned just beyond the northern stone-fence line of a D-shaped field."

Farnsworth twisted in his saddle. "Be ready boys! Let's gallop." He turned to his bugler. "No bugle calls."

Wary and cautious, they half-galloped down the dirt road toward Big Round Top. The road turned south. Ahead was Bushman's Hill and Kilpatrick's division. His thoughts careened about in his addled brain. General Law's infantry brigades were hugging the bottom of the hill. Ahead one hundred yards was a D-shaped stone-walled field they had passed riding north during the first charge. If they could get past the walled field, they would be almost to the safety of their lines.

5:28 p.m.
Captain Henry Parsons, leading half of his battalion
One hundred fifty yards west of the D-shaped field

Parsons spotted the Vermont regimental flag fluttering as the vanguard approached from the north. Lieutenant Colonel Addison Preston reined up.

"Henry," Preston said, "General Farnsworth was unhorsed a couple yards north of the Slyder house. Captain Cushman and some of his troopers are escorting Farnsworth back down the track that the general took when he rode north toward Little Round Top. I want you to ride south and then curve back toward the D-shaped field. You're to provide additional troopers for Farnsworth's small detachment."

"Yes, sir." He turned to Sergeant George Duncan. "George, form up the squadron."

Parsons turned to Lieutenant Stephen Clark. "Stephen, we are going to advance in a column of fours. I want your Company F to be the third company in the column. Your company will act as a ready reserve to respond to any contingencies that may pop up."

"Yes, sir." Clark saluted and departed.

"Captain, the three companies are ready to move out," Duncan reported.

Parsons's hands gripped the reins tight as he led the First Battalion squadron through the woods. He turned to Duncan. "Sergeant, let's ride south for two hundred yards. When we pass the left flank of the Fifteenth Alabama skirmisher line, we will turn east toward Big Round Top. When we arrive at the southern end of the D-shaped Field we will turn north and ride along the western edge of the field."

"I'm riding ahead to mark the turn toward Big Round Top." Duncan dashed through the trees.

The column proceeded south. He spotted Duncan and his mount standing still and staring toward Big Round Top. He reined up as rifles cracked and men screamed. Great flaky streams of fire and white banks of convolving smoke blanketed the base of the mount.

Duncan pointed. "Major Wells and his troopers are attacking the Fifteenth Alabama main battle line defending Big Round Top."

"Let's ride to support General Farnsworth before he tangles with the Fifteenth Alabama. Bugler, 'Charge'!"

He clapped his spurs and dashed toward Big Round Top. The horse's wind, like his own, ran ragged as they pounded toward Wells's troopers sabering and firing their pistols. Rebel bayonets glimmered in the western sun. *Maybe the sun will blind them as we approach.* Several cracking pops. A bullet whizzed over-head. Flames and smoke erupted from the boulders and rocks. Rebel sharpshooters had spotted his squadron. He cursed under his breath. The graybacks fired and peppered the air over his troopers. A steady Rebel fire began whipping at his Vermonters. Desperation made any scrap of possibility look like hope. Even the relentless heat.

Through the smoke he spotted the south end of the D-Shape field. He shouted, "Sergeant Duncan, veer left." He pulled on the reins and wheeled his horse.

A rifle cracked and a trooper shouted, "I'm hit."

Damn. Parsons galloped north along the stone wall of the D-shaped field on his right. The stone wall streamed by like a passing train. As he sprinted along the narrow lane along the stone wall of the D-shaped field, grayback skirmishers threw up the butts of their rifles and surrendered. He twisted in his saddle and glanced at Vermonters pulling out of the column and rounding up the Rebel prisoners. He narrowed his eyes down the sloping field and spotted the north end of the stone wall.

Duncan shouted, "Look, Captain. That's General Farnsworth and Captain Cushman at the northeast corner of the D-shaped field. See Cushman's white jacket? And the general's white neck-erchief flapping in the breeze?"

Parsons's eyes flicked to the white jacket. His pulse pitched forward like a hurled spear. "You're right. Let's leap the wall and join them."

He wheeled to the right and glided over the stone wall into the open D-shaped field.

Duncan rode up next to him. "Sir, the Fifteenth Alabama battle line at the bottom of the D-shaped field is swinging away from Wells's troopers and wheeling toward us."

Parsons swallowed hard. A horde of Rebels were darting toward the south end of the D-shaped field.

Duncan said, "When they are in position, they will block an escape at the bottom of the enclosed field."

Anxious torment gripped him. "We will ride with Farnsworth's troopers and cut our way through the enemy."

5:35 p.m.
Farnsworth
Approaching the D-shaped field

Farnsworth heaved ragged breaths and powered south toward the D-shaped field. He tensed his jaw but was unable to ease his splitting headache. He felt like he was adrift in rising sea swells, bobbing and plummeting in the melee. He aimed for the eastern side of the stone wall that ran parallel to Big Round Top.

Cushman shouted, "General, that's Captain Parsons and his squadron leaping into the D-shaped field on the western side of the stone wall."

Galloping near the eastern side of the stone wall, Farnsworth shot a glance to his right at Parson's column racing into the open field. Parsons pulled even on the opposite side of the stone wall about two hundred paces away. Good. Reinforcements. He sucked in a deep breath.

He shouted, "Captain Cushman. Charge!"

He raised his saber and raced up the sloping D-shaped field. He glanced off to his right and Parson's column erupted into a yell and charged with sabers raised.

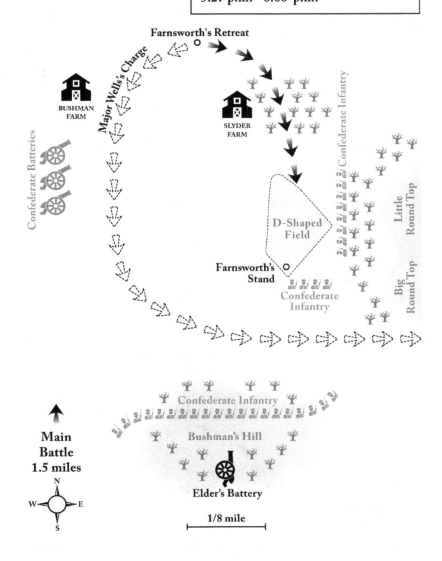

South Cavalry Field
Farnsworth's Retreat, Wells's Charge
July 3, 1863
5:27 p.m. - 6:00 p.m.

Farnsworth's Retreat

Major Wells's Charge

BUSHMAN FARM

Confederate Batteries

SLYDER FARM

Confederate Infantry

D-Shaped Field

Farnsworth's Stand

Confederate Infantry

Little Round Top

Big Round Top

Confederate Infantry

Bushman's Hill

Elder's Battery

Main Battle 1.5 miles

N
W — E
S

1/8 mile

5:35 p.m.
*Captain Henry Parsons, charging with General Farnsworth
D-shaped open field*

Threads of sunlight streaked through trees up and down the D-shaped field. Parsons squinted through the sparkling light, eyeing ghostlike Rebels forming into a defensive line. He gripped his saber and glided toward the southern end of the D-shaped field. General Farnsworth and his detachment were hugging the eastern edge of the D-shaped field as they charged south. The Fifteenth Alabama had wheeled into position behind a stone wall at the bottom of the field. They had blocked their escape. His heart quivered. Could they leap through a field of Confederates?

Duncan dashed past him, standing in his stirrups with his saber raised. The sergeant's cheeks glowed red. He cocked his head and shouted, "I'm with you!"

The Alabamian rifles cracked and unleashed a rattling volley. Bullets filled the air like swarming locusts. Duncan screamed and threw up his left arm. He flew off his mount and plunged into the ground in front of his horse.

"Duncan!" Parsons shouted.

Parson's horse recoiled and reared, standing on his rear legs while his front legs raked the air. He leaned forward, dropped his saber, and wrapped his arms around the mount's neck. He screamed, "Please God, don't trample poor Duncan." The mount started tipping backward. He loosened the reins. Firefly fell forward, her front legs hitting the ground beyond Duncan's body. He wheeled the mare around and stepped away from the sergeant. My God. A bullet had ripped through Duncan's torso and dark blood soaked the back of his blue jacket.

"Damn you Rebels," Parsons muttered.

He looked up and felt his heart recoil. His Vermonters had surged past and were headed for the south part of the meadow. He was alone.

A Rebel captain raced toward him with his sword raised. Two infantrymen armed with Enfields surrounded him.

The Rebel captain bellowed, "Surrender."

"Go to hell." He raised his saber. A Rebel thrust his rifle against his chest. Crack…crack! He screamed. It felt like a lightning bolt jolted through him. He squeezed the reins and spurred his horse into the Rebels, racing toward the south stone wall. He held his breath, and his mount leaped the wall and galloped up the sloping hill.

5:39 p.m.
Farnsworth
Charging in the D-shaped field

The corner of the D-shaped field loomed ahead, and beyond was the safety of Bushman's Hill. A knot tightened inside him. The Rebels circling the corner wall were like frenzied sharks, smelling blood in the water and harrying their prey.

"General," Cushman shouted, "the Fifteenth Alabama are scurrying over the wall and advancing like a slavering pack of dogs."

Farnsworth stared, blurry-eyed and riddled with fright. "We will cut our way through. Speed is our weapon."

His heart skipped a beat and he charged toward the feeding frenzy, waving his saber like a berserker. A blurry, white-coated Cushman rode stirrup to stirrup, escorted by his orderly Corporal Walker.

Farnsworth aimed for the leaping shadows of a Confederate officer advancing next to a traitorous red battle flag ten yards ahead of the enemy skirmish line. The Rebel's devilish mouth was curved like a sickle and his face sported a sharply pointed Spanish-style beard.

Like Satan.

Gripping his saber in his right hand and his revolver in his left hand, Farnsworth reined up, aimed his pistol, and shouted, "Surrender, Lieutenant!"

Several rifles cracked. He crashed to the ground, wincing and shivering. He glanced at his blue jacket. Christ's blood! His body was bullet-ridden. Blood streamed from his leg, his gut, his shoulder. He gripped his revolver and tried to stand on one knee.

He groaned. It felt as if the spikes of a medieval torture device had pierced the pit of his stomach.

The Rebel lieutenant said, "Sir, will you surrender?"

He shook his head and raised his trembling revolver. His arms quivered and his fluttering heart hitched and locked. A shivering mist was gathering around him. *Oh, no...* He closed his eyes; Kill-Cavalry's snarling face floated by. *You killed my Vermonters ... and me ... should have disobeyed your damned orders ... justified ... I should have ... listened ... Custer ... Hang the luck...*

Blackness.

5:40 p.m.
Corporal George Walker
D-shaped field near General Farnsworth

Walker spurred his Morgan, gripping his saber. He veered and leaped over a fallen horse. He glanced back over his shoulder. Twenty yards away, a dozen Rebels fired their rifles at Farnsworth. The general and his horse fell. Walker reined up and wheeled toward him. Farnsworth raised his revolver and then dropped it.

A Rebel lieutenant shouted, "He's dead."

My God. Every muscle seized up. He shot a glance behind Farnsworth and the circle of Confederates. Captain Cushman was darting toward the downed Farnsworth. The Rebels turned and fired their rifles. Cushman screamed and grabbed his face. His horse crashed to the ground, pinning Cushman underneath. The captain fired his pistol twice, hitting one Rebel skirmisher. Cushman moaned, dropped his pistol, and closed his eyes. His head fell sideways on the ground, his magical white jacket drenched in blood. *Damn. He must be dead.*

Walker raced south and leaped the south end of the stone wall. Ahead a wounded Union officer listed on his walking horse. He rode up on the officer's left side.

"Captain Parsons. It's Corporal Walker. Are you hurt bad?"

Parsons glanced up. His face was ash white. "I was shot in the chest," he muttered.

"I will help you back." He gripped Parson's left arm and they trotted forward.

"What happened to General Farnsworth?" Parsons asked.

"Both General Farnsworth and Captain Cushman were shot and killed. They fell next to each other."

"This was a suicide charge," Parsons groaned. "We should have never made it."

5:45 p.m.
Major William Wells
South of the D-shaped field

Crackling volleys of rifle fire roared across the D-shaped field and the brow of the Big Round Top. The eeriness taunted Wells, full of fear and anguish. Something wasn't right. Lieutenant Stephen Clark pulled up with his company. *Where in the hell were they going?*

Clark halted and saluted.

Wells returned the salute. "Stephen, where are you going?"

Clark pointed at the Rebel battery belching fire and iron near the Bushman farm. "General Farnsworth was killed, six bullets striking him at once."

Wells recoiled in horror, his mind swearing on God's bones. *Kill-Cavalry murdered General Farnsworth.* "We must get out of this. You ride with me." He turned and shouted to his troopers. "Vermont, rally!"

While the Vermonters formed up, he said, "Stephen, what happened?"

"Captain Parsons formed his three companies into columns of four," Clark answered. "My company was third in the column. Parsons jumped the stone wall of the D-shaped field. We all followed. About the same time, General Farnsworth's small command arrived on the eastern side of the stone wall. Farnsworth shouted 'Charge,' and his group and Parson's three companies charged together. Parson's column was near the western side of the D-Shaped field, about two hundred paces away from Farnsworth's column. Parsons and the front of the column melted away as the Rebels fired volley after volley."

"Did you see Farnsworth and Parsons fall?"

"Yes. After they fell, we charged the Fifteenth Alabama behind the southern stone wall line. We fired and sabered our way over the fence. Then I spotted you."

Wells nodded. "We're going to ride around to the southeast of Little Round Top and hopefully pass through the Union lines where the Sixth Corps is positioned."

He spurred his mount and shot forward. Sweat poured off his brow and his face burned. His nostrils flared and he sucked in a deep breath and held it. *Damn Kilpatrick murdered Farnsworth and several Vermonters.* Tears streaked down his cheek. A searing shard had pierced his soul, letting an unholy darkness seep in. He had never hated a person more in his life than vainglorious Kill-Cavalry. Wasn't Farnsworth justified in defying the suicide order charge?

66

Kilpatrick — Friday, July 3

Kilpatrick smirked. *General Hooker once asked the question: "Who ever saw a dead cavalryman?" Well, there are plenty of dead cavalrymen this afternoon because damn Custer disobeyed orders and refused to bring his brigade to Bushman's Hill. Then Farnsworth was insubordinate, and I had to browbeat him into charging.*

Anger raged through him. *Meade made a grave mistake promoting Custer and Farnsworth from captain to general.* His jaw tightened. He would court-martial Custer and run his ass out of the army. It was Custer's fault that he had not destroyed Lee's right flank.

Kilpatrick's orderly pointed. "General, Major Wells and Lieutenant Colonel Preston are arriving."

He turned as Preston and Wells reined up and saluted.

"The Vermont's three battalions charged and have been repulsed," Preston said. "My early estimate of Vermont casualties is 13 killed, 25 wounded, and 27 missing or captured."

"Did you hear that General Farnsworth was killed?" Wells said.

Kilpatrick's jaw tightened. He fought hard to control his temper. Farnsworth was dead. No need to disparage an insubordinate general. "Yes, that's sad news," he answered in an empathetic tone. "He was a good soldier, a faithful friend, and had a great heart. He died a hero. He will be missed. But this was a glorious charge you made. Farnsworth's brigade penetrated a good mile to two miles in the enemy's rear. If the Federal infantry sitting up on Little Round Top and anchoring the left part of Cemetery Ridge had attacked with me, we could have rolled up the enemy."

Wells's face reddened and his nostrils flared. "I agree with one of my troopers, who said that during this charge it seemed as though all the powers of hell were waked to madness."

Kilpatrick's heated face flashed as if scorched by a branding iron. He shouted, "Major Wells, I had written orders to attack, and by God, that's what I did. When I ordered General Farnsworth to attack, the enemy was retreating."

Preston and Wells stared and said nothing.

"You're dismissed. Make sure the troopers get some rest. I'm expecting orders soon. With Lee's infantry charge defeated, we will be moving out to the west to engage the enemy."

6:30 p.m.
Major William Wells
Departing from Kilpatrick's headquarters

Wells trotted toward the Vermont headquarters, his ears ringing in the deadly silence. "Colonel Preston, today's charge was a senseless slaughter of good troopers. That attack accomplished nothing."

"Kilpatrick should have never given the order," Preston replied. "A mounted charge through thick woods, across rocky ground and fences, against infantry and artillery, was suicide. Did Kilpatrick skip the West Point lesson of the disastrous Light Cavalry Brigade charge against infantry and artillery in the Crimean War? The British had their Valley of Death and now the Vermonters have theirs."

Wells seethed. "Kilpatrick is one hell of a damn fool. I cringe at the thought of writing letters to the families of dead Vermonters. They died for Kilpatrick's glory. Nothing more. He is a vain, self-serving, and reckless officer."

Preston shook his head in plain disgust. "I've refused to call Kilpatrick by his unflattering nickname. But today he earned it: Kill-Cavalry."

Wells glanced westward toward South Mountain, where the last flare of hard-angled sunlight was streaking over the narrow ridge. As the gold flames melted behind the far-away ridge, would anyone remember the heroic General Farnsworth leading the courageous Green Mountain troopers in a suicide charge? He stared unseeing into the fading light. Military history was rarely kind to failures. Was Farnsworth's charge as notorious as the British cavalry charge of the Light Brigade? Perhaps. But Kill-Cavalry's price for glory was not worth the life of a stellar boy general and the blood of sixty-five casualties from the three hundred Vermonters making the charge.

Colonel William d'Alton Mann

67

Gregg — Friday, July 3

4:00 p.m. (Two and one half hours earlier)
General David Gregg
Strategic intersection

Gregg gripped his binoculars and scanned Rummel field as the battered Seventh Michigan skirted back on their panting and sweating mounts, struggling toward Low Dutch Road. The line of straggling wounded toiled several yards behind. A lump rose in his throat. Thank God for McIntosh's troopers at the Lott house, providing a steady crackle of gunfire and peppering the enemy chasing the injured Wolverines. The pursuing Rebels were halting and pooling up like a rising pond behind a beaver dam.

Below the Lott house, Chester's battery cracked and roared, feeding the thundering storm with volleys of hot lead. Burnt sulphur and smoldering saltpeter hung in the acid-hazed air like falling volcanic ash. Gregg's eyes stung as he peered through the smoke-shrouded clouds, spotting the ghostlike shadows of two riders sifting down the Low Dutch Road. One was wearing a bright red kerchief. He exhaled, letting out a breath he didn't know he was holding. His skin prickled. Custer was alive.

A pause hovered over the Rummel field. The weight of Jeb Stuart's will pressed against Gregg's chest like a heavy stone. The endgame would soon begin. Could his troopers withstand a final crushing attack?

He counted his remaining chess pieces. The mauled Seventh Michigan led by Custer was straggling back. The Fifth Michigan was defending the left wing and the Sixth Michigan was covering the rear. The First Michigan stood in reserve. McIntosh's brigade defended the right wing and the Low Dutch Road. He lit his pipe. The opening and middle-games of the match had ended and he had successfully maneuvered his defense and thwarted the Rebel attacks against the strategic intersection. Planning and coordinating were keys to the middle-game, and keeping Custer in check from recklessly charging at every opportunity. Now, after several exchanges and captures, Stuart would begin his end-game moves.

He puffed on his pipe. Jeb Stuart would try to convert his numerical advantage into a victory, probably with an all-out assault of all his cavalry forces. The great eighteenth-century French chess master François-André Philidor said, "the pawns are the soul of the game." He was right. A mobile mass of pawns formed the basis for attack, and isolated pawns led to defeat. He smiled. He had successfully kept his pawns massed as they maneuvered.

Captain Henry Weir pointed. "Custer is approaching."

He nodded. Custer had performed well. *Shades of the Battle of Aldie.*

Custer reined up, grinned giddily, and saluted. "The Seventh Michigan shocked the hell out of Stuart's boys." He wiped his grimy face.

Gregg clawed his beard. In a deep, grinding voice, he said, "That was a ripsnorter of a charge. You were outnumbered, but the Wolverines didn't flinch. During your retreat, it appeared that the Rebels tried to ride you down with superior numbers. Thank God for McIntosh's troopers covering my right flank and Chester's guns. What were your casualties?"

"The Seventh Michigan lost close to a quarter of its troopers in ten minutes."

Horror momentarily squeezed Gregg's throat. "My God, nearly eighty casualties."

"I think we could have whipped them if that stone fence hadn't blocked our charge. At one point in the fight, we were overpowering them. Mann couldn't get enough troopers through the gap they busted in the fence. That's when the Wolverines started to fall back."

Gregg puffed on his pipe. "Halfway across the plain, I saw you veer off to the left with a couple squadrons as Colonel Mann drove ahead with the rest of the regiment and hit the fence. Did you plan to split your forces during the charge?"

"No. I was leading the charge and I looked to my left beyond the Rummel house and spotted six artillery guns in a line along Cress Ridge. I didn't see any dismounted troopers protecting the far-left guns, so I veered toward it. After I crossed Little Run, I turned north and headed for the Rebel artillery guns."

He smiled. "Your tactics worked in preventing the Rebel cavalry from crossing the Hanover Road. It was as if Colonel Mann had grabbed the Rebel cavalry by the shirt collar by one hand, enabling your free hand to charge the Rummel farm and threaten their batteries."

Custer flashed a devil-may-care grin on his grimy face. "If I hadn't run into the second fence one hundred yards in front of the enemy batteries, I would have captured them."

Gregg's pulse quickened and he pointed. "George, a large cavalry force is emerging from the Cress woods. It looks like this is going to be Stuart's big chess move. He's going for the knockout blow."

Custer raised his binoculars and scanned the ridge. He straightened in the saddle and spat out the words. "Should we attack again with the First Michigan before Stuart tries to sweep the field?"

"Not yet."

He glanced at Custer fidgeting in his saddle. Plainly, the impulsive flames of boyish haste blazed inside him. He puffed on his pipe several times, billowing smoke like Chester's batteries. A rush of something resembling irksomeness swelled inside him. *Damn, Custer is like a chained bull terrier begging to be unleashed.*

"Stuart is baiting us into advancing closer before he attacks. I'm not going to play along. My goal is to hold the strategic crossroads. It's not to destroy a force twice the size of mine."

Custer frowned as if he had been rebuked by the schoolmaster.

"If Stuart conducts a second cavalry charge, I will wait until he has moved halfway down the slope before counterattacking with a cavalry charge. That way, Pennington and Randol's artillery guns can do the maximum damage."

He stiffened, staring at Custer. The boy general rocked back and forth in his saddle, plainly itching to hit Stuart immediately. Gregg pointed.

"George, is that the same huge saber I saw you twirling at the Battle of Aldie?"

Custer grinned boyishly and unsheathed his sword. "Here, hold it."

He reached out and gripped it with both hands. "This is heavy."

"When I was on McClellan's staff, I captured a secesh horse. Along with the big bay, I looted a Moroccan saddle, a silver-inlaid shotgun, and this thirty-seven-inch Toledo blade."

"How heavy is it?"

"Two pounds and eight and three-quarters ounces."

He shook his head. "I swear, there is hardly an arm in the Reb cavalry or ours that is strong enough to wield that blade."

"I prefer one swing and a fatal blow over dueling with a lighter sword. Also, my Toledo is great at parrying blows."

Gregg handed the saber back. He gripped his field glasses and scanned northward. A sloping forest of flashing steel glittered in the scorching sun. He held his breath.

"George, ride over to the First Michigan and tell Colonel Charles Town to ready his regiment."

Custer doffed his hat and slapped it against his leg. A wide grin stretched his lips as he pitched in the saddle.

"Damn't, George. Do not order the First Michigan to charge. I need to have our artillery guns do as much damage as possible before countercharging."

"Understood, sir."

"If I order Colonel Town's First Michigan to charge, I want you to order the Fifth and Seventh Michigan as flankers on the left flank. I'll hold the Sixth Michigan in reserve to protect Pennington's batteries."

"What about Colonel McIntosh's forces?"

"I will order Colonel McIntosh to deploy flankers from the Third Pennsylvania on the right flank. The plan is for the First

Michigan to smash Stuart's center and for the flankers to scatter the enemy pieces like thistles in a wild wind. Any questions?"

Custer shook his head and touched his hat. He wheeled Roanoke around and bolted up the Hanover Road toward Brinkerhoff's Ridge.

A messenger reined up and saluted. "Sir, General Pleasonton reports that a Rebel infantry force of about fifteen thousand soldiers is walking across the battlefield and is apparently aiming for a copse of trees that General Gibbon's division is defending."

"Why the copse of trees?"

"That's the middle of General Meade's line."

"How many troops are defending the middle of the line?"

"About six thousand or so."

"Christ almighty!"

"Meade is rushing reserves to the middle."

"I hope the hell they arrive in time. Please inform General Pleasonton that Custer's Seventh Michigan blunted Jeb Stuart's first attack. Stuart is preparing to attack with a much larger force. I'm ordering the First Michigan to attack the Confederates."

The messenger saluted and departed.

Thousands of voices erupted into a shrill, ringing scream, sounding like Indian war-whoops. He glanced over his shoulder toward Cemetery Ridge, south of the Gettysburg town. Thousands of rifles cracked, and a thunderstorm of bullets whistled and hissed. All hell was breaking out along Meade's front. He muttered a silent prayer for Meade's reserves to arrive in time.

He turned to Captain Henry Weir. "Henry, we are in quite a pickle. Not only are we outnumbered, but we also lack fresh troopers. The Seventh Michigan Regiments suffered heavy losses and have yet to re-form up. The Fifth Michigan was severely punished. Custer's largest regiment is the Sixth but they are needed to protect Pennington's guns and the strategic intersection. The Sixth Michigan is my strategic reserve. I just wish I had Colonel Irvin Gregg's Brigade here acting as the strategic reserve instead of one regiment."

"The First Michigan is Custer's veteran combat regiment," Weir said. "I would match Colonel Town's troopers against Stuart's best cavalrymen."

Gregg's eyes locked on the advancing enemy cavalrymen. He took a quick breath and stiffened.

"It appears the Rebels are going to try to take out Lieutenant James Chester's artillery battery just south of the Lott house." He twisted in his saddle. "Captain Meyer, order Lieutenant Chester to withdraw his guns."

Meyer saluted and departed.

He glanced forward at the advancing Rebels. "Henry, let's ride over to the First Michigan."

As he rode toward Colonel Town's Wolverines, he glanced up the slope at Cress Ridge. The ridgeline sparkled with thousands of sabers glinting in the fevered sunlight. Fear's shadow descended on him like a death shroud. His throat tightened. The dull gray legions were deploying, horse touching horse, column after column, red flags waving, marking regiment after regiment. The sloping forest of flickering steel was preparing to sweep down upon the outnumbered Federals like the gray tide of a swelling ocean.

His heart lurched and he struggled to inhale. Had he played this wrong? Should he have disobeyed Pleasonton's orders and moved Colonel Gregg's brigade to the Rummel field? Too late now. His outnumbered defensive line would buckle and then break apart like broken glass when the flying wall of gray troopers smashed it. The situation was dire. He had no other option but to sacrifice the First Michigan and order them to attack the swirl of red battle flags sliding down the slope. Death's jaws would swallow the charging Wolverines in one bite.

My God, my God, forgive me.

68

Miller — Friday, July 3

4:10 p.m.
Captain William Miller
A squadron on the northeastern edge of the Lott woods

A shiver skittered down Miller's back as he stood on a knoll next to Lieutenant William Brooke-Rawle, scanning the Rummel field. A sinister silence weighed on the battle-field like cold morning air after a heavy spring snow. The un-relenting sun had started slipping toward Brinkerhoff's Ridge. Sweat trickled into his already stinging eyes. He wiped his brow and gripped his field glasses. Two hundred yards south along the tree line he spotted Captain James Hart's New Jersey squadron occupying the grounds of the Lott house. A reassuring warmth quickened his heart. Hart's ferocious troopers were protecting his flank.

Lieutenant Brooke-Rawle said, "Will the Rebels attack again?"

He nodded. "Custer's Seventh Michigan charge bloodied Stuart's nose. Now Stuart's Invincibles' dander is up, and he will pitch his entire division at us." Miller scanned the sloping mead-owlands toward the wooded brow of Cress Ridge, swallowing back the paralyzing horror soaring in his throat. He turned and pointed. "Look, William."

Brooke-Rawle stared, open-mouthed. "I see them."

"It appears as if Stuart is preparing to charge again."

On the wooded summit behind the Rummel house, two Rebel brigades emerged. They were formed in close columns of squadrons and pointed toward General Custer's headquarters at the Spangler house along Hanover Road. The enemy troopers sat straight in their saddles as their horses pranced. The formation was perfect, intervals and alignments exact. The Rebels checked

553

their pistols and unsheathed their sabers. The Confederate lines trotted forward, striking and cocksure.

"What a grand spectacle." Miller twisted in his saddle and glanced at his one hundred mounted troopers hidden in the shady spot of a swale along the western edge of the Lott farm's rectangular woods. The Rebels marched at a jog trot with well-aligned fronts and steady reins. Their polished saber blades dazzled in the piercing rays of a bright summer sun.

Miller's limbs tensed. *Pure cussedness.* An ominous pause rolled over the battlefield, as if a hooded headsman had raised his two-handed axe and was about to bring it down.

Brook-Rawle said, "They're in close squadrons, advancing as if in review."

Captain Miller stared at the sloping forest of flashing steel and the waving red battle flags. The Rebels leaned forward in their saddles, sabers and pistols pointed forward, and lunged into a half-gallop. Several thousand Rebel wolf cries erupted. An icy undercurrent coursed through his veins.

"Here they come," shouted Brook-Rawle.

Swearing between gritted teeth, Miller reined his horse around toward Hanover Road and spotted Union artillery-men aiming their batteries. Without warning, Pennington and Randol's batteries vomited cracking thunder and billowing clouds. Yellow streaks of fire a yard long and a foot thick belched forth through thick white smoke. The ground rumbled and shook. He twisted his head back toward the Rebel mounted charge and licked his dry lips. A hailstorm of percussion shells and double-shotted cannister plunged into the charging Rebels. Hot iron hissed, slicing into the plumed cavaliers as men and horses fell to the ground, screaming and shrieking. On the enemy's left flank, a shell exploded under a horse and shattered the animal to pieces. The rider flipped over the horse's head and was trampled by another horse, galloping. The Union batteries pelted the Rebels with sheets of fiery hailstones. Sheer wonderment and horror rendered him dazed and motionless. Still, the graybacks came on, whirling through the battle-thunder.

"Now starts the final act," said Brook-Rawle, his voice filled with fear.

Miller flinched as the knot inside him tightened.

4:15 p.m.
General David Gregg
With Colonel Town's First Michigan at the strategic intersection

Gregg trotted toward Colonel Charles Town, staring northward at the advancing Rebel horsemen. Town was the rook chess piece he would use to check Jeb Stuart. On the flanks of Town's First Michigan troopers, Pennington's and Chester's artillery guns blasted, spewing yellow fire and white smoke like lava fountains. The projectiles shrieked long and sharp. Galloping hooves pounded, and he glanced sideways as a breathless and sweat-soaked Custer rushed past and pulled up beside Town.

Gregg reined up on the other side of Town. The colonel's face was pale and fragile, like cold moonlight, a heartrending display of courage. Town had tied himself into his saddle. Gregg stiffened, horrified. *Oh, my God.*

"Charles, are you able to lead this charge?"

In a voice laced with pain, Town replied. "By all means, General. I refuse to leave the field because of my consumption affliction. I will lead this charge."

Gregg's beard hitched with a slight smile of bittersweet awe and admiration. *This man has dauntless pluck.*

He pointed and, with respect twinged with regret, gave the order. "Colonel Town," he admonished, "put those people out of there."

"Yes, sir!"

Colonel Town unsheathed his sword, trotted forward two rods, and halted. Custer lurched forward, pulling up spur to spur with Town, leaning toward him and pointing northward. Custer's face was wild with excitement, his ice-blue eyes flashing fire, his blond mustache quivering as he spoke intently to Town. Town nodded slowly and saluted Custer. The boy general returned a hand salute and trotted forward a horse length and paused. He cocked his head, grinned, unsheathed his saber, and pointed toward the charging Rebels.

My God, is Custer going to lead the charge? A chill lanced Gregg's heart. *Damn't, if I'd wanted Custer to lead the charge, I would have ordered him to do so. Custer is a brigade commander, not a regimental commander.*

Damn't.

Gregg nodded and cracked a tight-lipped smile. There was no stopping that whirling dervish now. Just like the Battle of Aldie and leading the Seventh Michigan charge, Custer was uncontrollable when his blood was up. No orders from any superior at this moment could halt Custer from charging.

Gregg drew a deep breath, held it in, and prayed with all his heart and mind. *God be with you, General Custer, and Colonel Town, and with your Wolverines.*

❦ 69 ❦

Custer — Friday, July 3

4:15 p.m. (Moments earlier)
Custer
At the front of Colonel Town's First Michigan at the strategic inter-
section

Custer gently heeled Roanoke and, through narrowed eyes, observed Gregg riding toward Colonel Town. He glanced up at the grand spectacle of thousands of butternut-clad troopers marching down the slope on their prancing horses. Their sabers flared forward and glistened like silver in the murderous sunlight. Dark, fleecy thunderheads streaked over Cress Ridge. He flashed a jaunty smile and licked his dry lips. An impetuous fever for action against Jeb's infernal devils flowed inside him like raging lava. Only God knew how he could see glory where sudden death lurked.

He eased his mount next to Gregg and Town as the general ordered Town to charge. A thrilling rush jolted through his body, tingling his skin like a sharp static shock. *What a rare opportunity for immortal fame. This moment must be exploited before it vanishes like noon shadows on glass.*

Town unsheathed his saber, trotted forward several yards, and halted. Custer raced to join Colonel Town and his guidon carrying the regiment's headquarters flag. He was fidgeting like an irate cat switching its tail as he pulled up stirrup to stirrup with Town. *My God, this brave colonel is tied to his saddle.* The colonel was white-faced and grimacing, plainly in pain. Custer's breath rasped. This was the type of bravery that would propel an outnumbered force to glory. But it was his responsibility as Town's immediate senior to order Town to charge, not Gregg's.

"Colonel Town, the Seventh Cavalry has broken. I shall have to ask you to *charge* the Rebels. This hell-bent attack might be one of the greatest cavalry charges in history."

Town nodded with a grim smile "By all means, General, the First Michigan will do its duty."

"Great heavens!" a Wolverine within earshot shrilled. "This is a blunderhead charge. We will all be swallowed up!"

Not even attempting to hide his sarcasm, another Wolverine snarled, "Ours is not to reason why, but ours is to do and die."

Custer was oblivious to their contempt. His body thrummed like the vibrating strings of a fiddle. God, he craved moments like this. He would be center stage in the greatest mounted attack since Murat's glorious charge at Eylau.

Town sword-saluted, slowly and with great effort.

In response, Custer whisked out his shimmering Toledo with his right hand and raised the saber's grip close to his neck, inclining the blade thirty degrees from his slouch hat. He paused for a heartbeat, then slashed the sword downward toward his right boot and snapped it back, the blade glinting with a bright flourish in the sun. Though he kept his countenance neutral, in his mind, he was smiling; he had performed the perfect West Point sword salute.

Custer's mind raced. Should he get Gregg's permission to lead the charge? Hell, no! Gregg had given him permission to lead the Seventh Michigan charge. *Don't risk asking permission to lead the First Michigan charge. Just do it. If you're successful, forgiveness will follow as it always does with Custer luck.* He glanced up Cress Ridge. The gray troopers were in close columns of squadrons, flying their red battle flags. Adrenaline electrified his body. This was a scene right out of Lever's *The Irish Dragoon.* He glanced skyward. He hoped Marshal Murat was looking on with delight.

It was time to charge. He trotted forward a horse length, turned his head, caught Gregg's eye, winked, and pointed his Toledo directly at the oncoming Rebels. Old Steady nodded with a slight smile. Gregg was plainly admitting he was unwilling to stop the Union's beau sabreur from charging.

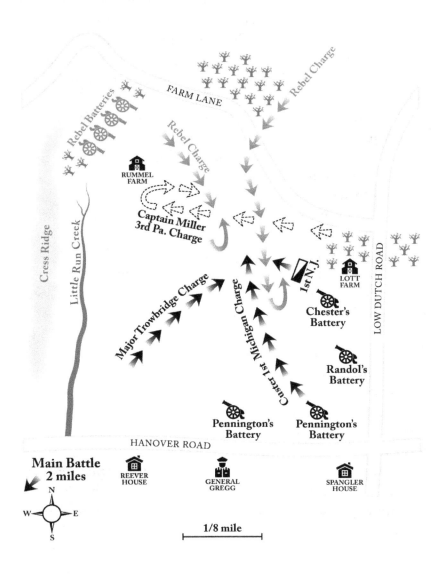

Custer Leads 1st Michigan Charge
July 3, 1863
4:00 p.m. - 5:00 p.m.

Rebel Charge

FARM LANE

Rebel Batteries

Rebel Charge

RUMMEL
FARM

Cress Ridge

Little Run Creek

Captain Miller
3rd Pa. Charge

Major Trowbridge Charge

Custer 1st Michigan Charge

1st N.J.

LOTT
FARM

LOW DUTCH ROAD

Chester's
Battery

Randol's
Battery

Pennington's
Battery

Pennington's
Battery

HANOVER ROAD

Main Battle
2 miles

N
W ● E
S

REEVER
HOUSE

GENERAL
GREGG

SPANGLER
HOUSE

1/8 mile

"Colonel Town, as the commander of the Michigan Brigade, it's my responsibility to lead this charge. The enemy has the advantage of high ground and numbers. Their blood is running hot because they repulsed the Seventh Michigan." He smirked. "The Devil be damned. We are going to give these horn-headed graybacks an ass-whipping."

Town's eyes widened and he stared, plainly surprised. In an instant, he smiled. "Yes, sir, General. Let's give 'em hell."

Custer wheeled about and glanced at the faces of Wolverines trotting behind him. A blazing hearth fire seemed to warm his very soul.

In a cavalier tone, he said, "You Wolverines are panting for a chance to cross sabers with the Rebels."

Colonel Town turned his head. "Sergeant Major Dewitt Smith. Wheel out the regiment by columns of squadrons and cross north across the Hanover Road."

Custer shivered as Sergeant Major Smith gave the orders and the First Michigan formed up.

In a raspy whisper, Town cried, "Draw sabers!"

"Draw sabers!" Sergeant Major Smith echoed.

A clinking rattle reverberated as hundreds of sabers were unsheathed.

Town cried out, "Remember, men; be steady, be calm, be firm! Think of Michigan! Forward!"

Colonel Town trotted forward with his saber drawn and his regimental guidon snapping in the breeze beside him.

Custer smiled, looking over Cress Ridge. His heart rate quickened as nervous energy coursed in spurts and gushes. It was a majestic sight, a swirl of red battle flags sailing like wispy scud clouds leading a thunderstorm. *What a glorious moment.* He dashed in front of Colonel Town, stuffed his hat into his jacket, and pointed his saber. Out of the corner of his eye, he saw Private Churchill trotting half a horse length behind on his left, his sword raised. A rising river of inner fierceness swelled inside him. He felt like a cougar preparing to pounce and deliver the fatal bite.

"Now, Norvell, for a bit of fun! Stick close. You're my good luck charm."

"Certainly, General."

He nudged Roanoke into a trot toward the massive line of graybacks swishing down the slope. He beamed. Never again would he have the chance to lead a Napoleonic grand charge against such overwhelming numbers. Outnumbered four to one, his thundering Wolverines would shock the Rebels with a head-long lightning strike. *Thank you, God, for this moment. And thank you for forging me into your creature of glory. This charge is a stepping-stone to greatness of epic proportions.*

4:16 p.m.
Lieutenant James Chester, commanding two 12-pounder artillery guns from Randol's battery
South of the Lott house and west of the Low Dutch Road

White smoke hung over Chester's two thundering 12-pounder artillery guns. The blast blew hot winds against his face. He breathed quickly as he looked through his binoculars. The advancing enemy cavalry was veering left toward the Lott house. His heartbeat faltered. *God Almighty!* The Rebel assault was aimed at his battery.

"Shift to cannister," he shouted.

Pounding hooves echoed from behind. He twisted in his saddle. Captain Henry Meyer reined up.

Meyer shouted, "Lieutenant Chester, General Gregg orders you to withdraw your guns back toward the Hanover Road. He is worried the Rebel cavalry will overrun your guns."

Chester glared, his face reddening. "Dammit, Captain, it's too late to withdraw. If I withdraw, my guns will be captured or destroyed."

"I'm giving you a direct order from General Gregg."

"Tell the general to go to hell!"

Meyer froze, plainly shocked by the blatant defiance of a direct order. He shook his head, wheeled his horse, and clapped both spurs to the horse's flanks.

Chester shouted, "Double cannister!"

Orange-tinged gray smoke purled from the batteries' blasting barrels. Gregg's ears pulsed as he lumbered toward Pennington's seasoned gunners. They were clambering about like madmen, firing shells as fast as a dripping water tap. The ground rumbled in bubbling bursts like a smoldering lava field. He smiled to himself. Pennington's boys were doing a fine job. The arching projectiles would cover Custer's advance like an umbrella for the first five hundred yards of the Michigan charge. Sweat dripped from the gunners' blackened faces, and whitish smoke swirled the air.

Pennington rode among his guns, pointing and shouting. As soon as the flames erupted from their iron jaws, the guns lurched backwards a rod. Four cannoneers rushed up, grabbed the two wooden wheels of each gun, and rolled it forward until the rims hit the stop logs. Gunners rushed forward and swabbed the hot bores with wet sponges. Steam erupted from barrels like a line of smoking volcanoes.

Gregg reined up at the gun closest to him.

"Spherical case!" Pennington bellowed.

A sergeant shouted, "Range, one thousand yards."

A corporal checked the Table of Fire, glued inside the lid of the limber chest, for one thousand yards. "Elevation, three degrees. Time of flight, four seconds."

A private adjusted the fuse gauge for four seconds and cut the fuse.

The sergeant checked the aim and raised both hands. He shouted, "Fire!"

The artillery gun boomed out blind fury. Smoke deepened and rolled about the iron jaws spouting fire. Gregg spied the streaking trail. The hissing shell followed an arc toward Cress Ridge and burst, pouring out its cracking thunder and flying iron above the cantering Rebel horses. Gaps appeared in the Rebel advance like holes in Swiss cheese. Cavaliers and horses were torn to pieces. Riderless horses broke formation and plunged through the fields.

Half a minute later, the gun was swabbed, loaded, and fired. Pennington's six guns raced, each creating a hailstorm of raging fire upon the graybacks. Gregg glanced northeast. Randol's four howitzers were flaming west of the Low Dutch Road, creating numerous white, puffy clouds. The thundering din pounded against his eardrums, drowning out the shrieks of the wounded and the moans of the dying.

He turned to Captain Weir. "Henry, if Pennington and Randol's battery can keep up this rate of fire it will give Custer's Wolverines a chance to blunt the Rebel advance."

4:20 p.m.
Custer, advancing with the First Michigan
North of the Hanover Road

Beyond the advancing Rebels an eerie glow blossomed as a dark fleece swallowed the blue sky. A thunderstorm approached. Nature was not going to rain on his show.

He grinned. "Keep to your sabers, boys!"

Pure, thrilling excitement pulsed through him as he brandished his sword and hurled to the front of another cavalry charge. Custer squinted toward the wooded brow of Cress Ridge. The Rebel cavalry brigade was fifteen hundred yards ahead, slithering down the slope like a den of gray serpents. A blood-soaked spirit flooded his veins and his thirsty mind relaxed, savoring the thrill of leading another death-defying charge. He urged Roanoke into a canter.

The Wolverines behind him erupted into a cheer. Pennington's artillery shells roared over the heads of the gaiting Wolverines and plunged a hailstorm of death into the gray masses. Mangled men and horses flew into the air, dousing the ground with their spurting blood.

He glanced to his left, where Norvell was riding gracefully a few yards behind, on his flank. Norvell smiled and tipped his saber. Custer's heart swelled. He had never seen a man fitter to wield a weapon. Norvell had become a part of Custer luck. He was invincible with Norvell at his side.

A blast thundered ahead on his right. He spotted Lieutenant Chester's guns just south of the Lott farm, hugging the Low Dutch Road. Chester's iron jaws belched smoke. The cannister broadside decimated the Rebel vanguard. *Thank God for Pennington and Randol's batteries. Their guns might even the odds.*

Churchill shouted, "The Rebels are aiming for Chester's battery."

Custer agreed. The Rebels were veering southeast toward the Union batteries along Low Dutch Road. A plan popped into his head. He would ride ahead on the thin, tapered edge of the Wolverine wedge. The triangular-shaped attack would split the Rebel brigade like a sharp sledgehammer. With the Rebel cavalry cut in half, the Fifth and Sixth Michigan and McIntosh's brigade could attack the Rebel flanks.

One hundred yards ahead, the Rebel yell erupted, and the cantering Rebel cavalry lurched into a breakneck gallop. It was as if the Rummel field was covered with a glistening glacier, capped with fluttering red pennants. It cracked and a slab three hundred yards across was barreling down the slope at the speed of a deadly avalanche.

He sucked in a deep breath, holding it a moment as the growing swell of churning hooves closed to fifty yards. He glanced over his shoulder. The Wolverines were twirling their swords over their heads. A sharp thrill shuddered down his spine.

"Come on, you Wolverines!" he shouted. "Charge!"

Bugler Joseph Fought trumpeted the shrilling clangor of the advance.

Custer drew the reins into his mouth and gripped them with his teeth. With his saber gripped in his right hand and the revolver in his left, he spurred Roanoke into a sweeping gallop. His heart pounded in his ears. Roanoke leaped four lengths out ahead of the Wolverines. His mad daredevils dashed up the slope with a huge hurrah. The thundering horse hooves vibrated his body. They flew in torrents as if blown by the wind of a perfect hurricane. He twisted his head. No Wolverine waivered. What a glorious and beautiful spectacle. The two forces were rising rogue waves, about to collide into a monstrous swell.

A thunderclap and shell burst ahead toward the left end of the Wolverine line. He ducked. Clumps of dirt pelted his jacket and snapped against his cheeks. Unearthly cries pierced through the all-engulfing roar.

"You Rebel bastards!"

A numbing fury raged inside, thrusting him fearlessly forward and deadening all senses, as though the storm had swallowed him. His sharp spurs sliced Roanoke's flanks, and his shrill scream tore the thick air. The wind whistled through his locks as galloping gave way to hell-bent flight. His savage soul roared as his wild steed bounded frantically beneath him toward the battle thunder. The foul odor of death reeked over the battlefield, burning his nose. He was a primordial beast stalking its prey. God, he loved cavalry charges.

4:21 p.m.
General David Gregg
Spangler house, near the strategic crossroads

Gregg's eyes burned as he gripped his binoculars, eyeing the First Michigan's rollicking devil-may-care charge. Custer raced four horse lengths ahead. Norvell was half a length behind on one side, and on the other side Colonel Town's regimental flag whisked in the wind beside his galloping charger. Custer's long saber was gleaming in the bright sunshine. Custer, a creature of glory, was bareheaded, his hair flowing like a gold-colored battle flag.

Gregg twisted toward Captain Weir, heart racing. "This is the most daring cavalry charge I've ever witnessed. Custer is fearless. He's like mighty Achilles, daring death to touch him as he charged over the plains of Troy."

"Custer craves being the hero," Weir agreed. "His daring and gallantry in battle is unmatched. His brigade loves him."

"That's what counts. He is a young, fiercely ambitious officer. He is perfectly reckless in his contempt of danger, and watching him today, he seems to take infinite pleasure in exposing himself to it. His Wolverines believe in Custer luck." Gregg shook his head in wonder. "I'm hoping it holds during this counter-charge and it's not his *final* charge. Thank God Pennington and Randol's batteries are doing a splendid job culling the exposed Rebel ranks."

Several enemy shells screamed and burst close to the charging Wolverines. A private racing ahead of the pack tumbled forward off his horse. A piece of shrapnel struck the horse, gutting the animal as clean as a butcher would. The troopers behind the fallen private jumped over him and his horse as if they were steeplechasing.

4:25 p.m.
Custer, leading the Wolverine wedge
One thousand yards southeast of the Rummel Farm

Custer lurched forward into the saddle, his face cutting the wind like the bow of a clipper ship. He flew with an unguarded burst of speed.

"Come on, Roanoke. Fly!" A soothing excitement flooded his soul like wicked sin.

A whooping Wolverine bolted ahead, brandishing his sword. *Go, young Wolverine, go.* A high-arching shell whistled as it plunged. His instincts screamed *Veer!* No time. In a heartbeat, the whistling shell exploded and the blast slapped his face with hot air. An unearthly cry shrieked, resonating above the din of battle. A fragment had struck the Wolverine racing ahead. The trooper's raised sword-hand dropped the saber, but the sword arm remained erect as if pointing at the heavens. His other limbs spasmed and curled in a contorted tuck as he tumbled to the ground.

My God! He was thunderstruck with shock. The dragoon's demonic screech clawed at his soul, rending all hope the trooper cursed by fate would draw another breath. *Damn Rebels!* He squinted through the flood of smoke cloaking the valley of death between the two charging forces. The air hissed with deadly cannonballs.

Racing at such a thrilling pace was pure bliss. It felt like he was diving off a cliff and freefalling at the speed of a shooting star. He shouted, "Norvell, our momentum is greater than the Rebels'. We are going to smash through the middle and cut them in half."

"I'm with you, General. Let's give 'em hell!"

Custer stared through fissures of billowing smoke at the charging Rebels. The columns of the Confederates had blended while maintaining perfect alignment. Rebel catcalls and insults echoed overhead. The brigade of Confederates were scoffing the regiment charging them. Custer's face burned. "You Devil bastards!"

Several Union cannister shells erupted, spraying the front line of the charging Rebels. Custer squinted as an electrical jolt flashed in his brain. *They've been staggered by a hard punch to the face.* He gathered Roanoke well under him and gripped his saber tighter. He aimed for the middle of the Rebels' left flank. Thundering hooves rattled. The madness of this charge could be equaled only by its heroism. Seething blood coursed through his veins with increased speed. He picked out a Rebel officer wearing a large plume hat. His gut tightened and he girded himself for delivering a saber blow.

"Perish to hell!" he screamed, and the words roasted in his mouth.

A horse-length away, the two hostile columns tilted together. He sliced through the enemy line into hell's storm like a cutthroat razor. A slender, willowy Rebel charged, his eyes slitted, brandishing his saber. Custer leaned right and swung his sword, cutting soft flesh like a sickle harvesting wheat stalks. The Rebel clutched at his throat, uttered a harsh cry, and tumbled in an arching crash to the ground.

The surging blue wall rolling close behind collided into the Rebel horsemen. His ears rang as if several flying freight trains roared overhead. The gray waves crashed into Custer's Wolverines standing firm like a breakwater. Who would give first? Wolverines pitched themselves out of their saddles and hurled past Custer, hitting Rebels headfirst like battering rams. Horses turned end over end, crushing the riders beneath them.

"These Yankee sons of bitches!" a Rebel yelled.

Sabers clanged and sparked. Faces and chests cracked open. Horses reared and pawed in the air, squealing like animals in a slaughterhouse. Custer lunged forward and stabbed a Rebel in the side. A flash sparkled in the corner of his eye, and he dove his head into Roanoke's neck. A breeze blew against his cheek as a Rebel saber sliced over his head. A lane opened like a brilliant beam streaming through a storm cloud, and Roanoke kept stride and raced ahead through it. It felt as if the horses had agreed to pass through each other like one might pass the fingers of the right hand through those of the left.

Norvell shouted, "We've broken through the first line like a wedge through firewood."

"Keep charging!"

He cut and slashed fiendishly into the second line. His heart pounded in his ears. Swords flashed and sparked as he dashed between the enemy, sabering Rebels as they flew by.

He glanced over his shoulder. The Wolverines hung together, thrusting ahead like a shredding whirlwind. There was no longer any semblance of a line. Their flanks had folded back like hawk wings in a deep dive.

Figures lunged, weaved, and rocked. An instant expanded into timeless eternity as he slashed and parried and slashed. Roanoke's flanks were soapy with sweat. His blue sailor shirt was wringing wet, and his throat was as parched as a dry lake.

Custer shouted, "Norvell, we're at the pointy end of the wedge. Keep splitting the Rebels as far as we can."

"We're cutting them down like ninepins," Norvell yelled.

The air hissed as a shower of Wolverine bullets passed through the melee. The brawl was a cacophony of demonic screaming, cracking, whinnying, and oath-swearing as the Wolverines pushed forward, cutting, slashing, pointing, and parrying. Custer focused on a Rebel and lunged with his saber. The Rebel was late parrying and Custer's heavy sword shattered the soldier's lower jaw.

He glanced to his left; a Rebel color sergeant bearing a red battle flag was approaching. A Wolverine sergeant slewed toward the Rebel and fired his revolver. The color sergeant screamed, threw up his arms, and tumbled off his saddle. Custer spurred Roanoke, dipped his shoulder in a low lunge, and speared the falling flag with his Toledo blade.

He waved the flag and shouted, "Another Rebel prize for President Lincoln!"

Enemy troopers were belching forth. Several Rebel revolvers cracked like lightning and a wash of bullets whizzed by through a gush of smoke. Roanoke's front legs buckled, and the mount tumbled onto his head. He released the reins and bolted over the horse's head, soaring gracelessly for several yards like a fledging bird jumping from the nest. He held his breath and closed his eyes.

The ground jumped up and smacked his shoulder and he rolled free. Roanoke lay on the ground, whinnying. *Devil be damned.* Unhorsed again, he picked up his sword and leapt to his feet. A sizzling hot poker had fire-branded his left shoulder. He glanced at his collarbone and saw that a bullet had singed his black velvet jacket, carving a shallow pumpkin rib through the fabric. No blood. Just seared skin. Custer luck.

Screams knifed through the churning melee. His heart lurched. A deluge of mounted and unmounted horses came roaring past, like tornado winds rutting up dust. His mind shrieked, *Mount a horse or be crushed!* He glanced at a silhouetted horse bursting through the shrouded murkiness. He gulped a breath and lunged sideways as the heaving charger barreled toward him. A Wolverine's boot spur kissed his cheek, tinkling like a hand-held bell. He was in death's whirlpool, and it was sucking him down into the harrowing maelstrom.

A Rebel yell erupted from behind. He pivoted and glowered at a dismounted Rebel who was charging with a sneer splitting his lips and holding his saber like a lance. Custer sidestepped and thrusted his Toledo through the Rebel's gut. The Rebel screamed and tumbled. Roanoke whinnied and stood. His warhorse was bleeding from a bullet wound in his foreleg.

"Damnation. I should have never ridden you today, Roanoke. Sorry, boy! I will come back for you."

A snorting mount flew a hairbreadth away like a passing train. The Wolverine's wooden stirrups struck his back as the trooper vaulted by. The air in his lungs erupted from his mouth. He bent down on one knee, gasping. A saber swooshed over his head like an arching axe cutting a tree. He caught his breath, stood, and raised his saber, parrying the next blow. A pistol cracked and the Rebel screamed and plunged from his charger. Men and horses were falling like guillotined heads.

Gunfire clattered continuously. Ragged breath wheezed from his mouth. *Find a mount. The demons are giving no quarter if you are down.* He whirled and spotted a riderless horse darting toward him in a bull rush. He held his breath and steeled himself. He pounced forward like a big cat and snagged the bridle with his gloved hand. He yanked, tilting the horse's head without breaking stride. He held on and was nearly airborne as the steed tore ahead. His breath whistled in his throat as his boots and spurs dug into the ground like a plow cutting a shallow furrow. His left shoulder popped, and he let go as the horse raced by, whipping its tail across his eyes. *Find another horse or get trampled.* His heart pounded.

He swiveled his head and spotted a riderless horse milling about. Its tail was cut off by a saber cut. He lunged toward the bug-eyed mare and lurched into the saddle with the agility of a circus rider. With a mount under him again, his rigid shoulders relaxed. He stared into the melee, a chill coiling down the back of his neck. Norvell was nowhere. *Damn. Hopefully he's not wounded and is still leading the charge.* He raised his sword and spurred his borrowed mount, racing behind a charging Wolverine. The brawl rumbled like a swarm of howling banshees and growling curs. Hooves pounded and the ground trembled.

Through the smoke he spotted a mounted Rebel private wearing a gray frock coat with yellow trim, dark-blue trousers, and a black-brimmed hat. He gritted his teeth and his hackles rose up between his shoulders as he jounced in the big saddle. He pitched low, touching the horse's withers. He carried the saber blade on his right shoulder. His heart raced with swash-buckling excitement. He stood tall in his stirrups and twirled his saber over his head in a rear moulinet.

The rangy Rebel raised his saber, baying for his blood. Custer pulled hard on the reins, halting the mare. The Rebel gaped, plainly surprised. Custer roared and cut the blade down hard across the Rebel's back, spraying blood. The wounded Rebel crumbled.

He spurred his mount deeper into the battle-thunder, racing back to the tip of the wedge. *Can't lead fighting from back in the pack.* His troopers were holding their own, but for how long? He plunged on, slicing and cutting. The wedge had penetrated two-thirds of the enemy columns. Ahead he spotted Private Churchill rallying the Wolverines, and a dismounted Rebel aiming his revolver directly toward them. A sudden chill rushed over him. He veered his galloping mount toward the Rebel and charged, holding his saber parallel to the ground.

Shrieking a torrent of epithets, he gripped his mount tight with his legs, leaned to the right, and slashed across the Rebel's arm. The man screamed and dropped his revolver. Custer dashed toward Churchill, shouting, "Norvell, I'm here!"

Churchill's face erupted into a wide grin. "General, nice of you to rejoin the fray. I thought I had lost you. The charging Wolverine wedge nearly cleaved the Rebels into two pieces."

"A bullet hit Roanoke's front leg and I was unhorsed. Luckily, I managed to find this mare."

He wiped his wet face. His Wolverines had ridden a high tide through the enemy lines, stopping the Rebel advance, and were paused at the high-water mark of the glorious charge like swirling flotsam. *Time to work our way back to the Spangler house before more Rebels emerge from Cress Ridge and wash us away.*

Major Luther Stephen Trowbridge

70

Fifth Michigan — Friday, July 3

4:30 p.m.
Major Luther Trowbridge
Along Little Run

Trowbridge sprinted ahead of his dismounted troopers dashing in a jumbled throng south toward Hanover Road. His breaths were short; sweat poured down his face. His leg muscles burned as if a cluster of hornets were stinging him with red hot needles. Pennington's big guns thundered ahead, spewing yellow, streaking flames from their iron jaws. The projectiles screeched skyward, intoning long, drawn-out metallic whines as they arced toward Cress Ridge. The blasts buzzed in his ears. He glanced to his right at his orderly, Billy Dunn, whose face seemed pinched and drawn.

"Billy," he shouted, "when we arrive at the ammunition train, we are going to reload our Spencers and prepare for the Rebels breaking through the First Michigan."

Billy gulped. "Yes, sir."

A galloping horse blurred into his peripheral vision. Colonel Russel Alger reined up.

"Luther," Alger said, "Custer and the First Michigan are in one hell of a fight. Reload and mount up your squadron and charge the right flank of the Rebels."

"Yes, sir." He sucked in a deep breath and held it as Noah Ferry's image whirled in his mind. His brain heaved, pleading for the release of these demonic instincts to avenge Major Ferry's cruel death. He was Achilles in Homer's *Iliad*, seeking just retribution for the death of Patroclus. *I swear by God's bones, Noah, your beloved Wolverines will redress your death.*

Trowbridge lurched into the saddle and galloped at the head of his troopers toward the Rebels' right flank. He glanced over his shoulder at his screaming Wolverines riding in a saw-toothed line, brandishing their swords. *Damn*. No time to form up into a column. He snapped his head forward, spotting Custer's red scarf in the middle of the conflagration, twirling his slashing saber like a carnival dancer. The First Michigan were formed like a ship's hull, driving through the middle of the Rebels, forcing the graybacks to spread out into a large bow wave.

Fury swirled in his mouth. "Remember Major Ferry!"

"Kill the traitorous bastards!" Billy Dunn shouted.

The gaggle pressed on, rapid and fierce. The air quivered with screams and shouts. A violent surge of rage swept over Trowbridge. Revenge for Major Ferry's death was imminent. He grasped the leather grip of his Old Wristbreaker, its heavy, flat-backed blade pointed straight ahead. His Spencer repeater hung from a waist belt and the rifle's muzzle was secured by a carbine thimble attached to the off-side of the saddle. His loaded .44-caliber Colt revolver rested in its holster attached to his waist belt. He made a violent grimace. He was going to fire every round, killing as many Rebel bastards as he could. His eyes narrowed, his muscles stirred, and his lips quivered. He had to have satisfaction.

His heart pounded against his ribs as he galloped toward the Rebels' right flank. The graybacks were focused on Custer's troopers and didn't see his Wolverines attacking on their blind side. *Perfect*. In the sinuous clash of glittering steel, he aimed for a Rebel officer sporting a plumed hat and wagging his sword. He scudded up like a flying spear and uttered a roar like an attacking mountain lion, swinging a cutting blow, slicing the grayback's jugular. A Wolverine screamed and tumbled off his horse in front of him. He jerked on the reins and veered a quarter turn, raised up his saber and thrust down, slashing the Confederate who had been trailing the plumed Rebel officer. He skirted ahead between two Rebels, cutting and slashing on both sides. His mount leaped and cleared a fallen horse. Death's sickly sweet odor filled his nostrils, a sickening mixture of rotting gases and decaying flesh.

A galling fire cracked, and his horse's head dove into the ground. He tumbled over the mount's neck and landed on his shoulder blade. For a couple of heartbeats, he lay on his side, gasping for a breath. Blood poured from his nose. It felt as if his hazy head was detached from his body, and he was lying in a mudhole like a lazy boar hog. Hooves clattered all around him like hail pelting stained glass. He was awash in a welter of uncertainty. In some distant part of his fuddled brain a puny voice whispered *skedaddle or be trampled*. A spectre of terror ripped through his heart. Remembering Major Ferry, he was swept up in a fierce animus.

He scrambled to his feet, spitting dirt. He wheeled away from his dead mount and jerked his Spencer rifle from his waist belt. A Rebel bore down on him, thrusting his saber at his neck. He cocked the hammer back, dropped the lever down, and then ran the lever up, feeding the first cartridge into the chamber. He aimed and pulled the trigger. The bullet hit the Rebel in the shoulder. He cocked the hammer back, dropped the lever down, ejecting the spent cartridge, and ran the lever up. He wheeled and fired again. In eighteen seconds, he fired seven rounds, and five Rebels lay dead within ten yards, their riderless mounts following the mounted horses racing down the slope toward Hanover Road.

He unholstered his revolver. Revolvers and rifles cracked in a roaring din. His heart quaked. *My God, I'm a thousand yards from the balance of my regiment, surrounded by graybacks, and my horse is dead. A Richmond prison is waiting for me if I survive.* Billy Dunn burst up and parried a Rebel sword, slashing the charging Confederate across the face. The enemy screamed and fell. Dunn leapt from his horse.

Dunn shouted, "Major, take my horse. If they capture me, I will escape before dark."

He hesitated. A bullet feathered by, kissing his cheek. He flinched. Dunn grabbed his jacket and jerked him toward the horse.

"Mount the horse, Major!"

He swung into the saddle and gripped the reins. For a moment, silence flooded his mind, the type of silence where your thoughts and actions sharpen. He nodded. Yes, shifty Dunn would escape by dark. A gray wave of bristling sabers rushed forward, threatening to swamp him. He pulled on the reins, wheeled about, and spotted his blue troopers galloping toward their starting point.

He turned in the saddle and saluted Dunn. "I'm ordering you to return to our lines by midnight."

Dunn grinned and snapped a salute.

He spurred Dunn's mount into a gallop and rode like a demonic creature, cursing under his breath. Clearing the Rebel right flank, he pulled up to a trot and twisted in his saddle. Dunn was surrounded by Rebels with his hands in the air. A twinge of guilt unsteadied his mind. *For God's sake, don't shoot him.*[14]

---

14 Private Billy Dunn was captured and later escaped, making it back to his regiment just before dark. See Eric Wittenberg, *Protecting the Flank of Gettysburg: The Battles for Brinkerhoff's Ridge and East Cavalry Field, July 2-3, 1863*, Savas Beatie, El Dorado Hills, CA, 2013, page 100.

71

Miller — Friday, July 3

4:26 p.m. (4 minutes earlier)
Captain William Miller
Northeastern edge of Lott Woods

Miller's breath quickened as he scanned the Rummel field, ebbing and flooding with blue and gray troopers like some foul river. The pungent stench of gunpowder pricked his nostrils. Artillery bombardment and the crack of rifles echoed relentlessly over the battlefield. Mangled corpses littered the ground.

His heart fluttered like a hovering hawk. He turned to Lieutenant Brooke-Rawle. "William, let's ride forward." He trotted forward twenty yards and halted.

Brooke-Rawle reined up next to him. "Stuart's troopers just closed ranks and are barreling down the slope like a wall of water."

Miller glanced at a long, rolling gray wave, studded with fluttering pennants, sliding down the slope. The Seventh Michigan, drawn up in close column of squadrons near Pennington's battery, was posed like a blue breaker. Custer's red scarf and gold ringlets bounced freely as he led the First Michigan toward the charging Confederates. Miller pointed. "Custer's one regiment is going to be swallowed up by the three charging enemy regiments."

"It's impossible for Custer's Wolverines to stop the Rebel charge," Brook-Rawle admitted. "It's a forlorn task."

Miller pinched his lips together and peered up the Low Dutch Road. No Rebel cavalry. *Damn.* His troopers were mere spectators sitting on the sidelines of a great battle while their brother warriors were about to be slaughtered. The helplessness of being torn between obedience and decency tormented him. Was he justified in disobeying orders in order to help Custer and the First Michigan?

Bugles blasted. Bareheaded and glorious, Custer spurred his horse almost four lengths in front of the regiment. His yellow locks were flying like a battle flag. His long, straight saber gleamed in the sunshine. For a moment, Miller was invigorated with a rush of spirited frenzy. Custer's fearless bravery was infectious. There was something magical about the boy general and his captivating leadership that awed him, as if he were witnessing the birth of a mythical legend. The First Michigan bounded up the slope, screaming at the top of their voices.

But his awe began to crumble as disaster unfolded in front of him. "The Wolverines are riding so fast that they might get hit with the last sprays of canister from the Federal artillery guns."

Brooke-Rawle nodded. "In a moment the two opposing columns are going to collide head-on."

Scanning through his binoculars, Miller felt his heart skip a beat. "I see General Hampton's battle flag over the Rebel vanguard."

"I see it too!"

Custer spurred his gray warhorse repeatedly, racing at breakneck speed. The screaming Wolverines galloped right behind him. Miller drew in a big breath and held it. The forces closed rapidly, like two trains racing toward each other on the same track. A heartbeat later they smashed into each other. The violent crash roared like lumberjacks felling a thousand giant trees onto the ground. Horses turned end-over-end, crushing their riders beneath them. *Oh, my God. How can Custer's Wolverines survive?* The opposing forces collided like ocean waves breaking on a rock-bound coast, and men and horses rolled and tossed like foam upon the crest.

Custer's red scarf flowed at the pointy end of the pounding Michigan wedge splitting the Rebel cavalry. The Wolverines drove into the second line of Confederate cavalry like a deadly tornado, slashing and trampling the enemy in their path. Sabers clashed, pistols cracked, and screams for surrender echoed.

Miller's skin prickled. "The Wolverine momentum is ebbing. The Rebel's mass is too thick for Custer. The enemy will soon wash over the Wolverines like a dam bursting."

"Custer needs reinforcements," Brooke-Rawle said.

"Agreed." Miller caught a flicker of movement out of the corner of his eye and glanced toward the Lott farm. "A New Jersey squadron is attacking the Rebel's left flank." He turned to his first lieutenant. "Are we just going to sit here and watch the Rebel legions rush by? I've been ordered to hold this position. But if you will testify for me in case I'm court-martialed for disobedience, I will order a charge."

Brooke-Rawle grinned. "I will stand by you, Captain. Let's pitch in."

Brooke-Rawle wouldn't desert him. Reassurance overcame any remaining doubt. "Rally your squadron on the left." He turned to Sergeant Thomas Gregg. "Sergeant, rally the right squadron. I will lead your squadron in the charge."

He glanced beyond the Lott farm at the monstrous gray waves of Rebels rolling by.

"My squadron is ready, Captain," Brooke-Rawle shouted.

"Good. Let's surprise the Rebels and aim for the last fourth of their columns."

Sergeant Gregg called out, "My squadron is ready, sir."

Miller shouted, "Fire a volley."

The carbines cracked and ripped into the left flank of the Rebels.

"Draw sabers!"

Metal clinked and gleamed as the troopers raised their sabers skyward like a field of ripe cornstalks.

He turned to his bugler. "Sound 'Charge'!"

The bugler trumpeted a shrill "Charge." A great cheer erupted among his men.

He spurred his mount and sailed forward, leading Sergeant Gregg's squadron toward the last fourth of the enemy's column flank. He shot a quick glance to his left and spotted Brooke-Rawle leading the left wing. Galloping at full speed, he narrowed his eyes and spotted a stone-and-rail fence ahead and veered to the right. After his right wing cleared the fence, he twisted in his saddle. *Damn.* Brook-Rawle's trailing left wing had detoured to the left of the fence. A thirty-yard gap separated the two squadrons. He twisted back around and dug his spurs into his mount. His noble beast bolted ahead, tearing up the turf.

He tightened his ears for the horrid crash of two bursting sea swells. Holding his breath, he raised his saber with his right arm half bent, the wrist level with his forehead, the point of the blade in the air pointed at the late-afternoon sun. The hollow space between the two forces faded in a heartbeat. A yard away from a Rebel, he extended his arm to full length and fired a vertical cut, slicing to the right across the Rebel's cheek. The grayback yelled, and blood sprayed into the air like red rain as he tumbled from his mount.

After the first crash of horses, the Rebels had opened their files like a furrowed field. His troopers swept through the openings like jousting medieval knights, parrying and cutting. He spotted his next victim bending forward on his mount. As they passed, he swung a horizontal cut and slashed the Rebel across the arm.

He turned his head and saw that Sergeant Gregg's squadron was with him. *Good.* Where was Brooke-Rawle? His heart's thundering gallop matched his horse's pounding hooves. The ground vibrated beneath their thundering tramp. He continued racing forward across the rear portion of the Rebel charge, like a crosscut saw cutting against the grain.

Daylight emerged ahead and they surged through the mass of graybacks in a wild, boiling tempest. They had cut through, hacking the last line of gray scoundrels. *We must regroup.* He reined up. Sergeant Gregg pulled up next to him, sweat streaming from his face, his blue uniform covered in red blotches.

The sergeant shouted and twirled his saber above his head. His squadron pulled up.

"Sergeant Gregg, are you wounded?" Miller asked.

"No, sir."

"Good. Our charge has cut off the rear portion of the Rebel squadrons from their main body. They are racing back toward Cress Ridge like scared rabbits."

"Let's chase them!" Gregg clamored.

Miller's eyes flicked toward the Rummel farm. An unsupported Confederate battery consisting of four ordnance rifles stood one hundred yards ahead.

He pointed, shouting, "Aim for that Rebel battery beyond the Rummel farm."

Sergeant Gregg and Private E.G. Eyster raced their mounts forward. The Pennsylvanians erupted into a cheer, spurring their horses as if in a steeplechase.

Miller smiled. *If anyone can take the Rebel battery, it's Sergeant Gregg.*

4:35 p.m.
Sergeant Thomas Gregg
One hundred yards south of the Rummel barn

The wind whisked past him like a breeze in tall wheat as his horse carried him flying across the field. Gregg smiled, tight-lipped. He had a clear shot over the rolling fields at the Rummel farm. On Cress Ridge, beyond the farm, was a stand of dense woods. Private Eyster pulled ahead as they raced toward the enemy artillery battery in front of the trees.

He crested an earthen berm. A saber flashed in the sunlight and his heart jumped. A screaming Rebel galloping on a large black warhorse was ten yards away. Gregg pulled hard on the reins and veered to the right. Raising his saber, he parried the enemy's sword. He gritted his teeth and swung a level, backhanded stroke, slicing the Rebel's throat. The Rebel half choked and plunged to the ground, dead.

Ahead, Private Eyster had halted and was holding his carbine on a dismounted Confederate. A mounted Rebel charged Eyster on his blind side.

Gregg shouted, "Behind you, Private Eyster."

Eyster twisted in his saddle and fired his carbine, hitting the enemy in the chest. The dismounted Rebel drew his revolver and shot Eyster's horse. Eyster tumbled to the ground. He reached for his carbine.

The Rebel shouted, "You're my prisoner! Drop your rifle!"

Gregg's stomach knotted. He spurred his horse and slashed the Rebel with his saber. He started to turn his head, but a flashing sword made him flinch. A Rebel yelled and, with a right cut, sliced off the top of his scalp. He tumbled to the ground, gasping for air. Heat like scorching flames licked his face. Blood cascaded down his face. His mind clouded as the battlefield thundering feathered into a dull din.

A distant voice said, "You're my prisoner. An ambulance will take you to a surgeon."

4:41 p.m.
Captain William Miller
Entrance of the Rummel wagon shed

Miller dashed toward the unsupported enemy artillery battery with Sergeant Heagy galloping at his side. Two other sergeants were trailing, sabers pointed toward the target. A long, thunderous roar blasted from the battery. Shells whizzed overhead. Miller's skin prickled, and uncertainty haunted him. His detachment was between the Rebels charging south and the Rebel rear guard sitting on Cress Ridge. It felt like a head vice had been fitted to his skull and the Rebels would start compressing the torture device at any time. *Must keep riding fast or be squeezed to death.*

Heagy pointed with his saber. "Let's barrel over those Rebels."

Twenty yards ahead, a thickset Confederate officer was trying to rally his men. His battery had not been firing. Miller's veins pulsed with furor. *We can capture it.* He licked his cracked lips. His throat was chafed leather, and smoke stung his eyes.

Bullets sang past. A ripple of uneasiness shuddered overhead like the cold breeze of a threatening storm front. He glanced toward Little Run. Rattling fire had erupted from dismounted enemy behind a fence.

He shrilled a cry. "Head for the Rummel Barn!"

Miller's lungs gasped for air as he rushed to the Rummel barn. Eight troopers reined up next to him. *My God, that's all?* He scanned the area, searching desperately for more.

A trooper pointed and shouted, "There's Sergeant Heagy."

Sergeant Heagy and the two other sergeants rode fifteen yards beyond the Rummel Barn. The Rebels were throwing stones at them. The other enemy gunners were limbering up their artillery pieces and withdrawing them.

"Hell," Miller muttered, "if only I had more troopers, we could take that battery."

A whizzing minié ball breathed hotly on his neck. He gasped and jerked his head. His neck trembled as he touched the skin under his scarf. *Thank God, no blood.* But his neck throbbed like a razor cut. He glanced up. A dismounted enemy swarm was rushing from Cress Woods toward the battery.

He pointed. "Sergeant Heagy. Back to the Rummel barn."

He trailed the three sergeants as they sprinted back toward the barn. He reined up, and from behind the shed a mounted Rebel emerged with his sword raised for a vertical cut. A chill shot down his back. His horse snorted and fidgeted as he pulled hard on the reins. He raised his sword. The Rebel screamed and swung his saber, and Miller parried it. His hand shook and his saber snapped in two. *Damn.* He threw the saber hilt at the Rebel, who ducked. He gripped his revolver and aimed it.

"You are my prisoner," he shouted. "Drop your saber and revolver and dismount."

The Rebel glared for a few heartbeats and then complied.

"Now go inside the wagon shed." The prisoner stepped into the wagon shed. Miller turned his mount and slapped the hindquarters of the Rebel's horse. It galloped riderless toward Cress Ridge. Clapping hooves echoed as the remaining troopers of his squadron arrived and formed a line of thirty yards. The battle-thunder roared like an approaching tornado as the Confederates raced northward like horses fleeing through an open gate. He shuddered. They would have to cut their way through the crumbling Rebels before the enemy could tighten the head vice and crush his skull.

He gulped a bucket of air and shouted, "Sergeant Heagy. Follow me! We're riding back to the Lott farm."

He clapped his spurs and his mount started trotting in a northeasterly loop around the melee toward the Low Dutch Road. He glanced back over his shoulder, where his troopers were riding in a line a horse-length behind. Their mounts' hooves thumped on the field and leaped over corpses strewn across the battlefield. He tugged on the reins and trotted by two fallen troopers. He shuddered.

"Oh, my God," he muttered. "Everything is going to the Devil."

A Third Pennsylvania private and a Rebel trooper had cut each other down with their sabers and were lying with their feet together, their heads in opposite directions, and the bloodstained saber of each still tight in his grip. *Poor souls.*

He dug his heels into his mount's flanks and slashed through the mounted Rebels fleeing like a long string of ants scrambling back to the safety of their mound. The graybacks appeared licked and bone-weary, many marked with blood-soaked splotches on their gray jackets.

A Confederate on a black mount blocked his path and charged with his sword raised. A demonic rage flooded his veins. He gripped the captured Rebel officer's sword, leaned to his left, and fired a backhanded saber cut as the horses streaked by like a medieval jousting duel. A scream erupted. He pointed the sword forward and glanced at the blade dipping blood.

Sergeant Heagy shouted, "You slashed the Rebel in the thigh."

He nodded as his squadron continued angling toward the rectangular woods above the Lott woods. After galloping for a few moments, the Confederate troopers started passing behind his squadron as the graybacks galloped toward Cress Ridge.

"Sergeant Heagy," he shouted, "when we arrive at our line of departure, spread out the troopers in the same formation we had before."

"Yes, sir."

4:26 p.m. (15 minutes earlier)
Lieutenant William Brooke-Rawle
Northwestern edge of the Lott Woods

Brooke-Rawle pitched forward in his saddle and screamed above the racketing roar as he raced toward the Rebel left flank. His peripheral vision caught Miller's right wing, veering right, piercing into the Confederate flank, and disappearing in the melee.

Rebels shouted, "We're attacked in the rear!"

Brooke-Rawle's breath pitched. General Hampton was furiously brandishing his sword next to his brigade flag in the swirling middle of Custer's Wolverines. Wolverines and Rebels were locked together, friend and foe, falling and crushing beneath the angry tread. The charging New Jersey squadron dashed toward the traitorous red flag. Hampton was cutting and slashing Wolverines in the churning throng.

Several New Jersey troopers surged like demons of death, hemming Hampton against a fence. One trooper fired his sword in a high, swirling cut and sliced Hampton's scalp. Hampton screamed, blood streaming down his face. The Rebel general wheeled his horse and leaped over the fence. The Jerseyans erupted into a cheer.

Brooke-Rawle's bugler shouted, "Lieutenant, look to your left."

A river of graybacks twenty yards away was streaming to the rear, threatening to overrun his squadron. He raised his saber and parried a blow. Sparks flew as steel clashed on steel. He wielded his saber again, slashing the Rebel. A horse reared, pawed the air, its rider tumbling to the ground, trampled under the terrified hooves of a passing horse. Battle-thunder boomed. Cries and screams swelled.

Brooke-Rawle reined up as their cleaving momentum floundered. A continuous racket of clashing sabers, shouting men, and neighing horses filled the air. First Sergeant John Brandon, ten yards away, was turning his mount in circles. My God, everything was going to the Devil! They were caught in a whirlpool of retreating Rebels galloping north.

He shouted, "Stick together, lads!" He unholstered his revolver and fired the pistol at the fleeing Rebels, hitting two in the back. He pulled the trigger again. Click. *Damn.* The revolver was empty. A Rebel closed and swung his saber. He lunged to his left against the cut and parried the blow. The Rebel snarled and closed again, swinging his saber. With Brook-Rawle unable to make short work of the grayback, the two of them cut and thrust for several seconds. The duel paused, and his path was blocked by five Southerners flourishing their sabers in the air.

His dueling opponent shouted, "Surrender, you son of a whore."

His stomach knotted; scalding rage flared up his neck. He reached for a second pistol tucked into his boot. "Go to hell!"

His thumb yanked on the hammer. It didn't budge. *Damn. Can't cock it.* His heart quaked. He pitched the pistol. *Crack.* The weapon hit the scoundrel across the nose bridge. Blood spurted.

First Sergeant John Brandon and three other troopers burst past him firing their pistols, and dashed the Rebels back as coolly as the sturdy rock repels the ocean's foam. Two Confederates dropped dead, and the others scattered. The ground was strewn with fallen riders and their horses.

Brandon shouted, "Follow us, Lieutenant!"

He spurred his mare and raised his sword, firing it down upon the back of a retreating Rebel. He followed Brandon's mount. The first sergeant cut his way through the Rebel cavalry and paused thirty yards beyond the enemy's left flank.

Brooke-Rawle cast his gaze on the chaos. He spotted a hatless officer with golden, flowing hair and a red scarf, wheeling his saber, driving the Rebels north.

"First Sergeant Brandon! Let's join Custer and the First Michigan."

He elevated his right arm to full extension, with the saber pointing level to the ground. He thrust his boots home in the stirrups and crouched slightly in the saddle, bending forward from the waist. His left hand gripped the reins near the base of the mount's neck and grasped until the horse was on the bit. His eyes locked on Custer's red scarf.

72

Gregg — Friday, July 3

4:41 p.m.
General David Gregg, talking to Captain Henry Weir
Reever house

Calm yourself. Jeb's troopers have yet to broach the strategic inter-section. Gregg spotted Colonel McIntosh's brigade flag charging into the Confederates' right flank.

He pointed. "Henry, Colonel McIntosh is charging the right flank of the enemy with a small band of mounted troopers."

"A New Jersey mounted squadron is hitting Stuart's left flank," Weir informed him. "Beyond the New Jersey, Captain Miller's mounted attack is cutting a swath through the last fourth of the Rebel's left flank."

A warm breath of hope began to thaw Gregg's icy uncertainty. "With Custer leading the First Michigan and breaking the center of the Rebel charge, this battle is shaping up like Hannibal's great pincer victory over the Romans at Cannae."

"Wasn't the Roman force twice as large as the Carthaginians?"

"Yes. Hannibal was outnumbered two to one, like I am. Thank God for Custer and the First Michigan holding the middle against overwhelming numbers while Custer and McIntosh's remaining forces are winning the struggles on the flanks and in the rear."

"We don't have the number of forces to encircle and destroy the enemy as Hannibal did."

"Agreed. But these sharp flanking blows and Pennington's and Randol's devasting artillery barrages have halted the Rebel charge. If we can hold, we have achieved my goal of this chess match of preventing Stuart's cavalry from crossing the Hanover Road and attacking the rear of the Union army."

Captain George A. Custer

73

Custer — Friday, July 3

4:45 p.m.
Custer, pursuing the skedaddling Rebels
Six hundred yards southeast from the Rummel farm

Custer twisted in his saddle and glanced at the Rummel farm ahead, swarming with bluecoats.

He shouted, "Norvell, who are those Federal troopers?"

"I believe they are a squadron from the Third Pennsylvania that sliced through the last fourth of the Rebel formation."

Custer pulled up. Squadrons of bluecoats were attacking both enemy flanks. Graybacks were darting from the melee and scurrying north toward Cress Ridge.

"Norvell, I don't think Stuart expected flank attacks after the First Michigan charged their center."

Churchill pointed. "General Custer, the Third Pennsylvania troopers are departing the Rummel farm area and looping back toward the Lott farm."

Custer twirled his saber. "Wolverines, form a line facing south."

The First Michigan troopers formed a line and he trotted out in front of them.

Churchill said, "General, the line is formed."

"Charge!" Custer shouted."

He lurched ahead through the gap they had created when attacking north. A howling gray demon charged with his saber drawn. Custer lunged to his left and thrust his saber into the horseman's belly.

A mounted Rebel shouted, "General Hampton has been wounded. Retreat!"

Confederates were splitting like the Red Sea, creating a thoroughfare for his galloping Wolverines. Off to his left, Chester's

589

battery was thundering. He reined up and held up his saber. The Wolverines halted.

Custer shouted, "Form up."

The First Michigan formed up, facing north on a line west of Chester's battery. The troopers were bloodied and breathing hard.

"Are you going to charge again?" Churchill asked him.

He shook his head. "No. Let's wait here to see if Stuart is going to mount another assault."

"It looks like the lines are drifting apart, as if satisfied."

Custer grinned. "If Stuart wants to have another go, I'm more than willing."

5:00 p.m.
Custer
West of Chester's battery

A thunderous cheer burst forth from the First Michigan. The defeated Rebels on Cress Ridge were lingering about and not forming up. Custer grinned and turned, waving to the long line of mounted Wolverines. A thrill flushed through him.

"Norvell, Stuart is not going to attack again. We've won!"

"I thought I had lost you on this latest charge when you were unhorsed," Churchill said.

"Custer luck." He uttered a deep sigh. "Poor Roanoke. I shouldn't have ridden him on the second charge. As soon as the skirmish lines are set, would you please send someone to find him? I will meet you at the Spangler house after I speak with General Gregg."

He paused and scanned the Rummel field. Death quivered above the battleground in the rancid air. The bloody field was heaped with a horde of ghostly figures that had blossomed like wild mushrooms. The tangled blue and gray corpses lay sprawled in bizarre postures. Entrails lay spilled from ruptured bellies. *God, what a fight.* Would anyone remember that his fearless Wolverines had saved the right flank of the army at the Battle of Gettysburg?

74

Miller — Friday, July 3

5:00 p.m.
Miller's Third Pennsylvania receives a visit from Colonel McIntosh
Woods north of the Lott farm

Captain Miller and his squadron were dismounted at the edge of the Lott woods when Colonel McIntosh trotted toward them and reined up.

Miller saluted. "That was one hell of a fight, Colonel!"

McIntosh returned the salute and grinned. "William, I couldn't be prouder of the charge you made. You delivered the coup de grace against Stuart's left flank by slicing through his rear with your charge to the Rummel farm."

"Thank you, sir. I saw an opportunity to exploit the Rebels' rear and took the initiative to attack."

"I'm mighty glad you did, because I was tied up on the Rebel right flank, attacking with my staff."

Miller paused and scratched his chin. "You ordered me to protect the Low Dutch Road and I thought I could do that by attacking the Rebels before they attacked my position."

"Again, I compliment you on using your initiative to exploit an opportunity. I'm directing you to collect your men and assume your old position." The colonel winked. "No more attacks this evening unless I order them."

"Yes, sir."

Major General George A. Custer

75

Gregg — Friday, July 3

7:44 p.m. (Sunset)
General David Gregg
Reever house, Gregg's field headquarters

Twilight was kindling on the battlefield, but the nation's dawning light was shining on the heroic boy general. Gregg beamed. *What an incredible feat. There was not another dragoon this afternoon who contributed more to bring about this victory over Jeb Stuart than the very gallant George Custer.*

And when the boy general reined up, his face speckled with dried blood and his black velvet jacket covered in dust, dirt, and brownish-red splotches like rust, he dismounted and saluted, his words booming in a high-pitched voice. "Stuart is departing Cress Ridge for York Pike. He is conceding defeat. The gallant First Michigan are the masters of the field, having charged a force outnumbering them five to one." He paused and took a deep breath. "I'm proud to have led my Wolverines against the much-vaunted Jeb Stuart and his Invincibles. The Rebels departed the battlefield for safety, after being beaten in a headlong fight."

Gregg's beard split into a white-toothed grin. "Thank you, George, and thanks to your valiant Michigan Brigade. I don't believe the First Michigan charge you led has its equal in this war, if ever."

Custer wiped his face with a handkerchief. "It was a costly fight. We've been burying the dead and tending to the wounded. The First and Fifth suffered fifty casualties, the Sixth a dozen, and the Seventh one hundred."

"Between your brigade and McIntosh's brigade, you suffered almost ninety percent of the two hundred fifty casualties."

Custer nodded. "This cavalry battle truly mattered. We prevented Stuart from attacking the rear of Meade's army. The sheer shock power of the First Michigan frontal charge was in the tradition of Murat."

"Agreed. Stuart certainly failed to deliver a crushing kidney punch in Meade's backside. The good news is that I've learned the Rebel infantry attack against Meade's middle was also repulsed. After being in command for six days, Meade has won the greatest victory of the war."

Custer grinned. "That is great news!"

Gregg paused, letting the silence and tension build like an approaching thunderstorm. Praise turned to criticism. "I didn't expect you to lead either the Seventh Michigan or the First Michigan cavalry charges. That's why I ordered Colonel Mann and Colonel Town to make the charges. You're a brigade commander now, George."

Custer's devilish face beamed as he squeezed the grip on his sheathed saber. "I always lead a Wolverine attack because I don't want my dragoons to go where I can't lead."

Gregg's jaw tightened. "George, I know you're not afraid to fight like a private soldier."

Custer grimaced, plainly shocked at this rebuke.

Gregg studied the boy general fidgeting. *Custer is Kilpatrick's responsibility. Don't be overcritical. He just jumped several grades from captain to general and hasn't had time to learn the repose necessary in high command.*

"I want to compliment you on deploying your dismounted troopers and your employment of the new repeating Spencer rifle. Also, your tactical deployment of Pennington's battery was crucial to the victory. Well done, George."

Custer smiled.

"Again, thank you. You led by example, and you earned your spurs today in the long tradition of the cavalry."

"Thank you, sir."

"I sent an aide to General Kilpatrick, telling him that I have released you from the duties I assigned you protecting the army's right flank at the Rummel farm. I told him of the gallant performance of your Michigan Brigade and the two cavalry charges you led that prevented Stuart from attacking Meade's rear. I also informed General Kilpatrick that I had sent an aide to General Pleasonton to inform General Meade of your brigade's gallant performance."

"I'm most grateful you were impressed with my Wolverines."

"George, I'm directing you to return to Two Taverns along the Baltimore Pike and, once there, to report to General Kilpatrick for further orders."

Custer saluted and departed.

Gregg turned to Captain Weir. "Henry," he mused, knocking his pipe against his bootheel to empty it, "Custer loves fighting. War is a boyish adventure for him, and he is a romantic who is always seeking the glory of leading Napoleonic cavalry charges like Murat. Hell, he dresses like Murat. Custer possesses courage, but he is too impetuous. It is as though he believes he is invincible."

"Thank God General Custer is on our side, sir," Weir said. "You did a good job unleashing him as your knight in this chess game."

"I agree. As boyish as Custer is brave, he needs someone to restrain him." He shook his head, tamping down his pipe. "But I'm sending him back to General Kilpatrick, who is as impetuous as Custer and also likes to attack without deliberation. They are like two peas in a pod."

Weir grinned. "One difference, sir. Custer orders charges and leads his men and *is* glorious. Kilpatrick orders charges and sits back, *taking* the glory."

Gregg chuckled. "Kilpatrick can't take credit for Custer's heroics today. That was all Custer and his glorious Wolverines."

Private Norvell Francis Churchill

76

Custer — Friday, July 3

The western corner of the night sky was filling with dark, ominous thunderheads. Custer grimaced. Hopefully, the brigade would arrive at the Two Taverns bivouac before the torrential rains began. He trotted down the Low Dutch Road, leading the four regiments of his Michigan Brigade. He yawned. His shoulder ached from tumbling off Roanoke. *Poor Roanoke. Damn't.* He should have never ridden his iron-gray stallion in the second charge. Roanoke needed to rest after the Seventh Michigan charge. He touched the minié ball in his jacket pocket, the one that the surgeon removed from Roanoke's foreleg. Shards of grief swirled through him, slashing him empty. He wiped a tear. *I'm sorry, Roanoke.* He would send his glorious warhorse back to his father's farm to live the rest of his life in peace.

A breeze rolled in softly with the smell of rain in it. Darkness lay wholly around Churchill, trotting next to him. His good luck charm was riding with his eyes half closed. Every commander needed a Norvell Churchill along his side.

A cramp gripped his calf and he stood up in his stirrups. The spasm eased and he slumped back down in the saddle. He smiled. The daredevil elixir he gulped down today leading two cavalry charges had buoyed his spirits and barred his aching body from crushing his mind. His brain burst with brilliant flashes of pride and his skin tingled as glory's hypnotic power washed over him. This was the greatest moment in his life. Not even Murat had accomplished what he had today. Twenty-three years old and he

597

had proved his mettle. He defeated the undefeated. He was the nation's hero.

How soon could he lead another cavalry charge?

Custer trotted down the Baltimore Pike. Even though driving sheets of rain were gushing from the pitch-black sky, tonight's blackness seemed to shelter a strong, welcome silence, compared to today's seething air packed with thundering cannons, cracking revolvers, and hideous screams. How long would the silence last?

Hopefully not too long. There was more glory to be had. His taut muscles were finally loosening, like a constrictor uncoiling from a strangled prey. The bloodlust fever coursing through his veins this afternoon was dissipating. Now a joyous spirit pulsed through him, soothing his aching bones.

Churchill said, "General, Lieutenant Colerick and another rider are trotting up the road."

Colerick and Captain Llewellyn Estes, General Kilpatrick's assistant adjutant general, reined up and saluted.

"Your headquarters tent is pitched at the Two Taverns bivouac," Colerick said. "Your quartermaster has deployed his teamsters and commissary wagons to feed the four regiments. Your cook has whipped up a hot dinner for you and Johnny, and your dog Rose is waiting for you in your tent."

"Good." He turned to Captain Estes. "Llewellyn, what word do you have from General Kilpatrick?"

"General Kilpatrick is riding over from the Round Tops and should be here in about an hour. General Pleasonton informed General Kilpatrick that the Confederate cavalry might ride down the Baltimore Pike and try to attack your brigade."

Custer brightened. "I will send a squadron from the Fifth Michigan up the Pike and have them dismount and lie down beside the road and set up an ambush."

"General Kilpatrick directs that your brigade will remain in bivouac at Two Taverns this evening and then in the morning you will ride to Emmitsburg and meet up with General Farnsworth's old brigade," Estes said.

"What do you mean, 'old brigade'?"

Estes's voice broke. "General Farnsworth was killed leading an attack this afternoon."

Custer's mouth creased as acrid bile raced up his throat and a storm screamed in his ears. "My God, Elon's dead." He swallowed, trying to control his fury. "What a tragic loss."

"General Kilpatrick wanted me to ride ahead and tell Captain James Kidd about General Farnsworth's death. They were schoolmates at the University of Michigan."

"Understood. Captain Kidd commands Troop E in the Sixth Regiment."

Colerick said, "I will escort Captain Estes to visit with Captain Kidd."

"Very well."

Estes and Colerick departed.

He turned to Churchill, no longer able to hide his anger. A bitter fever heated his blood as he fought to control his impulses for rash revenge. "Norvell, I'm shocked with General Farnsworth's death."

Churchill nodded. "That's tragic news."

Custer's expression could not disguise that he thought it was much more than news, and much worse than tragic. If damn Kilpatrick had done what he suspected, it was downright unforgivable. "I will address Elon's death with Kilpatrick. It had better not be in vain."

"General, we almost lost you today," Churchill interjected. "I'm surprised you weren't trampled to death after being unhorsed. Several Wolverines and Rebels were crushed."

"It was Custer luck that a horse came my way," Custer muttered darkly, his eyes distant, seeing another killing field altogether.

Captain James Kidd

77

Kidd — Friday, July 3

10:50 p.m.
Captain James Kidd
Two Taverns Bivouac

Kidd stood under a large tree outside his tent, watching the rain pelt the field. He glanced at Web, inside the tent drinking coffee and eating a hot stew. Clapping hooves approached and he watched Second Lieutenant William Colerick and Captain Llewellyn Estes rein up and dismount.

He smiled. "Llewellyn, did you ride over to Wolverine Brigade to get some hot victuals?"

"I wish that was the case," Estes said. "I rode over to tell you that your college schoolmate, General Elon Farnsworth, was killed this afternoon conducting an attack. General Kilpatrick wanted me to tell you that sad news in person. I'm sorry, James."

Kidd's heart wrenched. "Oh, my God."

Web emerged from the tent. "I heard you say that General Farnsworth was killed. How did it happen?"

Estes shook his head. "About one p.m. the Rebels opened with a most terrific cannonade. Around three p.m., Rebel infantry were spotted advancing against the middle of Cemetery Ridge. General Kilpatrick was convinced that the Rebels' aim was to sweep away our cavalry and then turn on the Union position on Little Round Top. So, Kilpatrick decided Farnsworth should attack a strong Rebel force positioned behind a rock fence. If Kilpatrick could break through this defensive line, his hope was the Confederate right flank would collapse and give General Meade an opportunity to destroy Lee's army."

Kidd said, "Did Farnsworth lead this attack?"

"No. Colonel Nathaniel Richmond led his West Virginia Cavalry in the attack, and they were cut up by the Rebels behind the fence. Then Kilpatrick ordered Colonel Brinton, commanding the Eighteenth Pennsylvania Cavalry, to charge. The Rebels bogged down that charge and Brinton's troopers dismounted and formed a line and skirmished with the enemy. Then Kilpatrick wanted Farnsworth to charge an enemy battery. Farnsworth rode ahead to examine the ground and discovered it was heavily timbered and swampy. At this point, the West Virginians retreated from the stone wall. Kilpatrick then ordered Farnsworth to charge the wall with the Vermont Cavalry."

Kidd's jaw tensed. "What did Farnsworth say?"

"Farnsworth said he regarded the charge as simple murder. There was a loud, heated exchange. Kilpatrick shouted, 'Do you refuse to obey my orders? If you are afraid to lead this charge, I will lead it.' Farnsworth said, 'Take that back. I ask no man to lead my troops forward.'"

"Did Farnsworth lead the charge?" Kidd asked, knowing what the answer would be.

"Yes. He fell with his saber raised and was hit five times."

"Damn." Kidd shook his head. "Thank you for informing me of these events, Llewellyn."

Captain Estes nodded, mounted his horse, and departed.

Kidd turned to Web, bitter. "Damn Kilpatrick goaded Elon into making a suicide charge. Elon was proud and brave and possessed an intrepid spirit. He was true as steel to his country and his convictions of duty." He wiped a tear from his eye. "He was poised, like Custer, and had discretion as well as dash. But Elon was too brave a man and too conscientious to do anything else than obey orders to the letter." He stopped and drew a breath. "All Kilpatrick cared about was gaining glory by recklessly sacrificing the lives of his troopers for no good purpose whatsoever."

"Damn Kill-Cavalry!" Web frowned. "I misread Custer, knowing he graduated from West Point the same year as that heartless cur."

"I did, too," Kidd said, staring off into the distance. "When I first saw the boy general in his circus outfit, I thought he was a vainglory popinjay. I hated him when he instituted the rigid discipline upon taking command of the brigade." He turned back to Web. "But when he led the cavalry charge at Hunterstown and was unhorsed and staved off several attackers with his sword, my hatred turned to respect." He kept nodding, as if seeing each event over again. "And after he led the Seventh and First Regiments in cavalry charges today and defeated Jeb Stuart's Invincibles, I have the greatest admiration for him."

A thunderclap burst, and rain fell in sheets. "James," Web said, "what did you think of General Gregg's performance?"

Kidd smiled. "Gregg saw the immense risk of guarding the army's right flank with two decimated brigades of his own division. If Custer's presence on the field was providential, it is General Gregg to whom, under Providence, the credit for bringing Custer there is due."

Web nodded.

"Gregg's leadership and tactical sense were superb. He fought a well-planned battle. He maneuvered the different commands with the same shrewdness as a skillful chess player moving pawns upon a chessboard." Kidd paused and rubbed his chin as quiet hovered momentarily.

Web's lips broke into a faint half-smile. "Yes, Gregg's calm and methodical leadership was reassuring during the battle today. I was impressed with his ability to foresee what Stuart was planning and counter the enemy moves."

Kidd nodded. "Gregg never made a false play. From the time he turned Custer northward, until he sent the First Michigan charging against the brigades of Hampton and Fitzhugh Lee, his tactics were flawless. General Gregg distinguished himself for his quick perceptions at critical moments."

"I agree with you about General Gregg's strategic performance at the strategic intersection," Web said. "Gregg played his chess pieces brilliantly. Custer was a fearless chess piece, the glorious knight, who executed Gregg's orders with the flare of his hero, Charles O'Malley, the dashing dragoon."

Kidd grinned. "If there was any poetry or romance in war, Custer could develop it."

Custer and Libbie with his brother, Thomas W. Custer (standing)

78

Custer — Friday, July 3

Custer beamed, sitting at a small table inside his tent, gripping a quill pen between his first and second bony fingers, writing about his glorious Wolverines. A yellow flame flickered from a lantern sitting on the small writing table. His heart was nearly bursting with pride. He reread his last few sentences.

> *I cannot find language to express my high appreciation of the First Michigan Cavalry. They advanced to the charge of a vastly superior force with as much precision as if going on parade; and I challenge the annals of warfare to produce a more brilliant or successful charge of cavalry.*

He dipped the quill pen into the ink jar. Too bad he couldn't thank General Meade in person for taking a huge risk promoting him from captain to general. His glorious battlefield exploits of saving the right flank of the Union army had proven Meade had made the right decision. He drew the pen up, scraped the excess ink off the nib, and, using light pressure, started writing.

> *Let us hope our victorious work today is just the beginning and the Fates provide me many more opportunities to lead my Wolverines in cavalry charges.*

From just outside the tent, Private Fought shouted, "General Custer, it's Joseph and Johnny. The logistics train just arrived, and we have your personal trunk."

"Please enter." He pointed to Rose, who lay sprawled on a blanket. "Just put it next to Rose. Thank you, boys."

"Your cook said the rabbit stew will be ready soon," Fought said.

"I'm starved." Johnny wiped his nose with his shirt sleeve. "I haven't eaten since breakfast."

Custer grinned. "You don't call the hardtack I saw you munching on at noon eating?"

Johnny shook his head and squished his nose as if he had sniffed a vile odor. "It was salty and so hard it could stop a bullet. I threw it away."

Fought pulled on Johnny's sleeve. "Let's go. General Custer needs to finish his writing. You will get your fill of stew in a bit." Fought led Johnny out of the tent.

Custer picked up the lantern and sat it next to the trunk. He unbuckled the two straps circling the chest, unhitched the latch, and raised the lid. He reached inside and flicked open a hatbox. His fingers fished out a small black box. He carried the lantern to the writing table and gently opened the black box. His heart fluttered like a hovering hummingbird. He picked up Libbie's secret gift and knuckled his eyes at the initials *L* and *A* inscribed inside the gold ring. "*L* and *A*. Libbie and Autie," he whispered. It had been so long since he'd heard her sweet voice call him by that name. How much longer until he could hear it again?

He scowled. Would he ever be able to wear this cherished gift, publicly avowing his love for Libbie? It all depended on him overcoming Judge Bacon's unyielding disapproval. Perhaps today's battlefield exploits and his growing fame would enhance his status with the judge.

The lamplight splintered against the gold ring. Pride burned in his heart. His only fear was a farewell to glory. Fame was fleeting, like a sparkling star disappearing with the breaking dawn. Maintaining battlefield notoriety as the Union's beau sabreur required several repeat hell-bending performances. His stomach cramped as if a vice was tightening around it. Would he ever get a chance to lead another glorious cavalry charge like today's First Michigan charge on the Rummel field?

Colerick stepped into the opening of the tent. "General Custer. General Kilpatrick is arriving with some of his staff."

Custer glanced up and nodded, his nostrils flaring. He laid the quill down on the table and slipped the ring into his trouser pocket. The ember smoldering at the back of his mind flared to life again, an angry torch, a raging bonfire. *What villainous folly. Farnsworth shouldn't be dead. Kilpatrick's quest for glory killed Farnsworth.*

He stood up and stepped out of the tent.

General Kilpatrick swung slowly from his saddle, puddles spilling off the front brim of his hat onto his poor, drenched horse. Custer donned his own hat, strode toward him, and saluted. "Good evening, General. Please join me in my tent."

Kilpatrick returned the salute and trundled into the tent, cringed, and rubbed his lower back. After a moment, he sat down slowly at the table, plainly in pain. Custer sat down across from him and drew a deep breath. How would Judson Kilpatrick react to his justified defiance?

Custer laid his hands on top of his battle report. "I'm most proud of my Michigan Wolverines. I led them in two death-defying charges this afternoon against Stuart's troopers, and we beat them back."

Kilpatrick stared for a long moment, scowling, his right hand clenching and unclenching. The contempt seething in his eyes was clear, but he held his sharp tongue. Gregg must have told General Pleasonton about the Wolverines' great performance. Kilpatrick was in a pickle. *He can't discipline me for disobeying orders because Gregg covered for me and I'm a glorious hero.*

Kilpatrick's eyes narrowed and his brow furrowed like a freshly plowed field. "All praise is due to you, George, and your Wolverines and Captain Pennington's battery," he said, pausing. Rancor laced with envy dripped through his voice. The silence grew like a morning mist. "General Gregg sent an aide to General Pleasonton after his one brigade and *my* one brigade, commanded by you, defeated Jeb Stuart." For a moment, Kilpatrick sat frozen, his face flushed scarlet. "Both Pleasonton and Meade were most impressed with your courage and leadership in today's fight. How ironic and fortuitous for you that General Gregg said he ordered you to stay and fight after I ordered you to return to my division."

Custer beamed with devilish mischief as Kilpatrick frowned and tightened his white lips.

Kilpatrick went on. "I consider it a mistake and not disobedience that you didn't return immediately to my division when ordered to do so."

"I was just following a superior officer's orders, sir."

Kilpatrick slammed his hand on the table. The whooshing air fluttered the lantern's flames and the light flickered across Judson's hawkish nose. "That's hogwash, George. As your West Point schoolmate, I'm well aware that you follow the orders you like and break the ones you don't."

Custer cleared his throat and held his gaze. He struggled to curb the frigid tone of his voice. "I am most saddened that General Farnsworth was killed today."

Kilpatrick broke eye contact. "It was a great charge. We almost broke through the Rebels' right flank." He eased forward in his chair and wagged his finger. "If your brigade was alongside Farnsworth's brigade this afternoon, I'm sure I could have swept through Lee's rear guard and destroyed his logistics trains. My cavalry division could have delivered the coup d'état that would have destroyed Lee's army."

Custer sneered. "Didn't you have General Merritt's brigade supporting you?"

A sickly pallor washed over Kilpatrick's face, as though an embalmer had drained all the blood from his sallow skin. Kilpatrick scowled and speared him with a violent glare.

Dark silence crept in like a funeral parade, squeezing Custer's nerves as if heavier and heavier stones were pressing down onto his body. *Watch yourself. You've baited the banty rooster far enough.*

Custer squeezed his eyelids shut. "What are your orders for my brigade?"

"In the morning, ride to Emmitsburg, where you will meet up with Farnsworth's old brigade. From Emmitsburg, we are riding west and racing to the South Mountain passes before Lee's army does. Meade is not sure if Lee will retreat tomorrow, but if he does, we want to be waiting for him." Kilpatrick paused, his fiendish eyes narrowing into slits. His voice, hardened by sarcasm, could not hide his resentment. "You might get to lead another cavalry charge again, Fanny."

Custer's face flushed with contempt. Kilpatrick's jealous jab, using the name upperclassmen had taunted him with at West Point, still stung. His jaw tightened, but he forced the rage down and stared. *Fine, Judson. You know the national papers will not be writing about you today. They'll be writing about the boy general's long blond curls and his glorious battlefield exploits.*

Kilpatrick's face twisted into a mocking smirk.

Custer gripped his hands behind his back and felt an inner satisfaction beginning to bubble. He would get to lead another cavalry charge soon. And he would enact revenge on Kilpatrick by stealing all the glory again.

He grinned, thrilled at the possibility. "I would love that, General. Thank you."

Kilpatrick stood and glared. "Don't get up. I will see you tomorrow at Emmitsburg. I'm sure you won't get waylaid again and join Buford or Gregg's cavalry divisions." He turned and departed.

Custer's heart danced a jig. Colerick entered the tent, wearing a red scarf. "How did the meeting with General Kilpatrick go?"

"As expected, Kilpatrick is frustrated that I outshined him again today." He stared at Colerick and broke into a huge grin. "Where did you get the red scarf?"

"Private Fought fixed me up." Colerick paused and stared, tight-lipped. "I was chosen to be the sacrificial lamb. After you led the victorious First Michigan charge, several of the Wolverines asked Fought if he could locate more red scarves like the one you wear." A ghost of a smile crossed Colerick's lips. "You inspired your troopers. But they didn't know if you'd object to the brigade wearing them or not?"

Custer threw his hands in the air. "I'm thrilled. The Iron Brigade wears those damn black hats. The flying Wolverine brigade will wear red scarves."

Colerick let out a breath, plainly relieved. "You earned the Wolverines' respect by leading those two charges. I followed close behind you in both. In the second charge you were fearless, screaming like a Berserker." Colerick paused and a panicked shadow flittered across his rugged face. "Just before we collided with Jeb's Invincibles, I felt the Grim Reaper's cold breath. It was like death's waters were breaching a dam and going to wash us away. My body was seized by a rush of terror. But your unwavering courage inspired me and pulled me and the First Wolverines along."

Custer smiled. "Fear can be a source of courage. No trooper wants to fail and let his fellow Wolverines down. But I knew you wouldn't let me down. It takes a man of courage to admit his fears after performing heroically."

"It's a great honor to serve under you, General. All the Wolverines feel the same."

Custer leaned forward, his hands on his knees. "I'm going to tell you why I will lead all Wolverine charges. At West Point I read about Philip of Macedonia, the father of Alexander the Great. Philip said, 'An army of deer led by a lion is more to be feared than an army of lions led by a deer.'" He paused. "After today's battle on the Rummel farm, I would add that a cavalry of Michiganders led by a fearless wolverine is to be feared most of all, for it is unstoppable." A sudden warmth seeped into every corner of his being. He raised his arm as if he were gripping his Toledo saber. "Today, I put the fear of God into Jeb's Invincibles."

Colerick cracked a grin, saluted, and departed.

79

Custer — Friday, July 3

11:40 p.m.
Custer
In his tent at Two Taverns

"General Custer, I have some tasty rabbit stew for you."
Custer glanced up from his desk, grinned, and laid down the dip pen. "Johnny, please enter. I'm starved."

The boy ambled into the tent, looking like an orphaned ragamuffin, and set the steaming bowl and two slices of bread onto the desk.

"Your timing is impeccable, Johnny. I just finished writing my battle report." He whiffed and his gut gave out a low-pitched gurgle. "This smells even better than Mrs. Wirt's stew we had in Hanover."

"It is, General. I gulped down two bowls." Johnny licked his lips and rubbed his stomach. "I'm thinking of having one more." Johnny turned and ducked out into the ranting deluge.

Custer inhaled the zesty aroma, dipped a bread slice into the stew, and took a bite. The hot thickness slipped down his gullet, soothing his battered, bruised body. He dipped the second bread slice and swallowed. Johnny was right. The stew was better than Mrs. Wirt's.

He lifted the inkwell, poured the excess ink into a bottle, corked it, and placed the dip pen into its wooden case. He stole a glance at his watch. Nearly midnight and the fourth of July. Outside the tent opening, several flickering lanterns dangled from tree limbs like floating jack-o'-lanterns, casting an eerie glow over his snoring Wolverines. No sign of anyone moving.

His turbulent mind fidgeted. The steady stream of callers and admirers had trickled off, replaced by emptiness. It was his first

611

boring moment since leading his brigade to the Rummel farm this morning.

Cracking thunder ranted overhead, rocking the tent. He glanced blankly at the lamplight on the desk casting murky shadows on the canvas. His throat tightened. Stillness and uncertainty seeped into the tent, lingering like a valley fog, settling into the hollows of his bones. The thrilling excitement that had been coursing through him all day and night had ebbed. His heroic reflection in the eyes of others had faded into faint memory; had it even happened? He was alone in this empty tent, facing the uncertainty of not courting Libbie. The silence swelled to a deafening roar.

His shoulders slouched; he spooned a bite. The spicy taste could not conceal the bitter bile bubbling up in his throat. A chill shivered through him. For a moment, he fought to gain control over the self-pity welling up.

He muttered a swear. Gripping his Toledo saber, he extended his arm as if parrying a blow. Custer luck was a certainty. He loved being a dragoon daredevil—the thrill of combat; charging at a full gallop, drunk with excitement; recklessly slicing and stabbing; risking life and limb like a dapper riverboat gambler.

Yet, he was frozen with fear that was robbing his spirit as well as his body. He didn't fear death on the battlefield, but he did fear Judge Bacon forever banishing him from courting Libbie. What did Judge Bacon think of him changing his uniform bars for stars? Did the judge think his promotion was deserved or not? How soon would the judge read the papers about his exploits today?

A pang of urgency seized him. He was a creature of glory on the battlefield, possessing unique fighting powers and a superior mind. But in courting Libbie, Judge Bacon saw him as the son of a poor blacksmith, a low-life hellion unfit to court his high-society daughter. His breath caught in his throat. The beau sabreur of the Union army was Jonathan Swift's Gulliver, restrained by Judge Bacon's thousands of snobbish little threads.

Gallant charges were his only hope to win Judge Bacon's approval. But how many more were needed before the judge cut the threads?

Fought stepped into the tent. "I brought you a glass of milk. How is the stew, General?"

He glanced up and his face shifted into his command mask. "It's great." He gulped down another spoonful. "How are my headquarters staff doing?"

"Exhausted, but in great spirits. Most are asleep." Fought scratched his neck. "General, may I speak freely?"

"Sure."

Fought's eyes gleamed like a mirror in the dancing lamplight. It was almost as if he could see his dashing cavalier reflection in Fought's eyes.

"The brigade is singing your praises. A reporter hailed you this evening as the *Boy General of the Golden Locks*. Private William Gage, Company C, Seventh Michigan said he "could ask for no braver General than Custer. By God, Custer is a brick!""

Weightlessness struck Custer's heart and he let out a throaty laugh. "Oh, my God." He stood effortlessly, the injuries of the day forgotten, his eyes unfocused as if in a daydream. "The Boy General of the Golden Locks. Is it true?" He paused, catching his breath. "I'm a *brick*. That's great praise." He swallowed some milk. "Can you believe Fate's irony, Joseph? Promoting a captain to a general who twice defied orders, defeated a superior enemy cavalry, and gained national fame?" His eyes regained their focus; real possibility had grounded him again. "Is it possible Al Waud of *Harper's Weekly* sketched my charge leading the First Michigan as he did my charge at the Battle of Aldie?"

"Sir, I'm not sure about Waud sketching your charge. But reporters did witness your charges. I can tell you, with heartfelt respect, the troopers truly respect your courage and leadership!"

Custer's heart soared as if he were riding a winged horse. "Thank you for telling me how the Wolverines feel about me, Joseph."

Fought saluted and departed.

Impulsive light-bursts pierced his soul's lurking darkness. He was awash in approval. His troopers loved him leading two charges. Most important, his luck would let him do it again. He would lead the Flying Devils of Michigan soon in another cavalry charge, and they would love him even more. By the end of the Battle of Gettysburg, his Wolverines would follow the boy general through the gates of hell.

War was his tonic, his instrument for achieving national fame and winning Libbie's hand. And he could play that instrument like a maestro. He pressed his hand to his pulsing chest and let his heart pull his mind along. The darkness leaking from the seams of his soul after being unhorsed at Huntersville was now replaced by a bursting peremptory spirit. More than ever now, he believed in destiny. *Judge Bacon be damned. Libbie will soon be mine.*

He stared out of the tent opening. The hammering rain pelted the canvas tent, rapping like the drumming cadence of a death march. He caught sight of Churchill, huddling under a rain-soaked oak, gripping his hellfire Spencer, and his thoughts drifted to the fallen Farnsworth and all the young Vermonters who perished because of Kilpatrick's stupidity. *They didn't have to die today.* He shoveled in a few more mouthfuls of rabbit stew, now no warmer than the night air but still delicious, but he barely noticed it. *I warned Elon to stand up to that bully Kilpatrick. It was suicide — a mounted charge through that rocky ground and thick trees, with Confederate infantry hunkered down safe behind stone fences. Damn you, Kilpatrick! How many brave boys did you sacrifice today?*

Anger and restlessness yanked him to his feet.

Farnworth was justified in defying that order. His brigade could have made a dismounted attack over that wretched ground. God's bones! Elon could have pinned down the Rebel infantry, and Merritt's brigade could have brought a mounted charge that would have crushed Lee's right flank. Kilpatrick could have been one of the heroes of Gettysburg, just like he wanted.

Instead, Kilpatrick was a grandmother's goat.

614

Anger and resentment forced his restless feet into a circumscribed march, restricted to the confines of his tent.

Damn him. Drumming up cobbled plans and ordering unsupported assaults that he never leads. Judson is smart. But he doesn't understand the basics of leadership. And intellect without moral courage is worthless and dangerous. Moral courage is leading from the front.

Anger and frustration turned his pacing into something more resembling stomping.

Moral courage is also the will to say and do what is right, regardless of the personal consequences. And Judson Kilpatrick is a coward.

He rummaged through his trunk, found his toothbrush, and started chewing on the hard bristles.

Direct disobedience of orders can be justified by circumstances. The catch is that you must accept the results, in either victory or defeat.

But he did not plan to be defeated — not tomorrow and not ten years from now. He had been blessed with Custer luck. How many times had he defied the odds, rolled the dice, and won? Since he didn't plan to be defeated or killed, he was confident he could exercise justified defiance throughout the war. He refused to blindly follow orders that would cause defeat and destroy his Wolverines. *Poor Farnsworth. Damn it!*

His unspent fervor exploded and he pulled the tent flap aside. Jagged threads of lightning streaked through the inky skies, electrifying his soul. After a heartbeat of darkened silence, cracking thunder bellowed, vibrating his bones. The gods of battle were pleased.

He had fearlessly played the game of war — and won.

He had defied death as the lead actor performing on the world's stage.

He was glory's creature — the beau sabreur of the Union army. Nothing could touch him.

Fortune favors the bold.

Breathless exuberance launched him out of the tent. He drank in the lightning and lifted his face to welcome the relentless summer rain. Flashes of wildness threaded his nerves. What magnificent opportunities would tomorrow offer? How many more chances lay before him to charge, wild and fearless, into the face of Death and defy it? He was immortal. The bullet had not yet been molded to kill him. Doubt over winning Libbie's hand no longer held sway over him. What more could he ask for? He reached into his pocket and gently grasped Libbie's ring. What more could Destiny hold for him but even greater glory?

He glanced toward the massive oak where Churchill, faithful Churchill, stood patiently on duty in the unwavering rain. With Churchill by his side, and the wind of Custer luck at his back, there was nothing that could stop him. Norvell must know that they would be charging again, soon.

"Private Churchill!"

Churchill squinted through the rivulets of rain cascading from the brim of his hat.

"Please join me! I have good news!"

ᗖᕯᕣ Appendix A ᗝᕯᕣ

The widely accepted interpretation of the First Vermont Charge and map on South Cavalry Field on July 3, 1863, is from Captain Henry Parsons's First Vermont Cavalry article in "Farnsworth's Charge and Death," published in *Battles and Leaders of the Civil War: Volume 3*, Castle Publishing, 1883, pages 393-396. Parsons led the First Vermont Cavalry Battalion charge. Parsons's traditional interpretation of the Farnsworth charge and death is the basis for Farnsworth's story in *Thundering Courage*.

The author, however, wants the readers to know that a revisionist history has been proposed to the First Vermont charge. Gettysburg Licensed Battlefield Guide Andrea Custer wrote "Captain Parsons' *Battles & Leaders* Account," *Blue & Gray*, vol, 23, no. 1 (Spring 2006), 9-10. She also wrote the revisionist article, "Into the Mouth of Hell: Farnsworth Charge Revisited," *Blue & Gray*, vol, 23, no. 1 (Spring 2006), 6-8 and 11-23. Her main argument is that the starting point of the Farnsworth charge was one-half mile west from the traditional starting point on the crest of Bushman's Hill. She also argues that Farnsworth was not killed in the D-shaped field but perished in the early stages of the charge.

She bases her argument on the assertion that Captain Parsons's firsthand account of the charge and map is inaccurate because Parsons was wounded early in the charge. She argues Parsons's account is suspect because he gleaned much of his story from other Vermonters who survived the charge.

The author is aware of Eric Wittenberg and J. David Petruzzi's belief in the traditional interpretation of Parsons's charge and their strong rebuttal to Andrea Custer's article in Eric Wittenberg's *Gettysburg's Forgotten Cavalry Actions: Farnsworth's Charge, South Cavalry Field, and the Battle of Fairfield, July 3, 1863*, Appendix D, "Where did Farnsworth Make his Charge?

A Rebuttal to an Erroneous Account," Savas Beatie, California, 2011, pages 189-206.

Author Joseph D. Collea Jr. concludes that he also supports the traditional interpretation of the charge in Appendix E, "Farnsworth Charge" Revisited: *The Second Battle of Gettysburg*, pages 301-303 in his *The First Vermont Cavalry in the Civil War: A History*, McFarland & Company, North Carolina, 2010.

Despite Parsons being wounded early in the charge and going down, and that he gleaned some of his story from his fellow troopers making the charge, the author has chosen to base the Farnsworth charge and death on Captain Parsons's account and map and Eric Wittenberg's account of the charge in *Gettysburg's Forgotten Cavalry Actions*, and Joseph Collea Jr.'s account of the charge in *The First Vermont Cavalry in the Civil War: A History*.

Why? Captain Parsons and his fellow First Vermont cavalry veterans visited the battlefield on numerous occasions after the war. While some eyewitness accounts dispute the harsh language exchanged between Kilpatrick and Farnsworth prior to the charge, we have no record of any of them objecting to Parsons's written account of the charge and his map. Also, none of them objected to the placement of the Farnsworth monument in the D-shaped field (where Farnsworth was killed) and the Wells monument at the northern foot of Bushman's Hill (where Wells launched his battalion's charge). Thus, Parson's account stands the test of time and serves as the basis for the story in *Thundering Courage*.

❧ Acknowledgments ❧

With gratitude for the patience and encouragement of my brilliant critique group of friends and mentors who read the entire manuscript, I'm grateful to the following: Anthony Tingle, Steve Stigall, Dennis and Debra Barbello, Kenneth James, Tom McConn, Charlie Jones, Steve Alexander, Steve Rauschkolb, Mike Movius, and Lynne Pierce.

With special thanks to those who read the early chapters of the book and provided critiques and suggestions, I'm grateful to Reg Reilly, Kathleen Baldwin, General Gregory (Speedy) Martin, Gary Booth, and Richard Sisk.

A huge, heartfelt thank-you to Steve Rauschkolb, whose personal counsel and direction have been indispensable. Thank you for leading the creation of the maps and thank you to Max Shtym, Ukrainian graphic artist, for his map drawings.

My profound gratitude to Dr. Elliot Cohen, MD, a retired military psychiatrist, a student of the Civil War, and friend, who provided invaluable mentorship on understanding George Armstrong Custer's complex personality.

With special thanks to Kenneth James for providing his expertise on Civil War cavalry charges and the history of the Spencer repeating rifle used by Custer's Wolverines at Gettysburg.

Thank you to Chris Army, a Gettysburg Licensed Battlefield Guide, for providing your superb insights on the guided tour of East Cavalry Field and South Cavalry Field.

Thank you to Odessa Anderson for providing me several copies of *Gettysburg Magazine* articles on the Gettysburg Cavalry Battles.

Thank you to Tom McConn for his mentorship and providing his superb master's degree thesis of the Union Cavalry at Gettysburg.

Thank you to Dale and Anne Gallon for permitting me to use Dale's painting *Custer at Hanover* for the front cover.

I want to thank Pat Hedgecoth Stephens, Norvell Churchill's great-granddaughter, for providing several original documents and stories about Norvell. Your great-grandfather's courage saved

Custer's life at the Battle of Hunterstown. Norvell was at Custer's side during both the First and Seventh Cavalry charges on East Cavalry Field on July 3, 1863. Norvell was truly an unsung hero during the Gettysburg campaign.

Thank you to Fred and Peggy Rainbow and Chris Bohjalian for providing support and encouragement.

Heartfelt thanks to Lori Brown, the most gracious and capable editor an author could hope for. Your keen-eyed editing and tireless support through the whole writing process was magnificent. Thank you for crafting the superb back-cover copy. You're a true friend and champion.

A great debt of gratitude to my publisher, Lisa Norman. Thank you so much for championing this story about one of America's greatest willing heroes during the Civil War. Without your support, Custer's revelatory story during the Gettysburg campaign would still be hidden to many readers.

Thank you to Andrew Pierce, Jennie Pierce, Nathan Pierce, and Terrell Stevenson for your support and encouragement.

Gregg Bennett — friend, colleague, listener, and always a voice of encouragement. Thank you.

Classmates, friends, and mentors, Bruce Blackstone, Jim Freiburg, Scott Norquist, Mike Monroe, Tom Windus, Dave Mercer, Steve De Jarnatt, Bob and Lina O'Day, Dave and Jan Mart, Ron and Mackie Christenson, Randy and Laura Irons, Ken and Dianne McKay, Dave Allen, Jerry White, Andy Waskie, Craig and Kareen Maul, Paul Madera, Guy Walsh, Chris Miller, James Cole, Larry Fiore, Nancy Bennett, Joe Rapisarda, Tammi Findley Hatcher, Dave Gomis, Dr. Jeffrey Schriber, Dr. John Monroe, Karen Reilly, Kathy Sisk, Dave and Danielle Gomis, Ed Culbertson, Shelli Star, Dave Pellegrino, Ron and Karen Woodrell, Charles Coolidge, Michael Lattanzi, Dave Mirra, Erv Rokke, John Fox, Kim Murray, Grady Scuteri, and Sidney Chapin.

Last, but by no means least, my largest thanks go to my wife, Lynne, always a voice of encouragement, who has been fighting alongside General Custer for the past couple years, and who read every word.

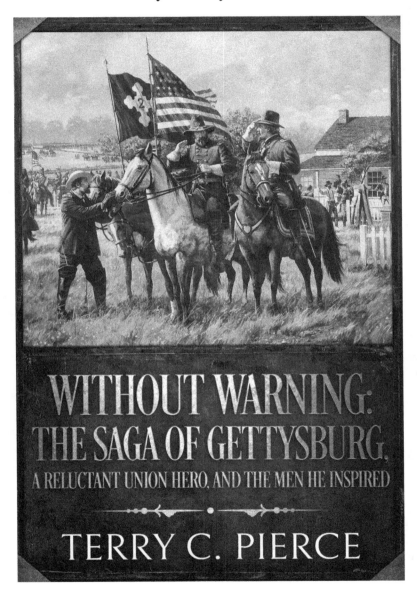

WITHOUT WARNING:
THE SAGA OF GETTYSBURG,
A RELUCTANT UNION HERO, AND THE MEN HE INSPIRED

TERRY C. PIERCE

Printed in the USA
CPSIA information can be obtained
at www.ICGtesting.com
LVHW092058311023
762563LV00004B/600

Untapped Power

Leveraging Diversity and Inclusion for Conflict and Development

Edited by

CARLA KOPPELL

OXFORD

UNIVERSITY PRESS

OXFORD
UNIVERSITY PRESS

Oxford University Press is a department of the University of Oxford. It furthers
the University's objective of excellence in research, scholarship, and education
by publishing worldwide. Oxford is a registered trade mark of Oxford University
Press in the UK and certain other countries.

Published in the United States of America by Oxford University Press
198 Madison Avenue, New York, NY 10016, United States of America.

Library of Congress Control Number: 2021923946
ISBN 978-0-19-761161-6 (pbk.)
ISBN 978-0-19-761160-9 (hbk.)

DOI: 10.1093/oso/9780197611609.001.0001

1 3 5 7 9 8 6 4 2

Paperback printed by LSC Communications, United States of America
Hardback printed by Bridgeport National Bindery, Inc., United States of America

For all the leaders whose voices must be heard for peace and prosperity to advance globally

Contents

Preface

The practice of international affairs is failing to keep pace with the twenty-first-century transformation of states and communities. This is true of work to develop poorer nations. It is equally true of global efforts to prevent conflicts, resolve those that occur, and rebuild following conflict.

Since the end of World War II, great progress has been made in shaping an international regime that honors the fundamental rights of individuals and communities globally. That framework also seeks to enable universal opportunity and progress.

The contemporary international legal, political, and organizational architecture provides a foundation for equity and inclusion; it has also raised the expectations and aspirations of people around the world. Unfortunately, economies and societies have not yet delivered on the promise. Inequity, exclusion, and discrimination persist, and they will continue to exist in the absence of a concerted push for progress.

Equity and inclusion aren't just ethical and moral goals; they are smart goals. Substantial research, analysis, and experience show that there are dividends for peace and prosperity that accrue from advancing the status of every member of the global community. There is also robust evidence that marginalization and exclusion have dramatic costs.

This volume was assembled to facilitate global progress toward equity and inclusion. The rich array of authors, who represent leading scholars, policymakers, and practitioners from around the world, are emblematic of the substantial global community calling for a focus on diversity, equity, and inclusion. Their reflections capture why such a focus is essential in global affairs. Their recommendations reveal critical strategies and tactics for advancing the cause.

It is my sincere hope that by capturing existing evidence as well as rich global experience and recommendations in this book, it becomes easier to advance an approach to international affairs that appropriately values diversity and advances equity and inclusion, delivering dividends for peace and prosperity globally.

Acknowledgments

This book was developed as part of a larger project to increase the focus on diversity, equity, and inclusion in international affairs education. The overall effort engages academics and practitioners from across the United States and around the world.

Because this is a topic that cuts across academic and professional subfields and engages scholars, practitioners, and academic leaders, a substantial number of people helped shape our thinking on this volume. First, the wonderful authors must be recognized for taking on the project as a labor of love and a commitment to the cause; they each put great care and thought into developing a body of work that will help the world advance. Further, thanks are owed to peer reviewers Naazneen Barma, University of Denver; Stephen Meyers, University of Washington; and Robert Nagel, Georgetown University. Each of these scholars put substantial time and brainpower into reviewing and helping shape the book. Additionally, great thanks are due to Melanne Verveer, Executive Director of the Georgetown Institute for Women, Peace and Security. She believed in and invested in the program on diversity, equity, and inclusion in international affairs from its inception; her wisdom and faith in the effort were essential. Further appreciation is offered to Carole Sargent of Georgetown University, who helped the editor navigate academic publishing for the first time; her wisdom and friendship were so very valuable. Additional thanks are owed to Amelia Corl, currently with the GHR Foundation, and Madison Schramm of the US Army War College, who dedicated substantial time to help advance the overall effort, in addition to coauthoring chapters.

Gratitude is also owed to the Rockefeller Foundation, which underwrote and hosted vital early-stage convening to shape the volume. In Bellagio, Italy, Zainab Bangura, Karen McGuiness, Carole Sargent, and Don Steinberg joined many of the chapter authors, providing critical early wisdom and guidance. Additionally, generous early stage guidance and support were provided by Jake Harris and Pamela Aal of the United States Institute of Peace, as well as Zia Khan of the Rockefeller Foundation.

A great deal of appreciation is also owed to the Georgetown Institute for Women, Peace and Security (GIWPS), which provided logistical, communications, and financial support for events, as well as publications, digital communications and research assistance. Special thanks to Satya Adabala, Kathryn Derewicz, Alexandra Smith, and Sarah Rutherford, who ably assisted with the project over many months and, in some cases, years. Also deserving of appreciation are many GIWPS current and former team members, including Claire Anderson, Sarah Brokenborough, Will Clifft, Emma Crawford, Mengjie Kang, Mentewab Kebede, Abigail Khouri,

Tyler McConville, Margaux Ochoa, Diksha Ramesh, Aida Ross, Amanda Suarez, Iryna Tiasko, and Kyilah Terry. Further, GIWPS organized and hosted a conference, Bridging Theory and Practice: Fostering Attention to Diversity, Equity and Inclusion in International Affairs, during which scholarly and practitioner experts including Julius Coles, Bonnie Jenkins, James Goldgeier, Sarah Mendelson, Don Steinberg, and Uzra Zeya, along with several chapter authors and academic leaders, enriched the foundation for the book.

Underpinning and underlying the book's development were also discussions involving academic leaders who worked with the editor over the past several years as part of the University Leadership Council for Diversity and Inclusion in International Affairs Education (ULC), which received generous support from the Robertson Foundation and from the Georgetown University School of Foreign Service. Gratitude to Matthew Auer, University of Georgia; Alyssa Ayres, George Washington University; Laura Bloomberg, University of Minnesota; Christopher Boone, Arizona State University; Christine B.-N. Chin, American University; Maria Cancian, Georgetown University; Miguel Centeno, Princeton University; Suzanne Cooper, Harvard University; Rita Kiki Edozie, University of Massachusetts, Boston; Lee Feinstein, Indiana University Bloomington; Leela Fernandes, University of Washington; Mark Giordano, Georgetown University; Elizabeth Halpin, Seton Hall University; Joel Hellman, Georgetown University; Merit Janow, Columbia University; Carolyn Kissane, New York University; Rosemary Kilkenny, Georgetown University; Ramayya Krishnan, Carnegie Mellon University; Rachel Kyte, Tufts University; Karen McGuinness, Princeton University; Tonija Hope Navas, Howard University; Anthony Pinder, Emerson College; Stephen Radelet, Georgetown University; George Shambaugh, Georgetown University; Carissa Slotterback, University of Pittsburgh; Courtney Smith, Seton Hall University; Cynthia Neal Spence, Spelman College; Scott Taylor, Georgetown University; Colleen B. Toomey, Columbia University; David Van Slyke, Syracuse University; Cynthia Watson, National War College; and Mark A. Welsh, Texas A&M University. Colleagues of ULC members who also helped shape ideas in this book include Frank Ashley, Texas A&M; Diana Beck, University of Minnesota; Alison Cullen, University of Washington; Leslie Evertz, Georgetown University; Ilana Feldman, George Washington University; Carole Gallaher, American University; Victoria Maria de Francesco Soto, University of Texas, Austin; Jackie Speedy, Carnegie Mellon University; and Jonathan Walker, George Washington University. Past members of the ULC also enriched reflection, including Sandy Archibald, University of Washington; Dan Benjamin, formerly at Dartmouth College; Reuben Brigety, University of the South; Ann Cudd, University of Pittsburgh; Angela Evans, formerly at the University of Texas, Austin; Ian Johnstone, Tufts University; Reşat Kasaba, University of Washington; John Keeler, University of Pittsburgh; Pardis Mahdavi, Arizona State University ; and Nancy McEldowney, formerly at Georgetown University.

Those giving permission for visuals are gratefully acknowledged. They include the Centre for Research on the Epidemiology of Disasters (CRED), the Inter-Parliamentary Union, Irene Grizelj, Lakshitha Saji Prelis, Khushboo Shah, Meaghan Shoemaker, Maria Stephan, Minority Rights Group, the OFDA/CRED International Disaster Database (EM-DAT), Our World in Data, the Population Reference Bureau, Pew Research Center, Université Catholique de Louvain—Brussels, Varieties of Democracy Dataset (V-Dem), and the World Bank.

Last but not least, thanks to the editor's husband, Giuseppe Topa, for his patience and support; to Benjamin Topa, Teodoro Topa, and Kristen Popham, who applied university students' eyes to draft chapters and outlines, helping sharpen the text; and to Alessandro Topa, for always making the editor smile.